Statistical Analysis

Statistical

Analysis

IDEAS and METHODS

E. VERNON LEWIS

Associate Professor of Mathematics

University of Delaware

D. VAN NOSTRAND COMPANY, INC.

Princeton, New Jersey

Toronto • New York • London

D. VAN NOSTRAND COMPANY, INC.
120 Alexander St., Princeton, New Jersey (*Principal office*)
24 West 40 Street, New York 18, New York

D. Van Nostrand Company, Ltd.
358, Kensington High Street, London, W.14, England

D. Van Nostrand Company (Canada), Ltd.
25 Hollinger Road, Toronto 16, Canada

Published simultaneously in Canada by
D. Van Nostrand Company (Canada), Ltd.

PRINTED IN THE UNITED STATES OF AMERICA

Preface

One who undertakes to write a textbook ought frequently to ask himself three questions: For whom is the book being written? Why is it being written? What does it have to offer that is not readily available elsewhere? Honest answers to these questions may keep the author humble and will surely improve his work. If the potential user of the book knows the answers, too, he will know better whether and how the book may serve him.

For whom, then, was this book written? It was written for undergraduate college students majoring in the social sciences or business administration who undertake a beginning course in statistics. At the University of Delaware, students majoring in sociology, psychology, economics, and business administration are required to take the first semester, and students in the latter two fields are required to take also the second. The statistics courses are open as electives for students who wish to acquire some knowledge of the subject but who have less mathematical background than majors in the physical sciences and engineering.

Why was it written? It is the author's conviction that workers in the social sciences and business administration will find themselves increasingly needful of an understanding of the basic ideas of statistics and of some facility in their use. Although one may wish that all who use statistical methods might have had a rigorous grounding in mathematical statistics followed by a thorough indoctrination in the application of the methods to their particular field, this condition is seldom encountered. Few students are either able or willing to undertake such study in addition to that required for their future vocation. The author believes that even the student who is "allergic" to mathematics can be led to understand and appreciate the thinking that went into the development of statistics and that, with such an understanding, the formulas of statistics and their interpretation will have more meaning for him. It is one of the purposes of this book to help students in this way. Colleagues who have used pilot editions in mimeographed form have been sufficiently enthusiastic to encourage the preparation of this present edition.

A second conviction of the writer is that at the time when students should become acquainted with the ideas of statistics (about their junior year) most of them have encountered only the rudiments of their major fields. Statistics texts that try to teach statistics through "live" problems in their future professional fields are apt to add the confusion about the subject matter to the mysteries of statistics, with unhappy results. In this text an effort has been made to illustrate the kinds of problems which statistics treats in terms of homely situations within the experience of the student. If he becomes adept at associating the statistical methods with problems he understands, he should be able, as his knowledge of his major field increases, to apply the statistical principles effectively and with justified confidence to problems that it offers.

What, then, does the book have to offer which is not readily available elsewhere? To the extent to which it has accomplished the purposes just discussed, it will lead the student to an understanding of the ideas of statistics and enable him to use many statistical methods soundly and effectively. The book is written in a rather informal style in the hope that it may induce the student to find in his growing appreciation of this new subject something of the real pleasure which the writer finds. Ultimately, it has been the intent to state the various principles compactly and clearly, but only after attempting to make the reader feel comfortable with them.

Another of the writer's convictions is that, although statistical principles can be illustrated with very simple "data" involving a few "observations," each with but one significant digit, the real purpose of statistics is to handle actual data, with several significant digits and reasonable numbers of observations. Desk calculators are useful in coming to grips with such sets of data. This text provides initial illustrations of the principles, particularly the early ones, that can be followed without a calculator, but examples with real data are included later. Problems of both types are offered for the student's use.

Now for a word about the plan of the book. The first five chapters, covering descriptive statistics, are written under the restriction that we are then dealing only with populations. Through a study of the noncomputational procedures of tabulating and diagrammatic representation, the student is helped to acquire a feeling for the meaning of a distribution and of the need of computational methods to deal more rapidly and effectively with the problem of describing a distribution. These methods are then provided.

Chapter 6, dealing with probability, constitutes the second part. Many instructors and their students will be content to study less than the entire chapter, possibly only the first 10 or 12 sections. Others may wish to supplement the material. It is even feasible to bypass the chapter, introducing the major results as they are needed later.

The third part deals with sampling and inference. First we consider thoughtfully why a sample is necessary, then how a good one is obtained, and how "good" statistics to estimate population parameters may be obtained. Then we learn to use these statistics for the two purposes of statistics: hypothesis testing and parameter estimation. This continues through one-, two-, and many-population problems. Then the problems of regression and correlation, dealing with the relation between two variables, is considered. Finally, we deal with enumeration data.

The last two sections deal with time series analysis and index numbers. The latter topic is discussed between the two portions of the discussion of time series. The book closes with a brief discussion of some of the problems of forecasting, including some realistic precautions.

A one-semester course would normally include the first 12 chapters, with possibly some material from one or more of the next four. Where two semesters are available for statistical analysis, the first 16 chapters can be covered thoroughly and the chapters on index numbers could be covered for their liberal value. In our second semester, for the business and economic majors, we cover Chapters 17 through 26, with extensive laboratory exercises; normally, an individual project is required of each student. Of course, each instructor must plan his own course to meet his own interests and needs.

A word about problems. It has been our purpose to include a representative group of problems after most of the chapters. The questions for General Study are designed to help insure that the ideas are understood. The Specific Problems give an opportunity to use these ideas, first on very simple pencil-and-paper data, then on more realistic data. The writer is convinced that the best teaching is done by instructors who provide their own new problems each year, reflecting the interests of their campus, and it is for this reason that extensive sets of problems are not included here.

Finally, if this book has any value, I owe several debts, which I gladly acknowledge. First, I am truly grateful to my students, who have taught me more than I can possibly have taught them, and who have been amazingly patient under the vicissitudes of working from the mimeographed pilot editions. Second, I am most deeply thankful to Professor R. M. Walter of Douglass College, Rutgers University. His constructive comments and warm encouragement were most welcome and very much appreciated. Much that is good in the book results from his suggestions and discussions: the mistakes are my own. Last but not least, I am indebted to my wife and daughter for their faith, encouragement, and phenomenal patience with my preoccupation and lack of patience during the long time this book was in preparation. I humbly hope that the book may be of some service to enough people to make all these people feel that their help was warranted.

E. VERNON LEWIS

Contents

PART A
Descriptive Statistics

1 *What Statistics Is and Does* 1
2 *Simple Ways to Study the Behavior of Data* 8
3 *Locating the Center of a Distribution* 32
4 *Measuring Scattering or Dispersion* 45
5 *Describing the Form of a Distribution* 60

PART B
Probability Rudiments

6 *Probability and Distributions* 83

PART C
Sampling and Inference

7 *What Is a Sample?* 121
8 *What Can a Sample Tell Us About the Mean of Its Population?* 129
9 *What Can a Sample Tell Us About the Variance of a Population?* 154
10 *Investigating the Mean of a Population Whose Variance Is Not Known* 170
11 *The Variances of Two Populations* 189
12 *Inferences Concerning the Means of Two Populations* 200
13 *Dealing With Samples From More Than Two Populations* 214
14 *Relationships Between Variables* 243
15 *Curvilinear Relationships* 275
16 *Treating Data Concerning Counts* 308

PART D
Time Series Analysis: Seasonal and Trend Components

17 *The Basic Idea of a Time Series* 329
18 *Components of a Time Series* 334
19 *Analysis of Seasonal Variation* 345
20 *The Secular Trend* 364
21 *Some Problems with the Calendar* 381

PART E
Index Numbers

22 *Index Numbers for Prices* 391
23 *Index Numbers for Volume* 404
24 *Some Important Index Numbers and Their Uses* 408

PART F
Time Series Analysis, Continued: Cyclical and Irregular Components and Forecasting

25 *Cyclical Variation* 415
26 *Hindsight and Foresight, or the Gentle Art of Forecasting the Future* 419

APPENDIXES

I Normal Ordinates 422
II Normal Areas 424
III Factorials and Their Logarithms 426
IV Random Sampling Numbers 427
V Chi-square and Chi-square-over-n 431
VI Student's t-Distribution 433
VII Cumulative F-Distribution 434
VIII Orthogonal Coefficients 442
IX Poisson Distribution 443
X Four-Place Logarithms Tables 445
XI Operation of Calculators 447
XII Square Roots 456
XIII Linear Interpolation 464
XIV The Greek Alphabet 467
XV The Crout Method 468
XVI Use of Logarithms 473

INDEX

INDEX 479

PART A

Descriptive Statistics

1

What Statistics Is and Does

1.1 Uncertain Numbers

Suppose that you have a checking account in some bank. The number of dollars that you have on deposit at any specific day and hour is a very definite number. It might, for example, be $525.69. True, you and the bank could disagree as to the amount and either or both of you could be wrong, but any discrepancy is not in the number, itself. It lies in a mistake in one or both efforts to record the number, and can be resolved by well-understood methods.

Now let us do a little pipe-dreaming and imagine that we are the committee responsible for investing the bank's funds in order to receive interest to cover the costs of operating our bank, paying interest to our depositors, and making a reasonable return to our stockholders. One of the facts we must know in order to establish a prudent investment policy is the amount of money on deposit with our bank. What *is* that amount? In an effort to ascertain it, we ask our accounting department for the total deposits at the close of business yesterday afternoon. They give us a specific number. If we were a little more thoughtful, we might ask for the deposits at the end of each business day for the past month. Quite likely we should find that we had some twenty different numbers. Our deposit totals vary from day to day and, in fact, from moment to moment as the end result of all the deposits and withdrawals made by all of our depositors, each acting in his own way. The resulting maze of figures is, to put it mildly, confusing.

But let's not lose sight of our question: how much money *is* on deposit in our bank? This number differs from the balance in our personal account, not only in magnitude but in the fact that the variations are a result of the combined effects of the needs and whims of many depositors, not just one. Yet the investment committee is entirely reasonable in thinking about "the" total amount on deposit, knowing all the while that there is no such fixed amount. How, then, are we to cope with this problem of variability?

As long as we have started imagining, let us suppose that we are now responsible for training new employees to perform an exacting step in a manufacturing process. One of our bright young training supervisors proposes a new method of training which he believes will accomplish better results than the methods now in use. In an effort to determine whether he is right, we examine the production records for a group of employees trained by the new method for their first week on regular wages, after their training period is over. We find variations in the numbers involved from employee to employee. When we study, for comparison, a set of similar figures for a group of employees trained by our standard method, we again find variations among the individual numbers. In the face of these variations, how shall we determine which method is better?

To take still another problem, suppose that our company needs, for making one of the devices it produces, some steel balls "exactly" 1/2 in. in diameter. A supply is received from a vendor, and we must determine whether to accept the lot as satisfactory or return it as unsatisfactory. One of our inspectors uses a fine pair of calipers and measures the diameter of the first ball he picks up as 0.5001 in. We ask him to measure it again, and this time he reports the value 0.4998 in. Continued remeasurement results in a series of figures which fluctuate around 0.5000 in. or some number close to it. Certainly it is reasonable to suppose the ball has a diameter: what *is* it? Our problem becomes more complicated when we measure other balls in the lot and find that they are subject to similar variations in observed diameters. In the face of this confusion, what should be our decision concerning the disposition of the lot?

In yet another situation, we might be concerned with assignment of employees to different job classifications, having different pay scales. An important criterion for proper assignment is manual dexterity: greater dexterity permits assignment to a job with a higher wage scale. Now suppose we have available two tests of manual dexterity. The first, which we have been using, requires considerable time and highly trained personnel to administer, but has the merit of a high order of reliability: employees are rarely misassigned as a result of its indications. The other test, a new one, is rapid and can be administered by employees with less specialized training. Would the quicker, simpler and cheaper test be adequate?

Here, what we need as a basis for our decision is the relationship between the scores on the two tests for a number of employees covering a range of dexterities. If we were to test each of these employees by both methods and compare the results, we would undoubtedly find that, often, high scores on one test were accompanied by high scores on the other, and that low scores were similarly related. But there would be disturbing exceptions. If we retested the individuals, we would obtain values which, in general, would not exactly duplicate the first set, particularly for our newer test, and our understanding of the relationship would be blurred by these variations. What, then, can we decide?

Obviously, we want to save money, and are attracted by the apparently cheaper test. But if the test result for some worker — say, Jones — indicated a higher degree of dexterity than he actually possessed, we would place him on a job, with a high wage, that his subsequent performance would not justify. This, itself, would be costly, and his discontent following the ultimate,unavoidable job and wage adjustment would quite likely cost us still more. Similarly, if, on the basis of the newer test, we were to assign an employee to a job requiring less dexterity than he really possessed, and hence paying a lower wage than he, Smith, could earn, we would again face a dual loss. First, we would not be gaining full advantage of Smith's dexterity and ability to produce for us. Second, we would suffer from the consequences of Smith's discontent when he realized that he was capable of holding the better job.

1.2 Kinds of Variation

These examples, we hope, have drawn your attention to the fact that numbers which result from observations are uncertain as a result of *variations*. Actually, we have seen examples of several kinds of variation, and we must now consider them more thoughtfully.

In the problem of the balance of our own checking account at a stated time, the possible variations were the result of *mistakes:* we forgot to record a check or a deposit, or made an error in arithmetic, or the bank made such an error, or both. The mistakes can be detected and corrected by careful verification procedures which are tedious but effective.

Passing to the diameter of a specific bearing ball, we found that successive remeasurements gave different results. Why? Quite possibly, the caliper was applied with slightly different pressures from time to time, or a minute film of dirt might have been present some times, or we may have varied slightly our angle of view past the indicator, or the temperature may have changed with corresponding changes in the dimensions of the ball and caliper. In one sense, it would be quite proper to think of the observed values other than the true one as mistakes, but they are a little different from the "goofs" in our checking accounts, for we do not know how to eliminate them completely. So, instead of calling them mistakes, we refer to the variations introduced by our measuring devices as *errors* of observation.

This is the first of many encounters we shall have with the problem of language. In any field in which we wish to carry on rather exact thinking, we must either coin a new word for each concept we wish to establish clearly, or we must use old words in a limited, and perhaps specialized, sense. Most of us have, at one time or another, heard or read some of the special language of the medical profession, which, for a variety of reasons, uses many coined terms. On the other hand, perhaps we have also heard some discussion of psychology, only to discover that, to the psychologist, some quite common words have very special meanings. In our study of statistics, we shall find that we shall quite often use a common word in a special sense, as in the case of error, and shall rarely coin a special word, like homoscedasticity. This may be troublesome at first but, with due thought, should not disturb you long.

Returning to the problem of the steel balls, when we considered the entire lot, we intuitively recognized that, as a result of variations in the operations by which they were made, the individuals varied in their true diameter. For the present, we might think of this as the *inherent variation* among the diameters. We see that our observations of diameters of several balls will be varying as the result of the combined effect of this inherent variability and the error of measurement. In order to make our decision as to the acceptability of the lot, what we really need is information about the *typical value* and inherent variation of the individual diameters, but, as we can see, our efforts to secure this information are harrassed by the error of observation.

The problem of the bank's investment committee did not involve errors of observation nor (they hope!) mistakes, but did involve two types of inherent variation. One kind is the time-to-time variation in the balance of each individual account. The other is the account-to-account variation in typical balance. The combination of these two variations produces the typical amount on deposit at the bank and the inherent variations in that amount.

In our problem of deciding between training methods for new employees, we can reason that each method has a "true" production rate that it will produce for newly trained employees, but that employees vary individually in their response to training, and vary from hour to hour in their effectiveness. Our problem of comparing the cheap and expensive methods for testing dexterity involved both the inherent variation among individuals and the error of measurement by each test method.

Almost instinctively, in the face of these varying observations, we tend to take more and more observations in deference, perhaps unconscious, to the old adage that "there is strength in numbers." But presently we become swamped with details: the superabundance of trees obliterates the woods, and the untold number of leaves masks the trees!

1.3 The Functions of Statistics

Statistics is sometimes defined as the art and science of treating quantitative observations which are subject to variation. It accomplishes its results through the appropriate application of a wide variety of procedures, some of the more useful of which we shall study in this book.

1. *Condensation.* If our banking committee obtained the 20 or more day-end deposit figures for a month, they would find the varying details already confusing. If they went further and obtained the some 250 or more such figures for a year, their confusion would be increased. The added wealth of detail has, in fact, resulted in a loss of effective information. What the committee really wants is to condense the information. It needs a single figure to

represent the *typical amount* on deposit and a single figure to indicate the *typical variation.*

2. *Tests of Hypotheses.* In our training problem, we had a proposal that the new training program was superior to the old in that higher production rates would result from its use. In formal terms, such a proposal would be called an hypothesis, and our objective would be to determine whether it is true. Observe that, if we can successfully condense the data on employees trained by each method to a single acceptable figure then, so far as these specific employees are concerned, we simply have to compare the two values. But this is not our real interest. These employees are, in our thinking, representative of the indefinitely larger group we hope to hire in the future. We are trying to infer from the results on this small group (which we shall learn is technically known as a *sample*) what would be the truth about the large group (technically, the *population*). A very little thought suggests that the variations in our observations may lead us to the wrong decision concerning our hypothesis, and we would very much like to know the *risk of error* associated with our decision.

3. *Estimation.* Our bank committee wants its typical deposit information not, primarily, as a matter of history but, rather, as a means of *estimating* from this past history (a sample) what the future (a population) will be. They will also recognize that the past variations introduce some uncertainties into this estimate, and so they will welcome a *measure of reliability.*

We shall see, as we study our subject further, that all of the problems we have considered involve these concepts of testing hypotheses or estimation of values in one way or another.

4. *Planning Observations.* We shall find that, in order for the methods of condensation, hypothesis testing, and estimation which we shall employ to be valid, the observations must be obtained in such a way that certain requirements are met. Furthermore, in order to be able to reduce the errors in testing hypotheses to required levels, or to attain the reliability needed in estimates, a sufficient number of observations must be made. However, additional observations only refine the results beyond the demands of the task, and introduce needless costs. Thus an important phase of statistics involves planning, so that an adequate number of properly secured observations will be obtained.

5. *Presentation.* Because of the time and expense involved in obtaining and interpreting sound observations, they are rarely made without a purpose in mind. The final accomplishment of this purpose must involve proper and effective presentation of the results, and this is by no means an unimportant part of statistical work.

In summary, then, we may say that statistics is the art and science of treating quantitative observations which are subject to variation. Hence, it involves planning the type, number and conditions of obtaining the observations to be made, their condensation into a limited number of wieldy values, their use in testing hypotheses or estimating values, with appropriate indications of reliability, and the effective presentation of the results.

1.4 Some Study Suggestions

This, then, being an overly brief statement as to what statistics is about, what problems shall we encounter in learning something about it, and how can we accomplish this learning with as little stress and as much satisfaction as possible? As you no doubt already know, the methods we use will often have a mathematical basis. Their original development and continuing improvement require a very high order of mathematical ability. But their use requires only arithmetic and a rudimentary understanding of algebra. It will be our purpose, in this book, to present a sufficient picture of the ideas which the mathematician uses to develop the methods to enable you to select, use, and interpret them correctly. You who have sufficient background and interest can study the mathematical details in texts devoted to that phase of the subject.

Since many of our real problems will concern the treatment of considerable numbers of individual observations, each observation often involving three or more digits, we shall need computing help. Thirty years ago, calculators were still relatively crude and costly, and many formulas were employed in statistics to circumvent the limitations of the available machines. It seems to us that, today, these formulas and procedures are both unnecessary and confusing to the student, so they have been omitted. Instead, we have included formulas which take advantage of the modern desk calculator, and we urge you to learn to operate such machines with accuracy, assurance, efficiency, and reasonable speed.

Furthermore, we urge you to do much of your studying of statistics at a place where a calculator is available, for then you will be able to work through the real problems and verify that you have grasped the ideas involved. However, because it is not always possible for you to study with a calculator at hand, and because too many figures often obscure ideas, we shall quite often provide examples worked with very simple figures, which you can check with pencil and paper. These examples should help you in two ways. First, they will directly illustrate the statistical method under study with very simple numerical values. Thus you should not get lost in a welter of arithmetic. Second, while you are learning to work with a calculator, you will find it helpful to work these simple problems first, before tackling the more real examples.

You will find, almost immediately, that you will have to develop orderly habits of tabulating original data, of formulating, performing, and recording computations, and presenting their results. Statistics can cope with inherent variations and with errors of measurement quite effectively, but cannot operate in the face of mistakes in recording and computing. Orderly habits and eternal vigilance are your only protections here.

Finally, part of your statistical work will often involve the presentation of the results of your work in clear English, devoid of statistical terminology. You will learn a number of statistical terms (which may seem, at first, gobbledygook) but your final answers should, in general, be free of such technical language. Why? Your chief asks you whether the proposed new method of training employees is better than the old one. If you reply, "The difference in favor of the new method was tested and found to be significant at the 0.01 level," unless you know that he is familiar with statistics, you will have only yourself to blame for what ought to happen to you! Your statement may be quite correct, but it is phrased in the special language of statistics, and would not convey its meaning to one not familiar with that language.

Special technical language, such as that of statistics, is designed to aid careful, exact thinking, but it has no place in final presentation of the results of that thinking for general use. So, keep "statisticsese" out of your reports. This habit will pay you an additional reward. Ideas that you can discuss only in the special language you may but partially understand; if you can discuss them clearly in plain English, you can be assured that you have grasped both the ideas and the special language. Incidentally, this habit could be applied profitably to all your study of specialized fields of information.

In this book, you will find, at the end of each chapter, some suggestions for general observation and consideration, some problems using simple numbers which can be handled without a calculator, and similar problems which require a calculator for efficient treatment. If you follow the suggestions for general study, you will find that the subject will become increasingly real and meaningful to you in relation both to your area of major study and to your general day-to-day experience. The specific problems will help you to check your understanding of the subject, and to increase your confidence in applying the ideas you will be meeting.

General Study

1. Examine some tables of original observations in your field of major interest. Do such tables convey much information to you?

2. Inspect the tables of populations of cities in a source such as *The World Almanac* and try to guess whether the cities in, say, Michigan are larger than those in Indiana. What meaning does the question have, if any?

3. Examine the stock market quotations in your daily paper. Could you give a reasonable answer to any or all of the following questions:

a. What was the price of stocks yesterday?
b. Has the price gone up or down since the day before?
c. Was the price of industrial stocks different from that of utilities yesterday?

2

Simple Ways to Study the Behavior of Data

2.1 Our Purpose

In our opening chapter, we drew your attention to a number of characteristics of the behavior of observations which were probably more or less well known to you, but concerning which you may well have done very little organized thinking until now. We merely suggested some ideas there, in quite broad terms, so that we might all share some views as to the nature of the task before us. Now we are about to come to grips with this task. In the present chapter, we propose to use some methods, chiefly tabulating and charting, which are often needed in the process of summarizing and presenting data. As a result, you will not only learn how the methods work, but you will become more clearly acquainted with some very fundamental aspects of the behavior of data. In later chapters, we shall find methods for dealing effectively with these aspects, as well as for accomplishing much of what we shall be doing here with less total effort.

2.2 Raw Data

Recall our problem of evaluating a new method for training new employees, which we discussed in our last chapter. Suppose that a group, designated in the company records as Class C-14, has been trained by this method and has completed its first week of work on regular wages. Because this work is paid for on a modified piece-work basis, our payroll office has a record of the number of units produced by each member of the class during that week. We transcribe these production figures in the order in which they are found in the payroll office which is, logically for them, that of the payroll numbers of the employees. Such a set of values, either as they originate or simply transcribed, are the material with which we work. Because we have not yet done anything with them, they constitute raw data, and would appear like Table 2-1. What can we see in this table?

Table 2-1 INITIAL PRODUCTION OF TRAINEES BY NEW METHOD

Number of units produced by operators trained in Group C-14 during their first week on regular rates.
Source: Synthetic

12,676	10,873	12,010	13,826	12,203
12,733	10,831	11,399	12,544	13,753
12,428	11,699	12,231	13,927	11,443
11,566	11,509	12,554	11,939	10,768
11,279	13,090	12,118	11,378	12,766
10,826	10,323	10,708	10,615	11,277
10,922	13,036	11,495	13,083	11,960
11,789	11,202	10,946	11,026	11,090
11,709	11,565	13,951	10,546	12,647
12,372	12,558	12,070	11,104	11,632

If we are honest, we can only say: not much! True, we may scan the table more or less carefully and find that all operators produced at least 10,000 units. Still closer scrutiny would show that some produced as many as 13,000 and more units, but that none produced more than 14,000 units. Even to be sure of these statements required a bothersome perusal of the jumbled figures, and they have told us but little. Of course, from the standpoint of the uses of the payroll office, the data were not jumbled; they were listed in order of payroll number, a most convenient order for that office. But we still haven't learned much that helps us to evaluate the training method, which is the purpose for which we obtained the data.

2.3 The Array

The confused order of the values of different size very effectively conceals most of their meaning from us. Now suppose that we go to the trouble of rearranging our data in order of magnitude. The result, known as an *array*, might appear as in Table 2-2. Let us first see what the array accomplishes,

Table 2-2 INITIAL PRODUCTION OF TRAINEES BY NEW METHOD

Number of units produced by operators trained in Group C-14 during their first week on regular rates. Arranged in order of increasing production.
Source: Synthetic

10,323	11,026	11,509	12,070	12,676
10,546	11,090	11,565	12,118	12,733
10,615	11,104	11,566	12,203	12,766
10,708	11,202	11,632	12,231	13,036
10,768	11,277	11,699	12,372	13,083
10,826	11,279	11,709	12,428	13,090
10,831	11,378	11,789	12,544	13,753
10,873	11,399	11,939	12,554	13,826
10,922	11,443	11,960	12,558	13,927
10,946	11,495	12,010	12,647	13,951

then consider some of the problems involved in its preparation. It is now easy, from the array, to see that the smallest, or *minimum*, production was 10,323 units, while the largest, or *maximum*, was 13,951 units. We can readily see that there were fewer production figures in the 10,000's and 13,000's than in the 11,000's or 12,000's. It is easy to see that there were as many figures below 11,700 as above it and, because we have divided our table into groups of five figures, we can sense the values below which 10%, 20%, and so on, of our productions lie. Still closer scrutiny reveals that no two of our workers actually achieved the same amount of production. Surely, this is a considerable gain in effective information, compared with that yielded by our table of raw data, even though the same facts were in both.

What about the work involved? Does the added information justify the effort? There are many ways of converting a table of raw data into an array. If there are comparatively few data, it is quite feasible to scan the raw data and place a "1" beside the smallest figure, then rescan and place a "2" beside the next, and so on. If, however, the table contains many entries, you will find that you are apt to overlook some values, notice them later, and make a lot of corrections. Sometimes a better way is to prepare an intermediate table, such as Table 2-3, in which the original data are divided into groups, each covering a

Table 2-3 INITIAL PRODUCTION OF TRAINEES BY NEW METHOD

Intermediate work sheet, with data from Table 2-1 placed in groups covering a range of 550 units, but in original order within groups

10,000–10,499	*10,500–10,999*	*11,000–11,499*	*11,500–11,999*
10,323	10,826	11,279	11,566
	10,922	11,202	11,789
	10,873	11,399	11,709
	10,831	11,495	11,699
	10,708	11,378	11,509
	10,946	11,026	11,565
	10,615	11,104	11,939
	10,546	11,443	11,960
	10,768	11,277	11,632
		11,090	

12,000–12,499	*12,500–12,999*	*13,000–13,499*	*13,500–13,999*
12,428	12,676	13,090	13,951
12,372	12,733	13,036	13,826
12,010	12,558	13,083	13,927
12,231	12,554		13,753
12,118	12,544		
12,070	12,766		
12,203	12,647		

range of 500 units in this case, from which it is then easy to arrange the figures into the final array. If the data are fairly extensive and subject to still other study, it often proves convenient to copy each figure onto an individual card and then sort the cards. Of course, with very extensive sets of data, the use of one or another form of punched card and sorting machines is desirable. However, many tasks do not warrant the use of the machinery, and still others must be done where no machinery is available. It is essential to know how to do the work.

2.4 The Frequency Table

The array which we just prepared added to the effectiveness of the available data by presenting them in an orderly manner, but we still have all the details. We are looking at all the trees and may be missing the woods. More formally, we have not done anything to condense our data. Realistically, in trying to visualize the results of our new training method, does it matter that one worker produced 10,708 units whereas another produced 10,768 units, or is that detail obscuring the general picture? Suppose we divide our observations into groups, as we did in one method of preparing our array, but now simply tabulate the number, or frequency, of observations in each group.

These groups are known technically as *classes*, and the number of observations in each class is known as the *class frequency*. We find that the description of the classes is not quite as simple as we might expect and that there are several methods in use for making the descriptions both exact and convenient. We might, incorrectly, describe our first class as "10,000–10,500" and our second as "10,500–11,000," and so on. This looks good, but suppose we had happened to have a production figure of exactly 10,500: to which class would it belong? We have an ambiguity, since, by our description, it could be placed in either class.

One way of avoiding this ambiguity is to note that the production figures are reported in whole numbers, without decimals or fractions. Thus we could say that our first class is to include all values from 10,000 to 10,499, inclusive, while our second includes the values from 10,500 to 10,999, inclusive, and so on. Of course, these descriptions would be more compactly written as "10,000–10,499," "10,500–10,999," and the like. Such sets of values which describe the classes in terms of the minimum and maximum possible value to be assigned to each class are known as *class limits*, and are very often employed.

Another way of avoiding ambiguity uses values midway between the adjacent class limits. Since the data cannot have these values, no ambiguity arises, and the classes look continuous. In our case, the values become "9,999.5–10,499.5," "10,499.5–10,999.5," and so on. Such values, which avoid the ambiguity problem by using values that the data will not have, are known as *class boundaries*.

Notice that the difference between the corresponding limits or boundaries of successive classes is, in each case, 500 units. Such differences are known as *class intervals*. The values midway between the limits or the boundaries for each class are known as the *class marks*. In our case, the class marks are 10,249.5, 10,749.5, etc.

Another common way of describing the classes is to indicate that the class includes all values from the lower to, but not including, the upper figure. This may be indicated, in our case, by such designations as "10,000–10,500$^-$," "10,500–11,000$^-$," and so on. A more elaborate notation uses the mathematical symbols "$\leq$," meaning "less than or equal to," and "$<$," meaning "less than," together with "X" to represent the values. In this notation, our first class would be described by the notation, "$10{,}000 \leq X < 10{,}500$" and the other classes would be similarly described. We can immediately see that this avoids ambiguity and makes the class interval evident, but it creates a difficulty with the class mark, because we do not know exactly where the class stops at the upper end. While this may not appear serious now, we shall find that it becomes serious when we come to make further use of the table we are in the process of preparing.

In Table 2-4, we have presented the results of our work as a *frequency table.* Actually, one would not normally use all three of the methods of describing the

Table 2-4 INITIAL PRODUCTION OF TRAINEES BY NEW METHOD

Frequency table for number of units produced by operators trained in Group C-14 during their first week on regular rates. Source: Synthetic

Class Limits	Class Boundaries	Class Mark	Class Frequency
10,000–10,499	9,999.5–10,499.5	10,249.5	1
10,500–10,999	10,499.5–10,999.5	10,749.5	9
11,000–11,499	10,999.5–11,499.5	11,249.5	10
11,500–11,999	11,499.5–11,999.5	11,749.5	9
12,000–12,499	11,999.5–12,499.5	12,249.5	7
12,500–12,999	12,499.5–12,999.5	12,749.5	7
13,000–13,499	12,999.5–13,499.5	13,249.5	3
13,500–13,999	13,499.5–13,999.5	13,749.5	4
			50

classes in a table. If the purpose of the table is simply to present the data, either the class limits or class boundaries and class frequencies would be sufficient, though the class mark is often added. If the table is used as the starting point for computations, as we shall see that it is, the class marks and frequencies are sufficient, though the limits or boundaries may be added.

A word about the preparation of such tables may be helpful. A commonly recommended procedure involves the use of a tally sheet such as is shown in Table 2-5, in which a tally mark is placed beside the appropriate class description as one reads down the table of raw data. This has the advantage of simplicity, but the simplicity is misleading. It is annoying, after you run through a table of raw data containing 50 entries, to discover that you have 49 or 51 tallies, and you may be surprised to find how often this will happen.

Table 2-5 INITIAL PRODUCTION OF TRAINEES BY NEW METHOD

Tally sheet for preparation of frequency table from raw data of Table 2-1

Class Limits	*Tallies*	*Frequency*
10,000–10,499	/	1
10,500–10,999	~~////~~ ////	9
11,000–11,499	~~////~~ ~~////~~	10
11,500–11,999	~~////~~ ////	9
12,000–12,499	~~////~~ //	7
12,500–12,999	~~////~~ //	7
13,000–13,499	///	3
13,500–13,999	////	4

Since one tally looks like another, the only way to come out with 50 is to start over again. A better way is to make a table like the intermediate table proposed in the previous section. Then, if you don't come out with 50 values, you have a good way of cross-checking the two tables to find the error. Still another way is to write the serial number of the observation instead of the tally. All this may sound a bit discouraging, but all of us do make mistakes, and a mistake in tabulation or numerical work undoes all the good thinking which has gone into the development of the methods we have used. These suggestions are based on practical experience and are offered in the hope that they may save you some of the embarrassment we have suffered! Of course, if you already have your data transcribed to individual cards, punched or otherwise, it is quite easy to sort the cards, count them, and verify the proper sorting.

2.5 The Histogram

There is allegedly an ancient Chinese proverb, "One picture is worth ten thousand words." Like most generalizations, that one is not always true, for a picture is, at best, a coded representation of an idea. For it to have meaning for us, we must know the code. Most of us are so used to "black and white" photographs that the code has become second nature, and when we see a photograph of a familiar person or scene, our mind readily visualizes the original.

Suppose we wanted to make a sort of model of our frequency table. We might take a board 3 in. wide by 10 in. long and mark off a row of 1-in. squares along its mid-line. Then we might designate each square in order to correspond with our possible classes. If we now obtained a series of discs, or counters, each 1 in. in diameter, we could place a disc on top of the appropriate square each time we read off an observation from our table of raw data. When we had placed and verified all 50 discs, we might cement them in place, and thus we would have a "statue" of our original data. After the cement had set, it might occur to us to saw the statue down its vertical mid-plane and add some designations of the scales to show what was being represented; then we would have an effective little model.

The only trouble with a model, of course, is that it involves too much equipment and work. So what we actually do is draw a scale picture of what the cut face would have looked like. The result, shown in Fig. 2-1, is known as a

Fig. 2-1. Initial Production of Trainees by New Method.

Histogram of number of operators producing indicated number of units of production during their first week on regular wages.
Class C-14. Source: Synthetic.

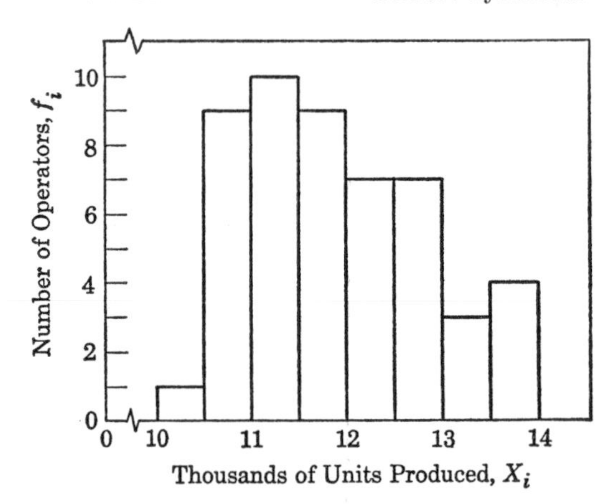

histogram. It presents the same information as the frequency table, Table 2-4, but in a way that makes some of the facts stand out with a real impact. Notice the fact that there is but a single observation below 10,500, that the greatest class frequency is in the 11,000–11,499 class, and that the class frequencies are not symmetrically arranged about this maximum frequency.

2.6 Comments on Frequency Tables and Histograms

In the manner we have drawn our historgram it is, of course, true that the height of the bars, read from the appropriate scale, gives the class frequency. But, because we have made all class intervals, and therefore all bar widths, equal, the areas of the bars are also proportional to the class frequencies. This is a most prudent practice. Some of the reasons why this is so can best be learned by experience.

We mentioned earlier the problem of the variations in individual check accounts at banks. Table 2-6 shows one of the cases of this variation. It records, in the order in which they were written, all checks written against one account during one calendar year. Of course, these are raw data, and are confusing, as usual. Since we are feeling our way into statistics, we might well

Table 2-6 Checks Drawn on One Personal Account During One Calendar Year, in the Order of Writing. Source: Owner's Checkbook

472.50	13.29	50.00	26.67	10.00	5.50	50.00	35.00
67.87	218.69	33.00	45.00	100.00	39.95	10.00	129.00
50.00	4.20	5.00	10.00	10.00	20.00	50.00	25.00
40.00	7.98	12.00	50.00	209.00	50.00	25.00	1,137.50
57.02	3.00	7.83	150.00	10.00	10.00	50.00	38.00
50.00	25.00	60.00	450.00	50.00	25.00	25.00	10.00
6.00	50.00	22.50	549.00	10.00	25.00	350.00	307.70
30.00	212.60	165.00	50.00	10.00	25.00	12.00	12.03
14.95	25.00	10.00	12.66	10.00	25.00	10.00	25.00
5.00	50.00	10.00	50.00	100.00	6,804.26	15.00	25.00
50.00	632.82	50.00	500.00	50.00	25.00	25.00	29.50
29.00	25.00	10.00	25.00	50.00	25.00	68.60	25.00
3.50	115.11	10.00	140.00	50.00	25.00	33.00	50.00
275.80	50.00	39.00	75.00	10.00	75.00	25.00	5.00
655.54	25.00	10.00	50.00	159.71	16.00	50.00	75.00
252.50	25.00	50.00	50.35	5.00	250.00	25.00	
50.00	100.00	100.00	50.00	5.00	500.00	10.00	
50.00	98.75	10.00	3.00	5.00	24.00	13.00	
48.49	6.00	5.00	30.00	400.00	5.00	2.25	
50.00	50.00	354.93	517.50	50.00	40.50	2.75	

make an array, as in Table 2-7. As before, we can make much more sense out of this table than out of the raw data, but we still find ourselves bothered by needless detail, so we decide to make a frequency table.

Table 2-7 Checks Drawn on One Personal Account During One Calendar Year, Arranged as an Array. Source: Owner's Checkbook

2.25	10.00	12.03	25.00	38.00	50.00	68.60	275.80
2.75	10.00	12.66	25.00	39.00	50.00	75.00	307.70
3.00	10.00	13.00	25.00	39.95	50.00	75.00	350.00
3.00	10.00	13.29	25.00	40.00	50.00	75.00	354.93
3.50	10.00	14.95	25.00	40.50	50.00	98.75	400.00
4.20	10.00	15.00	25.00	45.00	50.00	100.00	450.00
5.00	10.00	16.00	25.00	48.49	50.00	100.00	472.50
5.00	10.00	20.00	25.00	50.00	50.00	100.00	500.00
5.00	10.00	22.50	25.00	50.00	50.00	100.00	500.00
5.00	10.00	24.00	25.00	50.00	50.00	115.11	517.50
5.00	10.00	25.00	25.00	50.00	50.00	129.00	549.00
5.00	10.00	25.00	25.00	50.00	50.00	140.00	632.82
5.00	10.00	25.00	26.62	50.00	50.00	150.00	655.54
5.00	10.00	25.00	29.00	50.00	50.00	159.71	1,137.50
5.00	10.00	25.00	29.50	50.00	50.00	165.00	6,804.26
5.50	10.00	25.00	30.00	50.00	50.00	209.00	
6.00	10.00	25.00	30.00	50.00	50.35	212.60	
7.83	10.00	25.00	33.00	50.00	57.02	218.69	
7.98	12.00	25.00	33.00	50.00	60.00	250.00	
10.00	12.00	25.00	35.00	50.00	67.87	252.50	

We notice from our array that the smallest check was for $2.25 while the largest was for $6,804.26. After a little juggling of figures, we decide that a class interval of $750.00 would be a good starting point, because it gives us 10 classes, with attractively "round" lower limits. However, the results, in Table 2-8, are startling! The lower class accounts for all but two of the checks,

Table 2-8 CHECKS DRAWN ON ONE PERSONAL ACCOUNT DURING ONE CALENDAR YEAR. SOURCE: OWNER'S CHECKBOOK

Class Limits, $	*Class Mark*	*Class Frequency*
0.00– 749.99	374.995	153
750.00–1,499.99	1,124.995	1
1,500.00–2,249.99	1,874.995	0
2,250.00–2,999.99	2,624.995	0
3,000.00–3,749.99	3,374.995	0
3,750.00–4,499.99	4,124.995	0
4,500.00–5,249.99	4,874.995	0
5,250.00–5,999.99	5,624.995	0
6,000.00–6,749.99	6,374.995	0
6,750.00–7,499.99	7,124.995	1
		155

Note: Classes Poorly Chosen

of which one each is in the second and tenth class: the remaining seven classes are empty. This hardly gives us much of a picture of the actual distribution.

Of course, we realize that most of our checks were small, so we adopt the common but misleading practice of making non-uniform classes, with the result shown in Table 2-9. A normal person's quick scanning of this table

Table 2-9 CHECKS DRAWN ON ONE PERSONAL ACCOUNT DURING ONE CALENDAR YEAR. SOURCE: OWNER'S CHECKBOOK

Class Limits, $	*Class Mark*	*Class Frequency*
0.01– 5.00	2.505	15
5.01– 10.00	7.505	23
10.01– 24.00	17.005	12
24.01– 25.00	24.505	22
25.01– 49.00	37.005	15
49.01– 50.00	49.505	29
50.01– 200.00	125.005	19
200.01– 500.00	350.005	12
500.01–7,000.00	3,750.005	8
		155

Note: Classes Very Poorly Chosen

would quite probably leave him with the impression that the owner of the account wrote checks which were pretty uniformly distributed as to size. We, who have seen the array, know that this is not the case.

The use of these tables as the basis of histograms emphasizes the poor judgment we have used. Fig. 2-2, we could properly claim, is a correctly

Fig. 2-2. Checks Drawn on One Account During One Year.
Based on Table 2-8. Source: Owner's Checkbook.

Notice the ridiculous result of the poor choice of classes in Table 2-8.

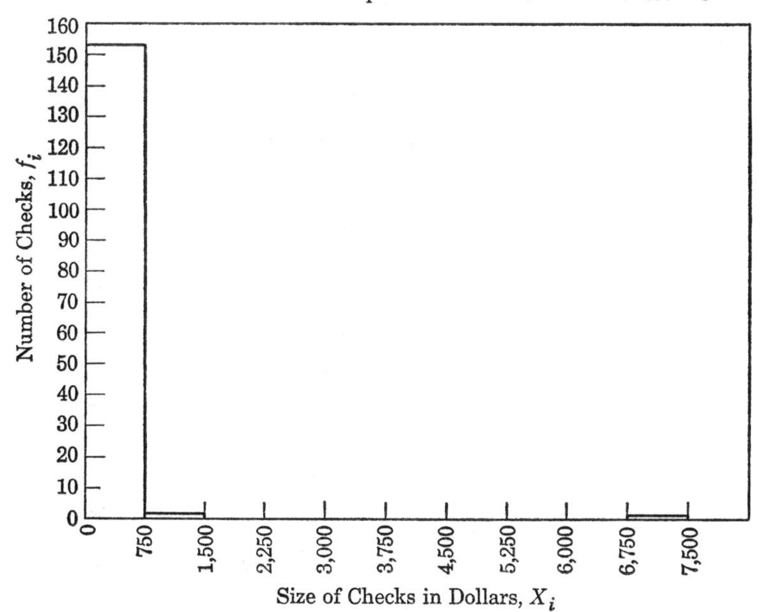

drawn histogram, because all bars are of uniform width, and the horizontal scale has not been distorted. Of course, its ridiculous appearance brings home to us the unwise decisions we made about our classes in preparing Table 2-8 on which it is based.

In Fig. 2-3 we can no longer claim that we have a properly drawn histogram. What we did was to lay off a number of bars of equal width, then mark their lower corners with the upper class limits of Table 2-9, and place their tops at the frequencies indicated in that table. True, our bars are of equal geometric width, but the scale units along the bottom scale are by no means evenly spaced. Here, our scale distortion aids and abets our not-too-cautious observer in coming away with the conclusion that our checks were pretty evenly distributed over their varying sizes.

We might attempt to improve the situation by restoring the uniformity to our scale of check sizes, letting the bar widths vary. In the case of these data, unless the chart were made on a very long piece of paper, several of the bars would be so narrow as to be indistinguishable from lines, and the chart would be illegible. Of course, we have used an extreme example, but you will find, as you study tables and charts more perceptively, that nonuniform class intervals

Fig. 2-3. Checks Drawn on One Account During One Year.
Based on Table 2-9. Source: Owner's Checkbook.

Notice that the use of bars of equal widths to represent widely different class intervals deceives the eye, even though the distorted scale is clearly marked.

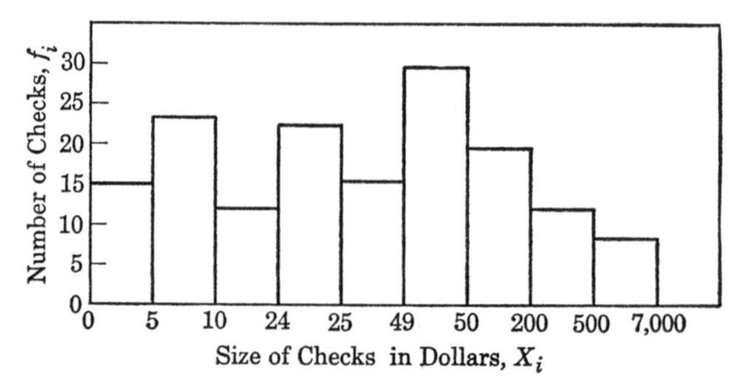

are deceptive. In scanning tables we tend, in spite of the designations in the tables, to interpret them as though the class intervals were equal. In "histograms" with unequal bar widths our minds tend to associate more importance,

Fig. 2-4. Individual Income Tax Returns, 1957.

Number of returns reporting adjusted gross incomes in indicated classes. From Table 2-10.
Orginal Source: Internal Revenue Service, U.S.T.D.

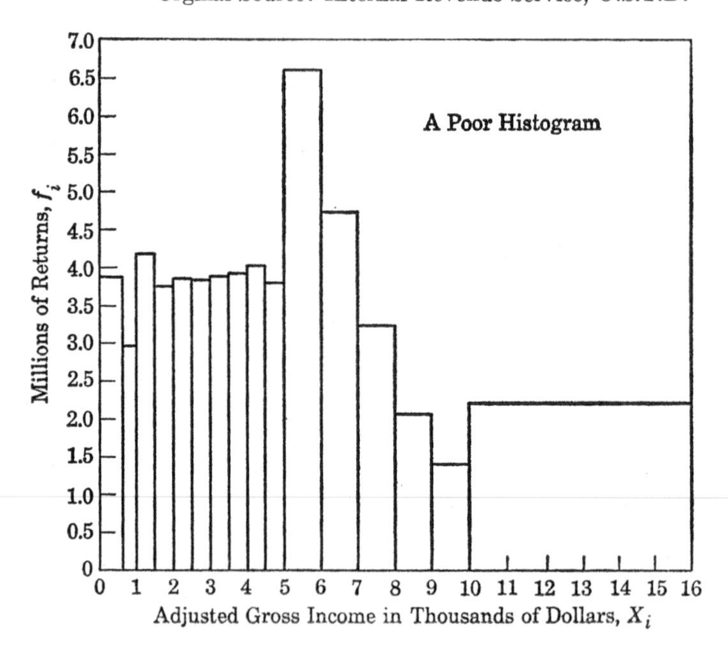

and hence higher frequencies, with the larger areas, regardless of the evidence that the producer of the chart intended otherwise.

How badly these tendencies can distort the truth in the presentation of data of more general interest will be seen from a study of Table 2-10 and of Fig. 2-4,

Table 2-10 INDIVIDUAL INCOME TAX RETURNS, 1957

Number of returns reporting adjusted gross incomes in the indicated classes. Source: Internal Revenue Service, U.S. Treasury Department

Adjusted Gross Income	*Number of Returns*
Under $600	3,833,400
$600 and under $1,000	2,989,651
$1,000 and under $1,500	4,178,054
$1,500 and under $2,000	3,698,934
$2,000 and under $2,500	3,843,211
$2,500 and under $3,000	3,815,406
$3,000 and under $3,500	3,886,778
$3,500 and under $4,000	3,905,197
$4,000 and under $4,500	3,991,220
$4,500 and under $5,000	3,877,207
$5,000 and under $6,000	6,555,283
$6,000 and under $7,000	4,709,612
$7,000 and under $8,000	3,206,964
$8,000 and under $9,000	2,091,262
$9,000 and under $10,000	1,334,622
$10,000 and under $15,000	2,213,510
$15,000 and under $20,000	543,746
$20,000 and under $25,000	250,860
$25,000 and under $50,000	366,399
$50,000 and under $100,000	93,421
$100,000 and under $150,000	14,127
$150,000 and under $200,000	4,004
$200,000 and under $500,000	3,997
$500,000 and under $1,000,000	585
$1,000,000 and over	223
Total	59,407,673

a "histogram" constructed from this table for incomes up to $15,000. The class intervals are nonuniform and we are careful readers, indeed, if we do not come away with the impression that incomes are quite evenly distributed over this range. Look more closely, and you will see that this is far from the truth.

To see what may be done, let us return to our check data, which is retabulated in Table 2-11 with classes of uniform interval, $25.00. True, this makes it necessary to use an "open" upper class, that is, one whose upper boundary is not defined, or to include a ridiculous number of empty classes. In the table, we make this conspicuous by using the words "and over" in the

Table 2-11 CHECKS DRAWN ON ONE PERSONAL ACCOUNT DURING ONE CALENDAR YEAR. SOURCE: OWNER'S CHECKBOOK

Class Limits, $	*Class Mark*	*Class Frequency*
0.00– 24.99	12.495	50
25.00– 49.99	37.495	37
50.00– 74.99	62.495	34
75.00– 99.99	87.495	4
100.00–124.99	112.495	5
125.00–149.99	137.495	2
150.00–174.99	162.495	3
175.00–199.99	187.495	0
200.00–224.99	212.495	3
225.00–249.99	237.495	0
250.00–274.99	262.495	2
275.00–299.99	287.495	1
300.00 and over	—	14
		155

designation of the limits or boundaries, while on the related histogram, Fig. 2-5, we show the right edge of the bar with a broken line.

Fig. 2-5. Checks Drawn on One Account During One Year.
Based on Table 2-11. Source: Owner's Checkbook.

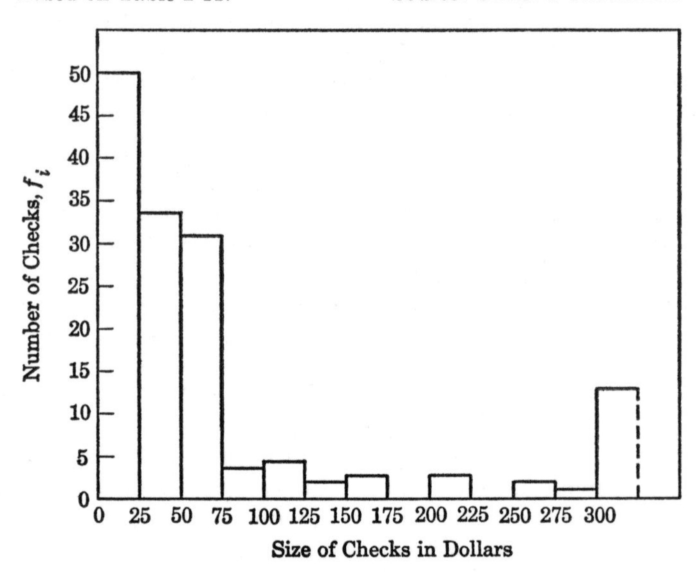

Quite possibly you are now rather disturbed to find that we cannot offer you a few rules which would insure that, whatever the nature of the observations you were studying, you could, by following the rules, prepare a satisfactory frequency table or histogram. While we sympathize with your feeling, the fact is that there are no such universal rules. The complex facts behind observations are so different from set to set, and the purposes for which the information concealed in the data are to be used vary so widely that no simple rules could possibly meet all requirements. We have been able to state some principles: you will find that they will be of very great service to you. But sometimes you will find data, like the check sizes we studied, that just are not going to respond completely satisfactorily to any effort to present them in a frequency table or histogram.

The fact is that our very inability to deal with such data effectively is one of the important reasons why other statistical methods we are to study were developed. In fact, as the information we seek becomes more complex, new methods for revealing the facts in the data are constantly being developed. As you continue your study of our subject, it might interest you to compare this text with those written thirty or forty years ago for the use of students like yourselves.

To return from our digression, however, we recognize that, in spite of the disadvantages brought to your attention, frequency tables and histograms are, in fact, often published with nonuniform class intervals. We suspect that this is too often the result of ignorance on the part of those preparing the tables and charts. But sometimes it arises from the necessity to economize on space while showing considerable detail in those parts of the data of greatest interest. The income data in Table 2-10 would be a case in point: moderate differences in income in the lower brackets produce far greater socio-economic effects than do the same differences in the higher brackets, hence the use of smaller class intervals in the region in which most of us exist.

Histograms for general use are often made striking in appearance by the use of colors or various forms of shading, or both. Sometimes the bars are replaced by rows of pictures of the kinds of units: houses, cattle, people, cars, coins, and so on. Sometimes the bars are given a three-dimensional appearance, as though they were blocks of marble standing on end, though this stunt can be misleading: does the area or volume of the block represent the frequency?

This leads us to bring to your attention a book with the engaging title, "How to Lie with Statistics," by Darrell Huff (W. W. Norton, Inc., New York, 1954). Written in a delightfully pleasant style and illustrated with amusing sketches, the book shows how we are so easily misled by just such matters as these nonuniform class intervals, or three-dimensional histogram bars, and many other slight departures from the best statistical procedures. Not only is it fun to read, but it will put you on your guard against being "taken in" and will have the still greater advantage of emphasizing for you many of the principles we shall be studying. We hope you will find and enjoy the little book.

2.7 Cumulative Frequencies and Relative Frequencies

Under many circumstances, we shall find ourselves more concerned with the number of values below (or above) several stated values than with the numbers in the individual classes. For example, we might be concerned with the number of checks written for less than \$25, \$50, \$75, and so on. Or we could start at the other end and count the checks for over \$1,000, over \$500, and work downward in value. In other words, we would be totalling, or accumulating, the frequencies as we move from one end to the other of the array or frequency table. The resulting values are, quite reasonably, called *cumulative frequencies.*

Just as care had to be used in describing our classes, so it is important that we distinguish between "below" and "at or below." Consider our check size data. There were, as the array of Table 2-7 makes it easy to determine, 50 checks written for amounts below \$25.00, but there were 72 checks for amounts at or below \$25.00. This arises from the fact that there were exactly 22 checks for \$25.00.

Another problem that arises in connection with frequencies stems from the fact that we often want to compare two sets of data with quite different total numbers of observations. We would want to compare the results of our group of 50 employees trained by our proposed new method with our records for the 1,274 employees who had been trained by our conventional method. Or we might be interested in comparing the sizes of checks written on the account we have studied with those of all checks written on all the private accounts in a given bank. The confusion resulting from the different total numbers in two or more sets can be reduced by considering the frequencies as fractions of the total number of observations. Such fractions are called *relative frequencies* if they are obtained by dividing a class frequency by the total number and *relative cumulative frequencies* if they involve a similar treatment of a cumulative frequency. Table 2-12 presents the information of Table 2-4 concerning

Table 2-12 INITIAL PRODUCTION OF TRAINEES BY NEW METHOD

Number of units produced by operators trained in Group C-14 during their first week on regular wages, shown as actual and relative frequencies and cumulative frequencies. Based on Table 2-4. Source: Synthetic

Class Limits		Class Freq.		Cumulative Freq. At or Below X_{Ui}		Cumulative Freq. Above X_{Ui}	
Lower X_{Li}	Upper X_{Ui}	Num. f_i	Rel. f_i/N	Num.	Rel.	Num.	Rel.
10,000	10,499	1	0.02	1	0.02	49	0.98
10,500	10,999	9	0.18	10	0.20	40	0.80
11,000	11,499	10	0.20	20	0.40	30	0.60
11,500	11,999	9	0.18	29	0.58	21	0.42
12,000	12,499	7	0.14	36	0.72	14	0.28
12,500	12,999	7	0.14	43	0.86	7	0.14
13,000	13,499	3	0.06	46	0.92	4	0.08
13,500	13,999	4	0.08	50	1.00	0	0.00

trainee production in terms of cumulative and relative values, while Table 2-13 does a similar thing for the check size data of Table 2-11.

Table 2-13 CHECKS DRAWN ON ONE PERSONAL ACCOUNT DURING ONE CALENDAR YEAR

Shown as actual and relative frequencies and cumulative frequencies. Based on Table 2-12.

Source: Owner's Checkbook

Class Limits, $		Class Freq.		Cumulative Freq. At or Below X_{Ui}		Cumulative Freq. At or Above X_{Ui}	
Lower X_{Li}	Upper X_{Ui}	Num. f_i	Rel. f_i/N	Num.	Rel.	Num.	Rel.
0.00	24.99	50	0.323	50	0.323	105	0.677
25.00	49.99	37	0.239	87	0.561	68	0.439
50.00	74.99	34	0.219	121	0.781	34	0.219
75.00	99.99	4	0.026	125	0.806	30	0.194
100.00	124.99	5	0.032	130	0.839	25	0.161
125.00	149.99	2	0.013	132	0.852	23	0.148
150.00	174.99	3	0.019	135	0.871	20	0.129
175.00	199.99	0	0.000	135	0.871	20	0.129
200.00	224.99	3	0.019	138	0.890	17	0.110
225.00	249.99	0	0.000	138	0.890	17	0.110
250.00	274.99	2	0.013	140	0.903	15	0.097
275.00	299.99	1	0.006	141	0.910	14	0.090
300.00	Higher	14	0.090	155	1.000	0	0.000
		155	0.999				

The discrepancies between the sum of relative frequencies and the relative cumulative frequencies are the result of rounding errors.

2.8 Step Diagrams

These cumulative and relative cumulative frequencies are shown in Fig. 2-6 and Fig. 2-7, respectively. Notice that the same line serves for either kind of frequency, and that one merely reads the values from the appropriate vertical scale. However, care must be taken to construct and read these charts properly. For example, consider Fig. 2-7. We know from Table 2-13 that through $24.99 we have accumulated 50 checks. Therefore, at $24.99 we plot a point at the level indicating 50 checks, then we make the "riser" of our step run from the axis to the point and the "tread" run from the point horizontally to the right. By the time we have reached $49.99, we have accumulated 37 more checks for a total of 87, so, at $49.99, we make a point at the 87 level, put in a "riser" up to it, and start a new "tread" to the right. Thus the only points that have meaning are those at the top of each riser: the lines are put in merely to guide our eye from point to point. The same points are the only ones which have meaning when we are reading from the scales indicating accumulation from the top down.

There seems to be no universal agreement as to a name for such diagrams. We have used the term "step diagram" because it seems to be highly descriptive. As we have made the diagrams, they are related to our histograms, which, in turn, are related to our frequency tables. It is possible but tedious and rarely useful to make such a step diagram with a riser for each new observation encountered. Sometimes it is useful to present the diagram with steps of equal rise, say every 0.10 on the relative scale, letting the treads vary in width. Fig. 2-8 is constructed like that for our data on the trainees. As you will see, it clearly brings out how much difference in production was associated with each tenth of the group.

Fig. 2-6. Initial Production of Trainees by New Method.

Step diagram showing cumulative and relative cumulative frequencies of indicated levels of production. Source: Synthetic.

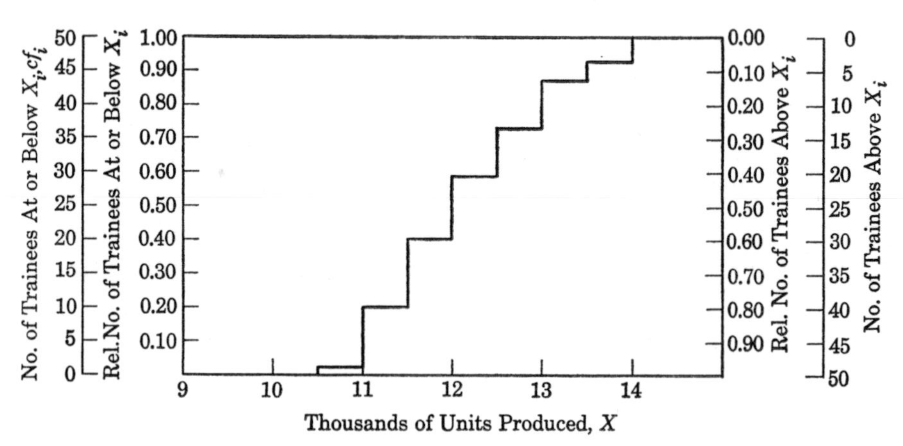

Fig. 2-7. Checks Drawn on One Personal Account During One Calendar Year.

Step diagram showing cumulative and relative cumulative frequencies of checks of indicated sizes. Source: Owner's Checkbook.

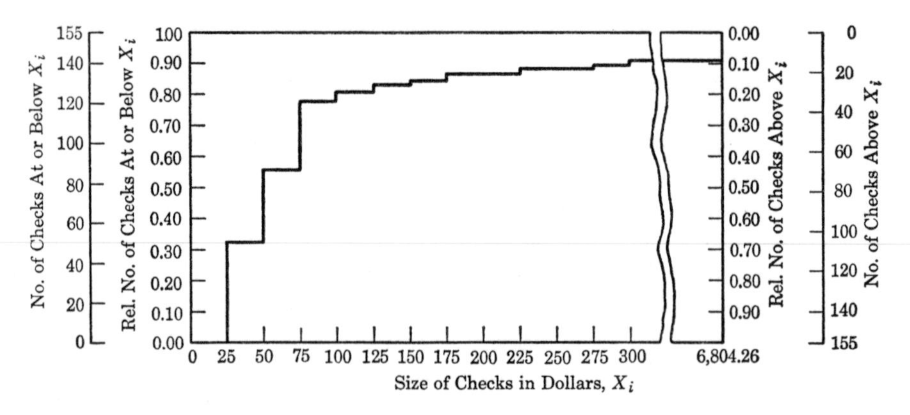

Fig. 2-8. Initial Production of Trainees by New Method.

Step diagram showing relative cumulative frequencies of indicated levels of production. Source: Synthetic.

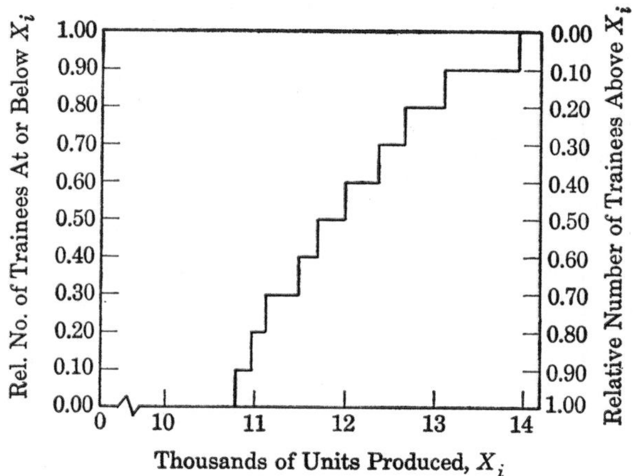

By now, it must surely be evident to you that we could present any of our histograms in terms of relative frequencies, as we now do in Fig. 2-9 for the trainee production data and in Fig. 2-10 for our check data. These are nothing but the original histograms, Fig. 2-1 and Fig. 2-5, respectively, redrawn with the scale of relative frequencies added. As a matter of fact, as we learn more about statistical methods, you will find that it is often desirable to think in terms of relative, rather than actual, frequencies, so this is a good time to start doing so.

Fig. 2-9. Initial Production of Trainees by New Method.

Histogram of number and fraction of operators producing indicated number of units of production during their first week on regular wages.
Class C-14. Source: Synthetic.

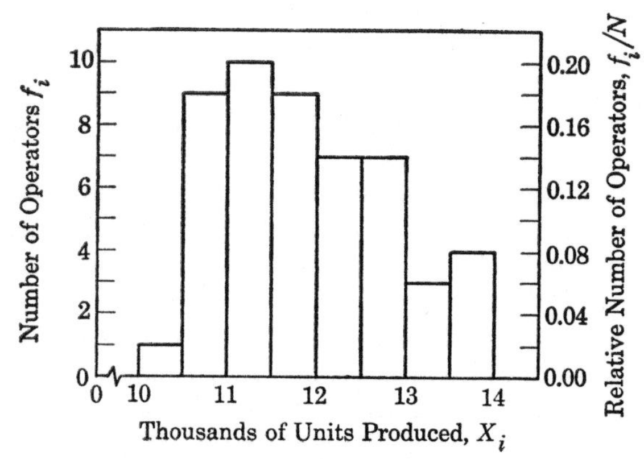

Fig. 2-10. Checks Drawn on One Account During One Year.
Source: Owner's Checkbook.

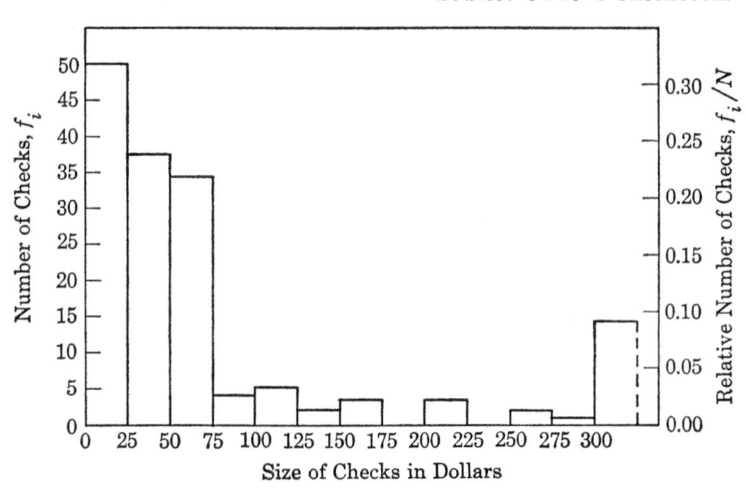

2.9 Frequency Polygons

When you come to make histograms of your own, you will find that, even in their simplest form — with plain open bars, devoid of pictorial efforts, shading, or color — they represent a considerable amount of rather tedious effort. That effort is, of course, rewarded by the ease with which even the untrained user can perceive much of the information contained in the data. The trained user can gather even more facts from a well-made histogram. But nevertheless, the effort of production is still great. What could be done to reduce it, and what might we lose thereby?

A common practice is to make a chart on the same layout that would be used for the histogram, but after plotting each class frequency at its class mark, simply to connect the resulting points. The resulting lines and the horizontal axis form a closed polygon; hence such a chart is called a *frequency polygon.* This has been done in Fig. 2-11 for the trainee data presented as a histogram in Fig. 2-9, and in Fig. 2-12 for the check data presented as a histogram in Fig. 2-10. The plotted points come, of course, at the position of the centers of the tops of the former histogram bars.

What are our gains and losses with the change from histograms to frequency polygons? As you will find, the polygons are quicker and easier to make — a gain. Also, the plotted points indicate frequency just as well as do the heights of the bars. But, in the histograms, the areas of the bars also represent frequency. Except by an occasional accident, the areas under the polygons bear no reliable relationship to frequencies, and that is not only a loss, but something of a fault, because your eye and mind are almost certain to try to associate meaning with these areas. There is an old adage, "Hard writing makes easy reading." We might properly paraphrase it to read, "Hard drawing makes easy seeing!" The frequency polygon, then, has its uses and conveniences, but its dangers.

In a quite similar way, we can produce *cumulative frequency polygons* and *relative cumulative frequency polygons* by plotting cumulative frequencies against observed values. These plotted points will be at the locations that we already explained were the only points with real meaning on our step diagrams.

Fig. 2-11. Initial Production of Trainees by New Method.

Frequency polygon of number and fraction of operators producing indicated number of units of production during their first week on regular wages.
Class C-14. Source: Synthetic.

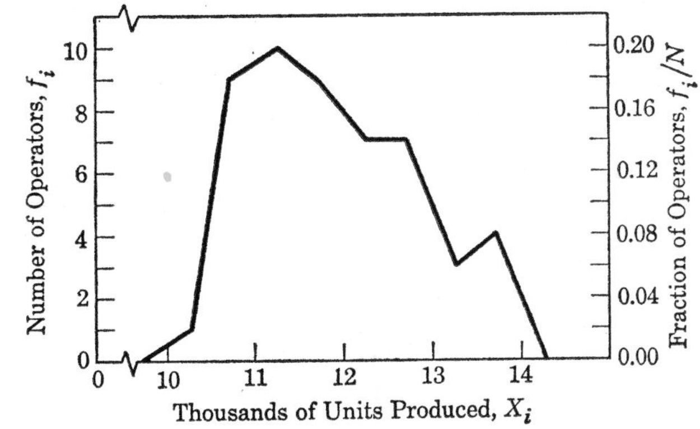

Number of Operators, f_i

0 2 4 6 8 10

Fraction of Operators, f_i/N

0.00 0.04 0.08 0.12 0.16 0.20

0 10 11 12 13 14

Thousands of Units Produced, X_i

Fig. 2-12. Checks Drawn on One Account During One Year.

Frequency polygon of number and fraction of checks of indicated sizes.
Source: Owner's Checkbook.

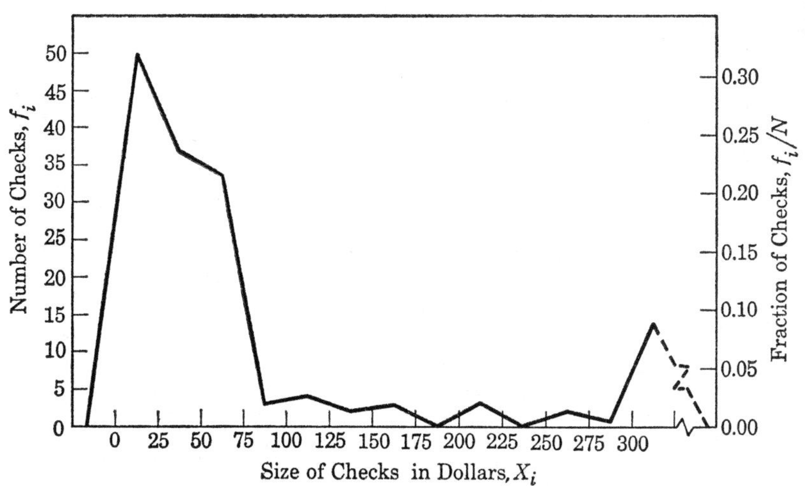

Figure 2-13 and Fig. 2-14 are cumulative (and relative cumulative, by virtue of the double vertical scales) frequency polygons equivalent to Fig. 2-6 and Fig. 2-7 concerning the trainee and check data, respectively. For these cumulative charts, there is less advantage of the polygon over the step diagram, while the sloping lines joining the plotted points give the eye an even greater urge to read off intermediate values, which is not legitimate.

Fig. 2-13. Initial Production of Trainees by New Method.

Polygon showing cumulative and relative cumulative frequencies at indicated levels of production. Source: Synthetic.

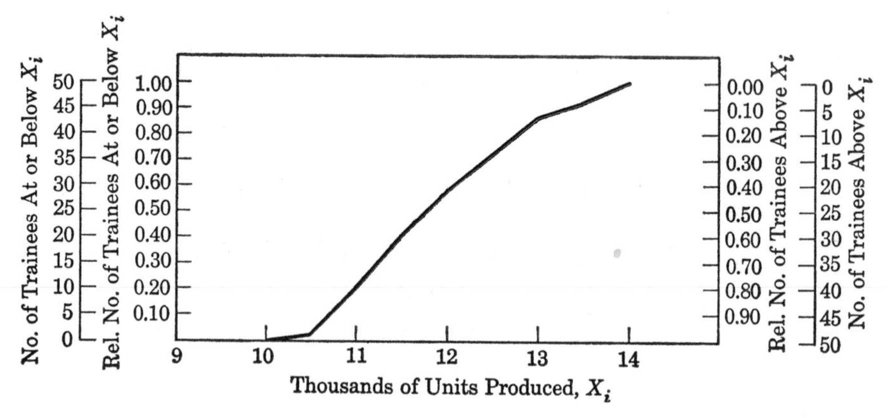

Fig. 2-14. Checks Drawn on One Account During One Year.

Polygon showing cumulative and relative cumulative frequencies of checks of indicated sizes. Source: Owner's Checkbook.

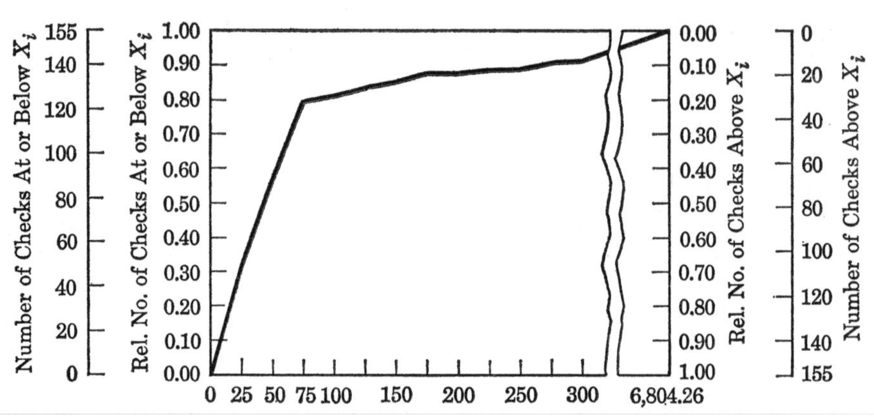

2.10 Some General Comments on Presentation of Data

We have tried, in the examples we have put before you, to show you sound practice in the presentation of data. Now we must call your attention explicitly to some of the things you have been seeing. Notice that each table and chart has had a concise *title*, which states compactly what information is involved. A *subtitle* gives more detail, and will contain some or all of the following information:

(a) an adequate description of the individuals on which the data were obtained,
(b) the nature of the measurements,
(c) the units of measurement,
(d) the date of the measurements.

As part of the subtitle, or elsewhere, always show the *source* of the data, for some sources of information command a much higher degree of respect than others, and you and your readers are entitled to this information.

In tables, each column should carry a *heading*, which describes it compactly. Sometimes this requires so much writing that an abbreviated heading, or even simply a column number, is given, and more elaborate explanation placed in footnotes. In some more elaborate tables, rows or groups of rows also have a meaning which is designated in what amounts to a heading but, because it is at the side of the table, is technically called a *stub*.

In graphs, the title, subtitle and source should be included without fail. Each scale should be clearly marked at an adequate number of division points, and a *scale label* should show the kind of information and units involved.

What this comes down to is the fact that tables and graphs should be self-contained, which means that adequate aids for their interpretation appear right on them. It should not be necessary to wade through pages of text to find out what a table or graph is all about. We could say that each should "stand up on its own legs and speak its piece!" When you prepare such material, you will be doing so in an effort to convey information to other people: assume that they are busy. If they really are busy, they will appreciate your effort to make their absorption of the information easy and will think well of you for your efforts. If they happen to be your superiors in your organization, that can do no harm! You will also find that these practices will revert to your own advantage when, in the future, you wish to find quickly some information that you recall having developed in the past; now you are the busy person, and you will be thankful that your own tables and charts are easy to recognize and differentiate.

2.11 The Distribution Concept

In the course of this chapter, we have been devoting some attention to three different sets of data. Diverse though they were in detail, they had a number of features in common. First and foremost, each set comprised observed values expressed in numerical terms — number of units of production made, number of dollars and cents for which a check was written, or number of dollars adjusted gross income. Second, the figures in each set applied to individuals in a stated category — workers trained by a new method putting in their first week at regular wages, checks written against one particular account, United States personal income taxpayers in 1957. Third, the individual observations varied one from another. Sets of observations having these three characteristics are what we call *distributions*, and they are the material with which we shall be working.

As you have studied these three distributions and their presentations as histograms and have seen other histograms, you must have already sensed that each distribution has some sort of central or typical value, some degree of scattering or dispersion of values, and a more or less clearly defined pattern of scattering. It will be our task, in the next three chapters, to learn how to find a numerical value for the center and for the amount of dispersion, and to give a compact and useful description of the scattering pattern, or form, of the distribution. When we have accomplished these objectives, we may well be surprised to find how readily we can do with computations the things we have been doing by more difficult procedures here. Having mastered these ideas and methods, we shall be in a position to undertake to answer some very penetrating and useful questions with the aid of data.

2.12 Retrospect

At this point, looking back over the chapter, we feel an irresistible urge to be honest with you. How much of what we have been discussing will you really use? If this had been written 40 years ago, and you were preparing for business or the social sciences, our answer would have had to be: all of it. Today, that is hardly true. As you deal with data, you will, indeed, often have to prepare and discuss frequency tables. We doubt that you will prepare histograms or other pictorial representations for more than two percent of the distributions you study. Why, then, have we so painstakingly discussed these ideas and methods?

You will find the answer in the fact that the other statistical methods we are about to consider accomplish what you could do with these simple but tedious methods, and accomplish much more, besides. But in order to understand these methods and how they work, you must have a feeling for distributions and their characteristics that we can help you to acquire only by using these devices first. This alone justifies their study. But it is also true that you will often see histograms, step charts, and polygons, and you will see many kinds of frequency tables. In order that you may recognize their worth and abstract their information from them, you must understand how they "work." We think you may find it wise to reconsider this chapter from time to time as you continue your study, when you may find new meaning in some of the points we have considered.

General Study

1. Examine several texts and journals in the field of major interest to you from the standpoint of the tables and charts contained in them. Find five examples of sound and effective tables and five of similar charts. Record the reasons for your decision in each case. Can you find five examples of unsound or ineffective tables and charts? If so, list your reasons for so considering them.

2. From text or advertising in current newspapers or magazines, similarly locate examples of sound and effective presentation. You might be interested to see whether you can find examples of unsound presentation which you suspect may have a deliberate purpose of deception!

Problems

1. From a morning paper, determine the closing prices of the first 100 stocks listed on the New York Stock Exchange the previous trading day. Present these figures (a) as raw data (in the order of their listing in your paper), (b) as an array, (c) as a frequency table with between 8 and 20 classes, (d) as a histogram, and (e) as a cumulative frequency polygon. Do you agree with our comments as to the results of each stage of presentation? Would you add any others?

2. Read the mileages on the odometers of each car in one of the parking lots on your campus and present the information in the several ways suggested in Problem 1.

3. Starting with Table 2-10, Individual Income Tax Returns, 1957, as given in the text, prepare the best table you can with uniform class intervals presenting the same information. Then prepare a histogram from this table, and, finally, a step diagram or cumulative frequency polygon. Discuss the advantages and disadvantages of this form of presentation as compared with that based on the original table.

4. Locate a frequency table with nonuniform classes presenting data of direct interest to you in connection with your major field. Make such diagrammatic presentation of this information as you need, and write an adequate discussion of the distribution as you now see it. Then make a revision to uniform class intervals as was done in Problem 4 above, and append to your previous description a statement containing any modifications you feel should be made.

3

Locating the Center of a Distribution

3.1 Populations and Samples

When we are working with distributions such as those we encountered in the previous chapter, we may be considering them from two different standpoints. Because they frequently lead to somewhat different statistical procedures, it is important that we learn to distinguish clearly between the two standpoints. In some cases, the data before us will constitute all the information conceivable on the subject, and our problem will be to condense the information so that our minds can cope with it more readily. The individual figures for the 59,407,673 tax returns from which Table 2-10 had already been partially condensed represented the complete information about taxable incomes in the United States in 1957. The production figures for our group trained by the new method represented all the information that ever will be available on their first week's production. Such sets of figures, or distributions, that contain all the information on a subject of interest to us are called *populations* or *universes*. The two terms, both borrowed from common language, will now have for us a special meaning, and will be used synonymously.

Under other circumstances, the data actually before us will constitute but a part of all the information in which we are interested. For example, in order to judge whether a lot of 10,000 bearing balls meets the diameter specifications under which they were purchased, we might plan to measure the diameters of 100 of the balls, infer from those measurements what the properties of the entire lot were, and make our decision on the basis of this partial information. Or, in the case of our trainee production data, we shall quite properly think of these data as 50 figures from a conceivably unending stream of first-week production data for newly trained employees. In fact, when we try to decide the merits of our new training plan on the basis of such a trial, we are thinking in just that way. When the information before us is but a part of that in which we are interested, we refer to the distribution we actually have as a *sample* from the larger population about which we are concerned. We hope that the sample represents the population, and it will be one of our later problems to determine what steps we can take to insure that this is so.

Sometimes we may be thinking about the same set of data in both ways. The adjusted incomes are a case in point. They constitute one element of our national economy for that year, and, under those circumstances, are properly considered as a population. But they may well be thought of as but one year's figures from a number of years under broadly similar economic conditions. Then the figures become a sample of the larger population of several years' figures.

In this chapter and in chapters IV and V, we shall always be considering our distributions as populations. If you will keep this fact clearly in your mind, it will help you to avoid some confusions that have plagued students of the subject since modern statistics began. You will, incidentally, considerably strengthen your own thinking about real data when you treat them.

3.2 Measures of Central Value; Averages

We mentioned at the end of the previous chapter that we were beginning to have a feeling that there was some central value for each distribution, about which the individual figures were dispersed. We shall now seek one or more methods for determining what this value is. Of course, we could take our array, or our frequency table, or one or another of our pictorial presentations of the distribution, and use our judgment to estimate where the center falls. But this procedure presents certain problems, because it involves so much subjective judgment. For one thing, two or more people, examining the same data, might select two different central values, and it might become difficult to agree upon a choice. Even more embarrassing is the fact that we might choose a central value today, report it to someone, forget what value we chose, then choose and report a different value next Tuesday, when the matter comes up again. This may seem trivial, but it can and does happen when we depend on subjective judgment. Yet another difficulty with the subjectively chosen value will arise when we do have to deal with samples, for then we shall be adding the vagaries of our judgment to the uncertainties resulting from incomplete information, and our problems of inference will become insoluble.

Therefore, what we need is one or more objective methods for selecting a single value to represent the center of our distribution. Such a figure will be called, in formal terms, a *measure of central value* (in some texts it is called a measure of central *tendency*) or, in less formal terms, an *average*. We shall find that there are different objective ways for arriving at averages, and each resulting average has its own particular name, which we shall learn.

3.3 The Mid-range

If we ask any "intelligent schoolboy" where the middle of a piece of string is, he will presumably tell us, "Half way between the two ends, of course!" Suppose we had a population consisting simply of the five values:

$$3, 5, 2, 9, 7 \tag{S3.3.1a}$$

We could conveniently arrange them in an array:

$$2, 3, 5, 7, 9 \tag{S3.3.1b}$$

Thus we can easily see that the smallest figure (minimum) is 2 and the largest (maximum) is 9. The difference between them, or range, is 7, and half it, 3.5. If we add this half-range to the minimum or subtract it from the maximum we arrive at the value 5.5, which is appropriately called the mid-range. This description shows the thinking behind the concept of the mid-range, but our procedure for finding it was needlessly clumsy: all we need to do is locate the maximum and minimum, add them, and divide by two. This is our definition of the *mid-range.*

This was simple enough for this set of figures, and it does, indeed, have the merit of plausibility. "Any fool can plainly see" that it makes sense. Unfortunately, what the fool can plainly see is not always the best of sense. Suppose we refer to our data in Table 2-1 (p. 9) concerning trainee production. Here we have only 50 figures, yet, from the table of raw data, it is no small task to pick out the two extreme values without making a mistake. Of course, the array, Table 2-2 (p. 9), shows clearly that the minimum was 10,323 and the maximum was 13,951 so that the mid-range is $(10{,}323 + 13{,}951)/2 = 12{,}137$. If we had had a still larger distribution, the problem of searching for the extreme values, with or without the preparation of an array, would have been much greater, so that the "simplicity" of the mid-range becomes rather more in thought than in use.

To see another difficulty with the mid-range, consider another set of figures, already in array form:

$$2, 3, 3, 3, 9 \tag{S3.3.2}$$

This set has the same mid-range, 5.5, but all but one of the values falls below it! A third set,

$$2, 8, 8, 9, 9 \tag{S3.3.3}$$

also has the same mid-range, 5.5, but the values are grouped near the maximum. Perhaps the center is not quite so simple as we thought: let us look further.

3.4 The Median

In arriving at the mid-range as a measure of central value, we were thinking in terms of the numerical values of our observations, and considered our center as midway between the extremes. This was plausible, but led to somewhat unsatisfactory results in the last two instances. Suppose, now, that we consider how many observations, or values, we have and take as our average that value which is at the middle of the array. That will mean that there will be as many values greater than it as there are less than it. For our set 3.3.1 the value will be 5, since the values 2 and 3 are below it and 7 and 9 are above it. When we come to sets 3.3.2 and 3.3.3 our values become 3 and 8, respectively, and we seem to have quite a simple procedure, but suppose that we have the values:

$$2, 3, 5, 7 \tag{S3.4.1}$$

What do we do? There are now four values in our distribution, and hence there is no one of the values which has equal numbers of values above and below itself. We can, however, extend our principle slightly and take the value midway between the top of the lower half and the bottom of the upper half of our array, 4 in this case. This is simple and reasonable.

This leads to a definition of this average, which is called the *median*, as the value at the middle of the array of an odd number of observations, or the value midway between the top of the lower half and bottom of the upper half of the array of an even number of observations. For the data of Table 2-1, we find by this definition that the median is $(11{,}699 + 11{,}709)/2 = 11{,}704$.

This average has the disadvantage that it practically requires that the data be arranged in an array, which we have already noticed is a tedious and time-consuming task. However, it does have the advantage of paying a little attention to all the values, not merely the two extremes. But it is not a completely satisfying measure of central value. Let's think further!

3.5 The Mode

In our discussion of the nature and purpose of statistics in Chapter 1, we mentioned that sometimes we need a "typical" value from our distribution. The case of the bank deposits was a good example. In the case of the trainee production data, we might well be interested in the typical figure for making future plans. We could, then, consider the typical figure as the one which occurs most often. Such a figure is called the *mode*, and is another average.

Set 3.3.1 and our data of Table 2-1 immediately show a disadvantage of this average: all values in these distributions show the same frequency: one! Another disadvantage is illustrated by the set:

$$2, 3, 3, 3, 5, 5, 7, 7, 7, 9 \tag{S3.5.1}$$

in which 3 and 7 each occur three times, and all other values occur fewer times. Hence there are two "modes" and we still haven't a center. Of course, S3.3.2 does have a clearly defined mode, which is indeed the typical value.

These simple illustrations developed the disadvantages of the mode. It requires, practically, that the data be arrayed, and it often results that there are several values, each having the same "maximum" frequency, so that the mode is not, in fact, well defined. Yet the basic idea is attractive, and we shall want to think about it more in the future.

3.6 The Arithmetic Mean

By this time, possibly, you are wondering when we are going to tell you to do what any "sensible" person would do: find the average. But let us remind you that, in our terms, all the values we have been determining in this chapter are averages! The one you have in mind has, in statistical terminology, the formal name *arithmetic mean.* (It may save you embarrassment to be told that the "arithmetic" in the name is an adjective, and the accent is on the "met.") There are several other kinds of means, but since this one is the most commonly used, we ordinarily refer to it by the less formal "nickname" as the mean, reserving the full name for those cases in which there might be misunderstanding.

We can find the mean for a number of distributions we have been studying, and Table 3-1 will show the necessary intermediate figures and final results.

Table 3-1 COMPUTATION OF ARITHMETIC MEAN FOR SET OF DATA USED IN TEXT

Data	Sum of Values	Number	Mean
Table 2-1	593,995	50	11,879.9
S3.3.1	26	5	5.2
S3.3.2	20	5	4.0
S3.3.3	36	5	7.2
S3.4.1	17	4	4.25
S3.5.1	51	10	5.1

What are the obvious advantages and disadvantages of the arithmetic mean as a measure of central value? It is immediately apparent that it can be computed directly from the raw data, without any form of rearrangement. Surely this is a real saving in time and trouble. Then another advantage is that it makes equal use of each observation: all the values are added together. Contrast that with the mid-range, which really uses only the two extreme values: the remaining values are not considered at all. Of course, unlike the mode, the mean is always clearly defined, a very real advantage in itself.

The mean has another very real but less obvious advantage. If we take the sum of all the differences between the mean and those values smaller than it we would find that it just equalled, numerically, the sum of the differences between the mean and all values larger than it. This has an interesting physical analogy. Suppose that our scale of possible values was arranged as a balance bar, with the fulcrum at the mean, and that the mean was placed at the middle of the bar. Now suppose that a series of equal weights was available, and that we hung a weight from the bar at the position corresponding to each observed value. For the data of set 3.3.2, the result would look like Fig. 3-1. We would

Fig. 3-1. The Mean of a Set as Its Balance Point, Illustrated with S3.3.2.

Each weight represents one value, and all weights are of equal size. The fulcrum of the balance is located at the mean, and the weights are in perfect balance.

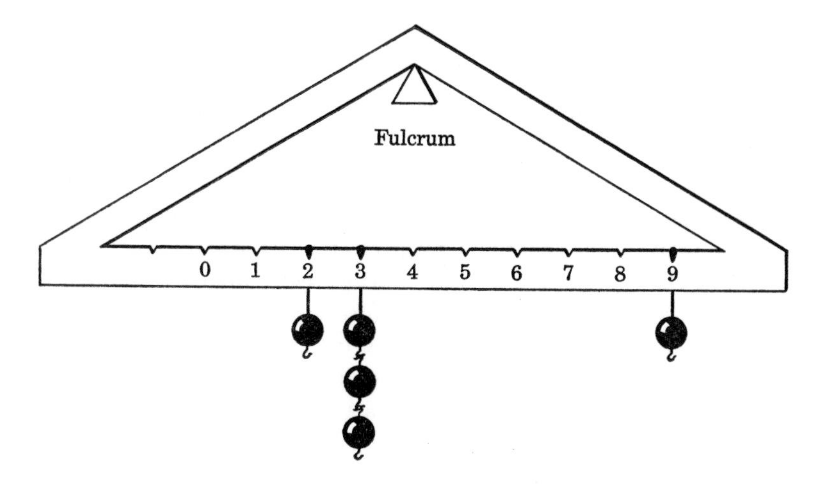

now find that our bar was exactly balanced and would tilt neither one way nor the other.

Why is that? In physics, it is shown that the turning action of a weight about a pivot is equal to the product of the weight times its distance from the pivot. But we made all the weights equal, so their turning actions depend on their distances. The sum of the distances on the right, whose weights would make the balance beam turn clockwise, is, by the nature of the mean, just equal to the sum of the distances on the left, whose weights would make the beam turn counterclockwise: so the beam doesn't turn. While this analogy may not seem too important to you yet, it is certainly comforting to realize that the mean does have this "point of balance" aspect. It has two other advantages which we cannot begin to appreciate until we have considered some other statistical ideas which form the content of the next two chapters. Suffice it to say, at present, that the mean has so many advantages that it is by all odds the most used average.

3.7 Some Mathematical Notation

We seem to have come quite far without introducing any frightening mathematical notation. A few plus signs and a fraction bar seem to have sufficed. This we could do because the ideas we have been dealing with have been so simple that we could describe the arithmetic operations involved without using too many words. But this will not continue to be true, so we may as well become used to some notation which will prove very convenient for us as time goes on.

The use of mathematical symbols arises from some simple physiological and psychological principles. Suppose you hold this book at normal reading distance and, keeping your eyes fixed on one word near the center of the page, try to determine how much of the page is really sharp and clear. Probably you will find it is about the area that could be covered by a 25¢ piece. Hence, if you wish to read the sentence,

> *The arithmetic mean of a population is obtained by adding together all the values in the population and dividing the resulting sum by the number of such observations.*

your eyes would have to start at the left of the first line, continually shift aim and focus as they scanned that line, return to the left of the second line, and so to the end of the sentence. Physical effort is really involved, though we are rarely directly conscious of it, and this effort is one of the factors which contribute to the literal fatigue resulting from careful study.

To reduce this fatigue and increase the amount of effective thinking that can be done in a given time, the mathematician uses more compact symbols. He starts by replacing the entire phrase "the arithmetic mean of a population" by the symbol "μ" which is a lower case Greek "m," named mu. By a certain consistency of selection of such symbols in statistics, we will usually associate a Greek letter with a characteristic of a population. Here the Greek mu is related to the initial letter of *m*ean. Next, we replace the idea "is obtained by" by the essentially equivalent idea "is equal to" and then replace it by the long-familiar symbol, =. Now we let X represent any value in our distribution but, in order to keep the individual values clearly in mind, we place the serial number of the observation as a subscript. We replace the phrase, "the number of such observations," by "N." Now we can replace "adding together all the values in our population" by the symbols:—

$$X_1 + X_2 + \ldots + X_i + \ldots + X_N \qquad (3.7.1)$$

where the rows of dots (. . .) replace the missing values and the subscript $_i$ stands for any subscript in our set. Now we can replace the phrase, "and dividing the resulting sum by," by writing the sum over a horizontal line and the quantity we are going to divide by, N, under it, or we can put the sum in parentheses, to indicate that something is going to be done with it, then write a slanting line (formally known as a solidus!), followed by the N. Thus our long sentence becomes

$$\mu = \frac{X_1 + X_2 + \ldots + X_i + \ldots + X_N}{N} \tag{3.7.2}$$

$$= (X_1 + X_2 + \ldots + X_i + \ldots + X_N)/N \tag{3.7.3}$$

This is a considerably more compact expression, you must agree. But even this does not satisfy us. This Greek letter idea has merit. Suppose we replace the phrase, "adding together," by the equivalent word, "summing," and then substitute for it the upper case Greek "S," Σ, or sigma. Then we follow the Σ by X_i and under the Σ we write "$i = 1$" and over it, N. Now we can write

$$\mu = \frac{\sum_{i=1}^{N} X_i}{N} \tag{3.7.4}$$

or

$$\mu = \sum_{i=1}^{N} X_i \Big/ N \tag{3.7.5}$$

Now we have a pretty compact expression. But we can go even farther in cases where we are sure no ambiguity can arise by eliminating the designations above and below the sigma, understanding that this means that we add all N of the values. Thus we have

$$\mu = \frac{\Sigma X}{N} \quad \text{or} \quad \mu = \Sigma X/N \tag{3.7.6}$$

Now we have a very compact expression. Yet, with the aid of our "code book" which we started when we described the meaning of each symbol, we can translate the compact expression directly back to the full directions in English.

It may seem to you that we have spent a long time in discussing this rather simple point. But we have seen so many friends so overwhelmed by mathematical notation which was intended to aid, not dismay, them that we felt impelled to try to make this point clear before the expressions we needed to translate became too complicated in English. What we have shown about these expressions is true of all mathematical notation: it is a condensed form of writing, a shorthand, if you like, which is capable of translation back and forth from clear English, and is intended to help us do our thinking more easily. All the expressions we shall have to use in this text will be like these in that they will be directions for performing some sequences of operations on sets of numbers: think of them as that, and you will find that they are a very real convenience.

3.8 Working from Frequency Tables

You will often find that it is difficult or impossible to obtain the complete data on subjects of interest to you when the data do not originate with you. For example, the income data presented in Table 2-10 are publicly and readily available, but we strongly suspect that the Internal Revenue Service would look with extreme disfavor upon a request for the nearly 60 million figures which that table condenses. Can we develop measures of central tendency from frequency tables? As we shall see, we cannot be assured of obtaining exactly the values that would have been obtained from the raw data, but we can obtain, for some of the measures, values that will often serve our purposes adequately. Instead of using the numerous and cumbersome values on trainee production rates of Table 2-1, let us see how the ideas work if we start from the related frequency table, Table 2-4. This will give us the added advantage that we already have our values computed from the corresponding raw data for comparison.

First, let us consider the mid-range. Here we can make only a poor approximation. The lower limit of the lower class is 10,000 units, while the upper limit of the upper class is 13,999 units. Using these values in place of the actual minimum and maximum, we could obtain $(10{,}000 + 13{,}999)/2 = 11{,}999.5$ as our approximation to the mid-range. The actual mid-range, from the complete data, was 12,137. It can be shown that the maximum discrepancy between the true value and that computed from the frequency table is one-half the class interval. This provides us with a gauge as to the possible consequences of the approximation.

The median can be approximated by the use of another simplifying assumption. Since there are 50 values, we need the value midway between the 25th and 26th of the values in the array. But we can't make the array if we have only the frequency table. But notice that the first three classes include 20 values and the first four classes include 29 values. The value we want must be in that fourth class: where? Suppose we act as though the values in that class were uniformly distributed through it. We can think of the value midway between the 25th and 26th as the "$25\frac{1}{2}$th" value, or $5\frac{1}{2}$ values above the bottom of the class. There are 9 values in the class and the class interval is 500 units, so if we take a value $(5\frac{1}{2}/9) \times 500 \doteq 305.6$ units above the lower class boundary, 11,499.5, we arrive at the value 11,805.1 as an approximation to the median, whose true value we found previously as 11,704. (The symbol, "$\doteq$" which we used above indicates approximately equal, when the last figure given is rounded.) Actually, the computation of the median from a frequency table could produce a discrepancy as great as one class interval, but with real data it is most unlikely to do so.

The mode can best be approached by thinking of the *modal class*, the class with the highest frequency. In our case, this is our third class, having 11,249.5 as the class mark. But notice: the data have no mode! If we had used different class intervals, or different class boundaries, we would have altered the position of our modal class. This is just another of the unsatisfactory aspects of the idea of the mode. Some workers use rather elaborate procedures in an effort to "pinpoint" the mode from frequency tables; we don't think they are justified and will therefore not trouble you with them.

The mean is subject to computation with an extension of the same simplifying assumption we used with the median. If we act as though the observations in each class are uniformly distributed through it, then their mean will be the class mark and their sum will be the product of the class mark times the class frequency. If we add all these products and divide the sum by the total frequency, or number of observations, we should have an approximation to the mean. We can express this process in our symbolic language as follows:—

Let X_i = the mark of the ith class

and f_i = the frequency of the ith class.

Then $\mu = \Sigma f_i X_i / \Sigma f_i$.

For our table, the results, with the intermediate computations, are shown in Table 3-2, and the value is 11,899.5, compared with the value 11,879.9 obtained from the raw data. No very simple statement can be made concerning the possible size of this discrepancy, but, as we become more familiar with other aspects of statistics, we shall be able to make an understandable statement.

Table 3-2 COMPUTATION OF ARITHMETIC MEAN FROM FREQUENCY TABLE 2-4

Class Mark, X_i	*Class Frequency,* f_i	$f_i X_i$
10,249.5	1	10,249.5
10,749.5	9	96,745.5
11,249.5	10	112,495.0
11,749.5	9	105,745.5
12,249.5	7	85,746.5
12,749.5	7	89,246.5
13,249.5	3	39,748.5
13,749.5	4	54,998.0
Sums	50	594,975.0

$\mu = 594{,}750.0/50 = 11{,}899.5$

This illustration should help you to understand that it is possible to approximate the four measures of central value from frequency tables, but that each measure is subject to the introduction of a discrepancy as the result of the grouping of observations into classes. Forty years ago, when good desk calculators were not available for handling ordinary sets of data and the high-capacity digital computers were unknown, statisticians made much use of these approximations to save the tremendous volume of work that would otherwise be needed. Further complications of formulas, but simplification of the arithmetic involved, were introduced in a justifiable effort to alleviate the tedium of calculation with the equipment then available. Fine machines are readily available today, and we believe it is a mistake to fill a text such as this with outdated procedures. Furthermore, each step of conversion of the data in the direction of "simplification" and the return from the "simplified" computations to the needed result represents a possibility for a mistake. This is a risk it does not seem prudent to take today.

3.9 Other Kinds of Averages

Although the four averages we have discussed (the mid-range, median, mode, and mean) are the most commonly used, and the arithmetic mean is the most useful, they do not exhaust the possibilities. One that seems most amazing is the *harmonic mean.* This is obtained by taking the reciprocal of each value (The reciprocal of X is $1/X$.), then finding the mean of the reciprocals, and taking its reciprocal! Ridiculous though this may sound, there are reasons for it. For example, in electrical work, if we have a resistor, we may think about either its resistance to the passage of electricity or its conductance, or ability to carry electricity. The conductance is the reciprocal of the resistance, and it so happens that, when resistors are connected "in parallel" it is their conductances which add. So the effect would be as though we had connected the same number of resistors with the same mean conductance in parallel. But, by long habit, people talk about resistance, so this mean conductance is converted back to a resistance by taking its reciprocal. We might say, then, that the only amazing thing is that people bothered to call the end result a harmonic mean!

We regret that we cannot resist the opportunity to point out that, in our electrical analog, if one of the resistances happens to be zero, you will have what is called a short circuit, and the results, when the voltage is applied, are always spectacular and sometimes disastrous! And there is a mathematical disaster, too: you cannot divide by zero, so, if any of your X's or the mean of their reciprocals happens to be zero, the harmonic mean can't be calculated.

Another average is the *geometric mean*, which is the Nth root of the product obtained by multiplying all N values together. This is a most unhandy average for two reasons. First, if any value is zero, the harmonic mean is zero, regardless of what all other values may be. Second, if there are an odd number of negative values but an even total number of values, the geometric mean is not a number of the kind with which we work in ordinary arithmetic and algebra. We mention these two averages, not with the idea that you will use them, but simply to acquaint you with terms which you may possibly encounter in some of your reading.

3.10 Recapitulation

We have presented a number of averages for your consideration, and have also suggested some auxiliary ideas, all in this one chapter. Here are restated the principle ideas about averages. An average, or measure of central value, of a distribution is a single value, obtained by defined objective methods, which represents the center of the distribution. The four most common averages are

1. The *mid-range*, calculated as half the sum of the minimum and maximum value.

2. The *median*, the value at the middle of the array. When the number of values, N, is odd, it is value number $(N + 1)/2$. When N is even, the median is half the sum of value number $N/2$ and value number $(N/2) + 1$.

3. The *mode* is the value which occurs most often.

4. The *mean*, or, more fully, the *arithmetic mean*, is the sum of the values divided by their number.

For many sets of data, these four measures will all be different. This is because of the different concepts of "center" on which they are based. The mid-range divides the range of values in half; the median, the number in half; the mode shows the typical value, in the sense of most "popular," while the mean is a balance point. The four measures for the sets of values considered in this chapter are shown in Table 3-3.

Table 3-3 MEASURES OF CENTRAL VALUE FOR SETS IN CHAPTER 3

Set	Mid-range	Median	Mode	Mean
3.3.1	5.5	5.0	None	5.2
3.3.2	5.5	3.0	3	4.0
3.3.3	5.5	8.0	None	7.2
3.4.1	4.5	4.0	None	4.25
3.5.1	5.5	5.0	None	5.1

General Study

1. As you read your newspaper, weekly magazines, and journals in your field, notice how many averages are used. Are the writers careful to state which kind of average they are using? Do the averages give you some feeling for the data they are discussing?

2. In a labor dispute, an employer could claim that the average earnings of its employees is $12,500 per year, while the union could claim that the figure is $5,000. Both could be strictly correct. Explain how this could be and illustrate with a simple table with assumed values.

Problems

1. Find the mid-range, median, mode, and mean of each of the following sets of values:

(a) 3, 7, 8, 7
(b) 2, 9, 5, 6, 7, 4, 5
(c) 2, 2, 4, 4, 9, 9, 7, 7, 5
(d) 1, 9, 5, 3, 5, 7, 3, 7, 5

2. Find the mid-range, median, mode, and mean of the data you obtained in the problems following Chapter 2.

3. Select 25 securities of interest to you and determine the mid-range, median, mode, and mean of the closing prices of these stocks on the New York Stock Exchange each day for one week.

4. Find the most recent population figures for the cities of your county or state and determine the measures of central value requested in the previous problems for them.

5. Record the shoe sizes of each member of your section and develop the four averages requested above for these data.

6. Record the number of cars passing a reasonably busy point near your campus each minute for 20 minutes and develop the four averages requested in previous problems.

7. Count the number of letters and spaces per line for 20 lines in this text. Determine the averages suggested in the foregoing problems.

8. For each set of data you have studied in such of the previous problems as you have done, state the average which you think best portrays the "center" of the distribution, and state why you selected this one.

4

Measuring Scattering or Dispersion

4.1 Measures of Dispersion

Our experience in finding measures of central value will have prepared us for many of the ideas we shall encounter in finding out how to describe the scattering of a set of values. What we shall seek is definite procedures which will yield, objectively, numbers which will be greater the more the values are scattered, or dispersed. When we find such procedures, their results will be called *measures of dispersion.* Our experience with averages will suggest that different ways of thinking about the amount of dispersion in a set of values may well lead to different measures, and this will, indeed, be true. But we are in for an even greater surprise: a way of thinking that, at first, will appear to lead to a terrifically complicated computation will, when we come to grips with it, turn out to be one of the simplest. That often happens when we do enough thinking about a problem.

4.2 The Range

In the last chapter, we used the mid-range as an average: why not use the range, itself, as a measure of dispersion? We can and do, and it has a great deal of merit, particularly when our distribution consists of a finite set of finite values. It does, of course, tell exactly the overall spread of our values, and is an idea that it is quite easy to understand.

Unfortunately, it suffers from all the disadvantages of the mid-range. It considers only the extreme values, and pays no attention to whether the other values are closely "bunched" or widely dispersed. If the observations are very numerous, it is a problem to make sure that the two extreme values have been correctly located. Furthermore, in dealing with observed values, we often have a lurking suspicion that the extreme values may be mistakes of observation or recording. (Note, in passing, that this idea is also an objection to the mid-range, but somewhat less serious, because of the possibility of counter-balancing errors.) Suppose we record the range for the sets of data used in the preceding chapter:

Set	*Values*	*Extremes*	*Range*
3.3.1	3, 5, 2, 9, 7	2, 9	7
3.3.2	2, 3, 3, 3, 9	2, 9	7
3.3.3	2, 8, 8, 9, 9	2, 9	7
3.4.1	2, 3, 5, 7	2, 7	5
3.5.1	2, 3, 3, 3, 5, 5, 7, 7, 7, 9	2, 9	7

Intuitively, most of us feel just a little dissatisfied with the idea that four of these sets have the same amount of dispersion. The first set seems to be fairly well spread through its range, while in the second set, three of the five values are just above the minimum and in the third set the maximum and the value one unit below it account for two each of the five values. All in all, we ought not to rest content with the range.

4.3 The Mean Absolute Deviation

In the range, we were thinking of the scattering or dispersion only in terms of the extreme values. Now we have already gone to considerable effort to locate the center of our distribution; why not measure our dispersion in terms of the amount by which the individual values deviate from the central value? This sounds like a good idea (it is!) and we hope you are even on your toes enough to suggest that we could use the mean value of the deviations of the observations from their mean. This would be expressed in our condensed symbols as

$$\Sigma(X_i - \mu)/N \tag{4.3.1}$$

This is good thinking, but it overlooked one piece of information already at your command. In our discussion of the mean, we pointed out that the sum of the differences between the mean and values smaller than it was numerically equal to that of the differences between the mean and values larger than it. Deviations of values below the mean will all have negative signs, while those above will all have positive signs, so the mean value of the deviations will be zero for every distribution. This is hardly a useful result!

But, of course, what you and we really meant was to find the mean of the amounts of deviation, ignoring the direction and attendant algebraic sign. In mathematical terms, the *amount* of deviation is the *absolute deviation*, and the mean of these amounts is the *mean absolute deviation*. The mathematician needs this idea of absolute, or numerical, value so often that he uses a symbol for it. Enclosing a quantity between parallel vertical lines indicates that the absolute, or numerical, value, disregarding sign, is to be used. If we let D

stand for the mean absolute deviation (this is not a universally used symbol, but happens to be convenient here), we can write our formula as

$$D = \Sigma \mid X_i - \mu \mid /N \tag{4.3.2}$$

Let us see how these computations would work out for set 3.3.1. The computations are shown in the working table below:

Value X_i	$X_i - \mu$	$\mid X_i - \mu \mid$	
3	−2.2	2.2	$\mu = 5.2$ by previous calculation
5	−0.2	0.2	
2	−3.2	3.2	
9	+3.8	3.8	
7	+1.8	1.8	
Sums	0.0	11.2	

$$D = 11.2/5 = 2.24$$

This computation was quite a bit of work, even for these few values. The only thing we can do to shorten it is to compute the deviations only for those values below (or above) the mean, double their sum, and divide by the total number of observations. This stems from the previously stated fact that the numerical sum of the deviations of values below the mean just equals that of values above. This brings out one of the disadvantages of this measure of dispersion. We must either make an array, a tedious task, or very carefully compute deviations for values on one side of the mean only, or compute all the deviations. None of these alternatives is very attractive for a large set of data.

However, let us go ahead and compute the mean absolute deviation for the other sets of values we used to investigate the range, and include the one just computed for comparison.

Set	*Mean* μ	*M.A.D.* D
3.3.1	5.2	2.24
3.3.2	4.0	2.00
3.3.3	7.2	2.08
3.4.1	4.25	1.75
3.5.1	5.1	1.92

The values probably seem to most of us to make more sense than did the range for these data. But we still have the problem of the work involved. Let's look further.

4.4 The Variance

Now comes the surprise! Suppose we square 2, that is, multiply 2 by itself: $2^2 = 4$. Now the laws of arithmetic tell us that the square of -2 is $(-2)^2 = 4$

also. This is interesting, for it says that, if we squared the deviations, we would automatically lose the signs. We might use the mean of the squares of these deviations as a measure of dispersion. We not only might, we will, and we'll call it the *variance* and use as its symbol σ^2, a lower case Greek "s" (sigma) with an exponent ^{2}, meaning "squared." In fact, we'll often refer to it in conversation, though rarely in writing, as "sigma squared." Its formula is

$$\sigma^2 = \Sigma(X_i - \mu)^2/N \tag{4.4.1}$$

You would now have every right to consider that we had taken leave of our senses! Here we objected to the mean absolute deviation because it involved finding all the differences, adding them, and dividing by the number of observations, and now we tell you to square the deviations before adding them, and imply that we have a better measure! Well, we do, but to show you that that is so, we must do a little algebra. Suppose we literally write down three of the terms, the first two and the last, of our sum:

$$\sigma^2 = [(X_1 - \mu)^2 + (X - \mu)^2 + \ldots + (X_N - \mu)^2]/N \tag{4.4.1a}$$

and then expand the squares, placing similar terms in the same column:

$$\sigma^2 = \begin{bmatrix} & X_1^2 & - & 2\mu X_1 & + & \mu^2 \\ + & X_2^2 & - & 2\mu X_2 & + & \mu^2 \\ + & \cdot & \cdot & \cdot & \cdot & \cdot \\ + & X_N^2 & - & 2\mu X_N & + & \mu^2 \end{bmatrix} \div N \tag{4.4.1b}$$

Now if we examine the first column on the right of 4.4.1b, we see that we have simply the squares of all the values, which are to be added together. We can express this notion by simply writing ΣX_i^2. The second column is just each value multiplied by twice the mean and preceded by a minus sign. We can remove the -2μ from this sum as a common factor and write the sum as $-2\mu\Sigma X_i$. The third column is simply the sum of N values of μ^2. So we can now rewrite our expression as

$$\sigma^2 = \frac{\Sigma X_i^2 - 2\mu\Sigma X_i + N\mu^2}{N} \tag{4.4.1c}$$

This doesn't look like much of a help yet, but let's continue by replacing one of the μ's in the last term in the numerator by its equivalent, $\Sigma X_i/N$, removing the common factor, N, from numerator and denominator of that term, and then combining like terms:

$$\sigma^2 = \frac{\Sigma X_i^2 - 2\mu\Sigma X_i + \cancel{N}(\Sigma X_i/\cancel{N})\mu}{N}$$

$$= \frac{\Sigma X_i^2 - \mu\Sigma X_i}{N} \tag{4.4.1d}$$

Surely you are now ready to say, "So what?" or something even less polite, and we don't much blame you. If we had had to answer your question even 30 years ago, our only proper answer would have had to be, "Not much!" But today, things really are different. With the aid of a modern desk calculator, we can accumulate simultaneously the sum of a set of values and the sum of their squares in a single run through the machine. Furthermore, by taking advantage of the fact that division of the sum by N, to find the mean, is equivalent to multiplying the sum by the reciprocal of N, and the fact that, when that reciprocal does not involve too many digits, the machine can so calculate the mean and then remove it without disturbing the sum and sum of squared values, we can begin to see some hope. Furthermore, a modern machine can then subtract the product of the mean by the sum in a way that is almost self-checking, and thus leave the value of $(\Sigma X_i^2 - \mu \Sigma X_i)$ ready to be divided by N. We have placed in Appendix XI a discussion of ways of operating the three principal types of American calculators which make this and other statistical computations quite easy. Your effort to acquire some facility in using such machines will reward you in many ways, both during your study of statistics and in your academic work generally, not to mention in your subsequent efforts in the "real world."

Suppose we look at the reciprocals of some possible values that N might have.

N	$1/N$
5	0.2
50	0.02
500	0.002
4	0.25
40	0.025
400	0.0025
8	0.125
16	0.0625
32	0.03125
7	0.142857142857 . . .
6	0.166666666666 . . .

Notice, first, that retaining the same sequence of digits in N, but moving the decimal, retains the same digits in $1/N$, but moves its decimal in the opposite direction. Notice, second, that the reciprocals of some numbers contain only one, others only two, or three, or some other specific number of significant digits. Up to three or four significant digits, we might consider reciprocals as wieldy for our purpose. But 1/7 comprises an unending repetition of the sequence, 142857. And 1/6 consists of 0.1 followed by an unending stream of 6's. Such reciprocals are unwieldy, for we always introduce some inaccuracy when we "chop" them off at some finite number of decimals, and the effect of the inaccuracy can be drastic for our present purposes.

But, fortunately, we have a way out of that difficulty, too. Suppose we replace all the μ's on the right of 4.4.1c by their equivalent, $\Sigma X_i/N$, and carry on as before:

$$\sigma^2 = \frac{\Sigma X_i^2 - 2(\Sigma X_i/N)\Sigma X_i + N(\Sigma X_i/N)(\Sigma X_i/N)}{N}$$

$$= \frac{\Sigma X_i^2 - 2(\Sigma X_i)^2/N + (\Sigma X_i)^2/N}{N}$$

$$= \frac{\Sigma X_i^2 - (\Sigma X_i)^2/N}{N} \tag{4.4.1e}$$

This is a form which looks better than it is, for our calculators cannot determine the value of $(\Sigma X_i)^2/N$ without removing the sum and sum of squared values from the machine. The sum of squared values must then be re-entered and the quotient subtracted from it. This adds to our time and the possibility of mistakes. However, we can multiply numerator and denominator by N, with the result that

$$\sigma^2 = [N\Sigma X_i^2 - (\Sigma X_i)^2]/N^2 \tag{4.4.1f}$$

and this is the form we shall use when N has an unwieldy reciprocal; we shall use, however, equation 4.4.1d when the reciprocal is wieldy. Perhaps we should emphasize that the terms, "wieldy" and "unwieldy," are not mathematical terms, but they do express the characteristics we are discussing.

Notice, carefully, that ΣX_i^2 means that the individual values are squared and the squares are added; whereas $(\Sigma X_i)^2$ means that the values are added and the sum is squared. Unless all values are identical, in which case statistical work is trivial, these two results will always differ. While we are dealing with possible confusion, we must mention a piece of statistical slang which is so convenient that it is now perfectly good usage. The quantity $\Sigma(X_i - \mu)^2$ is now universally referred to as the "sum of squares" which, like much slang, is a condensation of the full expression, sum of squares of differences between the observations and their mean. You will agree that the condensation is welcome! You will find yourself using the terms "sigma X" and "sigma X square" to denote the sum of values and sum of squared values, respectively, in unwritten discussions.

4.5 Use of Variance Formulas

The development of the formulas for computing the variance has occupied quite a bit of time and space. For readers not accustomed to algebraic manipulations, there is probably some distrust and confusion about the result. Therefore, before going on to discuss the merits of the variance as a measure of dispersion, let's put the formulas to use on some simple examples. We should always keep before ourselves the idea that the definition of the variance is that it is the mean of the squared differences between the observations and their mean, as stated symbolically in equation 4.4.1. The other formulas are algebraic identities, more convenient for use with modern calculators.

Table 4-1 APPLICATION OF VARIANCE FORMULAS TO THE DATA OF SET 3.3.1

	(1) X_i	(2) $(X_i - \mu)$	(3) $(X_i - \mu)^2$	(4) X_i^2
	3	−2.2	4.84	9
	5	−0.2	0.04	25
	2	−3.2	10.24	4
	9	+3.8	14.44	81
	7	+1.8	3.24	49
Sums	26	0.0	32.80	168

Computation of Mean

$$\mu = \Sigma X_i/N = 26/5 = 5.2$$

$$= (1/N)\Sigma X_i = 0.2 \times 26 = 5.2$$

Variance by Equation 4.4.1

$$\sigma^2 = (X_i - \mu)^2/N = 32.80/5 = 6.56$$

Variance by Equation 4.4.1d

$$\sigma^2 = (\Sigma X_i^2 - \mu\Sigma X_i)/N = (168 - 5.2 \times 26)/5$$

$$= (168 - 132.5)/5 = 32.8/5 = 6.56$$

Variance by Equation 4.4.1f

$$\sigma^2 = (NX_i^2 - (X_i)^2)/N^2$$

$$= (5 \times 168 - 26^2)/5^2 = (840 - 676)/25$$

$$= 164/25 = 6.56$$

Table 4-1 illustrates the application of these formulas to the data of set 3.3.1. The individual values, X_i, are recorded in column 1. To the right of the columnar portion of the table, the mean, μ, is calculated both by the definition formula and the equivalent formula using the reciprocal of N. The results are, of course, identical. Using this value of $\mu = 5.2$, the individual differences are computed and recorded in column 2. Their squares are recorded in column 3, whose sum is the numerator of the variance according to equation 4.4.1. Division by N $(= 5)$ gives the variance as 6.56. In column 4, the squares of the individual values are recorded. The sum of these squared values, together with the sum of the values and the mean, already obtained, provides the items needed for formula 4.4.1d, which may be used because the reciprocal of N is "tidy," and the result is again 6.56, identical with that obtained by definition. Finally, we use formula 4.4.1f, which is not really needed here, to show that it also produces the same result.

In Table 4-2 we introduce an example involving a new set of data, set 4.5.1, comprising seven observations. The reciprocal of 7, you will recall, is very

Table 4-2 COMPUTATION OF VARIANCE WHEN THE RECIPROCAL OF N IS A REPEATING DECIMAL AND ΣX IS NOT A MULTIPLE OF N

Part A. Using Equation 4.4.1 and Common Fractions. Data set 4.5.1

	X_i	$X_i - \mu$	$(X_i - \mu)^2$
	2	$-3\ 2/7 = -23/7$	529/49
	9	$+3\ 5/7 = +26/7$	676/49
	3	$-2\ 2/7 = -16/7$	256/49
	7	$+1\ 5/7 = +12/7$	144/49
	5	$-2/7 = -2/7$	4/49
	6	$+5/7 = +5/7$	25/49
	5	$-2/7 = -2/7$	4/49
Sums	37	0	1638/49

$$\mu = \Sigma X_i/N = 37/7 = 5\ 2/7 = 5.\dot{\overline{285714}}$$

$$\Sigma(X_i - \mu)^2 = 1638/49 = 33\ 21/49 = 33\ 3/7 = 33.\dot{\overline{428571}}$$

$$\sigma^2 = (1638/49)/7 = 1638/343 = 4\ 266/343 = 4\ 38/49 \doteq 4.7755102041$$

"untidy." In Part A of the table, equation 4.4.1 has been employed, using the exact common fractions throughout until the final expression of the variance as a repeating decimal. In this way we are always dealing with exact values until the final decimal approximation, but our computations with even these few values become very tedious. In Part B of the table, we avoided the difficulty of

Part B. Using Equation 4.4.1 and Decimal Fractions, Rounding μ to One, Two, and Five Decimal Places but Retaining All Resulting Places Thereafter

Decimal Places in μ	1		2		5	
X_i	$X_i - \mu$	$(X_i - \mu)^2$	$X_i - \mu$	$(X_i - \mu)^2$	$X_i - \mu$	$(X_i - \mu)^2$
2	−3.3	10.89	−3.29	10.8241	−3.28571	10.7958902041
9	+3.7	13.69	+3.71	13.7641	+3.71429	13.7959502041
3	−2.3	5.29	−2.29	5.2441	−2.28571	5.2244702041
7	+1.7	2.89	+1.71	2.9241	+1.71429	2.9387902041
5	−0.3	0.09	−0.29	0.0841	−0.28571	0.0816302041
6	+0.7	0.49	+0.71	0.5041	+0.71429	0.5102102041
5	−0.3	0.09	−0.29	0.0841	−0.28571	0.0816302041
Sums 37	−0.1	33.43	−0.03	33.4287	+0.00003	33.4285714287
Variances	$4.77\dot{\overline{571428}}$		$4.7755\dot{\overline{285714}}$		$4.775102041\dot{0}$	

handling the common fractions, but came face to face with the fact that the mean involves a repeating decimal. Notice our use of the symbol $\dot{\overline{\quad\quad}}$

to indicate that the group of digits under the bar (its formal name is *vinculum*) is repeated indefinitely. We had to make a decision: how many decimals to use in our computations.

May we, here, give you a word of sound advice which will undoubtedly appear rather peremptory and arbitrary? If you have learned any rounding rules in past courses, forget them when you come to statistical computations! Most rounding rules taught in other courses were designed for a limited and specific situation (thought that fact is rarely mentioned) and will get you into trouble in the work we are learning.

To illustrate the effect of this decimal rounding, we used one, two, and five decimals in μ, then proceeded to retain whatever number of figures they yielded in our remaining computations. You can see immediately that the use of only one decimal would give, in this instance, a value of the variance which agrees with the true value in the first three decimal places. This is fortunate, and will not always happen. The use of two decimals in μ only adds a fourth place of agreement in the variance, while the use of five decimals in the mean produces a variance correct to nine decimals in this example. *In no case is the variance wholly correct by this procedure, nor is there any simple way of determining the discrepancy.* Furthermore, with as many as five decimals in the mean and all others retained, this method is nearly as tedious as the use of common fractions.

In Part C, we decided to take advantage of our more convenient computing formula, but improperly chose 4.4.1d, which we were warned was improper here.

Part C. Using Equation 4.4.1d with $1/N$ Rounded at Indicated Number of Decimal Places

Decimal Places	$1/N$	$\mu = (1/N)\Sigma X_i$	$\mu\Sigma X_i$	$\Sigma X_i^2 - \mu\Sigma X_i$	σ^2
1	0.1	3.7	136.9	92.1	$13.1\overline{571428}$
2	0.14	5.18	191.66	37.34	$5.334\overline{285714}$
5	0.14286	5.28582	195.57534	33.42466	$4.77495\overline{142857}$

$$1/N = 0.\overline{142857} \qquad \Sigma X_i^2 = 229$$

Again we had to make a decision: how many decimals shall we retain in $1/N$? For comparison, we used one, two, and five, and retained all subsequent figures they produced. Here, the use of one significant digit produced a totally ridiculous variance, more than three times the proper size. The use of two digits reduced the discrepancy greatly, but even five digits produced only two correct decimal places in the final variance. This certainly was a poor procedure!

Finally, in Part D, we used the proper and expeditious formula, 4.4.1f.

Part D. Using Equation 4.4.1f

$$N\Sigma X_i^2 = 7 \times 229 = 1603$$

$$(\Sigma X_i)^2 = 37^2 = 1369$$

$$N\Sigma X_i^2 - (\Sigma X_i)^2 = 1603 - 1369 = 234$$

$$N^2 = 7^2 = 49$$

$$\sigma^2 = 234/49 = 4\ 38/49 \doteq 4.7755102041, \text{ as in Part A.}$$

Notice that throughout the computations we dealt only with exact values until our final decision to express the variance as a decimal approximation, and notice further that all values agreed exactly with those produced by the use of formula 4.4.1, the definition, with the exact, common fractions.

At this point, you may well ask what is wrong! Our algebra told us that all of our variance formulas were identically equal and, hence, interchangeable, but when we used them, we did not get the same results. Oh, well, many of us never did trust mathematics! But remember, when we translated the μ's in our formulas into 37/7 we were correct, but when we then translated 37/7 into a decimal with a finite number of decimals, we were no longer correct, nor could we tell how far astray this mistake would lead us. Similarly, the translation of 1/7 to a decimal with a finite number of places is not correct. So the fault was not in the algebra but in us.

In our discussion of the formulas, we carefully stated that formula 4.4.1d is properly used only when $1/N$ can be completely expressed with few enough significant figures so that we can use all of them, a fact that we summarized conveniently if informally by calling such reciprocals "tidy." Otherwise, 4.4.1f is required in practical computation. Of course, 4.4.1f may be used when $1/N$ is tidy: all you do is multiply and divide by N in a concealed way. If you don't make a mistake in doing the extra work, you will come out with the right result, as the final stage of Table 4-1 indicated.

4.6 The Standard Deviation

There is one slightly disturbing aspect of the variance which takes a little getting used to: its units are always the square of the units of measurement. If your data are in units of people, your variance is in square (!) people; if in dollars, square dollars, and so on. While this is more a matter of getting used to it than any really fundamental problem, the "old-timers" didn't like it too well, and sometimes we won't either. A simple expedient gets rid of the problem: take the square root of the variance. The result is known as the *standard deviation*, and it is symbolized by the plain, lower case, Greek "s," σ, whose square denoted the variance. Now, naturally, you see why the sigma got into the symbol for variance. As a matter of fact, some authors use a v for variance, but most American writers use the σ^2, and it does remind one of the squares involved.

So far as the standard deviation is concerned, its use does leap the mental barrier of the squared units, but you find that you soon get accustomed to that problem. It is necessary in a few uses to employ the standard deviation, and we shall take care to draw your attention to them as they arise. Obviously, if you use the standard deviation, you are required to extract square roots, a process which is not as difficult as you may recall, and which we discuss in Appendix X.

The standard deviation does have one interesting property which can be illustrated with the aid of the figures in Table 4-3, where we determined the

Table 4-3 Comparison of Arithmetic Mean and Square Root of the Mean Square of a Set of Positive Numbers

	X_i	X_i^2
	1	1
	2	4
	4	16
	8	64
	10	100
Sums	25	185
Means	5	37
Square Root	—	6.08^+

mean of the numbers themselves, then determined the mean of the squares of the numbers and took its square root. We shall always find that the square root of the mean of the squares of a set of positive numbers is greater than the mean of the numbers. You will increase your confidence in the truth of this statement by trying it on several simple sets of positive numbers, and you will begin to see that the larger values increase the squares, and hence the mean of the squares, at a faster rate than the taking of the square root can overcome; in other words, the square root of the mean of the squares of a set of values exaggerates the size of the larger values.

Now suppose these numbers had happened to be absolute deviations. This principle means that the standard deviation will be greater than the mean absolute deviation as a result of this same exaggeration of extreme deviations. This is often desirable. For example, suppose we are interested in the effect of an advertising program on sales. Possibly the new program, on the average, increases our sales in our various regions, but if the variation from region to region is increased, it may indicate that, in some regions, our sales have decreased as a result of objection to our program, and this could be very serious. Or we may be concerned with a new way of teaching a subject, and find that, on the average, it is better than the present method, but that, while it is much better for some students, it is also less effective for others. A method of measuring dispersion which somewhat emphasizes these extremes will be desirable. To remind us of this aspect of its behavior, the standard deviation is often called the "root-mean-square" deviation, abbreviated to "rms" deviation.

4.7 Comparison of Measures

Table 4-4 shows the range, mean absolute deviation, variance, and standard deviation for the several sets of simple data we have been studying. You will

Table 4-4 COMPARISON OF MEASURES OF DISPERSION

Set Number	Values	Range	M.A.D.	Variance	Standard Deviation
3.3.1	2, 3, 5, 7, 9	7	2.24	6.56	2.56124
3.3.2	2, 3, 3, 3, 9	7	2.00	6.4	2.52982
3.3.3	2, 8, 8, 9, 9	7	2.08	6.96	2.63818
3.4.1	2, 3, 5, 7	5	1.75	3.6875	1.92028
3.5.1	2, 3, 3, 3, 5 5, 7, 7, 7, 9	7	1.92	4.89	2.21133
Table 2-1	See Table	3,628	769.492	857,205+	925.85
Table 2-6	See Table	6,802.01	162.395+	48,527,387+	559.54+

see that the range is, as we have said, responsive only to the extremes, while the other measures all reflect the total pattern to some extent, with the standard deviation greater than the mean absolute deviation. There is one further advantage in the variance and standard deviation which we can appreciate better after our study of the next chapter. The balance of reasons will lead us almost always to use the variance or the standard deviation as our measure of dispersion, just as we decided to use the mean as our measure of central value.

It should be mentioned that, some years ago, efforts were made to overcome some of the objections to the range by such modifications as determining the difference between the upper boundary of the first quarter (quartile, it was called) and the lower boundary of the last quarter, and this was sometimes called the interquartile range. The similar difference between the inner boundaries of the first and last tenth (decile) of the values was also used for this purpose, but these procedures are rare today.

4.8 Working from a Frequency Table

Just as in the case of measures of central value, so in the case of measures of dispersion, we shall sometimes have only a frequency table to work from. We can approximate the range; in fact, we did so in the last chapter in the process of finding the mid-range. We can approximate the mean absolute deviation by finding the absolute deviation of each class mark from the mean, multiplying it by the class frequency, and adding the products, then dividing by the total frequency. This will introduce discrepancies, generally, for the reasons discussed in connection with the measures of central value. In a similar way, we can compute the variance by squaring the deviations before multiplying them by the frequencies, adding, and dividing by the total frequency. Some tedious algebra would show that equations 4.4.1d and 4.4.1f would be replaced by 4.8.1d and 4.8.1f, respectively, as given below. (Our regular numbering system has been slightly adjusted to keep similar numbers on these related formulas.)

$$\sigma^2 = \frac{\Sigma f_i X_i^2 - \mu \Sigma f_i X_i}{\Sigma f_i} \tag{4.8.1d}$$

$$\sigma^2 = \frac{\Sigma f_i \Sigma f_i X_i^2 - (\Sigma f_i X_i)^2}{(\Sigma f_i)^2} \tag{4.8.1f}$$

where X_i = the mark and f_i = the frequency of the i-th class. The calculations for the values used in Table 3-2 for calculating the mean are shown in Table 4-5.

Table 4-5 Computation of Variance and Standard Deviation from Frequency Table 3-2

	Class Mark, X_i	Class Frequency, f_i	$f_i X_i$	$f_i X_i^2$
	10,249.5	1	10,249.5	105,052,250.25
	10,749.5	9	96,745.5	1,039,965,752.25
	11,249.5	10	112,495.0	1,265,512,502.50
	11,749.5	9	105,745.5	1,242,456,752.25
	12,249.5	7	85,746.5	1,050,351,751.75
	12,749.5	7	89,246.5	1,137,848,251.75
	13,249.5	3	39,748.5	526,647,750.75
	13,749.5	4	54,998.0	756,195,001.00
Sums		50	594,975.0	7,124,030,012.50

$$\mu = (1/\Sigma f_i)\Sigma f_i X_i = 0.02 \times 594{,}975.0 = 11{,}899.5$$

$$\Sigma f_i X_i^2 - \mu \Sigma f_i X_i = 7{,}124{,}030{,}012.50 - 11{,}899.5 \times 594{,}975.0$$

$$= 44{,}125{,}000.00$$

$$\sigma^2 = (\Sigma f_i X_i^2 - \mu \Sigma f_i X_i)/\Sigma f_i = 44{,}125{,}000.00/50 = 882{,}500.00$$

$$\sigma = \sqrt{\sigma^2} = 882{,}500 \doteq 939.41$$

The values computed from the raw data were

$$\sigma^2 \doteq 857{,}205$$

$$\sigma \doteq 925.54$$

Note: In actual computation with a machine according to the suggestions in Appendix XI, the fourth column would not be recorded.

4.9 A New Fact About the Mean

This may seem a peculiar place to mention the matter, but it can be shown that the sum of squared differences between the numbers in any set and their mean is less than the sum of squared differences between the numbers and any other number whatsoever. Hence, the variance is smaller than the mean square of the differences between the values and any other measure of central value. For this reason, the mean is sometimes referred to as the "least squares" or "minimum variance" measure of central value. This is an added reason for the use of the mean and variance as measures of central value and dispersion, respectively.

4.10 Physical Meaning of the Standard Deviation

Just as the mean has a relation to the balance point of a set of equal weights, the standard deviation also is related to the physical behavior of a set of weights. Most of us are less familiar with the principle involved, but it may interest you to know of it. Suppose that our weights, instead of being hung from a balance beam, as we imagined in the last chapter, are now fastened securely along a rod at distances related to the values, as shown in Fig. 4-1.

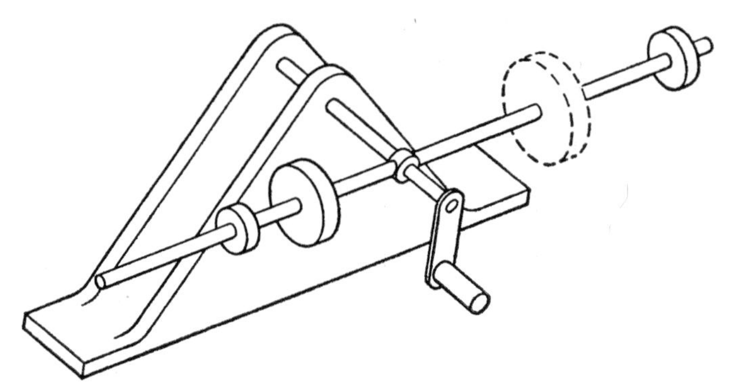

Fig. 4-1. Variance and moment of inertia.

The only difference we shall make is that, instead of using three weights at $X = 3$, we shall use a weight three times as heavy. This system would just balance at the position of the mean, 4. Now suppose that we fasten our rod to a transverse axle passing through $X = 4$, mount the axle in bearings, and put a crank at one end. If we imagine that the rod to which the weights are fastened has no weight and that the bearings have no friction, the physicists will tell us that, if we want to start the rod spinning on our axle, we shall have to apply effort on the crank. The amount of effort required to speed the rod up will vary directly as the squares of the distances of the weights from the axle. They will further tell us that if our separate weights are replaced by a single one of the size of the total of the separate ones, and this weight is placed at the square root of the mean of the squares of the separate distances, we would find the effort required to be just the same as with the separate weights, and that it would equal the total weight times the squares of the radius to the weight. This radius, known in physics as the radius of gyration, is equal in length to our standard deviation and its square is our variance. While this has no direct bearing on the utility of these measures of dispersion, to many of us it is good to know that they do have some connection with what could be thought of as a physical representation of our values.

General Study

1. As you see measures of dispersion mentioned in connection with data discussed in your reading outside this course, notice which ones are used. Are they clearly identified? Do the values begin to convey real information to you, now that you have started to master their underlying ideas?

2. Consider types of data of particular interest to you in connection with your major field. Which measure of dispersion would you, at present, consider most desirable to use for each type of data?

Problems

1. Find the range, mean absolute deviation, variance, and standard deviation of the sets of values in Problem 1 of Chapter 3.

2. Find the range, the mean absolute deviation, variance, and standard deviation of the data you obtained in the problems following Chapter 2.

5

Describing the Form of a Distribution

5.1 Some General Ideas

In our discussions so far, we have shown you several distributions, and have urged you to notice, in the texts and journals concerned with your field of interest, many others which present information valuable to you. We have also urged you to prepare some histograms and frequency polygons, yourself. If you have been doing these things thoughtfully, certain ideas must have become rather clear to you by now.

First, we think you will agree that, although the charts do present quite vividly a picture of the way in which the values in a distribution are dispersed about their center, which is what we mean, broadly, by the form of the distribution, these charts are difficult to prepare well. This is true even of the simple chart, the frequency polygon, and even more true of the more effective histogram. Even with efficient drafting equipment and with considerable practice, it requires no small amount of time and care to produce a proper chart. Of course, the resulting presentation is far clearer and more effective than a description of the form in words.

Second, study of many distributions representing a wide variety of subject matter will show you that the vast majority of them have certain features in common. For instance, they will have a modal class, that is, as we said before, a class with maximum frequency. This class will usually be near the center of the distribution, if not at it. On either side of this modal class the frequencies will fall off rapidly at first, then more slowly. The pattern may or may not be symmetrical about the modal class. True, the magnitude of the central value and measure of dispersion will vary from distribution to distribution, and there will be exceptions to our general statement. Some distributions will have two or more "humps," or all values may be on one side of the modal class.

But when we make the statement about the general similarities, we mean something of the kind of meaning we give to the statement, "All human faces are similar." In general, they have a forehead, two eyes with eyebrows, a nose, mouth and chin, and two cheeks. True, some people have but one eye, or no eyebrows, or may have sad malformations of other features. Others add mustaches or beards. But we recognize the similarities which constitute what we mean by "human face."

We can even go further and recognize groups of faces, such as Oriental, or those corresponding to certain ethnic groupings, which are recognizably closely similar within the group and different from other groups. Finally, we quite readily distinguish the particular details of the faces of our friends and loved ones.

Just so it is with distributions. We shall learn to recognize the common features of groups of distributions, as well as the distinguishing features of particular individuals. In order to do this, we must be sure that we understand the fundamental principles of a branch of mathematics known as analytic geometry.

5.2 Pictures of Equations: Analytic Geometry

When we were making histograms, frequency polygons, and the other pictorial devices we presented earlier, we tacitly assumed that you were adequately familiar with the principles of laying out scales and constructing graphs. But for what we need to do now, we must be sure that we all understand certain fundamentals which many of us never knew properly, or have forgotten. When these principles are understood, they make graphs and charts far more effective tools for us than they would otherwise be.

The configurations that can be formed by straight and curved lines, planes, and curved surfaces have had a fascination for man since earliest times. He has talked about them, grouped them, measured them, and even endowed them with occult or mystic properties. In ancient Greece, these figures held a particular fascination for a group of men who used them as a challenge to their ability to think in an orderly manner. They worked with a straightedge devoid of a scale of lengths, a compass, and dividers, but with no protractor; and they developed a beautifully orderly and proved discussion of the properties of many important figures. This work has come down through the years as Euclid's *Elements*, the basis of the plane and solid geometry of our high school days.

Other people were tremendously interested in numbers. What kinds of numbers were there? How could you do things with them? How could orderly rules be established for determining the unknown number which met the requirements of a problem? Out of this kind of question, arithmetic and algebra developed. It is not surprising that here, also, the occult and mysterious entered. (How many public buildings, particularly hotels, have no thirteenth floor!)

Now, while all this development was going on, the artisan, the engineer, and the "working people" generally surely kept the scales on their rulers and busily used their protractors and all the other tools and principles they could for dealing with these geometrical figures. They left the "pure" thinking to the "eggheads" of their day, whatever they may have called them. But it began to dawn on thinking people that perhaps this business of the straightedge and divider in geometry and the formal reasoning of algebra was a bit sterile. Perhaps the scale and protractor ought to be restored to geometry and perhaps geometry really could contribute to algebra.

The credit for the effective reunion of these two branches of mathematics goes to a Frenchman, René Descartes (1596–1650). The basis of his development was the orderly association of numerical values with geometrical positions through what we know as a coordinate system. The gridwork on which we construct graphs and charts, often called a *rectangular coordinate system,* is frequently named the *Cartesian coordinate system,* after Descartes.

Let us review the elemental steps by which such a system is, in principle, constructed. We begin by taking a line segment, ordinarily a horizontal one. We strictly say "line segment," rather than simply "line," because the line is visualized as extending indefinitely far in both directions: the portion we actually use we call a segment. We designate some point on the line by an "O" (capital letter), standing for "origin," to represent the beginning of our scale. If the values we represent are to be symbolized by x's, such as $x_1, x_2, \ldots x_i \ldots,$ we place an "X" at one end, normally the right end, and consider that the direction from O to X represents the "positive" direction. Now we select some length to represent one unit and, starting from O and moving in the positive direction, we mark off successive applications of this unit along the line, indicating the ends of each successive interval as $+1$, $+2$, and so on. We then start off over again at the origin and mark off unit intervals in the negative direction, marking the ends of the intervals -1, -2, and so on. The result, called an *X-axis*, might look like this:

Fig. 5-1. Numbered scale for values of *X*, the *X*-axis.

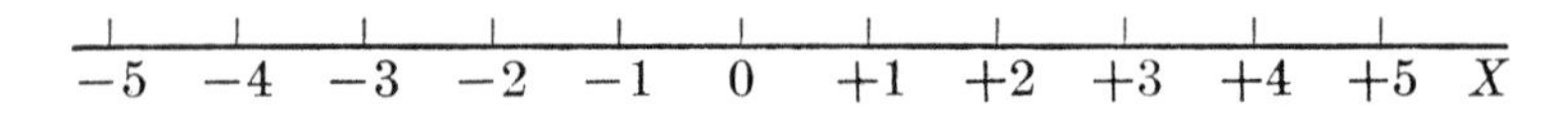

To use this scale to give a representation or picture of numerical values of the x's, we simply let the division points represent the numbers which are "whole numbers" or integers. If we have a number involving a fraction, such as $x_1 = -2\frac{3}{8}$, we could divide the interval from -2 to -3 into eight equal parts, and represent our number as at the end of the third such part to the left of -2. Suppose we have a number like $\sqrt{2}$, which cannot be expressed as a fraction (or "rational number") and is hence called an irrational number. We can approximate its position by representing its value as a decimal to as many places as we care to, and plotting the position corresponding to that (decimal)

fraction on the line. Very formal mathematics can establish that there really is one unique point on the line corresponding to $\sqrt{2}$, and that this point represents no other value. Thus we have what is called a "one-to-one correspondence" between the points on the line and the conceivable numerical values of x.

Frequently we find that we have a second set of numbers, $y_1, y_2, \ldots y_i \ldots$, which are related to our x's in such a way that there is one value of y associated with each value of our original x's. How could we represent that fact effectively in a geometrical picture? Like so many things, it's easy when you know how! We start by constructing another scale like the one we just made, but we make it on a line segment perpendicular to the first one, passing through the origin, and, normally, consider upward as the positive direction and mark the upper end of the segment with a Y.

Suppose that we wanted to represent the fact that $x_2 = +2$ corresponded to $y_2 = -3$. We know how to represent $x_2 = +2$ as a point on its axis, and the point $y_2 = -3$ as a point on its axis. To show that these two values belong together, we extend our ideas a bit, and decree that $x = 2$ shall be represented not only by that specific point on the X-axis, but by any point on a line perpendicular to the X-axis at $x = 2$. We similarly state that $y = -3$ shall be represented by any point on a line perpendicular to the Y-axis at $y = -3$.

Fig. 5-2. Rectangular coordinate system with several plotted points.

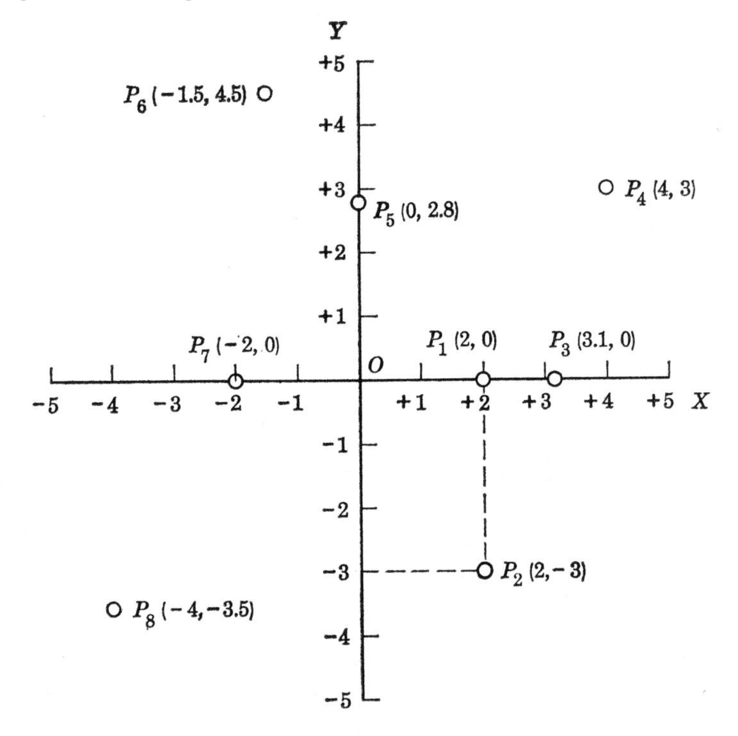

Since these two lines must intersect at one and only one point, and since that point has both the property that $x = 2$ and that $y = -3$, we reasonably consider that that point represents the simultaneous occurrence, or association, of those two values. It is common practice to designate the point by a capital letter, followed by parentheses containing first the value of x, then a comma, then the value of y, thus: $P_2(2, -3)$, though the capital letter is often omitted, leaving $(2, -3)$. This process of locating and marking the point corresponding at a pair of x and y values is called *plotting* the point or values. The values of x and y are referred to as the *abscissa* and *ordinate*, respectively, of the point. Figure 5-2 shows such a system and several points.

Now suppose that, instead of having a table of specific pairs of values of x and y, we have their relationship expressed in the form of an equation, such as

$$y = 2x - 3 \tag{5.2.1}$$

which simply tells us that if we take any value of x, double it, and subtract three, we shall have the corresponding value of y. Table 5-1 shows the result of

Table 5-1 Some Pairs of Values Which Satisfy the Equation $y = 2x - 3$. Intermediate Computations and Point Designations

x	$2x$	y	$P(x,y)$
+5	+10	+7	(5,7)
+3	+6	+3	(3,3)
+2	+4	+1	(2,1)
+1	+2	−1	(1,−1)
0	0	−3	(0,−3)
−1	−2	−5	(−1,−5)
−3	−6	−9	(−3,−9)

computing values in this way for several values of x. These values are plotted in Fig. 5-3. We notice that the points appear to fall on a straight line so we "fair in" the line. By reversing the plotting procedure, we can "read off" the coordinates of a number of points on the line and find that they all "satisfy" the equation, that is, the ordinate is the value of y that would be calculated from the value of x by the equation. We could keep this up forever and find no exception. Nor would we ever find a pair of values which satisfied the equation which was not on the line. The line, then, is actually a picture of the equation.

Notice, if you will, some interesting features of this line. If you move from one point to another on it, the rise, or difference in ordinates, is always twice the run, or difference in abscissas. This corresponds to the coefficient of x, namely 2, in our equation, and is so important that it is given a name, the *slope* of the line. Notice, also, that when $x = 0$, $y = -3$ and that the line crosses the Y-axis at this point. It is also important enough to have a name, the *y-intercept.*

Fig. 5-3. Graph of the line representing the equation $y = 2x - 3$ with the points computed in Table 5-3 specifically plotted.

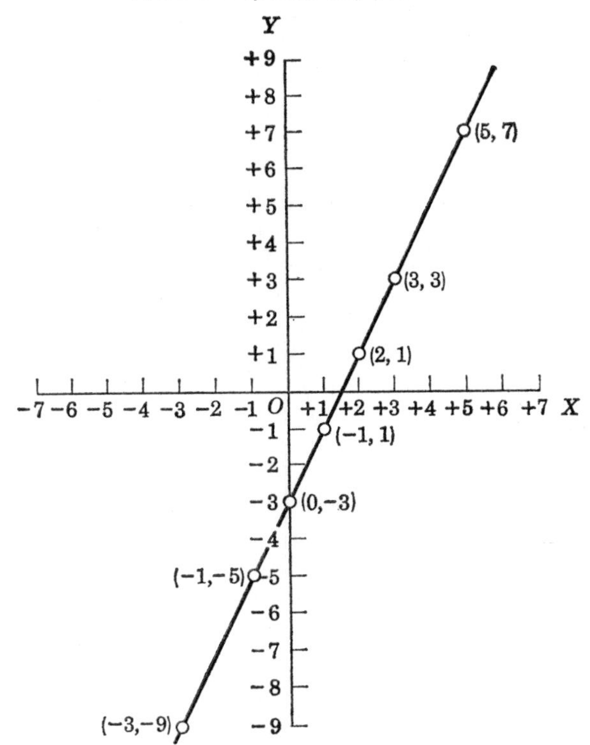

If we were to plot the curves, as the operation we have just performed is called, of equations such as

$$y = -2x + 3 \tag{5.2.2}$$

$$y = 3.5x + 1 \tag{5.2.3}$$

$$y = -0.5x \tag{5.2.4}$$

$$y = 2 \tag{5.2.5}$$

as we have done in Fig. 5.4, we would always get straight lines whose slopes would be the coefficient of x and whose y-intercept would be the constant term. From this, we might infer that any equation of the type

$$y = ax + b \tag{5.2.6}$$

represents a straight line with slope a and y-intercept b, whatever values a and b may have. This is correct, and it can be proved so by additional formal

Fig. 5-4. Plots of lines representing indicated equations.

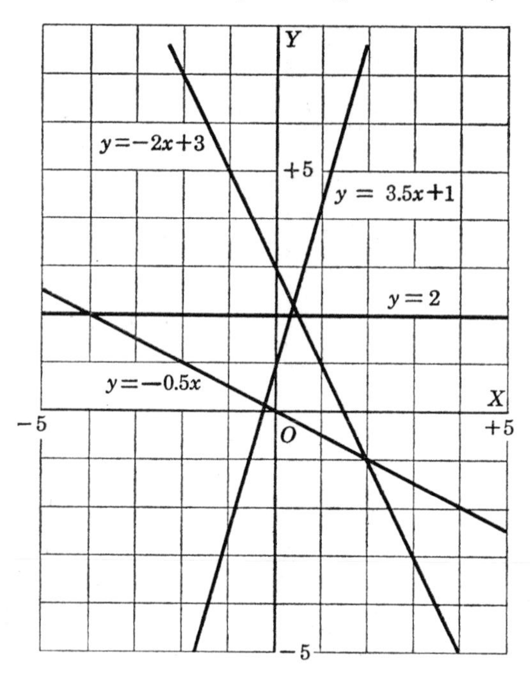

mathematics. This is our first example of the relation between the type, or form, of an equation and the form of its graph. In fact, the shape of its graph gives this kind of equation its name, *linear* equation.

By now you will not be surprised to know that, in general, each type of equation leads to a specific form of graph. For example, an equation of the form

$$y = ax^2 + b \tag{5.2.7}$$

will always represent a parabola whose axis lies along the Y-axis, whose vertex is at the point $P(0,b)$, which opens, or has its "arms" extending upward if a is positive and downward if a is negative, and which is more "pinched in" for large values of a than for small. Sometimes it is more convenient to represent a relationship between y and x by an equation which does not, as written, exactly "spell out" the relationship. For example,

$$y - k = a(x - h)^2 \tag{5.2.8a}$$

says that if you take a stated value of x, subtract h from it, square the result, and multiply by a you will have the value of y reduced by k. To find y, then, you add k. Such an equation is said to be in *implicit form*, because it implies a relationship, actually,

$$y = ax^2 - 2ahx + ah^2 + k \tag{5.2.8b}$$

whereas the equation is given in 5.2.8b is in the *explicit form* because it directly states how y may be obtained from x. The advantage of the implicit form, 5.2.8a, is that this equation represents the entire family of parabolas whose axes are parallel to the Y-axis. The vertex of any one of them will be at $P(h,k)$ and the axis will be the line $x = h$, and a will govern the direction and steepness of rise or fall as before. Some parabolas and their equations are shown in Fig. 5-5.

Fig. 5-5. Several parabolas and their equations.

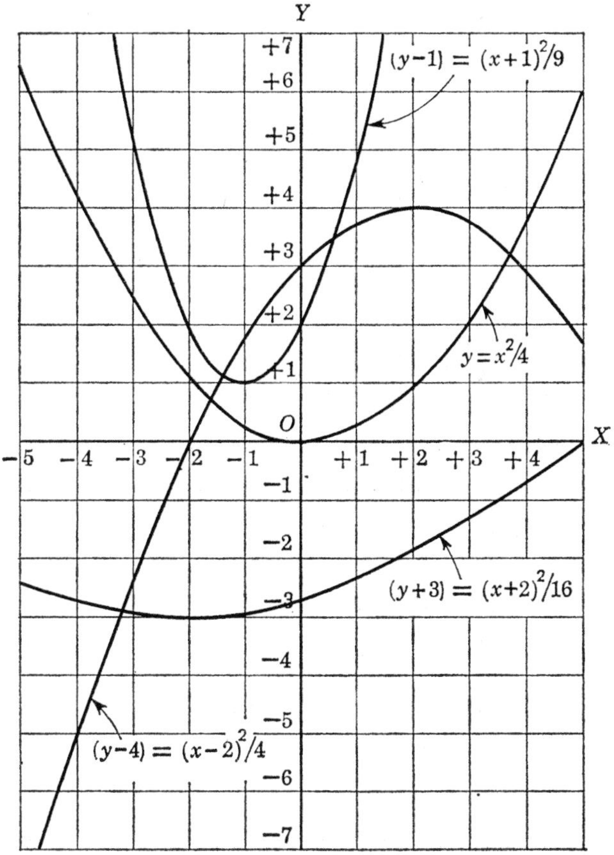

Equations of the form

$$(x - h)^2 + (y - k)^2 = r^2 \qquad (5.2.9)$$

always represent circles with their centers at $P(h,k)$ and radii of length r. Ellipses with their axes parallel to the coordinate axes have the equations

$$b^2(x - h)^2 + a^2(y - k)^2 = a^2b^2 \qquad (5.2.10)$$

and their centers will be at $P(h,k)$, their left and right "ends" will be a units either side of the center, and their "top" and "bottom" will be b units above and below the center. Fig. 5-6a shows some circles and ellipses with their equations.

Fig. 5-6. Effect of scale distortion on appearance of circles and ellipses.

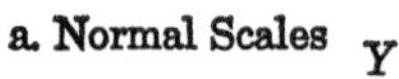

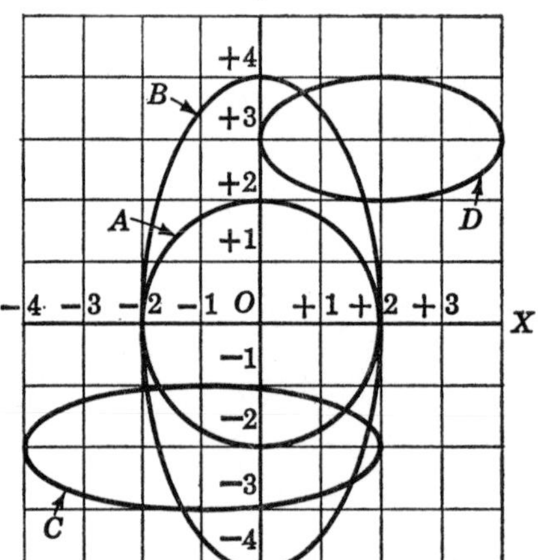

A: $x^2 + y^2 = 2^2$, a circle
B: $x^2/2^2 + y^2/4^2 = 1$, an ellipse
C: $(x - 2)^2 + (y - 3)^2 = 1$, an ellipse
D: $(x + 1)^2/3^2 + (y + 2)^2/4^2 = 1$, an ellipse

b. Scales Distorted in Ratio 2:1

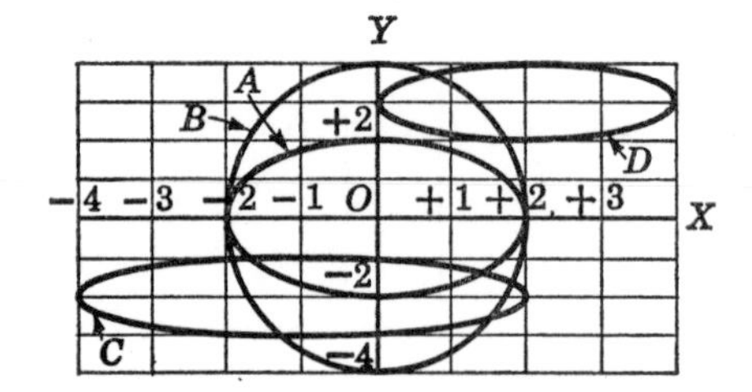

One of the great contributions of analytic geometry has been the development of these relationships between the shapes of graphs and the forms of the equations they represent. A great many mathematicians find that, when they see a graph, they instinctively think in terms of the equation it may represent, whereas, when they must deal with an equation, they think in terms of what its graph looks like. Herein lies the key to the description of the form of our distributions.

We should warn you of one thing in passing: when we say that the graph of an equation of the form shown as equation 5.2.9 is a circle, while that of an equation of form 5.2.10 is an ellipse, we are always assuming that the scale units in the x- and y-directions are the same. If this is not so, the equation of the circle may appear to produce an ellipse and that of an ellipse may appear to produce a circle, as is shown by replotting in Fig. 5-6b, with unequal scale units, the figures plotted with equal units in Fig. 5-6a.

5.3 Studying a Real Distribution

After this diversion in an effort to clarify our understanding of the rudiments of analytic geometry, let's return to some real data. Table 5-2 presents the

Table 5-2 FRESHMAN YEAR ACADEMIC INDEXES, CLASS OF 1956, UNIVERSITY OF X. FREQUENCY TABLES USING THREE DIFFERENT SETS OF CLASSES

Part A		Part B		Part C	
Class Mark X_i	Frequency f_i	Class Mark X_i	Frequency f_i	Class Mark X_i	Frequency f_i
0.205	1	0.405	1	0.105	0
				0.305	1
0.605	1	0.805	8	0.505	0
				0.705	1
1.005	25	1.205	39	0.905	7
				1.105	18
1.405	49	1.605	70	1.305	21
				1.505	28
1.805	90	2.005	98	1.705	42
				1.905	48
2.205	101	2.405	90	2.105	50
				2.305	51
2.605	72	2.805	74	2.505	39
				2.705	33
3.005	64	3.205	45	2.905	41
				3.105	23
3.405	34	3.605	15	3.305	22
				3.505	12
3.805	9	4.005	6	3.705	3
				3.905	6
	446		446		446

Part D. Means and Variances Calculated from the Frequency Tables Above

μ	2.26419	2.26239	2.26329
σ^2	0.473626	0.470069	0.461848

Values from raw data were $\mu = 2.25820$, $\sigma^2 = 0.460184$.

academic indexes earned by the members of the class of 1956 at one of our universities during their freshman year. The data are presented in the form of a frequency table, with a class mark of 0.205 for the lowest class, and with a class interval of 0.400 index units in Part A. The corresponding histogram is shown in Fig. 5-7a.

A question that should occur to you is: might the appearance of a distribution be seriously affected by the choice of class mark for the lowest class and of the class interval? One way to find out is to try it! Part B and Fig. 5-7b present the same data with the same class interval, but with the class marks midway between the marks previously used. The main features are not seriously altered by the change. If we cut our class interval in half, as in Part C and Fig. 5-7c, we seem to have disturbed matters seriously, but we really have not. How can that be? The histogram looks different from either of the previous ones! But let us think a moment. We said that we wanted to

Fig. 5-7a,b,c, and cc. Freshman Year Academic Indexes.
Class of 1956, U. of X. Source: Records Office.

Histograms based on Tables 5-2A, B, and C to show effect of change of classes and scale on appearance of histogram. Each shaded rectangle is equivalent to 25 students.

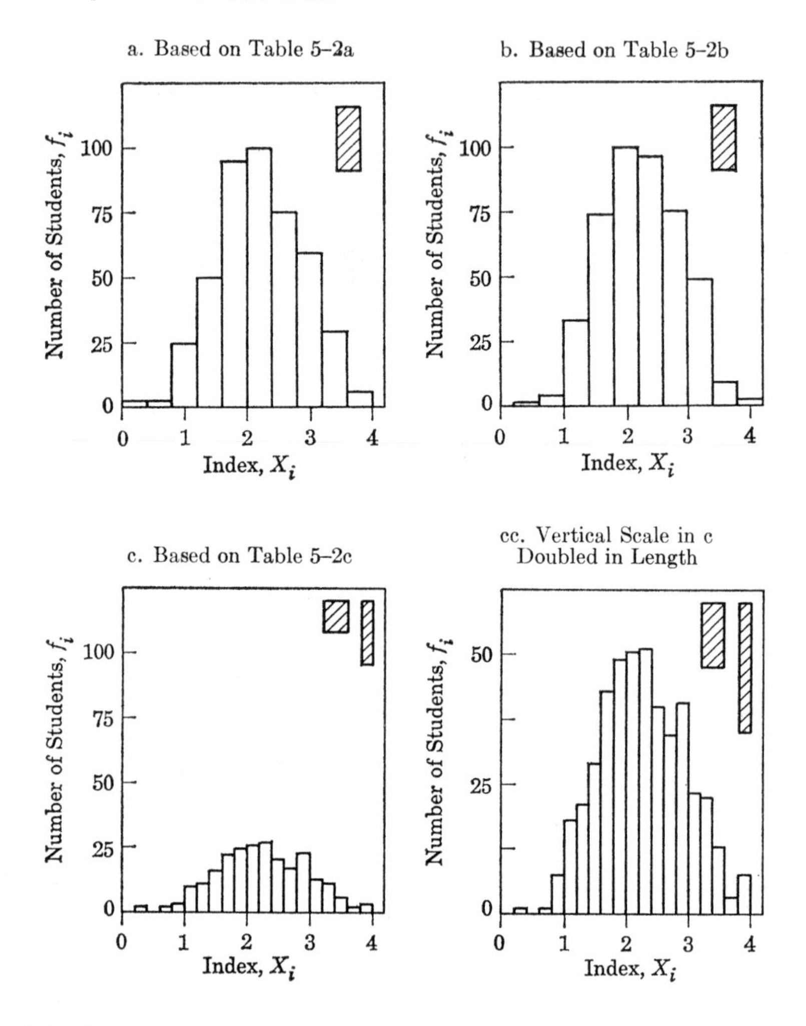

associate the area of the histogram bars with frequency. The bars on Fig. 5-7c are half as wide as the previous bars and, because we kept the same units on our frequency scale, this graph requires only half as much area to represent an observation as did the previous charts. We can adjust this system by doubling the length of the units on the frequency scale, as we did in Fig. 5-7cc, and we restore the histogram to an appearance very similar to either of the previous ones.

This raises another question: is there no limit to the number of classes and their location? The fact is that there are prudent limits for the number of classes. One should not have fewer than eight classes for any serious use, and preferably not fewer than ten. At the other extreme, 20 classes is considered a reasonable upper limit. Although these values are not absolutely "sacred," experience has shown that fewer than ten classes tend, by throwing the figures into too broad classes, to mask rather important aspects of the distribution, whereas more than 20 classes tend to overemphasize details. Furthermore, if the frequency table is to be used for the approximation of measures of central value and dispersion, the discrepancies introduced by grouping make fewer than ten classes a rather undesirable choice.

While we are on the subject, let us compare the mean, variance, and standard deviation of these data as approximated from the three frequency tables with the value that was obtained from the raw data. The results are shown in Part D. Although we do not yet have a formal basis for saying so, it is true that the discrepancies are not very great. In the rest of our work with these

Fig. 5-7d. Freshman Year Academic Indexes. Class of 1956, U. of X.

Histograms of Fig. 5-7a,b, and cc superposed on same chart to emphasize essential similarity.

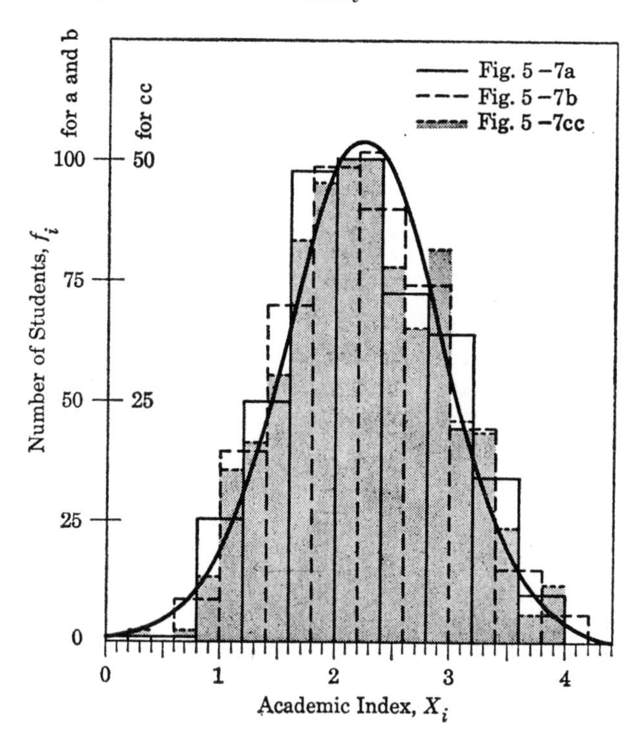

data, however, we shall use the values actually calculated from the raw data.

What should we consider in deciding the location of class marks? Because of the nature of many distributions, it would be desirable to have the mean itself as one of the class marks. But this would have the disadvantage, often, of making the marks and boundaries rather awkward. There is yet another requirement that must be met for some purposes, namely, that each class should preferably have upward of five values in it. This is more important than having the mean as a class mark, so we generally settle for reasonable values for class marks, with the mean near one of them. All this may seem arbitrary at this time, but as your knowledge of statistics increases, you will uncover the reasons behind the suggestions.

Perhaps it will help us to understand the similarity of the three different histograms if we place them all on one chart, as we have done in Fig. 5-7d. Notice that we must use two different scales in reading these frequencies, because we have made the histogram corresponding to Part C as it was made in Fig. 5-7cc. Now these histograms are all telling the same story. The peak frequency occurs in the class in the vicinity of the mean, 2.258. The frequency falls away on either side, quite rapidly at first, then more slowly. This change of pace occurs in the vicinity of academic indexes of 1.580 and 2.936, which are one standard deviation (0.678 units) below and above the mean, respectively.

5.4 Fitting a Normal Curve to a Real Distribution

As a result of our analysis in the preceding section, we found that the data under study could be represented by several different histograms, broadly similar, but differing in some details. Our broader observations, stimulated by the initial phases of our study of statistics, suggest that many other distributions may have a similar form, as would be brought out by their histograms. Now when a person of reasonable mathematical training encounters a situation such as this, he is not content to leave it in this stage.

In the first place, the tops of the histogram bars form a zig-zag line: artists find such lines irritating and disturbing, and so do mathematicians. Furthermore, the fact that the exact positions of the zigs and zags are dependent on the whimsy of our particular choice of class marks and intervals disturbs the mathematician — he wants results as independent as possible of such subjective judgments. Yet another objection arises from the fact that any one histogram tells us only about the frequencies in the classes for which it was constructed: the mathematician is interested in a more general result that will permit him to tell about the frequencies that would have been in any classes. Still another objection stems from the fact that equations for zig-zag lines are not simple to write: he would like a simple equation (this is true, popular opinion to the contrary notwithstanding!).

Suppose we had made each of the histograms which were superimposed in

Fig. 5-7d in the form of a bas-relief, with the bars consisting of a $\frac{1}{4}$ in.-thick layer of modelling clay laid on a smooth board containing the scales. Now suppose we worked with the clay, smoothing its upper edges while retaining the general shape of the histogram and the $\frac{1}{4}$ in. thickness, until we developed gently curved upper contours in place of the zig-zags of the histogram and, in fact, arrived at curves of the same size and shape for all three of the histograms we made. The result would be more pleasing in appearance, at least.

Then we could undertake to find out what equation would have as its graph the "remodelled" upper boundary of our clay figures. We might try several forms of "smoothing" the zig-zags, and might arrive at several different equations, some more convenient than others, and we might choose the most convenient one to represent the curve which tells smoothly the story that the several histograms tell roughly.

Of course, the mathematician doesn't use the clay, though a good one wouldn't hesitate to if it would help him to achieve a longed-for result, you may be sure! He seeks a curve which shall have the following characteristics:

1. Its equation should have in it parameters whose values he can determine to adjust his curves so that they will "fit" different distributions. (A parameter is a symbol like the a and b in the equation of a straight line, 5.2.6, which, as long as you are considering any one line, remains fixed in value, but which, by suitable changes in value, permits us to represent any line.)
2. The curve must reach its maximum height at the mean of the distribution.
3. The curve must fall away symmetrically on either side of the mean.
4. The curve must fall away with increasing rapidity to a point one standard deviation away from the mean on each side, then fall off more slowly. This makes the curve "concave downward" between $x = \mu - \sigma$ and $x = \mu + \sigma$, and "concave upward" elsewhere. The points on the curve at which the direction of concavity changes are called *inflection points*.
5. The total area under the curve and above the horizontal axis must be equal to the area of the histogram.

There are a number of curves whose equations have been found which would meet these requirements, but one which, in spite of its initial appearance, has so many advantages that it is commonly used is the curve whose equation is

$$Y = \frac{Ni}{\sigma\sqrt{2\pi}} e^{-1/2[(X-\mu)/\sigma]^2} \qquad (5.4.1a)$$

where

X = the quantity whose distribution is represented by the histogram. In our case, this is the academic index.

Y = the value to be plotted on the frequency scale.

π = the ratio of the circumference to the diameter of a circle, approximately 3.1416.

N = the total frequency. In our case, $N = 446$.

i = the class interval for the histogram being fitted.

μ = the mean of the distribution.

σ^2 = the variance of the distribution.

The symbol "e" which appears in the equation is quite possibly new to you. It is a fixed constant which happens to be the limit approached by $(1 + 1/z)^z$ as z becomes indefinitely large. Its numerical value is, like that of π, an unending decimal, approximately 2.7183. It has certain mathematical conveniences which we can take on faith, since it requires a grasp of calculus to appreciate them!

It is quite possible that you have been thinking, "If this is simple, I'm quitting right now!" But remember, we don't expect you to derive this equation right now, or even later, and we are about to show you some stunts that make this equation at least as easy to use as an interest table. So bear with us a little longer! First, let's rewrite the right side of equation 5.4.1a with the symbols grouped in a way that will help make their meaning clearer:

$$Y = \left(\frac{Ni}{\sigma}\right) \frac{1}{\sqrt{2\pi}} e^{-1/2[(X-\mu)/\sigma]^2} \qquad (5.4.1b)$$

Now the first parenthesis on the right involves only simple arithmetic operations. We multiply the total number of observations in our population by the class interval we used in drawing our histogram and divide by the standard deviation of our population. That's easy!

The second parenthesis looks more complicated, and it is. Let's forget about it for a few minutes, while we think about the temperature. Perhaps you will find that the temperature where you are is 72°, but a Frenchman would think of this as 22.2°. Why? Because in France the centigrade scale is commonly used on thermometers, while in our country the Fahrenheit scale is used, except in scientific work. We naturally think of temperatures in the scale to which we have been accustomed. The Fahrenheit scale considers the melting point of pure ice to be 32°F and the condensing point of pure steam at sea level and standard atmospheric pressure to be 212°F. On the centigrade scale, the corresponding temperatures are designated as 0° C and 100°C. Thermometers are made, sometimes, with both scales on them, one on each side of the stem. One covering quite a range of temperatures might look like Fig. 5-8, and if we wanted to find out what temperature on one scale was equivalent to some specified temperature on the other, we would only have to read across the stem.

But that is a nuisance, and we could only be sure within the limits of the

Fig. 5-8. Thermometer with Two Scales, Fahrenheit and Centigrade.

Notice that either scale reads temperature, though the numerical values are different, except at −40°.

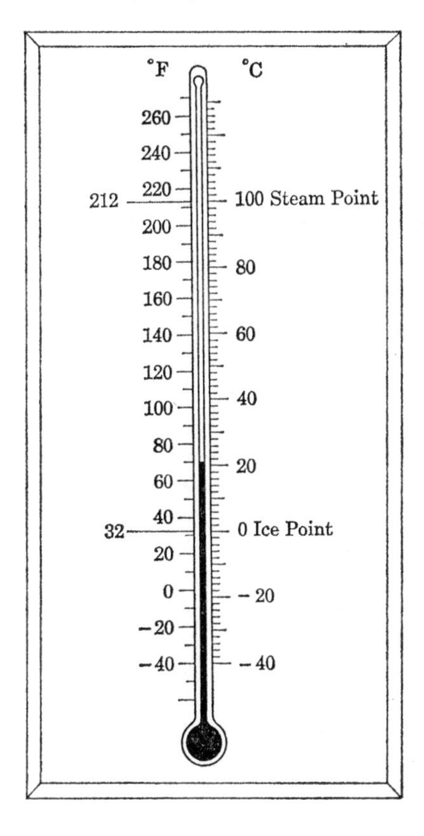

ability of our eye to read from one scale to the other. Suppose we try to find a way of calculating either temperature from the other. We can make the melting point of ice on the Fahrenheit scale, 32°F, over into its value on the centigrade scale, 0°C, by the simple task of subtracting 32 from it. At any temperature away from the melting point, there are more Fahrenheit degrees between that temperature and the "ice point" than there are centigrade degrees: in fact, for every 180°F (the difference between the "steam point" and the "ice point") there are only 100°C, or there are 9°F for every 5°C. So, if we subtract 32°F from any Fahrenheit temperature, than take 5/9 of the result, we shall have the centigrade temperature corresponding. This can be expressed as an equation:

$$C = (F - 32)5/9 \tag{5.4.2a}$$

where C = temperature in °C and F = temperature in °F.

In that equation, the 32 represents the difference in °F between the position of 0 on the two scales, while the 5/9 is the ratio of the size of the °F to that of the °C. Using principles of algebra we can turn this equation inside out by solving it for F:

$$F = 9C/5 + 32 \tag{5.4.2b}$$

so that we have a pair of equivalent formulas which permit us to go either way from one temperature scale to the other.

What, you may be wondering, has all this to do with our troublesome equation? Look at the part of the exponent of e which is inside the parentheses, namely, $(X - \mu)/\sigma$. When we drew our histogram, we plotted it in the units we were talking about, academic index units, where a value 0.00 corresponds to failure in every course and 4.00 corresponds to an A in every course. This was a reasonable scale for our purpose, just as we consider the Fahrenheit temperature scale reasonable. But suppose that we had decided to use a different scale. One intelligent choice of origin would be to place it at the mean of our distribution. After all, that is a central value, and the curve we are seeking is to be symmetric about its center. What about the choice of units? We have been interested in the inflection points of the curve, which we want to place at one standard deviation either side of our mean. Hence, if we make each unit on our new scale equal to σ units on the original scale, the inflection points would be at $+1$ and -1 on the new scale. If we call values on the new scale z's, to distinguish them from the x's on the original scale, our equations for transforming values become

$$z = \frac{X - \mu}{\sigma} \tag{5.4.3a}$$

and

$$X = \mu + z\sigma \tag{5.4.3b}$$

This makes it possible to rewrite our troublesome equation 5.4.1b in the form,

$$\left(\frac{Ni}{\sigma}\right)\left(\frac{1}{\sqrt{2\pi}}\, e^{-(1/2)z^2}\right) \tag{5.4.1c}$$

This looks less messy, but we may as well admit that many of us would have our troubles in computing $e^{-(1/2)z^2}$. But, aside from the tedious routine involved, that computation poses no challenge to persons with a moderate mathematical training. Furthermore, modern computing machinery removes the boredom and virtually eliminates the time involved in the computations, so that tables of the values of the right-hand parenthesis for all necessary values of z are commonly available. We can condense our equation still further by letting

$$y = \frac{1}{\sqrt{2\pi}}\, e^{-(1/2)z^2} \tag{5.4.1d}$$

our right-hand parenthesis, so that our equation is now

$$Y = (Ni/\sigma)y \tag{5.4.1e}$$

In Appendix 1 you will find a condensed table of values of y corresponding to a useful set of values of z. There is a curve drawn beside that table which deserves our attention. Recall that, on some of our histograms, we placed a second vertical scale, showing relative frequencies which are $1/N^{\text{th}}$ of the actual frequencies. If we wanted to plot our curve using that scale, instead of the actual frequency scale, we would have plotted values of what we might call

$$Y' = Y/N = (i/\sigma)y \tag{5.4.1f}$$

Of course, the points would be in the same place on the paper because of the relation of the scales. In our discussion of class intervals, we mentioned certain factors which governed their selection. We said that if we had too few classes, we lost detail, but didn't affect the main facts presented. Suppose we had made our class interval one standard deviation, and adjusted the units on our frequency scale again so that the same area on our paper still represented one observation as in Figure 5-7a. The resulting value to be plotted on the frequency scale (since $i = \sigma$ for this histogram), which we might call Y'', is

$$Y'' = Ny \tag{5.4.1g}$$

and the figure to be plotted against the relative frequency scale is simply $Y''/N = y$. In other words, the values of y in equation 5.4.1d are simply the values that would be plotted for a normal curve to fit a histogram for a normal distribution when the histogram is plotted in relative frequencies, with the observed values transformed to z values, and with the class interval one z unit, or one standard deviation in the original x units. This is the curve which is plotted in Appendix I. In plotting normal curves over any histogram, all we are really doing is transforming the scales by means of the equations we have given you.

It is for this reason that the equation, which we rewrite for you,

$$y = \frac{1}{\sqrt{2\pi}} e^{-(1/2)z^2} \tag{5.4.1d}$$

is often called the *standard normal distribution* equation. Our definition of the values of z also leads equation 5.4.1d to be known as the normal distribution with zero mean and unit variance (or standard deviation).

This discussion has, we are sure, seemed rather long and, for many of you, difficult. We urge you to go back and study it again, but before you do so, let us see the end result in terms of the actual fitting of the normal curves to our data. The necessary computations for fitting the histogram in Fig. 7-d are shown in Table 5-3. In constructing this table, we start in the middle, with column 3. Here we enter convenient values of z for which we have values of y in Appendix I, and write the corresponding values of y in column 4. The values of z which we used are adequate for many purposes. In the second

Table 5-3 COMPUTATIONS FOR FITTING NORMAL DISTRIBUTION CURVE TO HISTOGRAMS CORRESPONDING TO TABLE 5-2. COLUMN 5 FITS TABLE 5-2, PARTS A AND B; COLUMN 6, PART C.

$\mu \doteq 2.2582$	$\sigma \doteq 0.684$		$N = 446$	$i = 0.400$	$Ni/\sigma \doteq 260.8$	$i = 0.200$ $Ni/\sigma \doteq 130.4$
Column	1	2	3	4	5	6
Symbol	$\mu + z\sigma$	$z\sigma$	z	y	$(Ni/\sigma)y = Y$	$(Ni/\sigma)y = Y$
	4.3102	1.9836	3.0	0.0044	1.1	0.6
	4.0366	1.7784	2.6	0.0136	3.5	1.8
	3.7630	1.5048	2.2	0.0355	9.3	4.6
	3.4894	1.2312	1.8	0.0790	20.6	10.3
	3.2158	0.9576	1.4	0.150	39.1	19.6
	2.9422	0.6840	1.0	0.242	63.1	31.6
	2.8054	0.5472	0.8	0.290	75.6	37.8
	2.6686	0.4104	0.6	0.333	86.8	43.4
	2.5318	0.2736	0.4	0.368	96.0	48.0
	2.3950	0.1368	0.2	0.391	102.0	51.0
	2.2582	0.0000	0.0	0.399	104.1	52.0
	2.1214	−0.1368	−0.2	0.391	102.0	51.0
	1.9846	−0.2736	−0.4	0.368	96.0	48.0
	1.8478	−0.4104	−0.6	0.333	86.8	43.4
	1.7811	−0.5472	−0.8	0.290	75.6	37.8
	1.5742	−0.6840	−1.0	0.242	63.1	31.6
	1.3006	−0.9576	−1.4	0.150	39.1	19.6
	1.0270	−1.2312	−1.8	0.0790	20.6	10.3
	0.7534	−1.5048	−2.2	0.0355	9.3	4.6
	0.4798	−1.7784	−2.6	0.0136	3.5	1.8
	0.2062	−1.9836	−3.0	0.0044	1.1	0.6

column, we may record the values of $z\sigma$, though, if we are working with a modern automatic calculator, it is not necessary to record these values. In column 1, we place the values of $\mu - z\sigma$, or X. Somewhere, often at the top of the table, we calculate and record Ni/σ. Because we are going to fit two histograms with the same x-scale but different class intervals, we must compute this constant for each value of i. In column 5, we recorded $(Ni/\sigma)y = Y$ for $i = 0.400$, which gives us the values for fitting the histograms with that interval, corresponding to Parts A and B. Column 6 records the similarly computed values for $i = 0.200$, corresponding to Part C. Thus we have converted the z and y values for the standard curve to X and Y values for our specific curves. It is even easier to do than to describe! These values were used in plotting the curve in Fig. 5-7d.

You will probably agree that the curve reasonably resembles the histograms, as though it might indeed be the end result of the imaginary operation with modelling clay we discussed earlier. The question is, does it really resemble the histograms closely enough so that we could think and work in terms of the curve instead of the histogram without doing violence to the facts of student academic indexes? In order to answer that question intelligently, we must consider more thoughtfully just what we might do with the curve as a substitute for the histograms.

5.5 The Normal Distribution Area and Frequencies

In our histograms, we insisted upon the use of bars of equal width so that the area of the bars would be proportional to the class frequencies. Presumably, then, we ought to be able to interpret the area aspect of our normal curve in terms of our frequencies. In fact, the fifth requirement that we established (p. 73) for the curve to replace our histogram was that it must have the same area under it as our histogram did.

What is the area under the normal curve? This is a truly amazing thing, and it is going to take a bit of doing to understand it, but let's start. In the first place, what is the area under our histogram? If we are thinking of the histogram as plotted in the original, or X, units and in actual frequencies, each bar is i units wide, and there are bars totalling N frequency units in height, so the total area is Ni square units. In passing, let us notice that we depart from the strict practice of analytic geometry, which requires equal scale units in both directions and adjust our units to make effective use of our paper. This area could be represented by a rectangle N units high by i units wide, or $\frac{1}{2}N$ units high by $2i$ units wide, or any equivalent rectangle.

But what about the area under our curve? Unless you have mastered a good calculus course, you will know no way of calculating that area. Furthermore, if you were to study the properties of the normal equations more closely, you would find that it never does come down and touch the z-axis: no matter how far out we go, the curve is always getting closer to the axis, but never arrives. We say that it approaches the axis asymptotically. If that is so, how can the area be definite?

To answer both of those questions through formal mathematics would, as we have suggested, require that you take a pretty complete calculus course. You can do physically the equivalent of what is done mentally and with refinement in the calculus. We will suggest how it could be done. Suppose you constructed your histogram carefully on a well-made sheet of good graph paper of as large a size as you could conveniently find. Then, on another piece of the same graph paper, you very carefully plotted many points of the related normal curve, using the same scale, and faired in the curve as far as you could go just as accurately as you could. Of course, you couldn't complete the curve, because it goes out forever in both directions, but you could go so far that you could no longer see the gap between the curve and the axis.

Now you could count up the squares covered by your histogram, and could count the whole squares and combine parts of squares covered by the area under your curve. An even easier procedure for comparing the two areas, if the paper is so well made that its weight per unit area is quite uniform, would be to cut out both the histogram area and that under the curve, and weigh them. Your results should be nearly alike, but with the weight (and therefore area) of the area under the curve a little less than that of the histogram. Perhaps you might now look for larger pieces of graph paper, and so lessen the effect of errors of drawing and cutting your figures, and find that the discrepancy was reduced. The longer you were able to make the graph of your curve, the closer would the two values draw together.

Now this process is so tedious that we doubt you will actually perform it, but it is the nearest physical counterpart that is reasonably easy to perform of the task that calculus does by reasoning. So, let us accept the two facts that the curve does, indeed, have a finite area, and that that area is the same as the area of the histogram to which it was fitted. Just as, with calculus, we can find the area of the total curve, so we can find the area from the left up to a vertical line drawn at any required value. If we think of the standard normal curve, equation 5.4.1d, which is drawn in relative frequencies for an imagined class interval of one z unit, its area will be just one square unit. Areas under it to the left of any z value will then be fractions, and will correspond to relative cumulative frequencies at and below that value of z. Similarly, the difference between two such areas is the area under the curve between vertical lines at the two corresponding z values, and this will correspond to the relative frequencies of values between those to values of z. Of course, we can convert relative frequencies to frequencies simply by multiplying by the total number of observations, N, and we know how to go from z-values to X-values.

Table 5-4 Computation of Frequencies from the Fitted Normal Curve Corresponding to Table 5-2A for Freshman Year Academic Indexes, Class of 1956, University of X

Class Mark, X_i	Upper Boundary X_U	$X_U - \mu$	$z_U = (X_U - \mu)/\sigma$	Area Below z_U	Area in Class	Normal Frequency f_N	Observed Frequency f_0
—	$+\infty$	$+\infty$	$+\infty$	1.0000	0.0053	2.4	0
3.805	4.005	1.747	2.554	0.9947	0.0192	8.6	9
3.405	3.605	1.347	1.969	0.9755	0.0586	26.1	34
3.005	3.205	0.947	1.385	0.9169	0.1283	57.4	64
2.605	2.805	0.547	0.800	0.7881	0.2030	90.5	72
2.205	2.405	0.147	0.215	0.5851	0.2293	102.3	101
1.805	2.205	−0.253	−0.370	0.3558	0.1859	82.9	90
1.405	1.605	−0.653	−0.955	0.1699	0.1079	48.1	49
1.005	1.205	−1.053	−1.539	0.0620	0.0451	20.1	25
0.605	0.805	−1.453	−2.124	0.0169	0.0135	6.0	1
0.205	0.405	−1.853	−2.709	0.0034	0.0029	1.3	1
—	0.005	−2.253	−3.294	0.0005	0.0005	0.2	0
—	$-\infty$	$-\infty$	$-\infty$	0.000	—	—	—

Using the values from the raw data, $\mu \doteq 2.258$ and $\sigma \doteq 0.684$.

To see how this works out, let's construct and study Table 5-4, in which we compare the frequencies given by the curve we have fitted with those actually observed, according to Table 5-2a. Our first column gives the class marks of the successive classes in descending order. Notice that we leave the first and last two rows in this column blank. This allows room for us to deal with the "class" corresponding to the "tails" of the curve beyond our extreme actual classes. The second column gives the upper class boundaries, X_U, for the successive classes. For the upper "tail" we write $+\infty$ (plus infinity) as a reminder that the curve goes on forever, and similarly $-\infty$ at the other end. These do not constitute formal notation, but are simply shorthand reminders. The third column contains the differences between the X_U values and μ, and the fourth contains these values divided by σ and are therefore values of z_U, the upper boundaries of our classes on the z scale.

The fifth column is obtained from Appendix II, using linear interpolation between the tabulated z-values. (Appendix C gives a convenient machine interpolation method.) These values correspond to the cumulative relative frequencies to the upper class boundaries. By subtracting from these values in each line the values in the line below, we obtain the values in the sixth column, the areas between the boundaries of each class, which are the relative class frequencies. For example, the value on the first line is 1.0000 − 0.9947; that on the second line, 0.9947 − 0.9755, and so on. The seventh column gives the product of the relative frequencies of column six multiplied by the total number of observations, $N(= 446$ in our case). This figure is often called the "theoretical" frequency, but we think this is a most improper use of the term, theoretical, and we intend to use the designation "normal" to indicate that we calculated them from the fitted normal curve. We use the symbol f_N to remind us of this origin of the figures.

If we were going to answer the obvious question about how well the curve does fit the histogram, we would have to use a procedure that we are far from ready to learn, but when we use it, we find that we should have the fitted frequencies to one more figure than the actual, or observed frequencies. This means that we report f_N to tenths. This is always good for a laugh among the ignorant, because it looks as though we had a tenth of a student beyond the 26 complete ones in the class whose mark is 3.405. Actually, of course, the decimal arose from the mathematical equivalent of the manipulation of the modelling clay, which we proposed when we were first discussing the problem of fitting a curve to a histogram. We could round the values of f_N to whole numbers, but then we would be in trouble later, so — let them laugh: we'll laugh last.

In the final column, we copy the frequencies, which we now designated f_0, from the original Table 5-2 Part A as the actual or observed frequencies for comparison. At present, we can make only a subjective judgment, but you will probably agree that the agreement is quite good. Later, in Chapter 16, we shall test just how good it is.

5.6 Looking Both Ways

In thinking back over this chapter, we find that we have accomplished a good deal. We have developed some feeling for the idea that a smooth curve might represent a histogram and its frequency table, and do something more, besides. We have learned how to work with the equation for one kind of curve which does fit many types of data with which we shall be concerned.

But those of you who are complete students (not the fractions we just mentioned!) will be raising several questions, including the following:

1. We have seen a number of distributions which are by no means symmetrical and others which have more than one peak. What do we do about them?

2. Since academic indexes must be between 0 and 4, inclusive, by definition, why do we even think of fitting a curve calling for values out to infinity in both directions?

3. Is there any good reason for using this normal curve other than the fact that it often does fit pretty well? Did someone just grab it out of the air, or is there a rational basis for using it?

4. Prof. Whoosis in the Whatsis Department says, "There aren't any normal distributions, anyway, and since so much of statistics is based on them, statistics is no good." Is he right? (This is a real quotation of an actual statement, unfortunately.)

In order to arrive at intelligent answers to these questions, we need to consider some background ideas. This will be done in the following chapter. Be assured that all four questions deserve an answer. When you can give a proper one, you are well on the way to understanding the basis of statistical thinking.

General Study

1. As you carry on your general reading of news and publications, begin to notice to what extent distributions are presented and discussed with the aid of some type of smooth curve. How often is the curve used in addition to a histogram? In place of it?

2. Estimate to what extent the data of your field of particular interest are of such form that a normal distribution curve is likely to represent them fairly well. Try to describe the general characteristics of other types you believe you will encounter.

3. Consider the questions we asked in the last section of this chapter and, without looking ahead, see what you can do now toward starting to answer them.

Problems

1. Find the normal frequencies corresponding to the other parts of Table 5-2.

2. Find the normal frequencies corresponding to the distributions you found in the problems of Chapter 2.

PART B

Probability Rudiments

6

Probability and Distributions

6.1 Reorientation

It is a very prudent plan, in any effort to master a new subject, to pause periodically and consider what has been learned and what lies ahead. In this way, we see the subject as a united structure, not as individual bits and fragments. This is a particularly good time for such a pause in our efforts, as you will presently see.

Our opening chapter attempted to give you a picture, in very broad terms, of the purpose and methods of statistics: it supplied our orientation, if you will, linking some of our past experience with the statistical ideas that lay ahead. Our next four chapters introduced us to some phases of what is often called, appropriately, *descriptive statistics*, because our objective was to learn how to describe the data we were interested in in a compact, expeditious, and objective manner.

We first employed methods requiring very little grasp of mathematics: retabulation, grouping, and simple charting. These methods had the advantage of presenting much of the information in our data in a form that could be understood by intelligent readers with no statistical training. However, the processes involved were tedious and the results were not as condensed as we could sense that they might be.

The methods for determining measures of central value and dispersion followed next, and should not have posed too many difficulties for you. Finally, we came to the problem of describing the form of a distribution, and introduced the normal distribution equation. This, we suspect, proved a real challenge to many of you. In the first place, it is a type of equation which was probably quite unfamiliar to you, and the mere mechanics of interpreting its meaning and performing the indicated operations were beyond your mathematical experience. In the second place, the equation must have seemed to you something like the magician's rabbit: pulled out of the hat by legerdemain!

So far as your mathematical difficulties are concerned, let us suggest a way of approaching them. Very likely all of you drive a car with skill and confidence and, we surely hope, with safety. Could you design a car, or make a headlight bulb, or adjust the front-end alignment? We would be amazed if more than one out of all of our possible readers could do all these things, yet you drive well. So it is with our distribution equation: we believe you do not need to be able to derive it "from scratch" if you broadly understand its meaning and practice its use and interpretation. This we intend to continue to help you to accomplish.

Your second concern, that you don't really see where the equation came from, so that it is too much like the magician's rabbit, brings us to our present position. In order to understand why the normal equation is a reasonable one for our purpose, and not an arbitrary witches' brew of weird symbols, we must consider some of the ideas in a branch of mathematics known as probability theory. Out of this study, there will emerge both an understanding of the appropriateness of the normal equation as a description of many distributions and ways of coping with distributions which the normal equation does not describe.

The study of probability at this time will have the added advantage of providing a background that will make it easier for us to understand the ideas ahead of us. We must soon come to grips with the problem of dealing with the information in a sample, which is only part of the universe or population in which we are interested. Thus, our effort to learn something about probability will, in a very real sense, do three things for us:

1. It will provide a foundation on which to base our description of distribution forms, from which we can extend our methods.

2. It will make our future task of dealing with samples easier.

3. It will provide a firm link between the area we have been studying, descriptive statistics, and the new area, sampling theory.

Probability theory, like most branches of mathematics, is still being developed, extended, and refined. Books larger than this one are devoted to the presentation of the "elements" of the subject to readers already equipped with a rather extensive mathematical training. Obviously, we can hardly make a single chapter, long though it may become, accomplish the same thing! But we do intend to help you understand the most basic principles on which the subject rests, and the ways of thinking which lead to some of its most useful results for statistics. We think that, with this background, you will be prepared to use your statistical methods with more prudence and understanding, and with something of the justified confidence with which you drive your car. This, then, is where we are going.

6.2 Ways of Doing Things

Before we embark on the study of probability, itself, it will help us to become familiar with some expeditious methods for counting the number of ways in which things can be done. This may seem silly, to learn how to count, at our age. For simple problems, it may be silly, for we can list the ways and count them. But a problem does not need to be very complicated before the listing preparatory to actual counting becomes both tedious and extremely difficult. What we shall do, then, is to consider a simple problem, then more complicated ones, and let them lead us into the counting principles we need.

As an example, suppose that there are three routes leading from the metropolis of Bigton to the residential suburb of Homeville, and that there are then four routes leading to the pleasantly restful and attractive community of Farmdale. In how many different ways can we go from Bigton to Farmdale via Homeville?

This is really so simple we hardly seem to need to talk about it, but let's do so, anyway. We might identify the three routes from Bigton to Homeville by the letters A, B, and C, and the four routes from Homeville to Farmdale by the numbers 1, 2, 3, and 4. No matter how we go from Bigton to Homeville, we have four possible ways of continuing from there to Farmdale. We could list our route possibilities, as in Table 6-1, by giving the letter and number of

Table 6-1 Tabulation of Possible Routes from Bigton to Farmdale via Homeville

Routes from Bigton to Homeville: A, B, C

Routes from Homeville to Farmdale: 1, 2, 3, 4

Overall Routes:				
	$A1$	$A2$	$A3$	$A4$
	$B1$	$B2$	$B3$	$B4$
	$C1$	$C2$	$C3$	$C4$

the two components we used, making sure that with each letter we used each number once. Of course, there are 12 possible routes, which we notice is the product, 3×4, of the number of each of the two component parts.

Suppose we are selecting a dinner from a menu comprising three soups, four main courses (including entree and vegetables, with no substitutions permitted), two salads, five desserts, and three beverages. How many possible dinners, including one item of each kind, can we select? So far as the soup and main course are concerned, we could think of the problem as quite like our route problem above, and conclude that there are $3 \times 4 = 12$ possibilities. Now we could consider that we have twelve "soup-and-main-courses" (where we put in the hyphens temporarily to remind us that composite choice has now been accomplished) and have to decide about salads, of which there are two. Either salad could be chosen with each of the 12 soup-and-main-courses, giving us $12 \times 2 = 24$ soup-and-main-course-and-salads. In a similar way, we find

$24 \times 5 = 120$ possibilities for soup-and-main-course-and-salad-and-desserts and, finally, $120 \times 3 = 360$ soup-and-main-course-and-salad-and-dessert-and-beverages, or dinners.

What we have been seeing are two applications of a general principle. If we call the first part of each job "event A" (going from Bigton to Homeville, or choosing a soup), call the second part "event B" (going from Homeville to Farmdale, or choosing a main course) and so on, we can state our general principle as follows:

PRINCIPLE I. *If event A can be performed in n_A ways and thereafter event B can be performed in n_B ways, and so on, then events $A,B,\ldots$ can be performed in that order in a total of $n_A n_B \ldots$ different ways.*

6.3 Selecting and Arranging: Permutations

If you have five different books, which you are about to arrange along a straight shelf, in how many ways can you do it? The answer to this question arises from a very simple application of the foregoing principle. We might visualize the five positions waiting for books as five squares in a diagram like this:

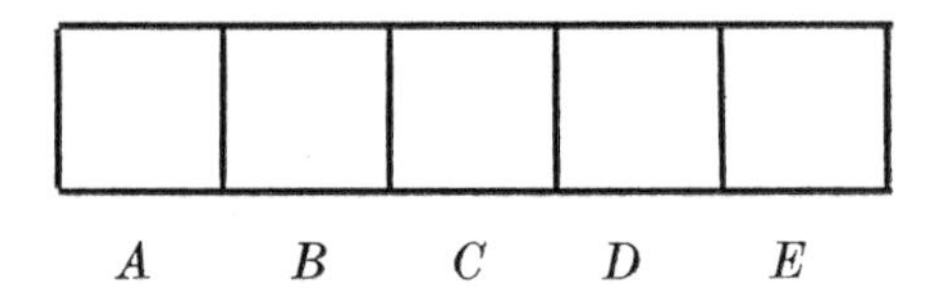

We may think of our task as consisting of five successive events. The first, event A, will be the selection of a book to fill space A. There are the five books of the entire set to choose from, so that $n_A = 5$. Then event B will be the selection of a book to fill space B, but there are now only four books left to choose from, so $n_B = 4$. The set of events and numbers of ways in which they can be accomplished are listed in some detail in Table 6-2, but, once you get

Table 6-2 WAYS OF ARRANGING FIVE BOOKS ON A SHELF CONSIDERED IN TERMS OF COMPONENT EVENTS

Event	*Description*	*Ways*
A	Choose book for first place	5, any of original books
B	Choose book for second place	4, any of remaining books
C	Choose book for third place	3, any of remaining books
D	Choose book for fourth place	2, either remaining book
E	"Choose" book for last place	1, the only remaining book

Total ways of arranging: $5 \times 4 \times 3 \times 2 \times 1 = 120$

used to the idea, filling in the successive numbers of ways of performing the events in the successive squares of our diagram is convenient:

5	4	3	2	1
A	B	C	D	E

Principle I tells us that the overall task of arranging the books can be performed in $5 \times 4 \times 3 \times 2 \times 1 = 120$ ways.

This is also a specific example of a more general principle. Before we state it, we should explain, in case you never knew or have forgotten, that the product of all the integers ("whole numbers") from a specific one, n, down to 1 (or from 1 up to n), inclusive, is so commonly needed that it is given both a name and a symbol. It is called *factorial n* or *n factorial.* Its symbol used to be $\underline{n|}$, but this is a great nuisance for both typists and compositors, so that $n!$ has been almost universal for some time. Our general principle can now be stated very simply:

PRINCIPLE II. *The number of orders in which n different objects can be arranged in a line is n!.*

Suppose that we now have a little more complicated task: we have a bookshelf with room for only five books, and we have 11 books at our disposal. Our problem could be thought of as the selection of the five books to be put on the shelf, followed by the choice of orders of arranging the five books. But this is a somewhat needlessly difficult approach. Another way of thinking would be to recognize that we again have five places to fill, but that now we have 11 choices available (any of the original books) for the first space, 10 for the second, and so on. Our block diagram, which was convenient before, would now look like this:

11	10	9	8	7
A	B	C	D	E

and our total number of ways of accomplishing our task, by Principle I, becomes $11 \times 10 \times 9 \times 8 \times 7 = 55{,}440$.

This number is built up in a rather interesting way. The first factor was the number of books we had available, 11, and the last was that number minus the number of places to be filled, 5, plus 1, that is, $11 - 5 + 1 = 7$. This is another specific example of a general principle. We shall define any specific selection and arrangement in line of a group of objects as a *permutation* of those objects. If we had n objects available from which we selected r objects and arranged them in line, we would say that we had a permutation of r objects from among n. Two such permutations are considered different if either (a) they involve a different arrangement of the same objects or (b) they involve different objects. Three of the possible permutations of $r = 5$ books from among $n = 11$ books available, using $a, b, \ldots k$ to designate the books, are: eigbk, bgike, and agieh. The first two permutations involve the same books in different orders, whereas in the third, books a and h are now used but books b and k are not.

If we represent the total number of permutations that may be made of r objects among n, where $r \leq n$, by the symbol $P(n,r)$, we may state our principle quite compactly by a formula:

$$P(n,r) = n(n-1) \ldots (n-r+1) \tag{6.3.1}$$

Notice that when $r = n$, $n - r + 1 = n - n + 1 = 1$, and $P(n,n) = n(n-1) \ldots 1 = n!$, which agrees with Principle II. Of course it must, because our choice, in that case, is to use all of the objects, and we have left only the problem of arranging them. Notice also that equation 6.3.1 indicates the arithmetic we need to perform in its simplest apparent form, but it is in some respects both unhandy to recall and unrevealing in form.

6.4 Developments from the Permutation Idea

Can we improve it for some purposes? Consider the next integer below $(n - r + 1)$, namely, $(n - r)$. The next is $(n - r - 1)$ and so on down to 1. But the product of these consecutive integers is just $(n - r)!$ and, if we were to multiply both sides of equation 6.3.1 by that quantity, we would have

$$P(n,r)(n-r)! = n(n-1) \ldots (n-r+1)(n-r) \ldots 1 = n! \tag{6.4.1a}$$

Now, if we divide both sides of this equation by $(n - r)!$ and actually do the division on the left, but simply indicate it on the right, we will have:

$$P(n,r) = n!/(n-r)! \tag{6.4.1b}$$

Really, because we have multiplied and divided by the same quantity we have (barring goofs!) left our values unchanged, but the right side looks different. What good has that done us? Actually, it has done two most valuable things. First, although equation 6.3.1 is in the form calling for the least arithmetic if we have to do it all ourselves, it still represents a great deal of work when n and r are very different. But with the aid of tables of factorials, such as Appendix III, equation 6.4.1b reduces the problem to a division of one number by another. Second, equation 6.4.1b can show us what is really happening. It shows us that the number of selections and arrangements of r objects from among n is really the total number of arrangements that can be made of all

n objects (which is $n!$) reduced by division by the number of arrangements that can be made of the $(n - r)$ objects not used (which is $(n - r)!$. Why should this be?

Before we attempt to answer that question, as we shall start to do in our next paragraph, we should like to draw to your attention another advantage of mathematical notation. Equation 6.3.1 described the number of permutations very simply and compactly. Then, by formal operations of rudimentary algebra, we were able to work with that expression, altering its appearance but not its meaning. This is the equivalent of rephrasing sentences in English and adding parenthetical elements to them. But it is often a troublesome, tedious, and even exasperating task to rework a sentence until it satisfies us. On the other hand, recall how easy it was to operate with our equation and, from its final form, to recast the idea in English. The idea was inherent in either the English or its mathematical "translation" all the time: it emerged and developed more readily with the mathematical expression.

To answer our question concerning the reasonableness of equation 6.4.1b, instead of considering quite so big a problem as the selection and arrangement of 5 books from among 11, let us consider selecting and arranging 4 books from among 7. We start to list the permutations of all 7 books, separating the first 4 by a little space to indicate that they are the books to be used as they will be on the shelf:

abcd efg	*acbd efg*
abcd egf	*acbd egf*
abcd feg	*acbd feg*
abcd fge	*acbd fge*
abcd gef	*acbd gef*
abcd gfe	*acbd gfe*

Notice that, in the first block of permutations, the first 4 letters, representing the books to be used, are identical, whereas the last 3 are the unused ones in their $3! = 6$ different arrangements. Thus, out of the 6 permutations of the 7 books, we have just 1 of the 4 books, *abcd*. In the second block, we place the same 4 books in a different order, thus obtaining a new permutation. Again, this order remains unchanged while we run through the 6 different orders of the remaining 3.

Still using books a, b, c, and d, their remaining permutations would bring the total up to 24, with each of which we would run through the same 6 permutations of e, f, and g. The permutations, including the 2 used above (of a, b, c, and d), are

abcd	*abdc*	*acdb*	*bcda*
acbd	*adbc*	*adcb*	*bcda*
bacd	*badc*	*cadb*	*cbda*
bcad	*bdac*	*cdab*	*cdba*
cabd	*dabc*	*dacb*	*dbca*
cbad	*dbac*	*dcab*	*dcba*

Each of these, accompanied by its 6 permutations of the books e, f, and g, contributes 6 permutations of the 7 books. But each set of 4 books we select repeats the same story: we have 24 permutations of the 4 books used, each accompanied by $3! = 6$ permutations of the 3 books not used. But we know that the total number of permutations of the 7 books is 7!. Therefore, the number of permutations of 4 books from among 7 is $7!/3! = 7 \times 6 \times 5 \times 4 = 840$. From the table of factorials, we could quickly substitute $7!/3 = 5040/6 = 840$.

6.5 Ways of Selecting: Combinations

It may seem strange that we have considered first the combined task of selecting and arranging before coming to the matter of selection by itself. But you saw that the formula for permutations came out quite readily from simple basic ideas. Let's carry them a bit further. Look back near the end of the preceding paragraph and you will see we began a sentence with the words, "Each different set of four books we select repeats the same story . . . "; but we never did discuss how many such sets there were. However, we know that each set of 4 books, once they are selected, can be arranged in $4! = 24$ ways, and we actually wrote out the 24 orders for books, a, b, c, and d. So, if we know that 4 books can be selected from among 7 and arranged in $840 = 7!/3!$ ways, and we know that each selection contributes 4! arrangements, the total number of selections must be

$$\frac{7!/3!}{4!} = \frac{7!}{3!4!} = \frac{840}{24} = 35$$

A selection without regard to order is called a *combination*. A common symbol for the number of combinations of r objects selected from among n was $C(n,r)$, but recent writers are tending to use the symbol $\binom{n}{r}$, and we shall generally do so. May we remark, in passing, that this symbol is rather interesting. It looks very simple and compact, and is very easy to write with a pen or pencil. But it does have certain disadvantages. In typewriting, it is a very real nuisance because, unlike the fraction, $\frac{n}{r}$, which may be written on one line with a slanted fraction bar (sometimes called a shilling bar) as n/r, there is no one-line typed equivalent for the combination symbol. We suspect it is a nuisance for a compositor, too. Even more important, it is often misread as a fraction, which it closely resembles. However, present usage makes it very common.

But to return from our digression, our example was, as you must suspect, a specific case of another general principle which we shall summarize in formulas:

$$\binom{n}{r} = P(n,r)/r! \tag{6.5.1a}$$

$$= n(n-1)\ldots(n-r+1)/r! \tag{6.5.1b}$$

$$= \frac{n!}{r!(n-r)!} \tag{6.5.1c}$$

Equation 6.5.1c is easy to recall and, if you have a calculator and table of factorials, is easy to use. Without the table and calculator, equation 6.5.1b, which is readily developed from 6.5.1c, is usually easiest. Equation 6.5.1a is good if you have already calculated the permutations, and, of course, recalls the relation between permutations and combinations.

Now we must ask how many combinations we can make from all n objects. Let us pretend that we have become "formula crazy," that is, we have finally developed so much faith in formulas that we use them without thinking. If we want to use all n objects, then $r = n$, so that equation 6.5.1c becomes

$$\binom{n}{n} = \frac{n!}{r!(n-r)!} = \frac{n!}{n!(n-n)!} \tag{6.5.2a}$$

Surely we may "cancel" $n!$ from numerator and denominator, and notice that $(n - n) = 0$, so that we have:—

$$\binom{n}{n} = \frac{1}{0!} \tag{6.5.2b}$$

and this worries us. What is 0!? We defined $n!$ as the product of the integers from one up to n, inclusive. But you can't start from one, go up in value, and get to zero. Our symbol, 0!, really does not have meaning under that definition yet our formula led to it in an attempt to answer a perfectly reasonable question.

Now we do what must always be done: we reconsider our problem sensibly. In how many ways is it possible to select all n objects? Of course, in just one way: you don't "select," you just use all of them. Our formula ought, then, to yield the value, one, or unity. It will if we adopt as an amendment to our definition of $n!$ that 0! shall be unity, that is, $0! = 1$. Do we have the right to do this? Yes, if this definition does not lead us into inconsistencies. Mathematicians examined the matter critically, and found that here and in other situations, this extension made sense, and nowhere did it fail to do so, and the extension has been accepted. Hence, our first three forms of equation 6.5.1 are all that we need. Notice an interesting consequence of our formulas:

$$\binom{n}{r} = \binom{n}{n-r} \tag{6.5.3}$$

that is, the number of combinations of r objects from among n is just equal to that of the remaining $n - r$ objects. Of course it is, for every time we make a selection of r objects to be used, we automatically make a selection of the remaining $(n - r)$ objects which, in the words of a famous Hollywood mogul, are to be "included out." Sound formulas both make sense and reveal facts, don't they?

If this were a course in college algebra, we could go on to consider very complicated problems of permutations and combinations, such as seating a party at a round dinner table, with certain restrictions imposed by personal attachments or incompatibilities, or the problem of the inebriated socialite and his circular key ring, but they are not necessary for our present purposes, so let us be on our way.

6.6 The Beginning of Probability

What is four? We could quite safely wager that you cannot define four. If you consult your dictionaries, you will not, we feel positive, find a satisfactory definition. Yet we all "know" what four is, and we proceed to operate with four and many other numbers without even thinking, until someone asks the question, that we can't define it. The whole numbers, or integers, are concepts that we accept intuitively and fundamentally, and we go on from there to develop the orderly principles which let us perform ultimately very complicated tasks with them. We bring this to your attention because, in a quite similar way, all effective thinking that we do starts from intuitively understood concepts and goes on to develop more complicated ideas from them in an orderly fashion. Probability theory is no exception, but the fact that its intuitive basis is clearly evident seems to bother many people; it shouldn't.

Like many branches of learning that are today quite "reputable," probability theory owes its origin to a "disreputable" past. Modern chemistry began with alchemy, the "art" of "transmuting" base metals, like lead, into gold. Astronomy has some of its roots in the observations of astrologers. And probability theory grew out of the efforts of the playboys of the past to "make a killing" at the gaming tables without such dishonorable procedures as the use of loaded dice and marked cards. And it is still true that the theory develops by the analysis of situations involving coins, cards, and dice, which are counterparts of highly involved problems in science, engineering, and commerce.

6.7 Fundamental Principles of Probability

Suppose we took a coin, a shiny half dollar, for instance, and tossed it: what could happen? It could land "heads" up, or it could land "tails" up, as we all know. But it could also fall into a crack in our floor and remain on edge, or it could flip and roll away and be lost, and we could think of various other possibilities. To make the situation still more complicated, we had a jeweler friend once who carefully kept two dimes in separate pockets. One had heads on both faces, while the other had tails, as a result of his careful machining of four original coins!

But if we want a mathematician to consider our question, he will tell us that mathematics can't help us as long as we consider all these possibilities as well as the possibility of controlling the outcome. However, if you will let him idealize the problem, he will discuss a "perfect" coin, "perfectly" tossed. By this concept, he will mean that

1. The coin has two faces, one called heads, the other, tails.
2. If the coin is tossed, it must fall either heads or tails. Standing on edge, getting lost, and the other freak possibilities are ruled out.
3. Nothing in the coin or its handling will in any way affect how it lands on a specific toss. Another way of expressing the third statement is that the coin is equally likely to land heads or tails.

He will think of the tossing of the coin as a *trial* of an *experiment* to determine what happens. Each possible outcome, or result, of the experiment he will call an *event*, and will often use a single symbol, or a simple collection of symbols, to identify each event, thus:

H = heads, means the coin falls "heads."

T = tails, means the coin falls "tails."

He will define the *probability* of heads occurring as $\frac{1}{2}$, the ratio of the number of events which are heads, one, to the total number of events, two, and he will use for it the symbol Pr {H}. Similarly, Pr {T} = $\frac{1}{2}$ will describe the probability of tails. Notice that the sum of the probabilities of the possible events is unity (one), as it will always be. Now in this exceedingly simple experiment, all he has really done is to restate his third condition in different words and symbols. This is no better and no worse than our attempts to define four. We don't really define four effectively, but we go on to use it: we don't really define this elemental probability, but we are going on to use it.

To see how we use it, suppose that we are interested in what would happen if we tossed a coin twice. Our mathematician would relate our proposal to the consideration of two successive ideal tosses of his ideal coin, or the performance of his simple experiment twice. He will place a further requirement:

4. The outcome of one toss shall in no way affect the outcome of the other, that is, the trials are *independent.*

This makes it possible for him to list the possible outcomes, or events, for the new experiment by writing the event for the first toss followed by the event for the second, thus:

HH HT TH TT

These events are called *compound events* because they can be visualized as built up, or compounded, from the *simple events*, the outcomes of the elements of the experiment. For the listed events, since the two simple events of which each is composed have the same probabilities and are independent, the mathematician again visualizes that all four are equally probable, and assigns the probability of each as $\frac{1}{4}$.

However, he could describe the possible outcomes of his experiment in a different way. He could consider event A as two heads, event B as one head and one tail, regardless of order, and event C as two tails. Notice that he has again compounded an already compound event. Of the possible events of the first stage of compounding (still equally probable), two are what we now call event B, while one each are event A and event C. So we can state that Pr $\{A\}$ $= 1/4$, Pr $\{B\} = 2/4 = 1/2$, and Pr $\{C\} = 1/4$. We might prefer to replace A, B, and C by 2H, 1H, and 0H to save having to remember how many heads were involved, and write Pr $\{2\text{H}\} = 1/4$, Pr $\{1\text{H}\} = 1/2$, and Pr $\{0\text{H}\} = 1/4$.

If we increased the number of tosses we were considering to three, our mathematician would do likewise with his ideal experiment and would list his possible outcomes or events as

HHH HHT HTH THH HTT THT TTH TTT

and would reason that each has a probability of 1/8. For the compound events with which we are often concerned, he would write

$$\Pr\{3\text{H}\} = 1/8$$

$$\Pr\{2\text{H}\} = 3/8$$

$$\Pr\{1\text{H}\} = 3/8$$

$$\Pr\{0\text{H}\} = 1/8$$

All this is quite simple and appears to support your suspicion that it is silly to learn how to count now. All right: we are interested in tossing a coin 100 times, so suppose we list . . . ! There *is* a task, for neither you nor we are going to write down the possible ways of getting 100, 99, 98, . . . 3, 2, 1 and 0 heads.

This is the time to think what is going on. We found, in our study of descriptive statistics, that our various procedures of tabulating and charting rapidly became tedious, and that our later mathematical procedures accomplished much of our work with far less effort, once we understood them. Perhaps they will do here, as well. Now look at the sentence after the one which was broken off at the dash. Doesn't "ways of getting," poor English though it is, call to mind "ways of selecting," or combinations? And before that, didn't we talk about ways of doing one thing followed by another, and another, and another? We did, and we did it on purpose.

Our compound experiment of tossing a coin some number of times, say n, can be visualized, as we have done, simply as the performance n successive times of the most simple experiment of tossing the coin once. Each of these simplest experiments has two possible outcomes, or events, so that the number of possible events for the compound experiment is $2 \times 2 \ldots 2$ for a total of n factors, or 2^n. For two tosses $2^2 = 4$, and for three tosses $2^3 = 8$, which agrees with our tabulations. But for 100 tosses 2^{100} equals a number greater than one followed by 30 zeros, which is big in either Texas or Alaska.

Returning to our reasonably sized experiments, notice that in our case involving the two tosses, obtaining one head involved, from one way of thinking, the selection of which toss out of the two was to get the head. This can be done in $\binom{2}{1} = 2$ ways, and there were $2^2 = 4$ ways in which the experiment could result. Hence, Pr {1H in 2 tosses} $= \binom{2}{1} 2^2 = 2/4 = 1/2$. Similarly, two heads can be assigned to two tosses in $\binom{2}{2} = 1$ way, and no heads can be assigned in $\binom{2}{0} = 1$ way, leading to the results previously obtained. For the three-toss experiments, $\binom{3}{3} = \binom{3}{0} = 1$ and $\binom{3}{2} = \binom{3}{1} = 3$, which, with the $2^3 = 8$, leads to the same values as before. The trouble with our 100-toss problem is that the arithmetic is still most unattractive. Let's just set it aside and think about something else for a bit.

6.8 Linking Probability to Experience

That "something else" will be the question of how we can get back from the very pure and ideal situation which the mathematician was discussing to the real world in which we live our daily lives. The mathematician thought about a very perfect coin, tossed under very perfect conditions, and defined probability in such a way that, at least in the cases we have discussed, it was easy to calculate it. Such probabilities are designated as *mathematical* or *a priori* (Latin for "in advance") probabilities. The latter designation stems from the fact that they can be calculated in advance of actual performance of an experiment.

In the real world, we might toss a coin many times and record the result of each toss. After a total of n tosses, we could count up the number, or frequency, of tosses in which the outcome had been heads, and call it n_{H}. The number, or frequency, of tails would be n_{T}. If we did not count as a toss any attempts which resulted in anything but heads or tails, then $n_{\mathrm{H}} + n_{\mathrm{T}}$ would equal n. Hence, the relative frequencies of heads and tails, n_{H}/n and n_{T}/n, respectively, would be two fractions whose sum would be one (unity). In the sense that their sum is 1, and that they are ratios of the numbers of events of different considered kinds to the total number of such events, they bear a strong resemblance to the probabilities the mathematician talked about. The difference is that they were the result of actual observations. All this leads to such relative frequencies being called *statistical* or *a posteriori* probabilities. The first name stems from the fact that statistics deals with observations. The other comes from the Latin for "afterward," reminding us that they can be established only after an actual experiment.

Now we come to the heart of the matter: is there any connection between the numerical values of the two kinds of probability? We have already shown that the mathematical probability of heads, Pr {H}, is $\frac{1}{2}$, as is also the mathematical probability of tails, Pr {T}. This paragraph was being written on a hot, "muggy" summer afternoon, and we decided to do an actual experiment as a relief from the monotony of thinking and typing. We found a shiny, 1959, Franklin-head half dollar, and proceeded to toss it 100 times and record the result, which is shown in Table 6-3.

Table 6-3 RESULTS OF 100 SUCCESSIVE TOSSES OF A 1959 FRANKLIN-HEAD HALF DOLLAR BY THE AUTHOR, JULY 28, 1960.
Results are in order down the successive columns.

H	T	T	H
T	T	H	T
H	T	H	H
H	T	H	H
H	H	T	T
H	H	H	T
T	H	T	T
T	H	T	T
H	H	H	T
T	T	T	T
H	T	H	H
H	H	H	T
T	T	H	T
H	T	T	T
T	T	H	T
T	H	H	H
H	H	H	H
H	T	H	T
H	H	T	T
H	H	T	T
H	T	H	H
H	T	T	H
H	T	H	T
H	H	H	H
T	H	T	T

In Table 6-4, we record n_H, and n_T and n after each toss, as well as, to four decimals, the relative frequencies. We used p_H and p_T (the "p" reminds us of

Table 6-4 COMPUTATION OF FREQUENCIES AND STATISTICAL PROBABILITIES FROM
Table 6-4 COMPUTATION OF FREQUENCIES AND STATISTICAL PROBABILITIES FROM DATA OF TABLE 6-3 ON COIN TOSSING

n	n_H	n_T	p_H	p_T	n	n_H	n_T	p_H	p_T
1	1	0	1.0000	0.0000	51	29	22	0.5686	0.4314
2	1	1	0.5000	0.5000	52	30	22	0.5769	0.4231
3	2	1	0.6667	0.3333	53	31	22	0.5849	0.4151
4	3	1	0.7500	0.2500	54	32	22	0.5926	0.4074
5	4	1	0.8000	0.2000	55	32	23	0.5818	0.4182

Table 6-4 (*Continued*)

n	n_H	n_T	p_H	p_T	n	n_H	n_T	p_H	p_T
6	5	1	0.8333	0.1667	56	33	23	0.5893	0.4107
7	5	2	0.7143	0.2857	57	33	24	0.5789	0.4211
8	5	3	0.6250	0.3750	58	33	25	0.5690	0.4310
9	6	3	0.6667	0.3333	59	34	25	0.5763	0.4237
10	6	4	0.6000	0.4000	60	34	26	0.5667	0.4333
11	7	4	0.6364	0.3636	61	35	26	0.5738	0.4262
12	8	4	0.6666	0.3333	62	36	26	0.5806	0.4194
13	8	5	0.6154	0.3846	63	37	26	0.5873	0.4127
14	9	5	0.6429	0.3571	64	37	27	0.5781	0.4219
15	9	6	0.6000	0.4000	65	38	27	0.5846	0.4154
16	9	7	0.5625	0.4375	66	39	27	0.5909	0.4091
17	10	7	0.5882	0.4118	67	40	27	0.5970	0.4030
18	11	7	0.6111	0.3889	68	41	27	0.6029	0.3971
19	12	7	0.6316	0.3784	69	41	28	0.5942	0.4058
20	13	7	0.6500	0.3500	70	41	29	0.5857	0.4143
21	14	7	0.6666	0.3333	71	42	29	0.5915	0.4085
22	15	7	0.6818	0.3181	72	42	30	0.5833	0.4167
23	16	7	0.6957	0.3043	73	43	30	0.5890	0.4110
24	17	7	0.7083	0.2917	74	44	30	0.5946	0.4054
25	17	8	0.6800	0.3200	75	44	31	0.5867	0.4133
26	17	9	0.6538	0.3462	76	45	31	0.5921	0.4089
27	17	10	0.6296	0.3704	77	45	32	0.5844	0.4156
28	17	11	0.6071	0.3929	78	46	32	0.5897	0.4103
29	17	12	0.5862	0.4138	79	47	32	0.5949	0.4051
30	18	12	0.6000	0.4000	80	47	33	0.5875	0.4125
31	19	12	0.6129	0.3871	81	47	34	0.5802	0.4198
32	20	12	0.6250	0.3750	82	47	35	0.5732	0.4268
33	21	12	0.6363	0.3636	83	47	36	0.5663	0.4337
34	22	12	0.6471	0.3529	84	47	37	0.5595	0.4405
35	22	13	0.6286	0.3714	85	47	38	0.5529	0.4471
36	22	14	0.6111	0.3888	86	48	38	0.5581	0.4419
37	23	14	0.6216	0.3784	87	48	39	0.5517	0.4483
38	23	15	0.6053	0.3947	88	48	40	0.5455	0.4545
39	23	16	0.5897	0.4103	89	48	41	0.5393	0.4607
40	23	17	0.5750	0.4250	90	48	42	0.5333	0.4667
41	24	17	0.5854	0.4146	91	49	42	0.5385	0.4615
42	25	17	0.5952	0.4048	92	50	42	0.5435	0.4565
43	25	18	0.5814	0.4186	93	50	43	0.5376	0.4624
44	26	18	0.5909	0.4091	94	50	44	0.5319	0.4681
45	27	18	0.6000	0.4000	95	50	45	0.5263	0.4737
46	27	19	0.5870	0.4130	96	51	45	0.5312	0.4788
47	27	20	0.5745	0.4255	97	52	45	0.5361	0.4639
48	27	21	0.5625	0.4375	98	52	46	0.5306	0.4694
49	28	21	0.5714	0.4286	99	53	46	0.5354	0.4746
50	29	21	0.5800	0.4200	100	53	47	0.5300	0.4700

fraction or *proportion*, as well as of statistical probability) for n_H/n and n_T/n, respectively. In Fig. 6-1, we have plotted p_H against n. The results are revealing.

Fig. 6-1. Experiment in tossing a 1959 Franklin-head Half Dollar 100 times. Plot of relative cumulative frequency of heads, p_H VS. Toss Number, n.

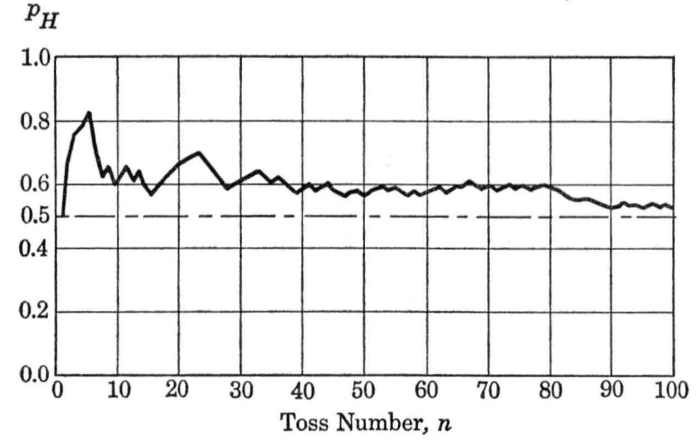

Notice that the first toss happened to fall heads and the second tails: p_H at the second toss was exactly 0.50, the value of Pr {H}, the mathematical probability of heads. But never again, throughout the entire remaining 98 tosses of the first 100 was this value reached: all values of p_H except the second were greater than 0.50. What could this mean? Some possibilities are listed below for your consideration:

1. The mathematician's "perfect" coin was so different from our "real" coin that the mathematician's reasoning is of no use in connection with the behavior of the real coin.

2. The mathematician's "perfect" toss was so different from our "real" toss that, again, his reasoning is of no use in connection with our experiment. Perhaps we did have skill in controlling the fall and were, unbeknownst to you, "fudging" the data.

3. We didn't toss the coin enough times to learn how it really behaves in the long run.

We must consider these possibilities seriously. So far as the first is concerned, examination of a half dollar critically suggests that the metal is distributed through the coin in a well-balanced fashion, and we are unable to recognize any condition which would tend to make it fall one way more often than another. Inquiry to the Director of the Mint led to our being informed that no positive effort is made, before adopting each new coin design, to insure that the coins do, indeed, conform to this requirement, but that in order for coins to mint properly, the metal must be fairly symmetrically distributed.

As to our being able to control the toss, if we have the gift, we are unconscious of it, and certainly have been unable to put it to profitable use!

This, then, brings us to the third alternative, that we didn't make enough tosses to permit us really to learn about the coin. If we look at Fig. 6-1 more closely, we gain the general impression that p_H is drawing toward 0.5 as the number of tosses increases. But we must be a little careful here, also, to be sure of what we really mean by "drawing toward."

6.9 Limits, Mathematical and Statistical

Consider the equation

$$y = (x + 1)/2x \tag{6.9.1a}$$

and let us investigate what happens to y as x takes on increasingly large positive values. Some values are shown in Table 6-5, and a graph of the curve of

Table 6-5 SOME CALCULATED VALUES SATISFYING THE EQUATION $y = (x + 1)/2x$

x	$x + 1$	$2x$	y
1	2	2	1.00000
2	3	4	0.75000
4	5	8	0.62500
5	6	10	0.60000
10	11	20	0.55000
50	51	100	0.51000
100	101	200	0.50500
500	501	1,000	0.50100
1,000	1,001	2,000	0.50050
5,000	5,001	10,000	0.50010
10,000	10,001	20,000	0.50005
50,000	50,001	100,000	0.50001
1,000,000	1,000,001	2,000,000	0.5000005

Fig. 6-2. Graph of the equation $y = (x + 1)/2x$.

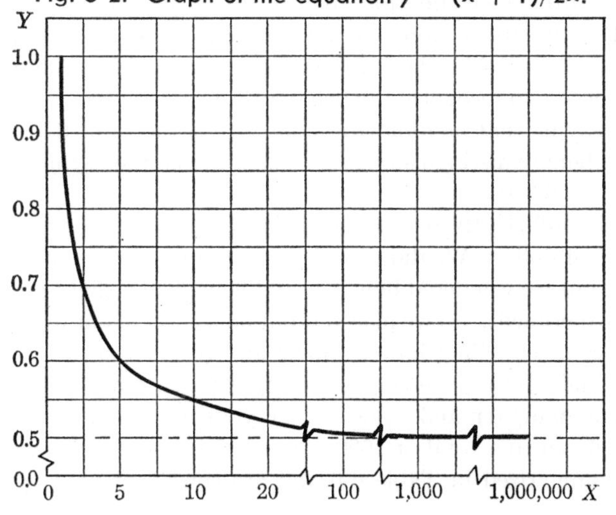

the equation is shown in Fig. 6-2. Here we sense that as x increases, y decreases persistently toward the value 1/2, and that it never wavers from that course. A little algebra will make the reason clearer:

$$y = \frac{x}{2x} + \frac{1}{2x} \tag{6.9.1b}$$

$$= \frac{1}{2} + \frac{1}{2x} \tag{6.9.1c}$$

$$y - \frac{1}{2} = \frac{1}{2x} \tag{6.9.1d}$$

by showing that the difference between y and $\frac{1}{2}$ is always $1/2x$. When x is positive, this amount is positive, and becomes smaller as x increases. In fact, it can be made as close to zero as we wish by the simple process of making x large enough. We express this fact by stating that y approaches 1/2 *asymptotically*. Another way of stating the fact is to say that the limit of y as x increases indefinitely is 1/2. A symbolic statement develops if we consider "approaches infinity" as meaning the same as "increases indefinitely" and write simply

$$\lim_{x \to \infty} y = 1/2.$$

This is a little dangerous, because it can lull us into thinking of infinity (∞) as some quite definite value, but we shall try to be careful.

Does p_H behave in this way as we increase n, the number of tosses? It did not on our attempt to follow its behavior. At $n = 2$, p_H was exactly 0.5, but that was the only time throughout the entire 100 tosses that this was so. Through $n = 6$, p_H increased, then it went through a series of short fluctuations to a lower value at $n = 16$, then rose steadily through $n = 24$, fell steadily through $n = 29$, and so on. But, in a quite real sense, we feel that 0.5 is a sort of "home" about which the successive values are wandering. We can not even say that after some stated number of tosses, p_H will never be more than some stated amount away from 0.5, much though we wish we could. But very extensive experiments like the brief one we performed have persuaded most interested workers to recognize the behavior we have sensed. We describe the behavior by saying that p_H *approaches statistically* the value 0.5 as n increases indefinitely, thereby distinguishing its behavior from the asymptotic behavior of y in equation 6.9.1.

You may be sufficiently tired of statistics at this point to wonder what became of the half dollar. We didn't feel that we could devote our own summer to tossing it, but we wondered how it would behave in a slight modification of the original experiment. So we placed it out on a chest in our living room, with an instruction sheet telling how to make and record the tosses on attached data sheets, and offering one cent payment for each ten tosses (!). The idea entranced our daughter and some of her younger friends, who, with their elders, built us up to a total of 1600 tosses before the novelty wore off. The results are summarized in Table 6-6 and are consistent with what we have

Table 6-6 RESULTS OF 1600 TOSSES OF 1959 FRANKLIN-HEAD HALF DOLLAR, SUMMER OF 1960

Frequencies and statistical probabilities computed after each group of 50 tosses

n	n_H	n_T	p_H	p_T
50	29	21	0.5800	0.4200
100	53	47	0.5300	0.4700
150	83	67	0.5533	0.4467
200	109	91	0.5450	0.4550
250	133	117	0.5320	0.4680
300	149	151	0.4967	0.5033
350	177	173	0.5057	0.4943
400	201	199	0.5025	0.4975
450	231	219	0.5133	0.4867
500	254	246	0.5080	0.4920
550	278	272	0.5054	0.4946
600	306	294	0.5100	0.4900
650	330	320	0.5077	0.4923
700	357	343	0.5100	0.4900
750	381	369	0.5080	0.4920
800	406	394	0.5075	0.4925
850	430	420	0.5059	0.4941
900	451	449	0.5011	0.4989
950	471	479	0.4958	0.5042
1000	459	505	0.4950	0.5050
1050	519	531	0.4943	0.5057
1100	550	550	0.5000	0.5000
1150	581	569	0.5043	0.4948
1200	608	592	0.5067	0.4933
1250	629	621	0.5032	0.4968
1300	647	653	0.4977	0.5023
1350	674	676	0.4993	0.5007
1400	702	698	0.5014	0.4986
1450	736	714	0.5076	0.4924
1500	764	736	0.5093	0.4907
1550	782	768	0.5045	0.4955
1600	809	791	0.5056	0.4944

been saying all along. So we may properly accept probabilities of the events resulting from one trial of an ideal experiment as the limit which would be approached statistically by the relative frequencies of the corresponding events in the indefinite repetition of the actual experiment which gave rise to the ideal one.

6.10 A More Complicated Problem

We shall presently return to our coin, but first we want to see what we can do with a die (singular of dice!), because it offers some possibilities not as readily obtainable with coins. A real die is a cube with its faces numbered from 1 through 6, usually indicated by a number of dots, in such a way that the sum of the numbers on opposite faces is 7 and that if 1 is up and 2 is toward you, 3 will be at your right. Let's see what we can do with probability and dice.

The simplest experiment we can consider is the rolling of a single die, which the mathematician visualizes as a perfect cube with marked faces which do not affect its behavior, rolled in such a way that the result is not predetermined. This experiment can result in six events, which we, sensibly, designate by the resulting number, as 1, 2, 3, 4, 5, and 6. Since these are equally likely, we assign a probability of 1/6 to each.

With a die, however, we have the opportunity to consider a number of compound events which still involve the single die and single roll. Remember that a compound event is one that, as we have implied before, can be described in terms of simpler events. Thus, we might consider event A as "two or less" and event B as "more than two," in which case event A consists of simple events 1 and 2, while event B consists of simple events 3, 4, 5, and 6. Event A can result from the roll of a die in $n_A = 2$ ways, while event B can result in $n_B = 4$ of the total of $n = 6$ ways in which the die can fall. Hence, $\Pr\{A\} = 2/6 = 1/3$ and $\Pr\{B\} = 4/6 = 2/3$. Notice, in passing, that $\Pr\{A\}$ does not equal $\Pr\{B\}$.

Suppose we next inquire about the probability of event A occurring various numbers of times in two rolls of the die. Our fundamental Principle I says that since each roll can result in any of six ways, in terms of the ultimate simple events, then the two rolls can result in $6 \times 6 = 6^2 = 36$ ways, which are listed in Table 6-7. The table also shows the results in terms of events A

Table 6-7 POSSIBLE EVENTS FOR THE EXPERIMENT CONSISTING OF ROLLING A DIE TWICE

Listed as the simple events and as Event A (two or less) and Event B (more than two)

11	AA	21	AA	31	BA
12	AA	22	AA	32	BA
13	AB	23	AB	33	BB
14	AB	24	AB	34	BB
15	AB	25	AB	35	BB
16	AB	26	AB	36	BB
41	BA	51	BA	61	BA
42	BA	52	BA	62	BA
43	BB	53	BB	63	BB
44	BB	54	BB	64	BB
45	BB	55	BB	65	BB
46	BB	56	BB	66	BB

Total Events: 36

Events Comprising $2A$'s: 4 $\Pr\{2A\} = 4/36 = 1/9$

Events Comprising $1A$: 16 $\Pr\{1A\} = 16/36 = 4/9$

Events Comprising $0A$: 16 $\Pr\{0A\} = 16/36 = 4/9$

and B. We can count and determine that of the 36 results, four were $2A$'s, 16 were $1A$'s, and 16 were $0A$'s, so we find that

$$\Pr\{2A\} = \frac{4}{36} = \frac{1}{9}$$

$$\Pr\{1A\} = \frac{16}{36} = \frac{4}{9}$$

$$\Pr\{0A\} = \frac{16}{36} = \frac{4}{9}$$

At the risk of being tedious, we inquire what might happen with three rolls of the die. The $6 \times 6 \times 6 = 6^3 = 216$ possible results are shown in Table 6-8,

Table 6-8 POSSIBLE EVENTS FOR THE EXPERIMENT CONSISTING OF ROLLING A DIE THREE TIMES

Listed as simple events and as Event A (two or less) and Event B (more than two)

111	AAA	121	AAA	131	ABA	141	ABA	151	ABA	161	ABA
112	AAA	122	AAA	132	ABA	142	ABA	152	ABA	162	ABA
113	AAB	123	AAB	133	ABB	143	ABB	153	ABB	163	ABB
114	AAB	124	AAB	134	ABB	144	ABB	154	ABB	164	ABB
115	AAB	125	AAB	135	ABB	145	ABB	155	ABB	165	ABB
116	AAB	126	AAB	136	ABB	146	ABB	156	ABB	166	ABB
211	AAA	221	AAA	231	ABA	241	ABA	251	ABA	261	ABA
212	AAA	222	AAA	232	ABA	242	ABA	252	ABA	262	ABA
213	AAB	223	AAB	233	ABB	243	ABB	253	ABB	263	ABB
214	AAB	224	AAB	234	ABB	244	ABB	254	ABB	264	ABB
215	AAB	225	AAB	235	ABB	245	ABB	255	ABB	265	ABB
216	AAB	226	AAB	236	ABB	246	ABB	256	ABB	266	ABB
311	BAA	321	BAA	331	BBA	341	BBA	351	BBA	361	BBA
312	BAA	322	BAA	332	BBA	342	BBA	352	BBA	362	BBA
313	BAB	323	BAB	333	BBB	343	BBB	353	BBB	363	BBB
314	BAB	324	BAB	334	BBB	344	BBB	354	BBB	364	BBB
315	BAB	325	BAB	335	BBB	345	BBB	355	BBB	365	BBB
316	BAB	326	BAB	336	BBB	346	BBB	356	BBB	366	BBB
411	BAA	421	BAA	431	BBA	441	BBA	451	BBA	461	BBA
412	BAA	422	BAA	432	BBA	442	BBA	452	BBA	462	BBA
413	BAB	423	BAB	433	BBB	443	BBB	453	BBB	463	BBB
414	BAB	424	BAB	434	BBB	444	BBB	454	BBB	464	BBB
415	BAB	425	BAB	435	BBB	445	BBB	455	BBB	465	BBB
416	BAB	426	BAB	436	BBB	446	BBB	456	BBB	466	BBB
511	BAA	521	BAA	531	BBA	541	BBA	551	BBA	561	BBA
512	BAA	522	BAA	532	BBA	542	BBA	552	BBA	562	BBA
513	BAB	523	BAB	533	BBB	543	BBB	553	BBB	563	BBB
514	BAB	524	BAB	534	BBB	544	BBB	554	BBB	564	BBB
515	BAB	525	BAB	535	BBB	545	BBB	555	BBB	565	BBB
516	BAB	526	BAB	536	BBB	546	BBB	556	BBB	566	BBB

Table 6-8 (*Continued*)

611	*BAA*	621	*BAA*	631	*BBA*	641	*BBA*	651	*BBA*	661	*BBA*
612	*BAA*	622	*BAA*	632	*BBA*	642	*BBA*	652	*BBA*	662	*BBA*
613	*BAB*	623	*BAB*	633	*BBB*	643	*BBB*	653	*BBB*	663	*BBB*
614	*BAB*	624	*BAB*	634	*BBB*	644	*BBB*	654	*BBB*	664	*BBB*
615	*BAB*	625	*BAB*	635	*BBB*	645	*BBB*	655	*BBB*	665	*BBB*
616	*BAB*	626	*BAB*	636	*BBB*	646	*BBB*	656	*BBB*	666	*BBB*

Total Events: 216

Events Comprising 3A's: 8 $\quad$ $\Pr\{3A\} = 8/216 = 1/27$

Events Comprising 2A's: 48 $\quad$ $\Pr\{2A\} = 48/216 = 6/27 = 2/9$

Events Comprising 1A: 96 $\quad$ $\Pr\{1A\} = 96/216 = 12/27 = 4/9$

Events Comprising 0A's: 64 $\quad$ $\Pr\{0A\} = 64/216 = 8/27$

and we can see that the probabilities are

$$\Pr\{3A\} = \frac{8}{216} = \frac{1}{27}$$

$$\Pr\{2A\} = \frac{48}{216} = \frac{6}{27} = \frac{2}{9}$$

$$\Pr\{1A\} = \frac{96}{216} = \frac{12}{27} = \frac{4}{9}$$

$$\Pr\{0A\} = \frac{64}{216} = \frac{8}{27}$$

By now, you should be ready for real relief from this tabulating and counting procedure!

6.11 Combinations and Probability

Recall that, when we were discussing our coin tossing, we found that our experiment could be related to a problem in selections: if we were to toss a coin n times and were interested in obtaining r heads, we found that the number of possible events resulting in r heads was the same as the number of ways of selecting r objects from among n: $\binom{n}{r}$. Here, in our problem of the die, life has become a little more complicated. We must visualize that we first select the number of rolls which will yield A's. If we consider specifically the problem of two rolls, we can "select" the rolls to yield A's if there are to be two, one and zero A's in just $\binom{2}{2} = 1$, $\binom{2}{1} = 2$, and $\binom{2}{0} = 1$ ways, respectively.

Then we recognize that, on the rolls selected to produce A's, two of the simple events constitute A's, so there are two ways in which an A can be obtained. Similarly, on the rolls selected to produce B's, four simple events constitute B's, so that B can be obtained in four ways. Our Principle I tells us that the three tasks of (1) choosing the rolls to give A's, (2) obtaining A's on those rolls, and (3) obtaining B's on the remaining rolls can be performed in a number of ways which can be computed by multiplying together the number of ways of performing each task, thus:

Obtain two A's

Choose rolls: $\binom{2}{2} = 1$ way. (A's on both rolls.)

Obtain first A: two ways.

Obtain second A: two ways.

Total ways: $\binom{2}{2} \times 2 \times 2 = 2^2 = 4$ ways.

Obtain one A.

Choose rolls: $\binom{2}{1} = 2$ ways. (one A and one B)

Obtain the A: two ways.

Obtain the B: four ways.

Total ways: $\binom{2}{1} \times 2 \times 4 = 2^4 = 16$ ways.

Obtain zero A's.

Choose rolls: $\binom{2}{0} = 1$ way. (B's on both rolls.)

Obtain first B: four ways.

Obtain second B: four ways.

Total ways: $\binom{2}{0} \times 4 \times 4 = 2^4 = 16$ ways.

The computations account for 36 possible outcomes of our experiment. But we know that if we roll the die twice, and each roll can result in six possible simple events, then the two rolls can result in $6 \times 6 = 6^2 = 36$ simple events, which agrees with the calculations made above. Now if we divide each of the numbers of ways of obtaining the possible numbers of A's by the total number of simple events, we will come out with the probability of obtaining the specified number of A's. But we can set up this computation in a way which is even more revealing. Suppose that we put one of the 6's from our $6^2 = 36$ under each of the numbers of ways of obtaining A's or B's in our previous formulations:—

$$\binom{2}{2} \times \frac{2}{6} \times \frac{2}{6} = 1 \times \frac{1}{3} \times \frac{1}{3} = \frac{1}{9} = \Pr\{2A\} \qquad (6.11.1a)$$

$$\binom{2}{1} \times \frac{2}{6} \times \frac{4}{6} = 2 \times \frac{1}{3} \times \frac{2}{3} = \frac{4}{9} = \Pr\{1A\} \qquad (6.11.1b)$$

$$\binom{2}{0} \times \frac{4}{6} \times \frac{4}{6} = 1 \times \frac{2}{3} \times \frac{2}{3} = \frac{4}{9} = \Pr\{0A\} \qquad (6.11.1c)$$

Quite possibly this may impress you as rather too much juggling of numbers for no useful result.

But now notice that the 1/3 and 2/3 which finally appeared in the formulas were simply the values of Pr $\{A\}$ and Pr $\{B\}$ which we have discussed earlier. Thus, it appears that the probability of obtaining r A's in 2 rolls of a die is given by the formula,

$$\Pr\{rA\} = \binom{2}{r}[\Pr\{A\}]^r[\Pr\{B\}]^{2-r} \tag{6.11.2}$$

You will rightly suspect that this is still a special case of a yet more general principle. To find the general formula, we shall raise $(P + Q)$ to the nth power, but shall indicate the operation by attaching to the P's and Q's subscripts indicating the factor in which they appear in the indicated expansion:

$$(P + Q)^n = (P_1 + Q_1)(P_2 + Q_2)\ (P_i + Q_i)\ (P_n + Q_n)$$

Then we shall carry out the first few steps of the actual multiplication, retaining these subscripts:

$$\begin{array}{l} P_1 + Q_1 \\ P_2 + Q_2 \\ \hline P_1P_2 + P_1Q_2 + P_2Q_1 + Q_1Q_2 \qquad = P^2 + 2PQ + Q^2 \\ P_3 + Q_3 \\ \hline P_1P_2P_3 + P_1P_3Q_2 + P_2P_3Q_1 + P_1P_2Q_3 + P_3Q_1Q_2 \\ \qquad + P_1Q_2Q_3 + P_2Q_1Q_3 + Q_1Q_2Q_3 \\ \qquad\qquad = P^3 + 3P^2Q + 3PQ^2 + Q^3 \end{array}$$

If you study these results, and continue one or two more steps, you will see that:

1. Each term, before final collection of terms and simplification, consists of n factors, P's or Q's or a mixture.
2. In each term, each of the subscripts, $1, 2 \ldots n$, occurs once and only once.
3. In each term, the sum of the powers of P and Q is n.
4. The number of terms in which P occurs r times, which therefore are of the form $P^rQ^{(n-r)}$, is just the number of ways of selecting the n factors from which the P is to be used, namely, $\binom{n}{r}$.

Putting all of this together tells us that

$$(P + Q)^n = \binom{n}{n}P^nQ^0 + \binom{n}{n-1}P^{(n-1)}Q^1 + \ldots$$
$$+ \binom{n}{r}P^rQ^{(n-r)} + \ldots + \binom{n}{0}P^0Q^n \tag{6.11.3a}$$

which we have demonstrated for a few powers and which formal but tedious algebra will prove holds for all positive integral values of n. If we choose to think of the right side of this equation as read from right to left, we can write it, with the aid of our summation symbol, in the very compact form:

$$(P + Q)^n = \sum_{r=0}^{n} \binom{n}{r} P^r Q^{(n-r)} \tag{6.11.3b}$$

which is known as the *binomial theorem.* You recall, we hope, that $a^0 = 1$, where a is any real number.

Now suppose that we let $P = \Pr\{A\}$ and $Q = \Pr\{B\} = 1 - P$. It is evident that the term involving P^r in the binomial theorem is precisely the probability of obtaining event A r times in n rolls. In fact, this idea is even more general, and can be stated as follows:

PRINCIPLE III. *If an ideal experiment results in one or the other of two events, A and B, and if the probabilities of these events in one trial are* $P = Pr\{A\}$ *and* $Q = 1 - P = Pr\{B\}$, *respectively, then the probability that event A will occur r times in n trials is the value of the term involving* P^r *in the expansion of* $(P + Q)^n$.

This principle can be stated very compactly, using symbols with the meanings they have had in this section, by the formulas

$$\Pr\{rA\} = \binom{n}{r} \Pr\{A\}^r \Pr\{B\}^{(n-r)} \tag{6.11.4a}$$

$$= \binom{n}{r} P^r Q^{(n-r)} \tag{6.11.4b}$$

6.12 The Binomial Distribution

The equation just given is very fine, and compactly describes the results of good mathematical reasoning, but it still does not do all that we need done. It is restricted to a consideration of the mathematician's ideal experiments. But recall that we found a relation between relative frequencies of occurrence of event A in indefinite repetitions of real experiments and the mathematical probabilities in ideal experiments: the relative frequencies approached the probabilities statistically.

So all we have to do to get a distribution is to write a formula quite similar to 6.11.4, but with relative frequencies in place of probabilities. While we are doing it, we shall, simply to bring our final result into conformity with symbols in which it is often written, let $x = r$, the number of times event A occurs in n trials. We shall also let $f(x)$ be our symbol for relative frequency, in place of $n_x/n = n_r/n$, which we might otherwise have used. With these substitutions and differences in interpretation, equation 6.11.4b becomes

$$f(x) = \binom{n}{x} P^x Q^{(n-x)} \tag{6.12.1}$$

where, to repeat,

n = the number of times an experiment is performed

x = the number of these times in which event A occurs

P = the mathematical, or *a priori*, probability that event A occurs on one trial

Q = the mathematical, or *a priori*, probability that the alternative event B occurs in one trial, so that $Q = 1 - P$

$f(x)$ = the statistical limit of the relative frequency of the occurrence of event A x times in n trials

Because this is an equation describing the pattern of distribution of possible observed numerical values, the number of A's, and because of its relation to the binomial theorem, it is called the *binomial distribution equation*, or, more conveniently, the *binomial distribution.*

Such an equation is often called a theoretical distribution. Unfortunately, words have a way of losing their effectiveness with the passage of time. The term charity, for instance, used to express one of the causes of the finest sort of conduct toward our fellows; now it too often is used to describe the "dime for a cuppa coffee" act. In the sense that "theoretical" means developed in terms of ideal conditions, divorced from minor disturbing factors, this distribution is a theoretical distribution. In the perverted sense of a statement of what must occur as the result of some deep, mystic principles, this is not a theoretical distribution. Whether it is suitable as a description of any real distribution can only be settled by experience.

In the case of a very simple problem, such as the tossing of our real half dollar, it is quite easy to see that the mathematician's ideal experiment could be quite closely related to our actual operations with the real coin, and the results of our actual experiments should make us content to use the binomial distribution in connection with problems in coin tossing. Notice, in passing, that the n in the distribution might refer to the number of coins tossed simultaneously in one trial and the x to the number that came heads. The mathematician's reasoning would simply have considered the selections of coins to fall heads, instead of the selections of the trials to result in heads: the end equation would be the same.

More valuable applications have been in the field of genetics, which studies the inheritance of characteristics, in the study of defective items in manufactured products, in the study of failure in various types of services, in weapon firing, and a host of other "practical" problems. Sometimes it is fairly easy to visualize the underlying "experiments" and to develop an *a priori* idea as to the value of P, whereas often, in practice, we let the observations suggest the value. But of this, more later!

6.13 From the Binomial to the Normal Distribution

Although the binomial distribution is simple in form, and requires only arithmetic of an elementary type for computation of its indicated values, the computations for appreciable values of n soon become, frankly, both tedious and boring. Under those circumstances, mistakes are likely to occur. Mathematicians, too, are lazy, but their laziness takes the form of directing them to easier ways of getting a job done. In order to see how the easier way developed, we have shown two sets of computational results.

The first set, in Table 6-9 and Fig. 6-3, shows a series of binomial distributions in which $P = Q = 1/2$ throughout, but in which n increased from distribution to distribution. Such distributions could represent increasing numbers of tosses of a coin, or the simultaneous tossing of increasing numbers of coins, or other conditions in which the two possibilities on a single trial were equally probable. In Table 6-10 and Fig. 6-4, we have kept n constant and varied P. This might correspond to rolling a die a fixed number of times, or rolling simultaneously a fixed number of dice, but varying the number of faces on the dice and the description of our event A, so as to change P.

You may wonder at the representation of these frequencies by histograms when the observations can only have zero and integral values of x, but this is quite proper. Recall that, in making frequency tables and histograms, we said nothing about where the values were within the classes; we only said that the boundaries were to be unambiguous and that the intervals should be uniform. Here our class boundaries are at $-1/2$, $1/2$, $3/2$, and so on, midway between our successive possible values of x.

In the case of each distribution, we went on to calculate the mean, variance, and standard deviation, and thence to fit the related normal distribution. This is the curve drawn over each histogram. We have so arranged the scales that the height of the top of this curve and the actual area under it is the same on each chart. Finally, we have calculated the frequency, f_N, from the normal distribution for each actual class, and for all values below and above the possible values of the binomial distribution.

The results can be described very simply, partly by direct observation of our work and partly because of thoughtful study of the whole problem by mathematicians, as follows:

1. In each case, the mean of the distribution is nP, the product of the number of trials by the probability of event A.
2. In each case, the variance is nPQ, the product of the number of trials by the probabilities of the two events considered.
3. At $P = Q = 1/2$, the frequencies calculated from the normal distribution approach those calculated from the binomial distribution as n increases, and the approach is asymptotic. We may symbolize this by the statement,

$$\lim_{n \to \infty} f_N = f(x) \tag{6.13.1}$$

Table 6-9 Effect of Changing n on Binomial Distribution with $P = Q = \frac{1}{2}$

Computation of binomial frequencies, $f(x)$, and tabulation of normal frequencies, f_N, for fitted normal distributions

	n	x	$\binom{n}{x}$	P^x	Q^{n-x}	$f(x)$	f_N
$\mu = 1.00$	2	< 0	—	—	—	—	0.0170
$\sigma^2 = 0.50$		0	1	1.00	0.25	0.25	0.2228
$\sigma \doteq 0.70710$		1	2	0.50	0.50	0.50	0.5204
		2	1	0.25	1.00	0.25	0.2228
		> 2	—	—	—	—	0.0170
$\mu = 1.5$	3	< 0	—	—	—	—	0.0105
$\sigma^2 = 0.750$		0	1	1.000	0.125	0.125	0.1136
$\sigma \doteq 0.86602$		1	3	0.500	0.250	0.375	0.3759
		2	3	0.250	0.500	0.375	0.3759
		3	1	0.125	1.000	0.125	0.1136
		> 3	—	—	—	—	0.0105
$\mu = 2.00$	4	< 0	—	—	—	—	0.0062
$\sigma^2 = 1.0000$		0	1	1.0000	0.0625	0.0625	0.0606
$\sigma \doteq 1.00000$		1	4	0.5000	0.1250	0.2500	0.2417
		2	6	0.2500	0.2500	0.3750	0.3830
		3	4	0.1250	0.5000	0.2500	0.2417
		4	1	0.0625	1.0000	0.0625	0.0606
		> 4	—	—	—	—	0.0062
$\mu = 2.5$	5	< 0	—	—	—	—	0.0037
$\sigma^2 = 1.2500$		0	1	1.00000	0.03125	0.03125	0.0331
$\sigma \doteq 1.11803$		1	5	0.50000	0.06250	0.15625	0.1489
		2	10	0.25000	0.12500	0.3125	0.3143
		3	10	0.12500	0.25000	0.3125	0.3143
		4	5	0.06250	0.50000	0.15625	0.1489
		5	1	0.03125	1.00000	0.03125	0.0331
		> 5	—	—	—	—	0.0037
$\mu = 5.00$	10	< 0	—	—	—	—	0.0004
$\sigma^2 = 2.5000$		0	1	1.0000000000	0.0009765625	0.0009765625	0.0018
$\sigma \doteq 1.58113$		1	10	0.5000000000	0.0019531250	0.0097656250	0.0112
		2	45	0.2500000000	0.0039062500	0.0439453125	0.0436
		3	120	0.1250000000	0.0078125000	0.1171875000	0.1144
		4	210	0.0625000000	0.0156250000	0.2050781250	0.2047
		5	252	0.0312500000	0.0312500000	0.2460937500	0.2478
		6	210	0.0156250000	0.0625000000	0.2050781250	0.2047
		7	120	0.0078125000	0.1250000000	0.1171875000	0.1144
		8	45	0.0038062500	0.2500000000	0.0439453125	0.0436
		9	10	0.0019531250	0.5000000000	0.0097656250	0.0112
		10	1	0.0009765625	1.0000000000	0.0009765625	0.0018
		> 10	—	—	—	—	0.0004

4. At a fixed value of n, the normal frequencies are closer to the binomial frequencies the closer P is to $1/2$, and the approach is closer at any given value of P the greater the value of n.

Fig. 6-3. Binomial Distribution with $P = 0.5$ and Various n.

Shown as a histogram with fitted normal distribution overlaid.

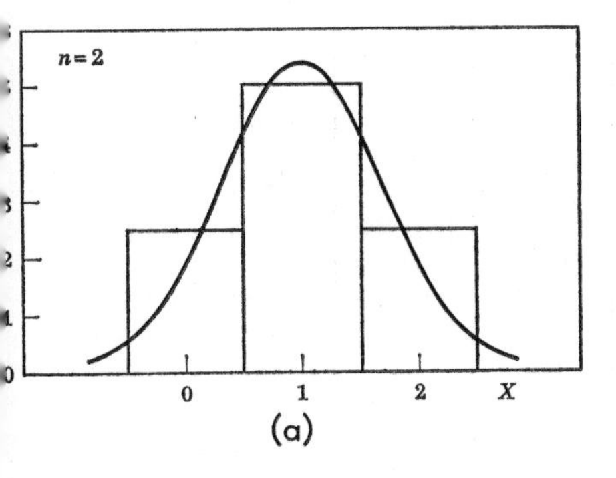

(a)

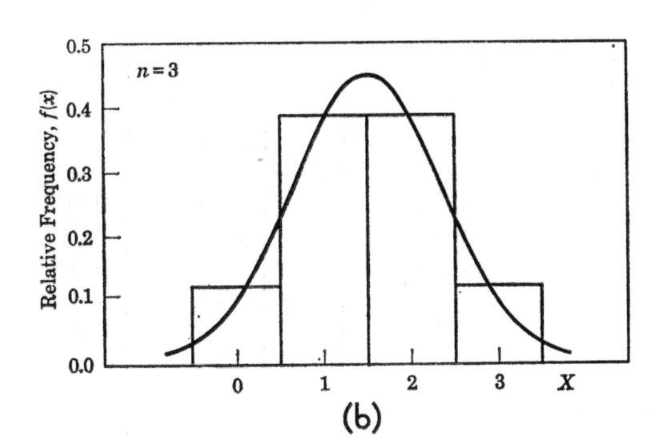

(b)

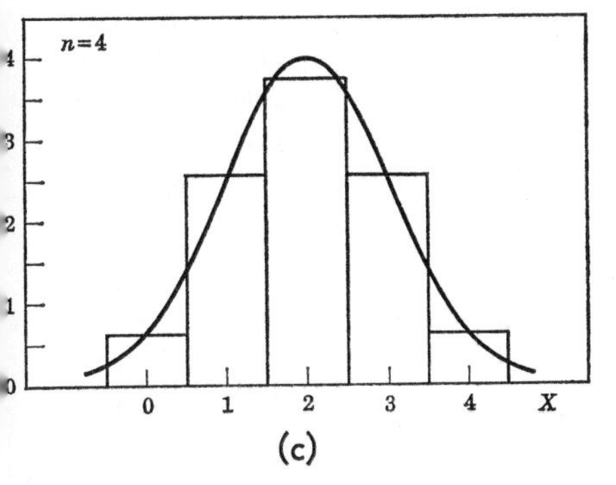

(c)

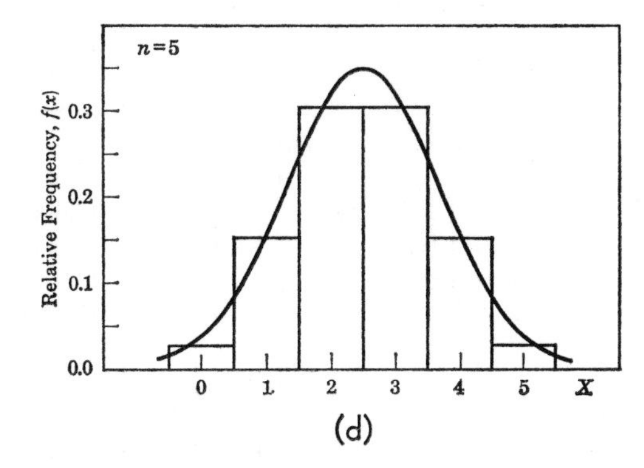

(d)

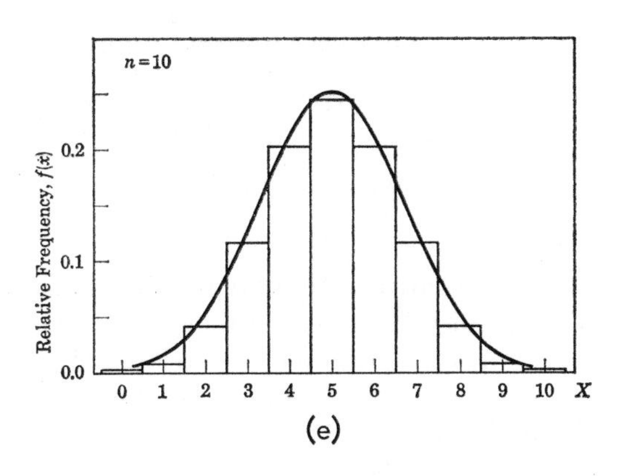

(e)

Table 6-10 EFFECT OF CHANGING P ON BINOMIAL DISTRIBUTION WITH $n = 5$

Computation of binomial frequencies, $f(x)$, and tabulation of normal frequencies, f_N, and Poisson frequencies, f_P for fitted distributions

	x	$\binom{n}{x}$	P	P^x	Q^{n-x}	$f(x)$	f_N	f_P
	<0	—	0.1	—	—	—	0.0681	—
	0	1		1.00000	0.59049	0.59049	0.4319	0.60653
$\mu = 0.5$	1	5		0.10000	0.65610	0.32805	0.4320	0.30327
$\sigma^2 = 0.45$	2	10		0.01000	0.72900	0.07290	0.0666	0.07582
$\sigma \doteq 0.67802$	3	10		0.00100	0.81000	0.00810	0.0014	0.01264
	4	5		0.00010	0.90000	0.00045	0.0000+	0.00158
	5	1		0.00001	1.00000	0.00001	0.0000+	0.00016
	>5	—		—	—	—	0.0000+	0.00000+
	<0	—	0.2	—	—	—	0.0468	—
	0	1		1.00000	0.32768	0.32768	0.2414	0.36788
$\mu = 1.0$	1	5		0.20000	0.40960	0.40960	0.4236	0.36788
$\sigma^2 = 0.80$	2	10		0.04000	0.51200	0.20480	0.2413	0.18394
$\sigma \doteq 0.89442$	3	10		0.00800	0.64000	0.05120	0.0443	0.06131
	4	5		0.00160	0.80000	0.00640	0.0025	0.01533
	5	1		0.00032	1.00000	0.00032	0.0001	0.00307
	>5	—		—	—	—	0.0000+	0.00059
	<0	—	0.3	—	—	—	0.0255	—
	0	1		1.00000	0.16807	0.16807	0.1391	0.22313
$\mu = 1.5$	1	5		0.30000	0.24010	0.36015	0.3354	0.33470
$\sigma^2 = 1.05$	2	10		0.09000	0.34300	0.30870	0.3353	0.25102
$\sigma \doteq 1.02469$	3	10		0.02700	0.49000	0.13230	0.1392	0.12551
	4	5		0.00810	0.70000	0.02835	0.0238	0.04707
	5	1		0.00243	1.00000	0.00243	0.0016	0.01412
	>5	—		—	—	—	0.0001	0.00445
	0	—	0.4	—	—	—	0.0112	—
	0	1		1.00000	0.07776	0.07776	0.0744	0.13534
$\mu = 2.0$	1	5		0.40000	0.12960	0.25920	0.2386	0.27067
$\sigma^2 = 1.20$	2	10		0.16000	0.21600	0.34560	0.3515	0.27067
$\sigma \doteq 1.09544$	3	10		0.06400	0.36000	0.23040	0.2387	0.18045
	4	5		0.02560	0.60000	0.07680	0.0744	0.09022
	5	1		0.01024	1.00000	0.01024	0.0104	0.03609
	5	—		—	—	—	0.0008	0.01656

Note: The Poisson frequencies will be discussed in section 6.14 but are included here for future convenience.

These findings led mathematicians to study the formal relationships between the equations of the two distributions, and they have been able to show that what we have sensed is a consequence of these relationships. In other words, the normal distribution may be thought of as the limit approached by a succession of binomial distributions with $P = Q = 1/2$ as n increases indefinitely. This is the end result of what was, historically, a long train of mathematical efforts. But before it becomes really ours, it must make sense for us. Is it reasonable?

Fig. 6-4. Binomial distribution with $n = 5$ and $P = 0.1$. Shown as a histogram with fitted normal distribution and points of Poisson distribution with $\mu = nP = 5P$ overlaid.

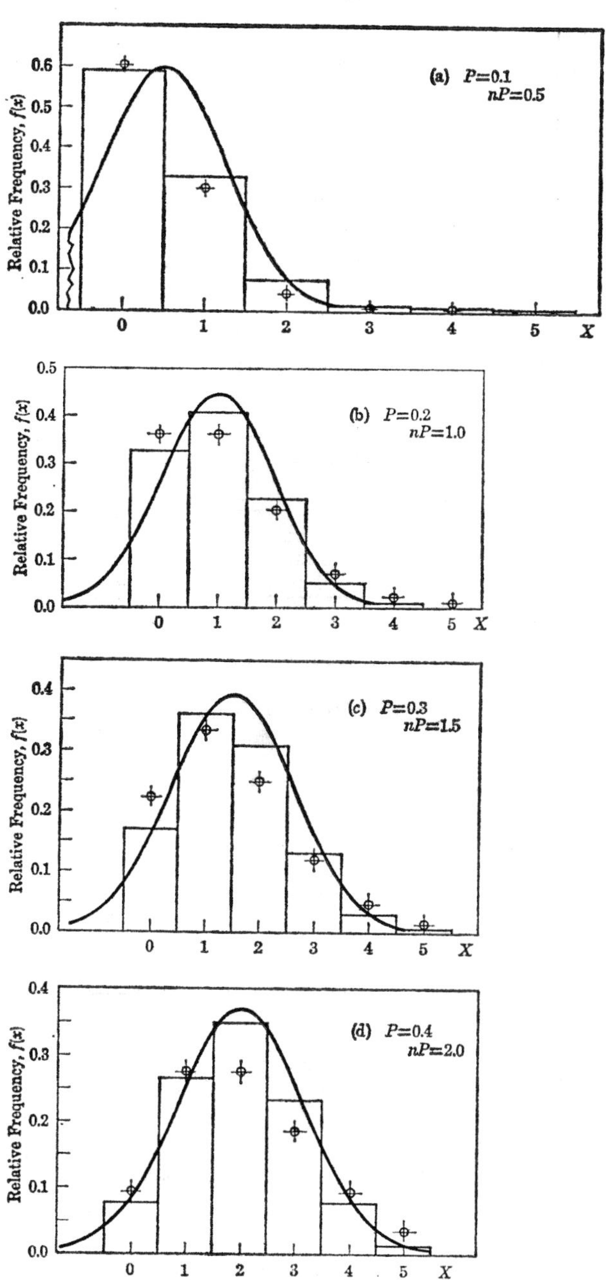

Suppose we think of the production of any observed numerical value as the combined result of the underlying true value plus a large number of disturbing elements. As a specific example, we might think of our measurement of the diameter of a bearing ball. The ball has a true diameter, say D. But as we try to measure it, the force with which we apply the caliper, the temperature of the caliper, the temperature of the ball, and the angle at which we happen to read past the index to the scale on our caliper, and our decision as to where to round the final estimated figure, not to mention a host of other details, will vary from one measurement to another. Suppose that we could visualize each possible disturbance as equally likely to occur or not in any one measurement. Suppose, further, that we consider that the effect of these disturbances upon the value is the same in all cases, producing a specific increase in value by one small unit when it is present and a similar decrease of one unit when it is absent, that is, $+1$ and -1, respectively. The number of disturbances acting will be represented by a binomial distribution with mean $nP = n/2$. The net effect of the disturbances acting in any measurement, x in number, will be

$$x(+1) + (n - x)(-1) = x - n + x = 2x - n \qquad (6.13.2)$$

and will therefore range from $+n$ when $x = n$ to $-n$ when $x = 0$, with a mean value 0, corresponding to the mean value of $x = nP = n/2$, and the individual effects will have exactly the same frequencies as the values of x which produced them. Thus the disturbances will cause variation in observation centered at the true measurement with a binomial pattern of distribution. But, as we have seen, the binomial distribution approaches the normal as the value of n increases. Therefore, it seems reasonable to recognize that the normal distribution "makes sense" in that it is the result of some simplification and idealization of the conditions of actual experience. We shall find that facts do indeed warrant our using the normal distribution to represent our data in many actual conditions, just as the binomial distribution does in other conditions.

Of course, we must not forget that we started this thinking because of our woes about the difficulties in performing the binomial calculations! Not only does the normal distribution represent the limit of the binomial as n increases, but it can be used as an approximation to the binomial when n is still quite small. We postpone a discussion of what restrictions we may place on its use for this purpose until we are better equipped to study it.

6.14 From the Binomial to the Poisson Distribution

Our computations summarized in Table 6-10 indicate that there will be many conditions under which the normal distribution would be a worse than poor approximation to the binomial, yet the binomial computations would be tedious. Again, mathematicians sought an easier way of dealing with the problem. They found that another equation serves as a good approximation to the binomial for many of these conditions. It is known as the *Poisson distribution*, after a French mathematician, and has the form,

$$f_P = p(x) = \frac{(nP)^x}{x!} e^{-nP} \tag{6.14.1a}$$

where x = the number of times event A occurs in n trials

P = the probability that event A occurs in one trial

f_P will be used to identify these frequencies when we wish to emphasize that they were calculated from the Poisson distribution.

For the moment, we shall think of f_P simply as a frequency calculated from this equation approximating the f_B of the binomial distribution. Of course, it was true of the binomial distribution, and is true of the Poisson, that $nP = \mu$, so we can write,

$$f_P = \frac{\mu^x}{x!} e^{-\mu} \tag{6.14.1b}$$

In Table 6-10 we included Poisson frequencies beside the binomial and normal frequencies for the distributions there tabulated to aid your comparisons.

Again, we should ask whether it is reasonable to use the Poisson distribution as an approximation to the binomial from anything in the fundamental nature of the distribution. The fact is that the Poisson distribution is derived directly from the idealization of an experiment different from the type we considered in arriving at the binomial. We might imagine a situation in which we had a very large volume of an oil in which were dispersed some very tiny particles of a solid with the same density as the oil. If we can assume that, in some minute volume, v, the probability of one of the particles being present is proportional to the size of v, and we restrict our thinking to values of v so small that the probability of two or more particles being present is zero, we may inquire what are the probabilities of finding x particles in a stated larger volume, V. The mathematical steps require skill beyond our scope here, but they do lead to the given form of the equation. Sufficient thought suggests a similarity between the two situations, though not an identity, and it is not surprising that under some conditions the Poisson distribution is an adequate approximation to the binomial distribution. In a later chapter, when we shall actually work with these distributions, we shall discuss how the computations are performed, and when the approximations are adequate.

6.15 Another Form for the Binomial Distribution

So far, we have considered the binomial distribution as a description of the frequency with which various possible numbers of events of a stated kind occur on n trials. Some most useful consequences will follow if we think, instead, of the fraction of trials, p, yielding this event. This simply represents a transformation of our variable from the number of these events, x, to their fraction, p, by the equation

$$p = x/n \tag{6.15.1}$$

For our later convenience, we can let:—

$$q = 1 - p = (n - x)/n \tag{6.15.2}$$

represent the fraction of the other events.

In Table 6-11 and Table 6-12, we have made this transformation of variable for the information in Table 6-9 and 6-10, respectively. We have added a

Table 6-11 CHANGE OF VARIABLE FROM x TO p IN THE BINOMIAL DISTRIBUTION WITH $P = Q = \frac{1}{2}$. COMPARE TABLE 6-9

n	x	p	$f(p)$	μ_p	σ_p^2	σ_p
2	0	0.00	0.25	0.50	0.125	0.35355
	1	0.50	0.50			
	2	1.00	0.25			
3	0	0.00	0.125	0.50	0.083	0.28867
	1	0.3	0.375			
	2	0.6	0.375			
	3	1.0	0.125			
4	0	0.00	0.0625	0.50	0.0625	0.25000
	1	0.25	0.2500			
	2	0.50	0.3750			
	3	0.75	0.2500			
	4	1.00	0.0625			
5	0	0.00	0.03125	0.50	0.0500	0.22360
	1	0.20	0.15625			
	2	0.40	0.31250			
	3	0.60	0.31250			
	4	0.80	0.15625			
	5	1.00	0.03125			
10	0	0.00	0.0009765625	0.50	0.0250	0.15811
	1	0.10	0.0097656250			
	2	0.20	0.0439453125			
	3	0.30	0.1171875000			
	4	0.40	0.2050781250			
	5	0.50	0.2460937500			
	6	0.60	0.2050781250			
	7	0.70	0.1171875000			
	8	0.80	0.0439453125			
	9	0.90	0.0097656250			
	10	1.00	0.0009765625			

subscript p to μ, σ^2, and σ to remind ourselves that we are now dealing with the new variable. The results are really striking. Notice that, in each case,

Table 6-12 Change of Variable from x to p in the Binomial Distribution with $n = 5$ and Various Values of P. Compare Table 6-10

x	p	$P = 0.1$ $f(p)$	$P = 0.2$ $f(p)$	$P = 0.3$ $f(p)$	$P = 0.4$ $f(p)$
0	0.00	0.59049	0.32768	0.16807	0.07776
1	0.20	0.32805	0.40960	0.36015	0.25920
2	0.40	0.07290	0.20480	0.30870	0.34560
3	0.60	0.00810	0.05120	0.13230	0.23040
4	0.80	0.00045	0.00640	0.02385	0.07680
5	1.00	0.00001	0.00032	0.00243	0.01024
	μ_p	0.50000	0.50000	0.50000	0.50000
	$\sigma_p{}^2$	0.01800	0.03200	0.04200	0.04800
	σ_p	0.13416	0.17888	0.20494	0.21908

$\mu_p = P$, the probability of occurrence of our event on a single trial. Notice further that our variance and standard deviation are, respectively,

$$\sigma^2 = PQ/n \tag{6.15.3}$$

and

$$\sigma_p = \sqrt{PQ/n}$$

and that decrease steadily as n increases. In Fig. 6-5 and Fig. 6-6 we have replotted Fig. 6-3d and Fig. 6-4b, respectively, with p-scales added. These plots emphasize the idea that we have not changed any fundamental facts by this change of variable, but simply altered our viewpoint.

The new viewpoint is enlightening, for it brings out the fact that increasing the number of trails of a simple experiment will not change the mean result, but will decrease the variability of the results when we measure that variability

Fig. 6-5. Binomial distribution with $n = 5$ and $P = 0.5$, with dual horizontal scale to show both x and p as the variable. Redrawn from Fig. 6-3d.

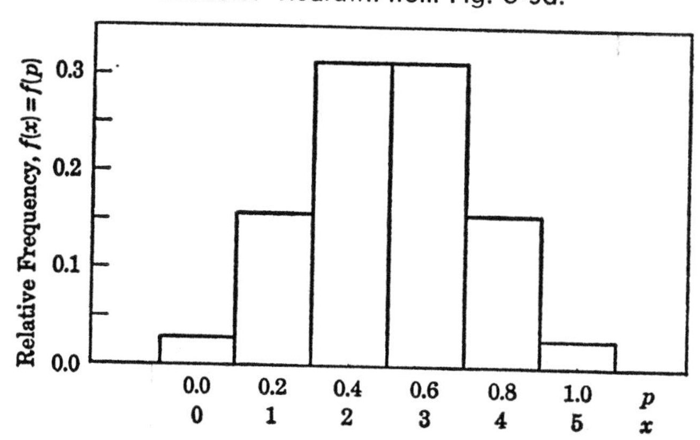

Fig. 6-6. Binomial distribution with $n = 5$ and $P = 0.2$. Shown as a histogram with dual horizontal scale to refer to both x and p as the variable. Redrawn from Fig. 6-4b.

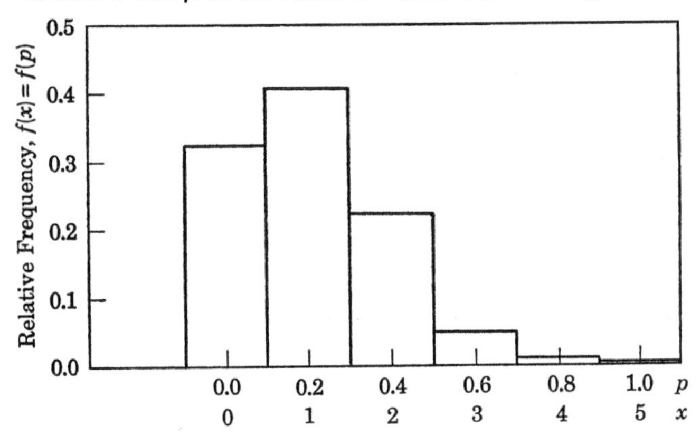

as variance or standard deviation. Of course, we can have $p = 0$ or $p = 1$ in any number of trials, so that our range is 1 regardless of n, but the variance reflects the "bunching" about the mean.

Suppose we wanted to write our binomial distribution equation in terms of p and q instead of x and $n - x$. The transformation of variable can be made in equation 6.12.1 with the following final result:

$$f(p) = \binom{n}{pn} P^{pn} Q^{qn} \tag{6.15.4}$$

Of course, substitution of the numerical values for needed computations into 6.15.4 produces exactly the same results as the equivalent substitutions into 6.12.1, as it must, for we are simply getting at the frequencies of the same compound events described in two different ways.

6.16 In Retrospect

We are quite sure that this chapter has been difficult for many of you — not, we honestly assure you, because we tried to make it so but because in it we are coming to grips with some very fundamental ideas. For your consolation, may we say that we have known no person, whatever his prior mathematical training and whoever his teacher may have been, who ever arrived at any real understanding of the elements of probability without some very real and, at times, discouraging effort. There are conscientious mathematicians who insist that it is impossible to understand probability without going through the long mathematical preparation to permit the full study of the mathematical development of the theory. Undoubtedly they are correct if by "understand" we must mean complete and precise comprehension of all the details and implications of the subject, and how it is developed.

But to us, this proposal that anyone who is to have any insight into probability must have complete training is not realistic, any more than it would be realistic to insist that, before one could be given a license to drive a car he must demonstrate his ability to design and make each part of the car and to assemble the final vehicle and adjust it to perfect running order. Frankly, we doubt that there is a person living who possesses all the necessary skills to accomplish this task, but millions of us understand enough of the basic ideas so that we drive our cars with skill, confidence and, we hope, safety. What we have tried to do here is to give you the probability equivalent of good "driver training," and even that requires concentration and thought.

Perhaps it will help you to look back over what we have been trying to do with this sketch in mind.

1. The mathematician, in attempting to provide useful tools for dealing with real situations in which uncertainty prevails, visualizes an idealized experiment which has as close a relationship as he can work with to the actual situation.

2. He lists, or otherwise considers, all the possible outcomes (events) to which the experiment could lead, and defines the probability of any outcome, simple or compound, as the ratio of the number of events of this type to the total number of events. The use of the concept of combinations considerably expedited this task in the situations leading to the binomial distribution.

3. When the compound event can be thought of as the result of the outcomes of a number of simpler unit experiments, he will seek expressions for the probabilities of the compound events in terms of the probabilities of the simpler events.

4. When the probabilities of his ideal experiments are closely paralleled by the relative frequencies observed in related actual experiments, we replace his probabilities by relative frequencies and consider the resulting equations to be distribution equations.

5. When the distribution so developed is awkward or tedious to use, we often seek a more convenient equation which will adequately approximate the exact equation. Such equations are often found among those developed by the mathematician to idealize other situations.

May we suggest one other thought for your consideration, again in terms of driving a car? You can learn just about so much about how to drive a car by reading about it: finally you have to get in a car and drive. We think that you will find that many of the ideas we have discussed here will gain clarity and meaning as you put them to use in the work that lies ahead. Try it!

General Study

1. We mentioned that probability was studied in terms of coin tossing, die rolling, card drawing, and such simple games because they resembled more serious problems with which we were concerned. Consider some problems of interest in your field of specialization and discuss a simple device involving coins, dice, cards, etc., which would parallel your actual problem. Some problems you might consider:
   (a) Inheritance of various characteristics, such as blood type, hair color, color blindness.
   (b) Conditioned reflexes in psychology.
   (c) Incidence of crime, fire, or accidents in a city.
   (d) Absence due to illness in an industrial plant.
   (e) Production of defective units of product in a manufacturing operation.

2. Watch for references to probability in your reading. Try to distinguish between those in which the terms are properly used and the discussion arises from an understanding of the basic ideas and those in which the term is loosely or incorrectly used.

3. What do we mean when we say, "It will probably rain tomorrow," or "I will probably get a B in European History"? Could the statements mean different things in different circumstances?

Specific Problems

1. A game involves the use of two "dice" in the form of regular tetrahedra (solid figures with four faces, each an equilateral triangle) with faces numbered from 1 through 4. List the possible results of rolling the two dice and verify your list with the use of combination formulas.

2. In the game in Problem 1 moves are based on the sum of the numbers produced by a roll of the two dice. Determine the probabilities of the various possible results.

3. Calculate the frequencies for a binomial distribution with $P = 0.3$ and $n = 10$ in terms of x. Convert each x to the equivalent p and draw the histogram of the distribution with both scales.

PART C

Sampling and Inference

7

What is a Sample?

7.1 Populations and Samples: a Reconsideration

At the beginning of Chapter III, we very briefly mentioned the distinction between populations and samples, and served notice that, throughout Chapters III, IV, and V, we should be considering only populations. Now the time has come when we must consider the two terms and the distinction between them more carefully. As is often the case with words, these two are each used, even in their technical sense, with two different but related meanings. It will be important for us to understand both meanings in order not to be confused in our later use of the words.

If you will re-examine Table 2-1, you will see that it presented the record of the number of units produced, during their first week on regular wages, of a group of 50 trainees. In the first sense of the word, our population comprises the 50 trainees, while, in the second sense, it consists of the 50 production records. Similarly, Table 2-6 presents the values, or sizes, of 155 checks written on a specific account during one calendar year. In the first sense, the population comprises the checks; in the second, their sizes. The same dual use of the term applies to any such tables of data.

In the first sense, the term population denotes the individual units or entities in some group sharing a common identifying characteristic or group of characteristics. In other words, they are in the same category in this respect. Our employees in Table 2-1 were all from Class C-14 trained by our company by a new method. In Table 2-6, all checks were written during a single calendar year on the same account.

In the second sense, the term population will refer to the numerical values associated, through measurement or counting, with such a collection of individuals. These measured or counted values will reflect the variations in some characteristic which has been defined but is not of the same magnitude for all individuals in the group. Although all trainees belonged to the same class, they did not produce the same amount during their first week. Although all checks were on the same account during the same year, they were not all for the same amount.

The term population (or its equivalent, universe) may thus apply at our pleasure either to the individuals under study or the numerical values of some property of them of interest to us. A single population, in the first sense, may lead to several populations in the second sense. For instance, the first-sense population of students of the class of '56 at the U. of X during their freshman year not only has the second-sense population of academic indexes, which we studied, associated with it. It also has the following, among others:

1. Students' heights.
2. Students' weights.
3. Number of siblings.
4. Socio-economic status.

While it may seem imprudent to use the same word in both senses in technical work, you will find that context, in any case where it matters, will make the meaning clear.

The word, sample, has exactly parallel applications to the individual units and to the data associated with them. Of course, a sample comprises a part of the population. Now that we have made that simple statement, we recall a remark attributed to Mark Twain: "All broad generalizations, including this one, are false." It happens that, as a matter of convenience in certain situations arising in inspection, when it is necessary to examine each item in a lot, the result is called a "100% sample." But, in general, a sample will not only consist of less than the entire population, but frequently of far less.

7.2 Why Are Samples Necessary?

One might be tempted to wonder why one needs to deal with samples: why not get all the data? There are several reasons why samples are often desirable and sometimes essential. We shall consider a few instances which will make the idea clear.

1. *Destructive Measurements.* An important characteristic of a good photoflash bulb is that it shall flash when a proper voltage is applied to it. We, quite properly, want to know that it will. The only way to be sure is to apply the voltage: if the bulb fires, it *was* good, but . . . A steel bar, for some uses, must have at least a specified strength. To be sure whether it has the strength, we break it in a machine which records the force required. Again, perhaps it *was* a good bar!

2. *High Cost of Measurement.* Intuitively, we can appreciate that the more individuals from our population we actually measure, the more reliable will be our information about the entire population. But suppose that the measurement is extremely costly, so that the cost of obtaining additional assurance

presently exceeds the real value of the assurance. Determining the durability of truck tires is a good example. It is a very expensive task to conduct a properly planned test of the life of a set of truck tires. In view of long experience with such tires, life of tires only moderately different in design and construction from established types is determined on comparatively small samples, and preliminary appraisal of radical departures is made on even smaller samples.

3. *Infinite Populations.* The ancient Egyptians had an amusing hieroglyph for the largest number they could think about; a pair of arms raised in the traditional "I give up" sign! We often use the terms infinite and infinity to convey not only their strict and complicated mathematical meaning but also the idea of something bigger than we can cope with. Thinking of our employee training method problem, we might visualize an indefinite succession of such employees down the years. We cannot, today, train them all and determine how well they produce. Our class C-14 can be thought of as a sample from that "infinite" population. Similarly, the academic indexes of the students of the class of '56 can be (and were!) thought of as a sample from the infinite population of future freshmen at that university, though the great-grandparents of one generation of them are still unborn!

So we must deal with samples when destructive measurement is involved, when the cost of measurement starts to exceed its value, and when the population is infinite. In dealing with them, our purpose will be to find out about the whole population from the part we have.

7.3 What Is a Good Sample?

If we are to judge the whole population from the sample, surely we want a sample to be a good sample. But what do we mean by "good"? Ideally, we no doubt visualize that our sample is just a small-scale copy of our population. We would like to believe that there were the same relative frequencies in a class in the sample as there were in the population. Some thoughtful consideration will show that this is in the nature of wishful thinking. We cannot be sure that our sample is such a miniature of our population unless we know all about the population: but then the sample would be unnecessary!

If, however, we modify our thinking a little, we develop a criterion of goodness which will be satisfying in two respects. First, it will be possible to secure good samples. Second, with them, it will be possible to accomplish our practical objectives from the samples.

Thinking back to the previous chapter, recall the problem of rolling a die. We had a real die in mind, from which our mathematician visualized an ideal die ideally rolled so that each face had an equal chance of coming up. We shall visualize a good sample as one in which each individual in the population has an equal chance, or probability, of being included in the sample. Such a sample is called a *random sample.* One of the important steps in any statistical project is that of insuring that any samples involved shall be random.

This may seem like a strange idea, for many of us think of something done at random as something done without conscious planning. It may surprise you, then, to learn that to insure that a sample is truly random, in our sense, usually requires very real thought and definite planning. Perhaps it is something like milady's "casual" sports costume! Let us see how such samples can be obtained, and some of the consequences of failing to take the proper precautions.

7.4 Obtaining a Random Sample Physically

Suppose we have a lot comprising 10,000 steel balls from which we need to obtain a sample of 100 for diameter measurement. Imagine a device like a concrete mixer, into which we can put the entire 10,000 balls and, by rotating the device, have them rolled and tumbled in all directions inside the drum as a result of the combined rotation, axial tilt, and internal helical baffles. Periodically, we could stop the drum, have blindfolded helper reach in, and remove one ball. Then we could continue mixing, and so on, until we had our sample.

If we observed the rotation and its consequences, through transparent panels, we could, with an appropriate design, be pretty well assured that this plan closely simulated the mathematician's visualization of ideal conditions and that our sample was random. However, there are certain objections to the plan.

Even with steel bearing balls, such a tumbling of the finished balls would work irreparable damage. If we were sampling eggs, the results would be worse, and the plan would be totally unfeasible for sampling the citizens of Bigton! How can we accomplish the desirable result without the detrimental side effects?

7.5 A Bad Plan and Its Consequences

Suppose that one of the men's furnishing stores near our campus was interested in attracting the campus trade and asked us, from a sample, to determine the distribution of sizes of men on the campus. We accept the job, and decide to obtain our sample as a result of the following considerations. First, there is a spot on the campus where several walks intersect near the center of the mall. We decide to obtain our sample there. The area is pleasantly shaded at about eleven o'clock in the morning, so we plan to set up a table and chairs before that time and use the first hundred male students who pass the spot and are willing to be measured as our sample. It sounds like a sensible plan, doesn't it? We execute it, prepare our report, and collect our pay. Some months later, we find that we have a most cool reception from the store manager who finds himself, in consequence of our report, overstocked on large sizes and short of needed smaller sizes. He takes a most dim view of the work for which he paid us.

What was wrong? Wasn't our sample random? It was not! As it happens, our path intersection was near the Engineering Building. Most of the Engineering seniors had just finished a ten o'clock class there, but had none at eleven, and were on their leisurely way to the snack bar, while most of the underclassmen were loaded with classes inside the building at both hours. Comparatively few men from other schools passed at that time. So we were most unlikely to find any underclassmen from the Engineering School in our sample and rather unlikely to obtain many students from other schools. Furthermore, there is some reason to suspect that engineering students, as a group, are generally larger than other groups. No wonder our merchant was misled.

7.6 Good Samples Through Indirect Physical Methods

It would properly occur to us to wonder how we might handle our male students in a way similar to that in which the mixing machine handled the bearing balls, without rousing the ire of the students. Some thought will suggest ways. We could, for example, transcribe the name of each student from the directory onto one of an adequate number of uniform slips of paper,

Fig. 7-1. Secretary of State Henry A. Stimson Drawing First 1940 Selective Service Number. Courtesy Wide World Photos, Inc.

then place each slip in a capsule from a batch of uniform capsules, and place the capsules in a tumbling device. The capsules could then be tumbled and drawn without protest from the men. In fact, we could make quite a production of it by enlisting the aid of some attractive coeds, etc.! Lest you think this is ridiculous, Fig. 7-1 shows the use of just such a scheme for determining the order of draft calls in World War I but with Cabinet members replacing the coeds.

The slip-and-capsule routine is pretty involved. Spheres or discs bearing serial numbers can be placed in a tumbling machine, and the names in the directory can be serially numbered. Such a set of discs or spheres can be used for many tasks, by replacing the units drawn after each task is completed. But even this is a bit elaborate. A common procedure involves the use of uniform cards, with either names or serial numbers, which can be well shuffled before each of the required number of cards is drawn. Other devices are balanced spinners with the digits from zero through nine and ten-faced tops in different colors to spin out the serial numbers.

7.7 A Simple Procedure

All of these physical procedures are fairly simple and, if well used, quite satisfactory. However, they do involve more or less bulky equipment and are rather time-consuming. In recent years, a much more convenient procedure has been developed which involves the use of what are known as tables of *random numbers*. Such a table is included here as Appendix IV. As generally prepared, these tables consist of digits tabulated in columns of two digits each, with a space after every fifth row. Modern tables have usually been prepared by digital computers set on a routine which simulates the action of the repeated spinning of a ten-faced top or rolling of a die in the form of a regular dodecahedron (a twenty-faced solid with all faces equal in size and shape) having each of the ten digits on two faces.

To illustrate the use of such a table, suppose that we had 1,427 male students at our institution, from whom we wished to select a random sample of 100. We would serially number the names of these students in our directory, then open our table to some unpredetermined page and, placing our finger anywhere on the open pages, would proceed to read the numbers down in order, using two of the columns of two to secure the necessary digits. Because the four digits would contain the numbers 1 to 10,000 (if we read 00 00 as 10,000), we shall be wasting many numbers, since we have only 1,427 students. We can improve our efficiency without destroying our randomness if we interpret as our serial number the remainder after dividing our random number by 2,000. Thus, the random numbers 00 01, 20 01, 40 01, 60 01, and 80 01 would be interpreted as serial number 1, while 41 97 would be interpreted as 197 and 51 24 would be interpreted as 1,124. If the numbers in our table were in the sequence shown below, and we were using this efficient speed-up plan, they would be considered equivalent to the number shown in the right-hand column:

Random Number	*Read As*	*Equivalent Serial Number*
54 99	5,499	1,499 — Not usable
06 49	649	649
96 74	9,674	1,674 — Not usable
24 28	2,428	428
62 66	6,266	266
93 18	9,318	1,318
84 39	8,439	439
30 41	3,041	1,041
40 12	4,012	12
70 06	7,006	1,006

Two questions arise that warrant a little further consideration. First, what shall we do if the same serial number appears twice? Strictly, it would be correct to use the data for the individual represented twice, rather than continuing to draw until we had 100 different serial numbers, but it is generally preferred to adopt the latter procedure. Second, what about the possibility that our book habits will end up with our virtually always starting at about the same place in our table: wouldn't that produce a degree of nonrandomness? It would, and if we wish to be strict purists, we can open our book "at random" and let the first number we touch indicate the page on which we are to start. Then we can similarly select a second number to indicate the column with which we start and a third for the row. This should satisfy almost anyone capable of being satisfied!

7.8 Temptations

There will develop many situations in which you will be strongly tempted to disregard the random requirement for samples. As an example, suppose you wish to obtain a sample of 10 drums from a batch of 1,000 drums stored in "blocks" five drums wide by three drums deep by three drums high in a warehouse. You serially number the positions of the drums, use your random numbers, and find that the resulting list requires the moving of many drums to reach each sample. The temptation will be great to "fudge" just a little, particularly when you bring your list to the warehouse foreman! But, as we shall show you later, the validity of the methods that you will use in working with the data from our samples will depend upon the validity of certain assumptions, one of which is invariably that the sample was a random sample. Although departures from validity here are most serious, it is an all too human tendency to yield to the foreman. Our best advice when the situation arises is: don't yield, or you'll regret it.

General Study

1. The *Literary Digest* conducted a poll prior to the presidential election of 1936. Their poll predicted a heavy majority for Landon, the Republican candidate, whereas the actual voting gave the majority to Roosevelt, the Democratic candidate. The poll used a sample of about ten million drawn from telephone directories and *Literary Digest* subscribers. The magazine never recovered from the fiasco. Was its sample random? Why?

2. A poll taker seeks a sample of 100 housewives in a certain city. She uses the first 100 housewives she finds at home between 2:00 p.m. and 4:00 p.m. on weekday afternoons. Is this sample random? Could you improve the method?

3. On a certain campus, one of the student organizations is anxious to evaluate the student stand on a number of questions of morals and ethics. It calls for volunteers to fill in a questionnaire on the subject. Will these volunteers comprise a random sample?

Specific Problems

1. Use the table of random numbers to select a sample of 20 from a population of 45,000. If this is done by the entire class, each person, or group working together, should arrange its sample in numerical order and the resulting sets should be compared. How could such a comparison be made effectively?

2. Use the table of random numbers to select samples of 10 from a population of 1,000. If, within a set of 10, no individual is repeated, how many sets did you take before the same individual appeared in two sets? Compare your results with those of other persons or teams.

3. Use whatever physical sampling scheme is most convenient for the facilities you have to draw samples of 5 from a population of 100 and compare the results with those obtained by using random numbers for the same purpose.

8

What Can a Sample Tell Us About the Mean of Its Population?

8.1 The Origin of Our Problem

In our study of statistics, so far, we have looked very broadly at what statistics is all about, and rather uncritically at how it works. Then we have gone on to study some of its nonmathematical technics, including retabulation, grouping, and visual presentation, in more detail. This prepared us to receive somewhat more readily some of the ideas of descriptive statistics, involving measures of central values and dispersion and a formal description of the shape of the distribution. But so far we have been under the rather limiting restriction that our methods must be used only when we have complete populations.

Then we took a break from our main activity and considered some of the basic ideas of probability theory, and learned a little about what probability is and how it relates to experience. Then we considered samples — why they must be used, what are the characteristics of good samples, and how such samples may be procured.

Before returning completely to our main task, let us pause yet a moment to think about how we think (!). Actually, much of our thinking follows one or another of two rather common patterns. Faced with a problem, we try to bring our pertinent background knowledge to bear upon it. Much of that knowledge we find embraced in rather general statements of principles, and we recognize in our problem a specific instance to which these principles apply. We reach our solution by a process of inference from our general principles to their specific consequences for our particular case. In such situations, we are engaged in *deductive reasoning*, or *deduction*. In other situations, we have a limited set of specific facts, and are trying to infer the larger principle of which they must be a specific result. When we are reasoning from such specific facts to a broader generalizing principle, we are engaged in *inductive reasoning*, or *induction*.

Now it often happens that, either because we have inadequate starting material, or because of some weakness in our chain of inference, we may not be quite sure of our conclusion. We state the conclusion we have reached as what is formally known as a *hypothesis*, a statement of a possible but not certain truth.

For example, when our training supervisor informs us that he has a new training method which he believes is superior to our present method, he is stating a hypothesis. Actually, his hypothesis could be considered to be a statement that the mean of the population of first-week productions of an indefinitely large succession of workers trained by this method will be larger than that of workers trained by our present method. When a salesman claims that the strength of a certain yarn is 5.00 units, he is really advancing a hypothesis that the mean of all strength tests that could be made on such yarn would be 5.00. In such circumstances, then, we have a suggested but unproved truth about a population. We shall seek evidence from a sample as to the truth of our hypotheses.

Under other circumstances, we may be able to form no hypotheses but may still need to know what the truth is. We have a new type of plastic: what is its strength? We have designed a new shape of telephone handset: what proportion of telephone subscribers will order one in place of their present handsets if the charge per month is $1.00? $0.75? $0.50? Here we may have no way at all, other than by sheer guess, to advance a hypothesis about the values. So we seek an estimate.

8.2 Our Plan for Testing Hypotheses

We shall first deal with the problem of testing, or verifying, hypotheses concerning a mean. When we have accomplished this, we shall find that only a bit more thinking is required to permit us to deal satisfactorily with the problem of estimating means when we have no hypotheses concerning them.

In order to test hypotheses, we shall first need to obtain from the sample the best possible estimate of the population mean. Then we shall have to learn how that estimate behaves if we take repeated samples from a population. With this information in hand, we shall be able to develop an objective procedure for reaching a decision concerning our hypothesis. Of course, because we are dealing with a sample, we shall recognize that even this decision may be wrong, and we shall obtain statements of the probabilities of the two kinds of error we may make.

8.3 A Specific Problem

It will be a very real help to have a specific problem to think about while we are learning the principles involved in testing hypotheses. Suppose that we have been led to the hypothesis that the mean of the population in which we are interested is $\mu = 5.00$ and that we have a random sample of $N = 4$ values from this population, namely,

$$4, 7, 8, 5 \tag{S8.3.1}$$

Obviously, these are purely synthetic values with which it is easy to work, and you will be able to follow the arithmetic without resorting to a calculator.

8.4 Statistics: Estimates of Parameters

Just as when we were dealing with populations we found it convenient to condense the many observations into a measure of central value, a measure of dispersion, and an equation describing form, so, in dealing with samples, we shall want similar condensations. Because the mean and variance of populations appear in the distribution equations as "constants" whose values distinguish one particular population of a given form from another, and because such "constants" in equations are properly called *parameters*, we call our measures of central value, dispersion, and other characteristics of populations parameters, also.

Now it would seem very reasonable, when we condense the data in a sample, to do our condensation in such a way that the resulting values are the best estimates we can obtain of related parameters. At the moment, we are concerned specifically with a population mean, and we want a single value from our sample to estimate that mean. Surely we want it to be the result of a defined, objective treatment of the data. A figure so obtained from a sample is called a *statistic.*

Intuitively, we feel that we should treat the sample like a population, that is, add the values and divide by N; "common sense" says that is what ought to be done. In this particular instance, but by no means always, "common sense" happens to be right. We call our result the *sample mean*, denote it, if we have called our individual values x_i, by $\bar{x}$, read "x bar," and write its formula as

$$\bar{x} = \Sigma x/N \tag{8.4.1}$$

For our specific problem,

$$\bar{x} = (4 + 7 + 8 + 5)/4 = 24/4 = 6.00 \tag{8.4.2}$$

which is all well and good. But how do we know it is the best estimate of the population mean?

8.5 Criteria of Good Statistics

In order to know that we have the best of something, be it dishwashers, paintings, or statistics, we must define goodness (not always easy to do!). Suppose we think about our problem generally in terms of some parameter, Υ, the Greek upsilon, and its estimating statistic, U. By the way, ordinarily we use a Greek letter to denote a parameter and the related Latin letter to denote its estimating statistic, usually choosing letters suggesting the name of the parameter. We follow custom with μ for *m*ean but, instead of using m for the sample mean, we bow to the science of mechanics in which the coordinates of centers of gravity, or balance points, were denoted by bars over the letters, and use $\bar{x}$. Recall the relation between means and balance points.

Ideally, we would like to have $U = \Upsilon$ for every sample, but in our real world, this is asking too much. Suppose we imagine taking a succession of samples and calculating U from each sample. These U's would build up a new population, which would have a mean value that we could denote as μ_U. We shall find that we can work quite well with samples provided that the statistical limit of μ_U on indefinite repetition of our sampling process is Υ. A statistic which behaves in this way is said to be *unbiased*, and the possession of this property is our first criterion of goodness in a statistic.

But surely it is not enough that our statistic behave properly in the long run: we want its values to be dispersed about the true value of the parameter as little as possible. We have accepted the variance of a population as a good measure of its dispersion. Therefore, we may say that for U to be the best statistic for estimating Υ, the statistical limit of its variance on repeated sampling, σ_U^2, should be smaller than that of any other statistic. Such a statistic is said to be (the most) *efficient*. Although we cannot fully appreciate the quantitative aspects of the idea until later, we can sense that, if the statistic U has a small variance, we would not need as large a sample to make us confident that our statistic was close to the true parameter as we would if U had a larger variance. In a sense, then, the statistic with the smallest variance makes the most efficient use of the data.

We have intuitively sensed that "there is strength in numbers," by which we mean that we feel surer of the information inferred from a large sample than of that inferred from a small sample from the same population. In order for this to be true, it is necessary that the variance of U, σ_U^2, should decrease steadily as the size of the sample increases. A statistic which behaves in this way is said to be *consistent*, and this is our third criterion of goodness.

Finally, it would be disturbing to find that any other statistic contained information about Υ that was not contained in U. A statistic that contains all the information about its parameter that any other statistic contains is said to be *sufficient*, and this is our fourth criterion.

8.6 Behavior of the Sample Mean

The exact behavior of sample means will depend upon the specific population from which they come. Suppose that we have a normally distributed population of values of x whose mean is μ and whose variance is σ^2, from which we draw an indefinite succession of random samples of size N. From the data of each sample, we calculate its sample mean, $\bar{x}$.

This succession of $\bar{x}$'s will form a new population, whose individual members will be the means of the samples drawn from the original, or *parent*, population. What will be the characteristics of this population of sample means? It can be shown by mathematical reasoning beyond the scope of our work that they will be as follows:

1. The distribution will be normal in form.
2. Its mean, which we may designate as $\mu_{\bar{x}}$, will be that of the parent population, that is, $\mu_{\bar{x}} = \mu$.
3. Its variance, which we may designate as $\sigma_{\bar{x}}^2$, will be one-N^{th} that of the parent population, that is, $\sigma_{\bar{x}}^2 = \sigma^2/N$.

You will see that we are now in a position to examine some aspects of the goodness of the sample mean as a statistic for estimating the population mean. In the first place, $\mu_{\bar{x}}$ does equal μ, so the statistic is unbiased. In the second place, because $\sigma_{\bar{x}}^2 = \sigma^2/N$, its value will decrease steadily as N increases, so $\bar{x}$ is consistent. In calculating $\bar{x}$, we made use of every observation in the sample equally. This fact alone should insure that it contains all the information any statistic could about the parameter it estimates, that is, that it is sufficient. In contrast, the mid-range uses only the two extreme values, and is an insufficient estimator of the mean. Finally, we can investigate other proposed statistics for estimating μ and we would find none which, for any given value of N, has a smaller variance. Hence, $\bar{x}$ is efficient. From this we conclude that, under our criteria, $\bar{x}$ is the best statistic for estimating μ.

It does, indeed, seem that we have had to take the results of some mathematical reasoning, which we have not followed, very much on faith. Although the details of the reasoning are beyond our scope in this book, we need not use completely blind faith. Recall our experience with coin tossing and our description of the results as the binomial distribution. If that distribution was written for $P = Q = 1/2$ in terms of the proportion, p, of heads in N throws, you will recall that the mean, as N increased, remained $1/2$, the value of P, while the variance, which was always PQ/N, steadily decreased as N increased. The relation between the binomial and normal distribution should hardly leave us surprised at the behavior of $\bar{x}$. Very shortly, however, we shall be able to do some actual experimenting which is quite easy and which will make us very content that the mathematician's reasoning is sound.

8.7 Possible Testing Errors

As our next step in arriving at the mechanics of testing hypotheses, let us consider what kinds of errors might occur in our final decision. Of course, we must face the fact that such errors are possible, because we have no guarantee that our $\bar{x}$ will equal μ, but only that it is one value from a population whose mean is μ. Broadly speaking, then, we must consider the difference between $\bar{x}$ and μ and decide that the difference is either so small that our hypothesis is probably true or so great that our hypothesis is probably false.

Here are our two possibilities of error, then, clearly and unavoidably present whenever we make such a decision. In some circumstances, we may have a sample from a population whose mean is, in fact, 5.00 as our hypothesis states. But, by the behavior of random samples, our $\bar{x}$ may be quite far from 5.00, and we shall reject our hypothesis as false. In other circumstances, we may have a sample from a population whose mean was not 5.00 but, again, the behavior of random samples happens to place $\bar{x}$ so close to 5.00 that we are not led to reject our hypothesis. In each of these instances, we shall have made an error. In the first, we rejected a true hypothesis, while in the second, we accepted as true a hypothesis which was false.

This would be an impossible situation in which to work but for a very important fact. This is that, although we cannot eliminate the possibility of error, we can so operate that the probability of making an error can be predetermined and reduced to as small a nonzero level as we wish. It has been convenient to agree to call the error of rejecting a true hypothesis a *Type I error* and the risk, expressed as a probability, of doing so an *alpha risk*. The error of failing to reject a false hypothesis we call a Type II error, and its associated risk we call a beta risk. The diagram of Fig. 8-1 may help fix these ideas in your mind. After we have studied the actual testing process, we shall return to consider how these errors can be controlled.

Fig. 8-1. Schematic diagram of possible results of testing a hypothesis, H_0.

		Our Decision	
		Accept H_0 as True	**Reject H_0 as False**
The Fact	**H_0 is True**	**Decision Correct**	**Decision Incorrect** **Type I Error** **Alpha Risk**
	H_0 is False	**Decision Incorrect** **Type II Error** **Beta Risk**	**Decision Correct**

8.8 The Testing Process

Suppose that we now make the assumption that our sample was a random sample from a population known to be normal in form. Let us make the further assumption that, although we do not know its mean, we do know its variance. For our specific example, assume that that value is $\sigma^2 = 1.00$. Is it, you should be wondering, reasonable to assume that one knows the form and variance of a distribution without knowing its mean? In a very real sense, it is reasonable, indeed, and is a situation often encountered in actual experience.

If you are giving the same test in a specific subject to students in different classes, you will, on well-designed tests, find essentially the same variance in the individual scores in all the classes, and the scores of each class will indicate an underlying normal distribution, but the means are quite certain to vary from class to class. Heights of male college undergraduates will show about the same variance and suggest a normal distribution whatever the college, but the mean will vary considerably from college to college. In a quite real sense, then, if we are dealing with observations of a kind with which we have had considerable past experience, we may say that we know the variance and form of the population, but don't know the mean. But, you will say, suppose this is a new situation, and we don't have this background: what then? We do, indeed, hope you have been saying this, for the answer to this question is, to us, tremendously exciting and satisfying, but we ask your leave to postpone answering just a little longer.

Now if our assumptions are correct, our mean will be one of a population of such means whose variance is $\sigma_{\bar{x}}^2 = \sigma^2/N = 1/4$ and whose standard deviation is, therefore, $\sigma_{\bar{x}} = 1/2 = 0.5$. If, also, our hypothesis is correct, the mean of that population will be $\mu_{\bar{x}} = \mu = 5.00$. Because the distribution of these means is normal, it will be convenient to convert our values into the standard z-values by the usual formula:

$$z = \frac{\bar{x} - \mu_{\bar{x}}}{\sigma_{\bar{x}}} \qquad (8.8.1)$$

This is just equation 5.4.3a with the subscript "tags" to identify the particular population we are dealing with. Our numerical value for our particular example is $z = (6 - 5)/0.5 = 1/0.5 = 2.00$.

Of course, we know that we could observe values of z from what we loosely call $-\infty$ to $+\infty$, but we also know that the farther we are from zero the fewer values there are more remote. Here we have the key to our method. Suppose we accept the fact that we must make Type I errors with some specific alpha risk, say α. Our error will result from the fact that, given a sufficiently large numerical value of z (that is, an algebraically very large or very small value) we shall *act as though* it couldn't have originated as a result of sampling from a population with our hypothetical mean. Suppose further that we agree to arrange that half of our mistakes shall be made in consequence of algebraically large (i. e., numerically large and positive) and the other half because of algebraically small (i. e., numerically large but negative) values of z.

This simply tells us to find the values of z beyond which a fraction of the values equal to $\alpha/2$ are in each "tail" of the distribution. Because of the relation between these relative frequencies and probabilities which we have already discussed, we can then say that the probability of observing z's beyond these values is α, and that is the probability of rejecting H_0 when it is true. The designated values of z are called *critical values* and the tails of the distribution are the *critical regions.*

If we choose an alpha risk of 0.05, Appendix II shows us that the critical values of z, namely $z_{0.025}$ and $z_{0.975}$ are -1.960 and $+1.960$, respectively. We shall often place a subscript on the symbol for a critical value in this way to indicate the fraction of our distribution falling below it. A general designation for these critical values in terms of the alpha risk would be $z_{\alpha/2}$ and $z_{(1-\alpha/2)}$, respectively. Our observed value, $z = 2.00$, is in the upper critical region, and our decision must be to reject the hypothesis.

If we had chosen, instead, an alpha risk of 0.01, our critical values would have been $z_{0.005}$ and $z_{0.995}$, or ± 2.576. Under these circumstances, our observed value, 2.00, is not in the critical region, and we accept our hypothesis as true.

8.9 A Discussion of Alpha Risks

This simple example brings us face to face with an important fact: the choice of our alpha risk has a profound effect upon our decision. Possibly this disturbs us: it may be that we had hoped that statistics, which is so hard for us to learn (!), would reward us by removing the worries of "Decisions, all the time decisions . . . !" It won't, but it will make the problem less confusing. Without this part of statistics, faced with the problem of deciding on the basis of our sample whether our population had a mean of 5.00, we should have had to argue about whether such a sample could have come from such a population. Statistics eliminates that argument: under our assumptions and hypothesis we know how sample means from our parent population behave. We know we can't be sure whether ours is a sample from this population, but we know how to make a decision with a stated risk of error. Therefore, although we cannot, and should not, escape the use of judgment, we can pinpoint the place at which it is to be used, namely, to answer the question, "How often, for the purpose in hand, can we afford to be wrong?"

The answer to that question will depend upon the particular activity in which we are engaged, and the financial, ethical and even moral principles involved. Suppose that $\mu = 5.00$ was a hypothesis concerning the level of effectiveness of a certain vaccine. If our vaccine is not actually up to this level, it will fail to give the protection for which it is intended, while a higher level will often be accompanied by dangerous side reactions. If we use a large alpha risk, we shall correspondingly often reject normal vaccine but, as we shall presently see, we shall thereby reduce the frequency of accepting off-standard vaccine. Just what alpha risk we choose will depend on such factors as the cost of the vaccine, the possibility of adjusting off-standard lots, the seriousness of the disease it combats and of the possible side effects.

Surely the factors in that situation would differ markedly from those which would govern our choice of an alpha risk if the hypothesis, $\mu = 5.00$, concerned the diameter of bearing balls in tenths of an inch, for, between the acceptance of a lot of such balls and the final use of the machine of which they become a part, there will be many opportunities to recognize and correct a false decision.

We cannot resist the opportunity to suggest a very homely illustration which may make an alpha risk have a more lively meaning to you. One morning in early spring you see a bird somewhat smaller than a pigeon. You are hoping to see your first robin, but this bird is all white, has pink eyes, and yellow claws. It can't be a robin, you decide, because robins have grey backs, black eyes, etc. But, you are wrong! The bird you saw was an albino robin, a rare bird, but one of a type which does exist, and a robin indeed. When we reject true hypotheses because of observed values of our test statistics in the critical regions, we are dealing with "rare birds," but we have the advantage of deciding just how rare they are to be.

8.10 The Related Beta Risks

Suppose that someone else had proposed the hypothesis that $\mu = 7.00$ and had happened to get a sample just like ours. If he had chosen an alpha risk of 0.05, leading to critical values of ± 1.960, his value of z, -2.00, would have been in his critical region, in the lower half, and he would have rejected his hypothesis, just as we did ours. If, however, he had chosen an alpha risk of 0.01, leading to critical values of ± 2.576, he would have accepted his hypothesis. But we accepted ours, that $\mu = 5.00$, also!

It is rather disturbing to see the same sample values lead to the acceptance of two different hypotheses: surely μ cannot be both 5.00 and 7.00, can it? Of course it can't, but remember, our decisions are always attended by risks of two kinds of error. When we propose the hypothesis that $\mu = 5.00$, we are dividing all possible values for μ into two parts, 5.00 and all other values. We might say that there are two hypotheses. By tradition, the one we test is designated by H with a zero subscript, H_0, meaning zero or "null," and is called the *null hypothesis*. The alternative might be designated as H_1. Thus we have

$$H_0 : \mu = 5.00$$

$$H_1 : \mu \neq 5.00$$

Of course, our alternative, H_1, is a mighty broad hypothesis. We might break it up into pieces, one of which is $H_{1a} : \mu = 7.00$. Now our decision rule might be as before with respect to H_0, but we could add the rider that, if the observed value of our test statistic, z, falls in the upper part of the critical region, we shall not only reject H_0 but accept H_{1a}. This now permits us to consider how often we would fail to accept H_{1a} when it is true. If we had used an alpha risk of 0.05, our upper critical value would have been at $z = z_{0.975} = +1.960$. This corresponds to $\bar{x} = \mu + z\sigma_{\bar{x}} = 5.00 + 1.960 \times 0.50 = 5.00 + 0.980 = 5.980$. For the alternative hypothesis, H_{1a}, this corresponds to $z = (7.00 - 5.98)/0.50 = -1.02/0.5 = -2.040$. The corresponding value of p is 0.0207. Since we fail to accept H_{1a} when it, rather than H_0, is true when our observed values are below this critical value, our 0.0207 becomes our beta risk with respect to this alternative.

The more remote our alternative is from our null hypothesis, the smaller our beta risk for a given alpha risk. Similarly, the smaller we make our alpha risk, the greater will be our beta risk. Thus, in our example, if we had chosen alpha as 0.010, our upper critical value, +2.576, would have corresponded to $\bar{x} = 5.00 + 2.576 \times 0.50 = 5.00 + 1.288 = 6.288$. With respect to H_{1a}, this would correspond to $z = (7.000 - 6.288)/0.50 = -0.712/0.50 = -1.424$ and the beta risk would be 0.0773, more than three times our previous risk. In order to control both the alpha and beta risks at fixed values in the face of a specified population variance, we must control our sample size, making $\sigma_{\bar{x}}$ thereby of such size that the critical value for the desired alpha risk will also be the critical value for the desired beta risk. This type of planning is involved in design of experiments or surveys, concerning which we can only present broad ideas in this text.

8.11 Summary of Test Procedure

We have not only described the testing procedure but have introduced so much discussion that the pattern may need retracing. Table 8-1 shows the

Table 8-1 PROCEDURE FOR TESTING HYPOTHESIS THAT MEAN OF A POPULATION HAS STATED VALUE

Process	*General*	*Specific Example*
1. State the hypothesis	$H_0: \mu = \mu_0$	$H_0 : \mu = 5.00$
2. Choose alpha risk	$\alpha = \alpha_0$	$\alpha = 0.05$
3. State assumptions	(a) Sample is random (b) Distribution is normal (c) Variance is known	(a) Sample is random (b) Distribution is normal (c) $\sigma^2 = 1.00$
4. Formulate test statistic	$z = (\bar{x} - \mu_0)/\sigma_{\bar{x}}$ $= (\bar{x} - \mu_0)/(\sigma/\sqrt{N})$	$z = (\bar{x} - 5.00)/(1.00/\sqrt{4})$ $= (\bar{x} - 5.00)/0.5$
5. Formulate and determine critical values	$z_L = z_{\alpha/2}$ $z_U = z_{(1-\alpha/2)}$	$z_L = z_{0.225} = -1.960$ $z_U = z_{0.965} = +1.960$
6. Describe critical regions	$z \leq z_L$ and $z \geq z_U$	$z \leq -1.960$ and $z \geq +1.960$
7. Obtain data and calculate observed value of test statistic	—	$z = (6.00 - 5.00)/0.50$ $= 1.00/0.50$ $= 2.00$
8. Make and state decision	Reject H_0 if z is in critical region	H_0 is rejected, and we consider that $\mu \neq 5.00$

steps, both in general symbols and for our specific example. A few comments should be made. In the first place, the first six steps should all be performed before the data are obtained. By adopting this policy, one protects oneself from any opportunity to let a "sneak preview" of his data affect his thinking about his problem. It may be that we are most eager to have our data support one conclusion and, if we had seen them first, would be strongly tempted to choose an alpha risk which would lead to this decision. Furthermore, in performing these six steps, we are forced to consider our problem objectively: just what is our hypothesis, how sure we need be about our decision, and what assumptions we can properly make. This is most salutary in real life.

Unfortunately, those of us who write books succumb to the pressure to present some data, then show how to analyze them. Our readers, quite reasonably, come away with the idea that the time to consider the plan of analysis is after the data are in. Nothing could be further from the truth, and from here on, we intend to take precautions to see that our plans are presented first and our data later.

8.12 A Different Kind of Hypothesis

In the problem just completed, we worked with a hypothesis that a mean had a specific value. Often, we are not so concerned about an exact value as that it shall be at least some specific value or at most that value. For example, if we are considering the strength of a steel beam, we will be quite concerned that it be at least the minimum required value. On the other hand, if we are dealing with impurities in a medicinal preparation, we want to be sure that they do not exceed a stated value.

Our testing procedure will be almost the same. The only differences are in the form of the hypothesis and the location of the critical regions. Our hypothesis will be one or the other of the two forms:

$$\mu \leq \mu_0 \quad \text{or} \quad \mu \geq \mu_0.$$

If we have the first form, small values of $\bar{x}$ leading to small values of z are just what would occur if that hypothesis were true. But if $\bar{x}$ is sufficiently larger than μ_0, resulting in a sufficiently large positive value of z, we would want to reject H_0. This means that our critical region would be confined to the upper tail of the distribution, and our critical value would be $z_{(1-\alpha)}$. Observed values equal to or greater than the critical value would cause us to reject our hypothesis. Similarly, for the second form, $H_0 : \mu \geq \mu_0$, our critical value would be z and we should reject H_0 if our observed value were equal to or smaller than it.

As an example, suppose we wish to test the hypothesis $H_0 : \mu \geq 10.00$ with an alpha risk chosen as 0.02. We have already stated our hypothesis and chosen our alpha risk. Our sample has been planned to comprise $N = 10$ observations. We assume that it comes from a normal distribution by a random process and that the variance of the distribution is 1.60. We can now formulate our test statistic as

$$z = (\bar{x} - \mu)/\sigma_{\bar{x}} = (\bar{x} - 10.00)/\sqrt{1.6/10}$$
$$= (\bar{x} - \mu)/0.40.$$

We know that our critical value will be $z_{0.02} = -2.054$; the critical region will be $z \leq -2.054$. Now we obtain our data and calculate their mean, which turns out to be 9.20. This leads to an observed value of $z = (9.20 - 10.00)/0.40 = -0.80/0.40 = -2.00$. This value is not in our critical region, so we accept our hypothesis and act as though $\mu \geq 10.00$.

8.13 Which Hypothesis?

No matter what hypothesis we state, there is always at least one alternative. How do we decide upon which to test? For example, with the hypothesis $H_0 : \mu_0 = 5.00$, the all-inclusive alternative is $H_1 : \mu \neq 5.00$. With the hypothesis $H_0 : \mu \geq 10.00$, there is the alternative $H_1 : \mu \leq 10.00$. We could just as well, we think, reverse the subscripts and test the alternative. What governs our choice?

Our first demand is that the hypothesis be definite. The hypothesis $\mu = 5.00$ is definite, and leads to a specific value for μ_0 to be substituted into our formulation of the test statistic. The hypothesis $\mu \neq 5.00$ includes all values but 5.00 and we have nothing definite to substitute in our formula. So we really have no alternative there.

But now we practically hear your thinking, "The hypothesis $H_0 : \mu \geq 10.00$ wasn't definite, either. How come you used it?" An excellent and legitimate criticism. But notice what we did. We considered only the "equal" part of "is greater than or equal to ($\geq$)" in substituting into our formulation of the test statistic. Then we let the "greater than" direct us to reject only for observed values in the lower tail of the distribution. This means that if μ is exactly 10.00 we shall reject H, in the long run, in a fraction of our tests exactly equal to 0.020, which was what we undertook to do. But if μ is greater than 10.00, it will actually produce fewer $\bar{x}$'s smaller than 10.00 by an amount sufficient to yield z's in the critical region, and we shall falsely reject our hypothesis even less often.

Now we come back to our opening question: which hypothesis shall we test? It is to be regretted that much conflicting advice has been offered on this matter. The conflict arises from the fact that some of the advice has been offered by highly competent mathematicians with too little grasp of the aims, and difficulties, of the workers in the physical and social sciences. Some of the advice has been offered by workers in those fields with a too shallow grasp of the ideas of statistics. The advice will be surely sound only when it arises from an adequate perception of both the principles of statistics and the aims and problems of the fields to which it is to be applied. Let us consider the question in the light of several factors which affect the answer and see if we can arrive at a sensible and intelligent answer.

In the first place, as we have said before and will doubtless say again, good data are costly in time, effort, and, often, investment in equipment and materials required to obtain them. Generally speaking, neither individuals nor corporations can afford these expenditures unless they can anticipate some real benefit from the result. Sometimes a hypothesis may have arisen out of a search for some kind of improvement. The improvement may be in the quality of a product a firm manufactures, or in the profit it makes. Or it may be a reduction in the occurrence or severity of highway accidents, or of some type of crime or disease in a community. We hope, in fact we believe, that our proposal will achieve the result, and this proposal is embodied in our hypothesis.

But there are classic instances in which a hypothesis was accepted because the limited number of observed facts were consistent with it, only to have subsequent experience develop the information that the facts were also consistent with other hypotheses, and that actually, one of them was the truth. This raises the distinct possibility that we should play "devil's advocate," and advance and test the hypothesis which we really hope is not true. A strong argument in favor of this plan is that if we test the unpopular hypothesis and are able to reject it with a very small risk of being wrong (our alpha risk), then we shall have a very powerful reason for accepting the one we hoped was true.

To examine this proposal critically, let us return to the problem of section 8.12, where we tested $H_0 : \mu \geq 10.00$. We used an alpha risk of 0.02 which led to a critical region, $z \leq -2.054$. This is equivalent to $\bar{x} \leq 9.1784$. Suppose that this was the hypothesis we hoped was not true, that is, that we were playing devil's advocate, and that the hypothesis we hoped was true was $H_1 : \mu \leq 10.00$. If we had elected to test H_1 as our null hypothesis, using the same alpha risk, our critical region would have been $z = +2.054$, equivalent to $\bar{x} = 10.8216$. In order to make it convenient, let us depart from our usual subscripts and designate the hypothesis we actually test in each plan with a zero subscript followed by a serial letter to denote the particular plan, and use the same serial letter on our alpha risks.

Under this plan, then, $H_{0a} : \mu \geq 10.00$, $\alpha_a = 0.02$ and critical region $z \leq -2.054$ equivalent to $\bar{x} \leq 9.1784$ describes our first plan. Our second plan is described by $H_{0b} : \mu \leq 10.00$, $\alpha_b = 0.02$, critical region $z \geq +2.054$ equivalent to $\bar{x} \geq 10.8216$. Let's compare the plans.

1. Under either plan, values of $\bar{x} \geq 10.8216$ will lead us to conclude that $\mu \geq 10.00$.

2. Under either plan, values of $\bar{x} \leq 9.1784$ will lead us to conclude that $\mu \leq 10.00$.

3. Under either plan $9.1784 < \bar{x} < 10.8216$ will lead us to conclude that the hypothesis being tested is true, and the results for the two plans will therefore disagree.

But now suppose we tested $H_{0c} : \mu \leq 10.00$, our hypothesis which we hope is true and which we tested in plan B, under a new plan, making the critical region identical with the noncritical region in plan A. This requires us to reject for $\bar{x} \geq 9.1784$, equivalent to $z \geq -2.054$, which corresponds to an alpha risk of 0.98. The diagram in Fig. 8-2 will help clarify the situation, we believe.

Fig. 8-2. Alternate plans for testing one-sided hypotheses.

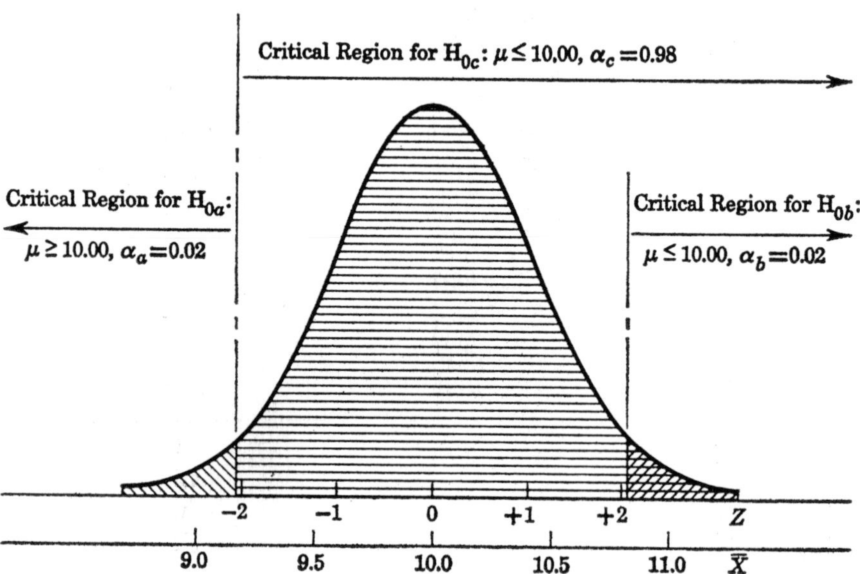

Incidentally, possibly we should tell you that an hypothesis involving an inequality is often called a *one-sided hypothesis*, and its test is called a *one-tailed test*, as distinguished from the *two-sided hypothesis* and *two-tailed test* dealing with equality.

In this specific example, we see that plans A and C accomplish exactly the same results, and that their two alpha risks total 1.00, as they must because they cover all possibilities. Of course, the alpha risk for one is the beta risk for the other, in our ordinary use of the terms. If, then, we can test either hypothesis, the one we hope is true or its alternate, and achieve exactly the same results by appropriate choice of risks, what difference does it make which we test? None, of course! Then why should conflicting advice have arisen? We believe that, as usual, it arose as the result of misunderstanding and nonunderstanding. In the first place, as we shall see later on, many of the tables of values of test statistics would become very bulky and expensive were they to be published as completely, even, as our z-table. In order to keep them reasonable in size and cost, it has become common to produce only those parts which would be needed for plans like plan A, involving small alpha risks. It would be prudent, then, to use a plan like A rather than one like C, simply because values needed are readily available. The choice is not dictated by any fundamental statistical, technical, or ethical principle.

In what we have been doing so far, we have considered two possible hypotheses, the one we were to test and its alternative. Since these hypotheses divide the possible values into two kinds, or cut the scale on which they are portrayed into two parts, we say that we are dealing with a dichotomy (from the Greek, meaning "to cut in two"). But more generally, we often cannot distinguish between what we like and what we don't like quite so sharply. Suppose that we are sure that if $\mu \geq 10.00$, our situation will surely be poor, while if $\mu \leq 9.00$, our situation will surely be good. For $9.00 < \mu < 10.00$, we are not sure whether our situation would be poor or good, but only that as μ takes on values nearer to 9.00, our situation improves. Under such conditions, we are really involved in a trichotomy represented by the three hypotheses:

$$H_0 : \mu \geq 10.00$$

$$H_1 : \mu \leq 9.00$$

$$H_2 : 9.00 < \mu < 10.00$$

As we have indicated, suppose we plan to test H_0.

Our procedure will be just as it was before, but in our interpretation of the results we "pretend" that H_2 isn't there and, if we reject H_0, we consider that we accept H_1. Our beta risk would then be calculated in terms of it. If, for example, we tested H_0 with an alpha risk of 0.02, as before, with a critical $z = -2.054$ equivalent to a critical $\bar{x} = 9.1784$, this value would stand at $z = (9.1784 - 9.00)/0.40 = 0.1784/0.4 = +0.446$ with respect to the alternative hypothesis. The corresponding beta risk is, therefore, 0.328, as you can and should verify. Figure 8-3 presents the ideas graphically.

It is common statistical practice, if we have rejected an hypothesis such as this, to say, "The mean is *significantly* below 10.00," and the smaller the alpha risk we used the higher the degree of significance we claim. Notice that the denominator of our test statistic, z, involved $\sigma_{\bar{x}}$, which, in sampling from a population of known variance, can be made as small as you please by making N large enough. It is true, then, that however little μ may be below 10.00, in our case, by taking a large enough sample we would ultimately be led to reject H_0, and declare μ "significantly" below 10.00. But, in our present problem, we have recognized that we aren't sure that values below 10.00 really affect us differently from values above 10.00 until they get down to 9.00. In other words, we must, in our thinking, distinguish between values *statistically*

Fig. 8-3. Diagram showing the risks involved in testing H_0: $\mu \geq 10.00$ against the alternative H_1: $\mu \leq 9.00$ when $\sigma^2 = 1.60$ and $N = 10$.

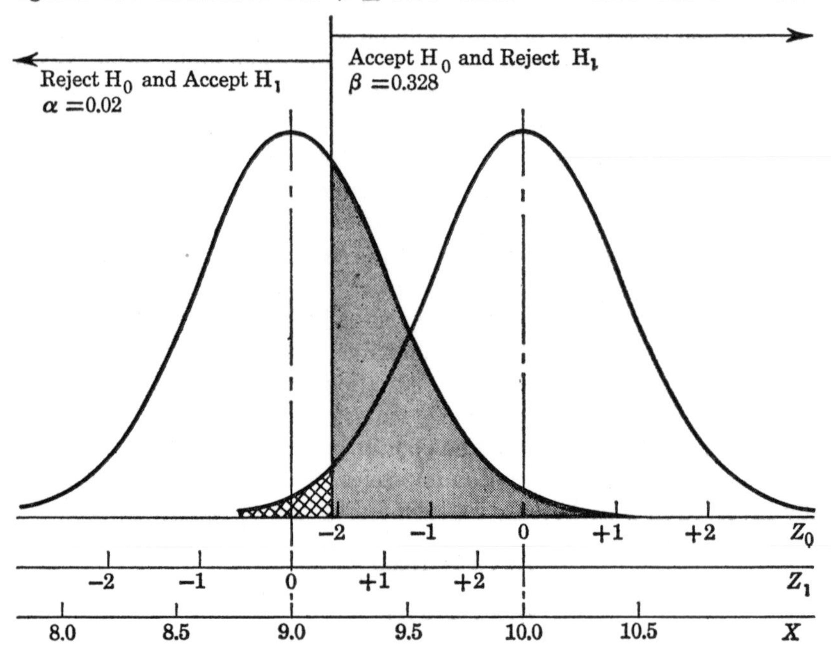

significantly below 10.00 and those which are *technically* (including economic aspects) *meaningfully* below 10.00. While this consideration is most important in planning the taking of data, it must be borne in mind in interpreting presentations of results coming to our attention.

8.14 Comments on the Method

While we are on the subject, quite possibly a warning about the words "accept," "reject," "prove," and "disprove" may not be amiss. Refer back to the summary of our testing procedure in Table 8-1, where you will be forcibly reminded that, in testing our hypotheses, we make certain assumptions and recognize that we have accepted certain risks. *If* all our assumptions are warranted and consistent with facts that, in general, we cannot know, then our risk of a wrong decision is exactly that stated, but if our assumptions, or any one of them, are unwarranted, then our risk is meaningless. Actually, then, we may reject our hypothesis for any of the following reasons:

1. The facts are that the hypothesis is false, and the test procedure properly detects the facts.

2. The facts are that the hypothesis is true, and all our assumptions are warranted, but we are experiencing one of the unavoidable errors contemplated in our alpha risk.

3. The combined effect of the facts concerning our hypothesis and the fact that one or more of our assumptions is unwarranted produces a value in the critical region.

It thus appears that the validity of our assumptions is very important. It has been our observation that most of us, when we are first learning about statistical methods, become very concerned about the assumption of the normal distribution, simply because that idea is new to us. Let us consider that assumption first, then.

There are methods, which we shall come to presently, for verifying whether this assumption is warranted whenever we are dealing with sufficiently large samples or whenever we have sufficient background information. Furthermore, we have two additional protections. It can be shown mathematically and verified by experience that even rather great departures from the normal form, in the face of samples of rather modest size (N at least, say five) lead to actual error frequencies little different from the assigned risk at levels of risk usually used. To replace "modest" and "little" in that sentence by more exact terms, we must specify the actual distribution form. It is also true that, when the form is definitely not normal, we can often use a transformation from x to a related variable, such as a power or root of x, or its logarithm, which is normally distributed and work with it. Thus, the worry about normality is hardly warranted.

As for the assumption that the variance is known, we shall presently establish a procedure for use when this assumption is unwarranted, so that is not a worry. Unfortunately, most of us, as beginners, pass lightly over the assumption of random sampling, but this is the *sine qua non* of the whole matter. If you have not a random sample, you have no right to use the method, and that is that! We have discussed ways of obtaining random samples, and you must make sure that your samples are random, because your stated risks will not be true for nonrandom samples and the actual risks for such samples are usually impossible to determine.

The result of all of these factors is that the terms "accept" or "prove" must be considered in the sense of convenient condensation of the description of the entire testing procedure. "Accept" simply means that, under our assumptions and with stated risks, we shall act as though our hypothesis is true. "Prove" means that we have posed an hypothesis and accepted it in the sense just stated. This is not the equivalent of the mathematical proof of a proposition in geometry, and cannot be.

We have mentioned before this problem of the meaning of words. It is perhaps an unusually troublesome problem in applied statistics, for one who works in this area is in the position of using methods developed in one area (probability and mathematical statistics) to serve another area (the field of application). Each of these areas has its own special language, and we find ourselves in all the difficulties of anyone working in two languages. One should be as careful as possible of his use of language, but should reserve the right to delimit the meaning of terms in his own field where that is necessary.

8.15 The Problems of Estimation

When we have calculated a sample mean, we have obtained from our sample the best, by our criteria, estimate of the mean of the population from which it came. Such an estimate, because it would be plotted as a single point on an axis of values of the quantity under consideration, is called a *point estimate.* We recognized that, although it was the best estimate, it need not be identical with the population mean, and this led us to find procedures for testing hypotheses with known levels of the risks of error involved.

Now we must consider the situations in which we have no preconceived ideas, or hypotheses, concerning the population mean, but do wish to ascertain its value. It is all well and good to say that the sample mean is our best estimate; the question remains, how good is it? Suppose we think some more about the problem in section 6.3 in which we had a sample of $N = 4$ values from which we calculated $\bar{x} = 6.00$. Our best guess is that $\mu = 6.00$. But if someone asks whether it could be that $\mu = 5.99999$ or 6.00001, we would say, with hardly a glance at the individual values in our sample, "Oh, sure!" If someone else were to inquire about 5.5 or 6.5 as possibilities, we would say something equivalent to, "Could be," and so on. After a bit, the proposal would strain our credulity, and we might say, "I doubt it." If yet another person asked if the mean could be 10.0, we would quite unconcernedly say, "Oh, no."

In this imaginary series of events, we see both the nature of our problem and a key to its solution. (How often it happens that really seeing our problem puts us well on the way to its solution.) We have been expressing increasing doubts that the real mean could be various values as those values became more remote from our sample mean. The only thing we need is a measure of the doubts and confidences involved.

Let's try a plan and see how it works and what it means. First, let's make the same assumptions we did in testing hypotheses, namely, that our sample is a random sample from a normal population whose variance is known to us. In the specific problem, let the variance be, as it was before, 1.00. Now imagine that a stream of people were to ask us to test the hypothesis that the population mean had different values, using an alpha risk of 0.05 in each instance. The first hypothetical value for μ below $\bar{x}$ that our sample would lead us to reject would be the value such that our $\bar{x}$ was just at the boundary of the upper critical region for the test statistic. This means that

$$z_{0.975} = +1.960 = \frac{\bar{x} - \mu}{\sigma_{\bar{x}}} \tag{8.15.1a}$$

or, substituting numerical values from our previous work,

$$1.960 = \frac{6.00 - \mu}{0.50} \qquad (8.15.1b)$$

and, solving for μ, we have

$$\mu = 6.00 - 1.960 \times 0.50 = 6.00 - 0.98 = 5.02 \qquad (8.15.1c)$$

Similarly, we might reason that the first hypothetical value for μ above $\bar{x}$ that would be rejected would be the one for which our $\bar{x}$ was the boundary of its lower critical region. This requires that

$$z_{0.025} = -1.960 = \frac{\bar{x} - \mu}{\sigma_{\bar{x}}} \qquad (8.15.1d)$$

which, by work similar to what has just been done, leads to

$$\mu = 6.00 + 1.960 \times 0.50 = 6.00 + 0.98 = 6.98 \qquad (8.15.1e)$$

Thus we know that we could reject any hypothesis alleging that μ was at or below 5.02 or at or above 6.98 with a risk of doing so wrongly of not more than 0.05. Let us now approach the problem in a little different way. From the behavior of the sample mean as discussed in section 8.6 and the properties of a normal distribution, we know that the relative frequency of values below $z = (\bar{x} - \mu)/\sigma_{\bar{x}} = -1.960$ is 0.025, as is also the relative frequency of values above $z = +1.960$. The relative frequency of values between these two is therefore 0.95. The relation between relative frequency and probability, then, permits us to make the statement.

$$\Pr\left\{-1.960 \leq \frac{\bar{x} - \mu}{\sigma_{\bar{x}}} \leq +1.960\right\} = 0.95 \qquad (8.15.2a)$$

Now all quantities involved in the statement inside the braces are known except μ. Suppose we operate on this statement by multiplying it through by $\sigma_{\bar{x}}$:

$$-1.960\sigma_{\bar{x}} \leq \bar{x} - \mu \leq 1.960\sigma_{\bar{x}} \qquad (8.15.3a)$$

then, subtracting $\bar{x}$ from each part,

$$-\bar{x} - 1.960\sigma_{\bar{x}} \leq -\mu \leq -\bar{x} + 1.960\sigma_{\bar{x}} \qquad (8.15.3b)$$

and finally, multiplying by -1, which reverses the direction of the inequalities,

$$\bar{x} + 1.960\sigma_{\bar{x}} \geq \mu \geq \bar{x} - 1.960 \qquad (8.15.3c)$$

This can simply be read in the reverse order so that we move through the expression in order of increasing value:

$$\bar{x} - 1.960\sigma_{\bar{x}} \leq \mu \leq \bar{x} + 1.960\sigma_{\bar{x}} \qquad (8.15.3d)$$

and this is just another way of saying the same thing as 8.15.3a. Hence we can substitute this form into the braces in 8.15.2a, obtaining

$$\Pr\{\bar{x} - 1.960\sigma_{\bar{x}} \leq \mu \leq \bar{x} + 1.960\sigma_{\bar{x}}\} = 0.95 \qquad (8.15.2b)$$

We have urged you to remember that all mathematical equations can be exactly translated into English. In the case of equation 8.15.2c, the proper translation is, "The probability that the interval from a sample mean reduced by 1.960 times its standard deviation to the mean increased by the same amount includes the true mean of the parent population is 0.95." You will often hear it *improperly* translated as, "The probability that the true mean is between, etc." This is improper because the mean is a fixed but unknown (to us) quantity. The element that is varying is $\bar{x}$, in consequence of which our interval varies, and our statement applies to the probability that our interval will include, or "trap," μ within its limits.

If we now complete the numerical work for our specific problem, we find that

$$\Pr\{5.02 \leq \mu \leq 6.98\} = 0.95 \tag{8.15.2c}$$

and you will notice that the ends of the interval are exactly the same as the values beyond which we would reject hypotheses concerning the value of μ with an alpha risk of 0.05. We have arrived at the same result by two different paths. The first time, we found out where we could say that μ *wasn't* with a probability of 0.05 of being wrong. The second time, we found out how we could say where μ *was* with a probability of 0.95 of being correct, and our two limits agreed.

Such an interval about a point estimate of a parameter which may be claimed to include the parameter with a known probability is known as a *confidence interval* estimate of the parameter, or confidence interval, for short. It is (deplorably, we think!) the custom to state the probabilities involved as percentages, so what we have computed are 95% confidence intervals. It is also traditional to place the interval so that failures to include the parameter will occur with equal probability at both ends of the interval. In general, this makes a shorter interval than any other for equal probability and, because we don't know where the parameter is, probably is as sensible as any plan in most cases.

Suppose we generalize our plan. If we want P% confidence limits for the population mean, and the population variance is known, we compute a related alpha risk as $\alpha = (100 - P)/100$, which expresses our "unconfidence" as a fraction. Our limits then become

$$\mu = \bar{x} \pm |\, z_{\alpha/2} \,|\, \sigma_{\bar{x}} \tag{8.15.4}$$

If we had wanted 99% confidence limits, our related alpha risk would have been 0.01, half it would have been 0.005, and the absolute value of the corresponding z would have been 2.576, leading to

$$\mu = 6.00 \pm 2.576 \times 0.40 = 6.00 \pm 1.0304$$

$$= 4.9696 \text{ and } 7.0304 \tag{8.15.5}$$

This will at first astonish you, we fear. We asked for a higher confidence and our limits are farther apart. Think of it this way, though, and you will see they must be. You don't *know* the value of μ. If you are required to be more positive about your assertion that your interval includes μ, you just must use a longer interval.

It is very much like fishing. If you are mildly interested in catching a fish for dinner, you might put out a short weir into the river by your camp. If you really would enjoy a fish, you put out a longer weir, and if you want to be as sure as possible, you put out the longest weir the law allows! Just so with our confidence limits: the surer we must be, the wider must be the range of our limits.

8.16 Applying the Methods

A. *A Problem in Test Development.* An organization is engaged in the preparation of a variety of tests of several types of ability as a service to manufacturing firms. It wishes that each new test be designed so that the mean score of people of the type for whom it is planned shall be 500. How shall it decide, on the basis of a trial on 50 people, whether one of these tests meets that requirement?

The requirement can be interpreted as meaning that the population mean, $\mu = 500$. Since that is a two-sided hypothesis, we must use it as our null hypothesis. We then assume that, as a result of their selection procedure, the 50 people used in the trial were a random sample from the type of people for whom the test is planned. We further assume that scores on this type of test will be normally distributed, and that the variance will be 10,000. Because it is a nuisance to its customers to have μ different from 500, and because it is relatively inexpensive to make adjustments after the trial, it is decided to choose the relatively large alpha risk of 0.10. The assumptions permit the use of

$$z = (\bar{x} - \mu_{\bar{x}})/\sigma_{\bar{x}} = (\bar{x} - 500)/\sqrt{10{,}000/50}$$
$$= (\bar{x} - 500)/14.14$$

as our test statistic. The alpha risk of 0.10 sets the critical values at $\pm \mid z_{0.05} \mid = \pm 1.645$. The test is now administered to the trial group, and $\bar{x}$ is found to be 525.2, which corresponds to $z = (525.2 - 500.0)/14.14 = 25.2/14.14 = 1.782$. Because this value is in the upper critical, the hypothesis must be rejected and the test must be considered to give too high a score.

It might also be of interest to determine the 90% confidence limits from these data for the population mean. $P = 90\%$ has an equivalent alpha risk of $(100 - 90)/100 = 0.10$, so that we use the same values of z which were employed as critical values in testing the hypothesis and can assert that the limits required are $\bar{x} \pm z_{0.05}\, \sigma_{\bar{x}} = 525.2 \pm 1.645 \times 14.14 = 501.9$ and 548.5. We are 90% sure that they will include the true population mean of the test. We might note that it is often prudent to compute confidence limits, even when our primary interest is in testing an hypothesis. It is a common reaction, when we have rejected an hypothesis for observed values just over a critical boundary, to be asked whether we shouldn't "stretch a point" *this* time (it's always only *this* time!) and let the hypothesis pass. The confidence limit brings home to us the idea that, although the value of μ might be 501.9, which, we admit, is close to 500, it might also be 548.5, which we won't admit is close to 500 for this purpose.

B. *A Problem in Sales Administration.* A sales manager believes that each of his salesmen ought to show mean weekly sales of at least $25,000 in order to keep the company's competitive position sound and to insure satisfying commissions to the men. If sales are not up to that level, it may be because of any or all of the following reasons:

1. The company has sold some inferior product in that salesman's territory, and has suffered a consequent loss of business.
2. Another firm has introduced a highly competitive product or instituted an unusually active and effective sales campaign.
3. A change in the activities of some former customers has reduced the potential volume of sales in the territory and a reassignment of territories should be made.
4. The salesman's performance has not been up to standard.

The manager plans to review the records of each salesman every eight weeks and, when it is appropriate, to call the salesman whose performance is below standard in for a review of the situation. While this plan should keep the manager well informed as to what is happening, it has certain disadvantages:

1. If a man is called in for such a review, he will lose time from his customer calls. This may lower his sales, to the harm of both the company and the man. In any event, the company would properly pay him for the time involved.
2. The manager's time in planning and conducting the review might well be devoted to more effective outlets.
3. There is an unavoidable adverse morale effect upon the salesman attendant upon such reviews.

As a result of these considerations, it is decided that, from a morale standpoint, particularly, it will be desirable to take as the null hypothesis $H_0 : \mu \geq$ $25,000 per week. This makes it possible to explain that you are only calling for reviews when there is real evidence that "things have slumped." Furthermore, in order to avoid the appearance of "riding" the men, it is decided to call the men in for review only if the null hypothesis must be rejected with an alpha risk of 0.02.

In order to be able to test the hypothesis, we must assume that each week's figure is a random sample of each man's performance. This requires a little thought, but if the sales are not subject to regular fluctuation from time to time during the year (or if, as we may learn to do later, they have been adjusted for such effects) and we know of no unusual factors operating, it is reasonable to assume this random character. We also assume, on the basis of our experience, that weekly sales are normally distributed with a standard deviation of $3,500.

This permits us to set up our test statistic as

$$z = \frac{\bar{x} - \mu_{\bar{x}}}{\sigma_{\bar{x}}} = \frac{\bar{x} - 25{,}000}{3{,}500/\sqrt{8}} = \frac{\bar{x} - 25{,}000}{1{,}237.4}$$

and the critical region as $z \leq z_{0.02}$, i.e., $z \leq -2.054$. In the present instance, we might as well translate this into its equivalent $\bar{x} = \mu_{\bar{x}} + z\sigma_{\bar{x}} = 25{,}000 - 2.054 \times 1237.4 = \$22{,}458$. This tells our manager to call in for review any salesman whose eight-week mean weekly sales fell at or below that figure.

Two comments should be made with respect to this sort of plan. First, as we pointed out in the discussion of one-tailed tests earlier, we could have accomplished exactly equivalent results by testing the hypothesis that $\mu \leq \$25{,}000$, rejecting it for values above $\bar{x} = \$22{,}458$, which corresponds to an alpha risk of 0.98. In translating a description of the two viewpoints into nontechnical language for the salesman, our first plan might be explained as indicating that we consider that sales are going well until we have strong evidence to the contrary, while the second plan must look as though we assume things are bad, even though we are, in fact, quite ready to depart from that idea. We simply discuss what we are doing honestly in terms calculated to be constructive.

Our second comment concerns a constructive use of the judgment factor involved in the choice of an alpha risk here. The manager might well plan to use two alpha risks for two different purposes on the same data. He might plan to send the salesman a simple note or give him a phone call when he had to reject $H_0 : \mu \geq \$25{,}000$ with an alpha risk as high as 0.05 or even higher, but only request the personal review at the risk we have proposed.

Again, the confidence limit idea is often helpful. Suppose Joe Doake shows up with an eight-week mean of $22,000. We might consider 96% confidence limits for his true production level: $22{,}000 \pm 2.054 \times 1{,}237.4 = \$19{,}458$ and $24,542 — which, as we should expect, indicate that his real sales volume could be very low.

C. *A Problem Involving a Guarantee.* It is most important that the weight of packages sold be not below that represented on them. As part of a program for insuring that it will not be subject to claims for short weight, a firm plans to set its automatic weighing machines for one-pound packages with due regard to statistical principles. It proposes to consider that the machines are delivering short weight unless a random sample of 25 packages at any time permits the rejection of the hypothesis, $H_0 : \mu \leq 1.000$ with an alpha risk of 0.005.

In order to have a decision procedure, they must assume a normal distribution of package weights from the machine, which past experience justifies. That experience also indicates a standard deviation of such weight of 0.0075 pounds. Thus we have as our test statistic

$$z = \frac{\bar{x} - \mu_{\bar{x}}}{\sigma_{\bar{x}}} = \frac{\bar{x} - 1.000}{0.0075/\sqrt{25}} = \frac{\bar{x} - 1.000}{0.0015}$$

and the critical region as $z \geq z_{0.995}$ or $z \geq +2.576$. Again, this is conveniently translated to $\bar{x} \geq 1.0039$, or about 0.06 oz. more than one pound.

8.17 In Review

In this chapter we have established fundamental principles with respect to methods for testing hypotheses and assigning confidence limits which will be used throughout the balance of our work. Our assumptions in different situations will lead to different test statistics, but the basic ideas will remain the same. We have also tried to make it clear that statistics does not operate in a vacuum on "pure" numbers: the numbers embody ideas, and often the welfare of people. Our judgment is involved, but it is channeled toward the choice of alpha risks and percentage confidence. As we showed you in one of our problems, because our results and methods of reaching them often have to be interpreted to people unacquainted with statistics, we should recognize that there are sometimes two different ways of describing precisely what we have done, and use the way more likely to elicit acceptance of our principles and results.

General Study

1. Consider various kinds of data with which you are or may become concerned. List several types in which you can reasonably assume known population variances and, for future use, several in which this assumption would be unreasonable.

2. Consider areas in the subject of your major field that are the subjects of active research. List the factors in each field which would govern your choice of alpha risks for some typical hypotheses.

3. Examine some advertising claims allegedly supported by the results of experiments. Are enough data given to permit the reader to verify the claim? In cases where data are given, can you estimate what alpha risks would be used in testing the appropriate hypothesis in order to "justify" the claim? Do you consider these risks to be reasonable?

Specific Problems

1–6. Use the data given below, in each case, to test the stated hypothesis with the given alpha risk if the variance may be considered to have the stated value.

Problem	*Data*	H_0	α	σ^2
1	2, 6, 7, 4, 5	$\mu = 6.0$	0.050	2.00
2	5, 4, 6, 8	$\mu \leq 4.0$	0.010	1.60
3	7, 5, 4, 2, 6, 8, 6	$\mu \geq 8.0$	0.100	3.43
4	4, 5, 5	$\mu = 3.0$	0.001	1.92
5	12, 15, 16, 20	$\mu \leq 14.0$	0.050	5.76
6	15, 20	$\mu \geq 20.0$	0.100	8.00

7–12. Use the information in Problems 1–6 to provide confidence limits for the mean. In each case, use a level of confidence such that the alpha risks in Problems 1–6 become the related alpha risks for the new problems, and state the confidence level.

13. A certain qualifying test for candidates for college entrance is so scored that the standard deviation of scores is 300. A school boasts that the mean grade of its graduates is above 600. Select an appropriate alpha risk and determine whether a sample mean, $\bar{x} - 620$, for $N = 25$ of their graduates justifies the statement. Calculate 90%, 95%, and 99% confidence limits for this school's mean.

14. A firm buys a raw material in tank-car lots. The material is in the form of a solution specified to contain 25% of the active material. If the variance of determinations of the material is known to be 0.50%, and the mean of five determinations is 24.7%, should the lot be accepted or rejected if an alpha risk of 0.01 is to be used in testing the appropriate hypothesis? Would it be better to write a one-sided specification for this material? In what form?

9

What Can a Sample Tell Us About the Variance of a Population?

9.1 Background

In discussing the use of a sample to gain information about the mean of a population, we treated the specific case in which we could assume that the population variance was known. We also suggested that a modification of the procedure would be needed when we could not make that assumption. Of course, if we don't know the variance, we must expect to have to estimate it from our sample, and our present purpose is to determine how to do so.

Although we seem more often to think of the means of populations than of their variances, it is, in fact, often quite as necessary to know about how a population varies. For example, Honolulu, Hawaii, and Brownsville, Texas, have nearly the same mean temperatures, but the variation in Brownsville is far greater than that in Honolulu, which affects many aspects of living. Two gas stations may sell the same average amount of gasoline per day, but if the business of one is quite consistent, while that of the other is highly variable, there may well be a resultant difference in operating costs and net profits for the two stations.

9.2 The Estimating Statistic

In approaching the problem of estimating a population mean from a sample, we let "common sense" guide us, in that we made the same computations on the sample that we would have made for a complete population, and it worked out very well. If we try that here, however, we find that, since the variance is the mean of the squared differences between the observations and the population mean, we are stopped before we start: we don't know the population mean! But you have learned something about statistics, and you might quite reasonably suggest that, although we don't know the population mean, we can calculate the sample mean. Because the sample mean is unbiased, efficient, consistent, and sufficient, you very reasonably suggest that we might use it in the formula in place of the population mean. This is even better than "common sense," for it showed real reasoning.

Let us try the idea, calling our result, temporarily, w^2 and calculating it according to the formula,

$$w^2 = \frac{\Sigma(x - \bar{x})^2}{N} = \frac{\Sigma x^2 - \bar{x}\Sigma x}{N} = \frac{N\Sigma x^2 - (\Sigma x)^2}{N^2}$$

using the particular modification proper for our N. We can make a very small actual population, such as

$$3, 4, 5 \tag{S9.2.1}$$

act like an infinite population if, each time we draw a value, we record it then return the value to the population. We could physically obtain a close equivalent to random samples by putting these numbers on identical cards, spheres, cubes, or other objects, placing them in a hat, box, or other container, shuffling them well, and, without looking at the objects, drawing one. After recording its number, we could return it to the group and repeat the process. If we wanted samples of $N = 3$, we could draw a line after each third value, and we would have the desired result.

But, because we have become acquainted with some ideas of permutations, combinations, and probability, we can figure out what would happen if we kept up such a process indefinitely without doing it at all! Since there are always the three values present each time we draw, there are three equally likely possibilities on each draw. If we were interested in samples of $N = 3$, there would be 3^3 such samples, or 27, possible, and they, too, would be equally likely. It is no great problem to list them, as we have done in Table 9-1, where we have also calculated $\bar{x}$ and w^2 for each sample. Now the relative frequency of values of $\bar{x}$ and w^2 in this table would correspond to the relative frequency of these values in an indefinitely large number of drawings of samples of $N = 3$ from an infinite population comprising equal numbers of 3's, 4's, and 5's and no other values.

The results of our sampling experiment are condensed into frequency tables at the bottom of Table 9-1, and the statistics of the distribution of $\bar{x}$ and w^2 have been calculated. The pertinent histograms are shown in Fig. 9-1. The results are worth your consideration. Notice that $\mu_{\bar{x}} = 4.00 = \mu$ and that $\sigma_{\bar{x}}^2 = 0.\dot{2} = \sigma^2/N$. This is what would have happened if our population had been normal, and, in fact, it will happen regardless of the form of our distribution. But what about w^2, our "common sense" estimate of variance? It didn't work out so well, for its mean value, μ_{w^2} turns out to be $0.\dot{4}$, which is pretty discouraging. Not only did "common sense" suggest the idea, but we recognized its reasonableness in view of what little statistics we already know.

Table 9-1 SAMPLING EXPERIMENT ON POPULATION COMPRISING EQUAL NUMBERS OF THREES, FOURS, AND FIVES AND NO OTHER VALUES; $N = 3$

Part A. Samples and Initial Computations

No.	x_1	x_2	x_3	Σx	x^2	$\bar{x}$*	$\Sigma(x - \bar{x})^2$	w^{2}*	s^{2}*
1	3	3	3	9	27	3.0	0	0.0	0.0
2	3	3	4	10	34	3.3	2	0.2	0.3
3	3	3	5	11	43	3.6	8	0.8	1.3
4	3	4	3	10	34	3.3	2	0.2	0.3
5	3	4	4	11	41	3.6	2	0.2	0.3
6	3	4	5	12	50	4.0	6	0.6	1.0
7	3	5	3	11	43	3.6	8	0.8	1.3
8	3	5	4	12	50	4.0	6	0.6	1.0
9	3	5	5	13	59	4.3	8	0.8	1.3
10	4	3	3	10	34	3.3	2	0.2	0.3
11	4	3	4	11	41	3.6	2	0.2	0.3
12	4	3	5	12	50	4.0	6	0.6	1.0
13	4	4	3	11	41	3.6	2	0.2	0.3
14	4	4	4	12	48	4.0	0	0.0	0.0
15	4	4	5	13	57	4.3	2	0.2	0.3
16	4	5	3	12	50	4.0	6	0.6	1.0
17	4	5	4	13	57	4.3	2	0.2	0.3
18	4	5	5	14	66	4.6	2	0.2	0.3
19	5	3	3	11	43	3.6	8	0.8	1.3
20	5	3	4	12	50	4.0	6	0.6	1.0
21	5	3	5	13	59	4.3	8	0.8	1.3
22	5	4	3	12	50	4.0	6	0.6	1.0
23	5	4	4	13	57	4.3	2	0.2	0.3
24	5	4	5	14	66	4.6	2	0.2	0.3
25	5	5	3	13	59	4.3	8	0.8	1.3
26	5	5	4	14	66	4.6	2	0.2	0.3
27	5	5	5	15	75	5.0	0	0.0	0.0

Part B. Frequency Tables for Sample Statistics from Above

Mean, $\bar{x}$		Trial Statistic, w^2		Sample Variance, s^2	
$\bar{x}^{2}$*	f	w^{2}*	f	s^{2}*	f
3.6	1	0.0	3	0.0	3
3.3	3	0.2	12	0.3	12
3.6	6	0.6	6	1.0	6
4.0	7	0.8	6	1.3	6
4.3	6				
4.6	3				
5.0	1				

*Note: All decimals in these columns should have the given digit repeated indefinitely.

Part C. Parameters of Sampling Distributions

$\mu_{\bar{x}} = 4.00$ $\mu_{w^2} = 0.\dot{4}$ $\mu_{s^2} = 0.\dot{6}$ $\sigma_{\bar{x}}^2 = 0.\dot{2}$

Fig. 9-1. Histograms of Frequency Distributions of Sample Statistics.
Based on Table 9-1c. Samples of $N = 3$ from population comprising equal numbers of 3's, 4's, 5's and no other values.

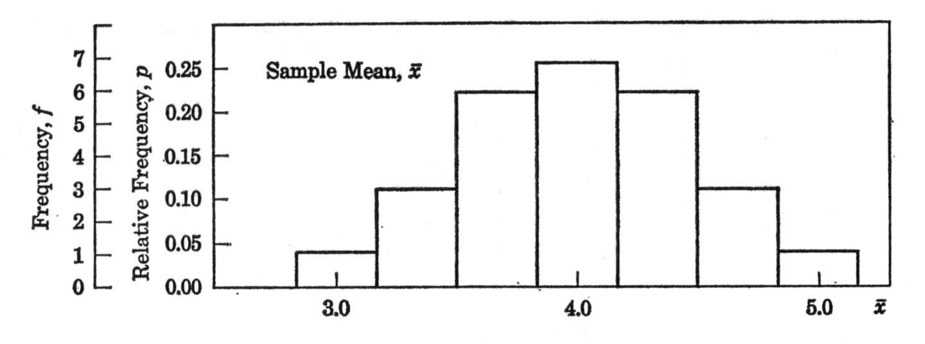

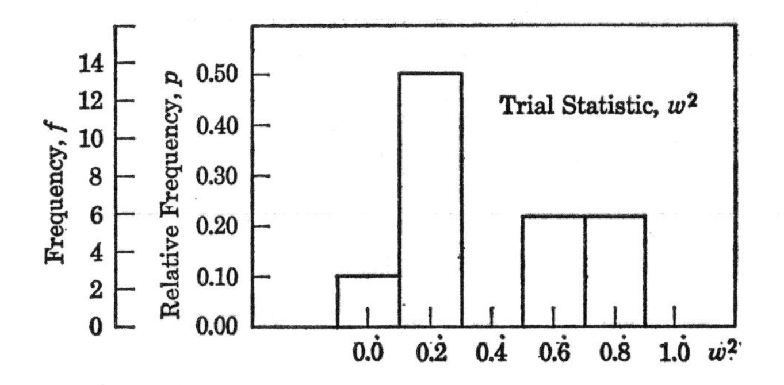

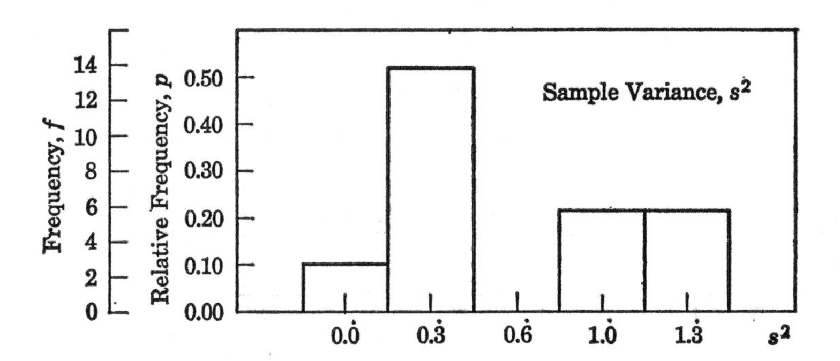

Before we give up, let's just try the idea on samples of $N = 2$ from this population. There are only $3^2 = 9$ such samples, and they are shown in Table 9-2, together with computations like those in Table 9-1. The pertinent histograms are shown in Fig. 9-2. Our sample means, $\bar{x}$, again behave as we would expect, with $\mu_{\bar{x}} = 4.00 = \mu$ and $\sigma_{\bar{x}}^2 = 0.\dot{3} = \sigma^2/N$. But again, w^2 mis-

Table 9-2 SAMPLING EXPERIMENT ON POPULATION COMPRISING EQUAL NUMBERS OF THREES, FOURS, AND FIVES AND NO OTHER VALUES; $N = 2$

Part A. Samples and Initial Computations

No.	x_1	x_2	x	x^2	$\bar{x}$	$(x - \bar{x})^2$	w^2	s^2
1	3	3	6	18	3.0	0.0	0.0	0.0
2	3	4	7	25	3.5	0.5	0.25	0.5
3	3	5	8	34	4.0	2.0	1.00	2.0
4	4	3	7	25	3.5	0.5	0.25	0.5
5	4	4	8	32	4.0	0.0	0.00	0.0
6	4	5	9	41	4.5	0.5	0.25	0.5
7	5	3	8	34	4.0	2.0	1.00	1.0
8	5	4	9	41	4.5	0.5	0.25	0.5
9	5	5	10	50	5.0	0.0	0.00	0.0

Part B. Frequency Tables from Sample Statistics from Above

Mean, $\bar{x}$		Trial Statistic, w^2		Sample Variance, s^2	
$\bar{x}$	f	w^2	f	s^2	f
3.0	1	0.00	3	0.00	3
3.5	2	0.25	4	0.50	4
4.0	3	1.00	2	2.00	2
4.5	2				
5.0	1				

Part C. Parameters of Sampling Distributions

$\mu_{\bar{x}} = 4.0$ $\mu_{w^2} = 0.\dot{3}$ $\mu_{s^2} = 0.\dot{6}$ $\sigma_{\bar{x}}^2 = 0.\dot{3}$

behaves: $\mu_{w^2} = 0.\dot{3}$, not $0.\dot{6}$, which is discouraging. But notice that, for the two values we tried, the mean becomes closer to the true value as N increases. This is just the sort of behavior that spurs a mathematician on, and presently, after more trying such as we have done, the key comes to him. In each case, $\mu_{w^2} = \frac{N-1}{N}\sigma^2$, without fail. So, if we multiply μ_{w^2} by $\frac{N}{N-1}$ we shall have σ^2. But what is even more important, if we multiply each w^2 by the same factor, we shall have a new statistic, which will be an unbiased estimate of σ^2:

$$\frac{N}{N-1}w^2 = \frac{N}{N-1}\cdot\frac{\Sigma(x-\bar{x})^2}{N} = \frac{\Sigma(x-\bar{x})^2}{N-1}$$

This is so important that competent mathematicians have investigated the matter further by more refined methods and found that this statistic is, indeed, unbiased and that, in sampling from normal distributions, it is efficient, consistent, and sufficient: it is our best statistic for estimating variance.

You may have noticed that we have not numbered the formulas involving w^2. This was deliberate, because it is not a statistic we shall use. The unbiased

Fig. 9-2. Histograms of Frequency Distributions of Sample Statistics.

Based on Table 9-2, Part B. Samples of $N = 2$ from population comprising equal numbers of 3's, 4's, 5's and no other values.

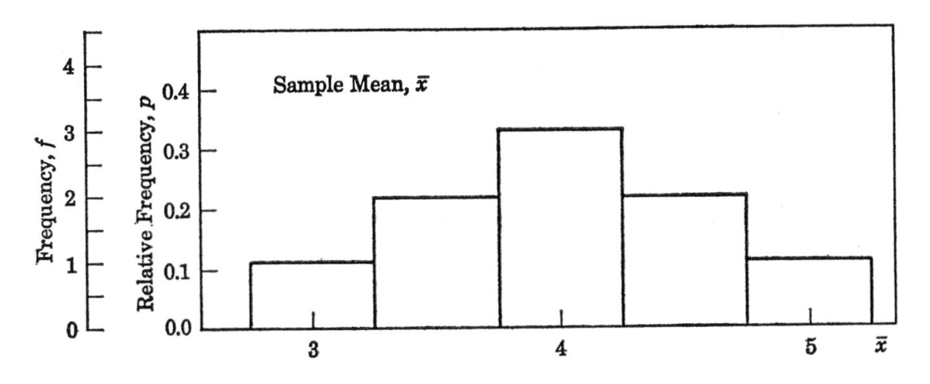

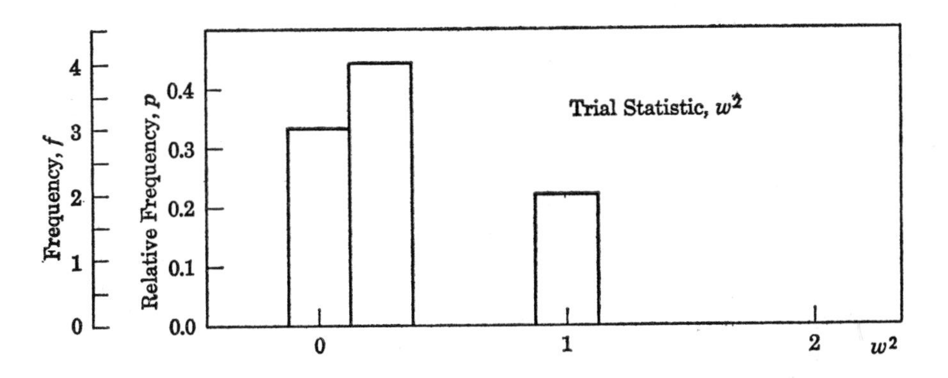

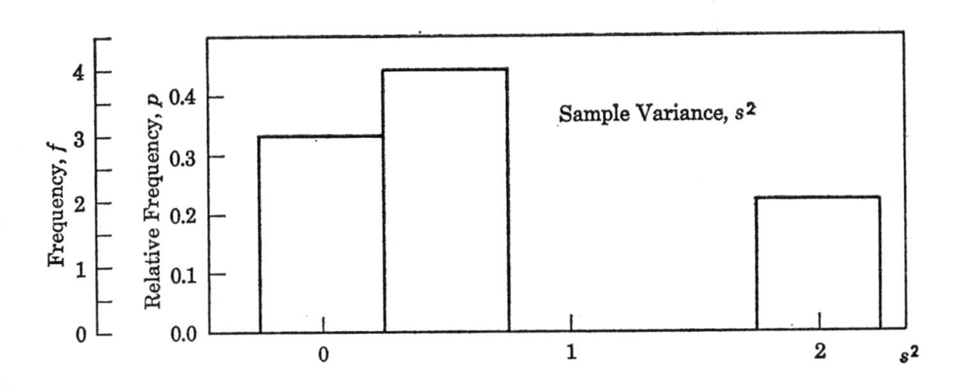

statistic derived from it is our *sample variance*, which we shall denote by s^2 in accordance with convention, is given by the following formulas:

$$s^2 = \frac{\Sigma(x - \bar{x})^2}{(N - 1)} \tag{9.2.1a}$$

$$= \frac{\Sigma x^2 - \bar{x}\Sigma x}{N - 1} \tag{9.2.1b}$$

$$= \frac{N\Sigma x^2 - (\Sigma x)^2}{N(N - 1)} \tag{9.2.1c}$$

where equation 9.2.1a is the embodiment of the basic idea and is useful for small samples with no calculator available. Equation 9.2.1b is useful when the reciprocal of N is wieldy and equation 9.2.1c is better when the reciprocal is unwieldy and we are using a calculator.

9.3 Degrees of Freedom

The quantity, $N - 1$, in the denominators of the formulas for s^2, is a number of a kind which will appear very often. They are called numbers of *degrees of* freedom. In this, our first case, replacement of the number of observations by the number of degrees of freedom in our naive, or "common sense," formulas for variance produced sound formulas. Other important uses for degrees of freedom will emerge as we continue.

The name is somewhat interesting. In our present instance, notice that, before we could compute s^2 from our sample, we had to compute $\bar{x}$. A little arithmetic will show you that, if we have N values, we may allow all but one of them to be freely assigned, provided we may control the last one, and we can control $\bar{x}$. For example, if $N = 3$ and we wish $\bar{x}$ to be 5.0, all that is required is that $\Sigma x = 15.0$. If we are given the first two values as 7 and 4, the third must be 4, whereas if the first two are -1, and -3, the third must be $+19$. A general procedure for determining the number of degrees of freedom associated with any statistic is to subtract the number of statistics that must be calculated from the sample, before the one in question can be calculated, from the total number of observations. We shall find it very convenient to use the symbol N to represent our number of observations and n to represent the number of degrees of freedom in our future work. In this problem of estimating the variance from a sample, $n = N - 1$.

9.4 The Distribution of the Sample Variance, s^2

We have seen, in our two little examples, some aspects of the behavior of s^2 in repeated samples. By its very nature, involving a sum of squares, s^2 cannot be less than zero, so obviously it cannot have a normal distribution. However, it can be shown, again by mathematics beyond the scope of our book, that the ratio of ns^2 to σ^2, for random samples of size N from a normal distribution follows a pattern known, from its symbol, as the *chi-square distribution* (or χ^2 distribution), a fact that we represent by the statement that

$$\chi^2 = ns^2/\sigma^2 \tag{9.4.1a}$$

$$= \Sigma(x - \bar{x})^2/\sigma^2 \tag{9.4.1b}$$

The equation describing the χ^2 distribution, in the form required to fit an histogram plotted in relative frequencies, is

$$y = \frac{1}{2^{n/2}\Gamma(n/2)}(x^2)^{n/2-1}e^{-(x^2/2)} \tag{9.4.2}$$

which makes the normal distribution equation look simple(!). The expression $\Gamma(n/2)$, read as "gamma function of $n/2$," refers to a quantity whose value depends on n and which is $(n/2 - 1)!$ if $n/2$ is an integer and is, in effect, read from a smooth curve passing through those points otherwise. Since we do not need to plot the curves of χ^2, we need have little concern with the equation. However, for your interest, a few have been plotted in Fig. 9-3. These curves always have their maximum height at $\chi^2 = n - 2$, and the mean value of the distribution is, in each case, $\mu_{\chi^2} = n$.

Fig. 9-3. Plots of the χ^2 distribution curve for the first five even numbers of degrees of freedom.

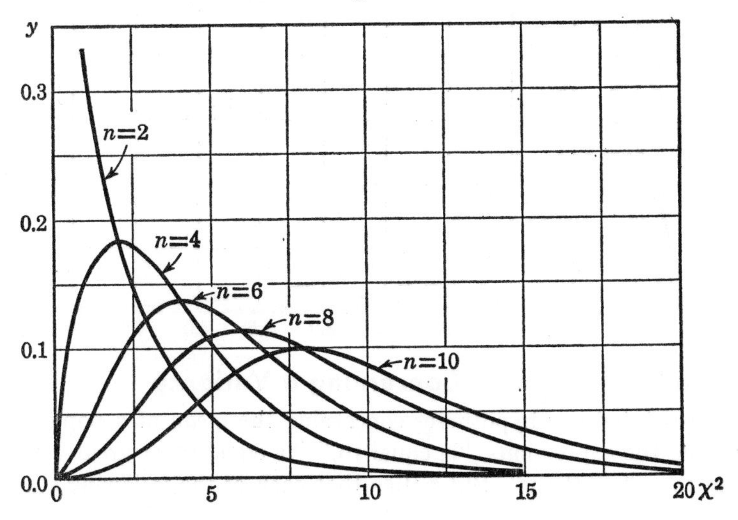

But now look at equations 9.4.1a and 9.4.1b a little more closely. Does it not seem strange, since we are interested in the relation of our estimate, s^2, to the true value, σ^2, of our population variance, we should deal with a distribution of the ratio of ns^2 or $\Sigma(x - \bar{x})^2$ to σ^2? It should seem strange, and it is, but it is an interesting example of history and human nature! Historically, the χ^2 distribution was developed for quite a different purpose, for which it was quite reasonable. So the necessary tables came to be published and available. Until very recently, people have been quite accustomed to using the formulas we have given and the available tables. But suppose we divide both sides of equation 9.4.1a by the number of degrees of freedom, n, to obtain

$$\frac{\chi^2}{n} = \frac{ns^2}{n\sigma^2} = \frac{s^2}{\sigma^2} \tag{9.4.3}$$

Now we have an expression which directly reflects the ratio of our estimate to the true value. It is no problem to express our distribution equation and the areas under it, which are our prime concern, in terms of χ^2/n. The mean of χ^2/n is, in every case, 1.00, and the maximum of its curve will also be at $\chi^2/n = (n - 2)/n = 1 - n/2$. The curves in Fig. 9-4 are for the distributions of χ^2/n equivalent to those for χ^2 plotted in Fig. 9-3, and they tell the same story in slightly different mathematical "words."

Fig. 9-4. Plots of the χ^2/n distribution curves for the first five even numbers of degrees of freedom.

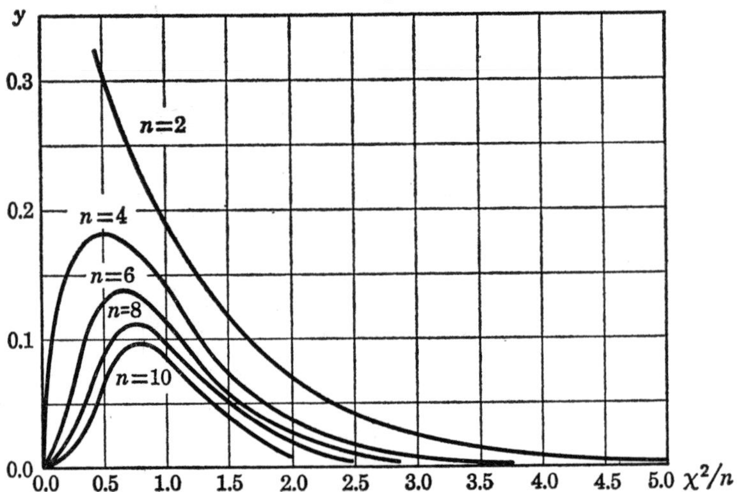

9.5 Testing Hypotheses Concerning a Variance

When we stated our hypotheses concerning the mean of a population, we always used the expressions, "is equal to," "is equal to or greater than," or "is equal to or less than." But notice that each of the following statements says the same thing:

$$A = B \tag{9.5.1a}$$

$$A - B = 0 \tag{9.5.1b}$$

$$B - A = 0 \tag{9.5.1c}$$

$$A/B = 1 \quad (\text{if } B \neq 0) \tag{9.5.1d}$$

$$B/A = 1 \quad (\text{if } A \neq 0) \tag{9.5.1e}$$

They simply say it in different ways. Because, as you expect, our test statistic is going to be χ^2/n, which involves a ratio, we shall express the hypothesis that our population variance has a specific value, say σ_0^2, in the form $H_0 : \sigma^2/\sigma_0^2 = 1$.

In the case of our tests of hypotheses concerning means, it was necessary to make certain assumptions in order to have a distribution available to describe the behavior of our sample statistic. We must do the same thing now, but our assumptions now are but two: (1) that the sample is a random sample and (2) that it came from a population which was normally distributed. Again as in the case of our means, we must choose our alpha risk. On the basis of our assumptions, our test statistic is χ^2/n, and our critical values are those below which and above which a proportion corresponding to half our alpha risk occur, that is, $(\chi^2/n)_{\alpha/2,n}$ and $(\chi^2/n)_{(1-\alpha/2),n}$, where the n reminds us that the values depend on n. We then obtain our data, calculate our value of s^2 and from it χ^2/n, compare with the critical values, and make our decision.

Suppose we wish to test the idea that the variance of a population is 2.00 on the basis of a sample that will consist of $N = 4$ values. Our number of degrees of freedom is $n = N - 1 = 4 - 1 = 3$. Table 9-3 shows the steps

Table 9-3 PROCEDURE FOR TESTING THE HYPOTHESIS THAT THE VARIANCE OF A POPULATION HAS A STATED VALUE

Process	*General*	*Specific Example*
1. State the hypothesis	$H_0 : \sigma^2/\sigma_0^2 = 1.00$	$H_0 : \sigma^2/2.00 = 1.00$
2. Choose the alpha risk	$\alpha = \alpha_0$	$\alpha = 0.050$
3. State the assumptions	(a) Sample is random (b) Distribution is normal	(a) Sample is random (b) Distribution is normal
4. Formulate test statistic	$(\chi^2/n) = s^2/\sigma_0^2$	$(\chi^2/n) = s^2/2.00$
5. Formulate and determine critical values	$(\chi^2/n)_{\alpha/2,n}$ $(\chi^2/n)_{(1-\alpha/2),n}$	$(\chi^2/n)_{0.025,3} = 0.0719$ $(\chi^2/n)_{0.975,3} = 3.12$
6. Describe critical regions	$(\chi^2/n) \leq (\chi^2/n)_{\alpha/2,n}$ $(\chi^2/n) \geq (\chi^2/n)_{(1-\alpha/2),n}$	$(\chi^2/n)\ \ 0.0719$ $(\chi^2/n)\ \ 3.12$
7. Obtain data and calculate observed value of test statistic	—	$(\chi^2/n) = 0.91\dot{6}/2.00$ $= 0.458\dot{3}$
8. Make and state decision	Reject H_0 if and only if observed value is in critical region	$0.458\dot{3}$ is not in critical region, so H_0 is not rejected, and we consider that $\sigma^2 = 2.00$

in our procedure, both in general terms and for our specific example. As in the case of the tests on hypotheses concerning means, the first six steps should be taken before the data are obtained. Now suppose that our data are

$$7, 9, 7, 8 \tag{S9.5.1}$$

We calculate

$$s^2 = \frac{\Sigma x^2 - \bar{x}\Sigma x}{n} = \frac{243 - 7.75 \times 31}{3} = \frac{243 - 240.25}{3} = \frac{2.75}{3} = 0.91\dot{6}$$

and

$$\chi^2/n = \frac{s^2}{\sigma_0^2} = \frac{0.91\dot{6}}{2.00} = 0.458\dot{3}$$

Because our observed value is not in the critical region but between its two parts, we do not reject our null hypothesis, and we do act as though $\sigma^2 = 2.00$.

The modifications to be made for testing one-sided hypotheses by one-tailed tests are quite natural. For $H_0 : \sigma^2/\sigma_0^2 \geq 1$, the critical region is $\chi^2/n \leq (\chi^2/n)_\alpha$ whereas for $H_0 : \sigma^2/\sigma_0^2 \leq 1$, the critical region is $\chi^2/n \geq (\chi^2/n)_{(1-\alpha)}$. We shall encounter these formulas in connection with the real problems later in the chapter.

9.6 Confidence Limits for the Variance

Our approach to confidence limits is again quite similar to that we used with the mean. If we require $P\%$ confidence limits, we calculate the related alpha risk as $\alpha = (100 - P)/100$. Using, as we did for means, the relation between relative frequencies and probabilities, we can say that

$$\Pr\{(\chi^2/n)_{\alpha/2} \leq s^2/\sigma^2 \leq (\chi^2/n)_{(1-\alpha/2)}\} = P \tag{9.6.1a}$$

We can operate on the expression inside the braces by taking the reciprocal of each part, which will have the effect of reversing the direction of the signs of inequality:

$$\frac{1}{(\chi^2/n)_{\alpha/2}} \geq \frac{\sigma^2}{s^2} \geq \frac{1}{(\chi^2/n)_{(1-\alpha/2)}} \tag{9.6.1b}$$

and then we can multiply by s^2 to obtain

$$\frac{s^2}{(\chi^2/n)_{\alpha/2}} \geq \sigma^2 \geq \frac{s^2}{(\chi^2/n)_{(1-\alpha/2)}} \tag{9.6.1c}$$

which is exactly equivalent to our original statement inside the braces. We can put it there, reversing our order of writing so as to proceed from small to large values:

$$\Pr\{s^2/(\chi^2/n)_{(1-\alpha/2)} \leq \sigma^2 = s^2/(\chi^2/n)_{\alpha/2}\} = P \tag{9.6.1d}$$

The first and last terms inside the brace give our required limits.

Suppose we required the 95% confidence limits for the variance from the data of the simple example we used in section 9.5. Our related alpha risk is 0.05 and the required values of χ^2/n for $n = 3$ degrees of freedom are 0.0719 and 3.12. Division of $s^2 = 0.91\dot{6}$ by these two values yields 12.75^- and 0.294 as our limits. Clearly four values scattering as much as these four do not establish a variance very closely!

9.7 A Comment About Standard Deviations

You will notice that our chapter title and all our discussion have concerned variances. We have indicated that s^2 is an unbiased estimate of σ^2. If you will recall our discussion in section 4.6, where we pointed out that the square root of the mean of the squares of a set of numbers is not equal to the mean of the numbers, you may suspect that, although $\mu_{s^2} = \sigma^2$, μ_s will not equal σ, the standard deviation. You will be quite correct. Table 9-4 shows the distributions of s for our sampling experiment discussed earlier in the chapter, and you will see that s is not an unbiased estimate of σ.

Table 9-4 DISTRIBUTION OF s FOR SAMPLING EXPERIMENTS DETAILED IN TABLES 9-1 AND 9-2

Part A. $N = 3$, as in Table 9-1

s^2	s	f	
$0.\dot{0}$	$0.\dot{0}$	3	
$0.\dot{3}$	0.57735	12	
1.0	1.0	6	$\mu_s \doteq 0.73542$
$1.\dot{3}$	1.15470	6	cf. $\sigma = 0.81649$

Part B. $N = 2$, as in Table 9-2

s^2	s	f	
0.00	0.00000	3	
0.50	0.70710	4	$\mu_s \doteq 0.62853$
2.00	1.41421	2	cf. $\sigma = 0.81649$

This will cause you some concern, later on, when we appear to be using s in some of our computations. It should cause you concern, but the fact is that, although we shall be using s to aid our understanding of our problem at certain stages of our learning, the methods were developed so that they are correct if, where an estimate of the standard deviation appears, the square root of the unbiased estimate of variance is used. It is quite reasonable for you to wonder why we don't develop a method for using an unbiased estimate of the standard deviation if any estimate of the standard deviation is going to appear in our working formulas. The answer is that all of the mathematics involved becomes much more cumbersome, in fact, "messy," and the same result can be obtained much more conveniently by the processes we actually use. At the appropriate time, quite a bit later, we intend to recall this thought to your mind and to show you the underlying principle which will draw these ideas together, but it would be most difficult to do now.

9.8 Applying the Methods

A. *A Problem in Test Development.* In the previous chapter we considered a problem of a firm engaged in the development of tests of various kinds of ability. That problem involved the establishment of the mean value of the scores on a new test in which it was assumed that the variance was known. Now let us suppose that, in another area, the firm is considering a new test which is quite a radical departure from others it has used for the same purpose. It wishes to insure that the new test will also have a variance of 10,000. Suppose that it again has a group of 50 people available as a trial group to take the test. How shall they proceed?

Here again, we must test the two-sided hypothesis, $H_0 : \sigma^2 = 10{,}000$ or $\sigma^2/10{,}000 = 1.00$. In the present instance, however, because we are in the preliminary stage of development, we shall use a smaller sample, specifically, $N = 20$, but shall retain the same alpha risk 0.10. We assume that our 20 takers of the test are a random sample of the population of potential takers, and that the distribution of test results will be normal. Our test statistic is, in consequence,

$$\chi^2/n = \frac{s^2}{\sigma_0{}^2} = \frac{s^2}{10{,}000}$$

and our critical values are $(\chi^2/n)_{0.050,19}$ and $(\chi^2/n)_{0.950,19}$, or 0.532 and 1.59, respectively. If we administer the test and observe a sample variance $s^2 = 5{,}300$, which leads to $(\chi^2/n) = 0.530$, a value in our lower critical region, we must reject our null hypothesis and consider our variance too small. A too-small variance on such tests is considered, by some authorities, to give the test too little power to discriminate various levels of ability. More important, if you are the test-producing firm, you will have accustomed your clients to interpreting tests whose variance is 10,000 and it is desirable not to have to re-educate them.

Our observed variance would have 90% confidence limits obtained by dividing it by our two critical values of χ^2/n, since the related alpha risk is 0.10. The resulting values would be 9,962 and 3,333, as you should confirm (!).

B. *A Problem in Sales Administration.* Our sales manager who established the procedure for calling for performance reviews that we discussed in the previous chapter attended a meeting with the company production managers in which concern was expressed that, although sales were maintaining satisfactory levels and growth, their short-term fluctuations were so great as to cause serious production scheduling problems and increased costs. He thought the problem over and decided to include, in his eight-week analyses of his men's performances, a consideration of their variances.

He had previously considered that a standard deviation of weekly sales of \$3,500, equivalent to a variance of 12,250,000, was typical, but he now plans to review cases of high variance. With the same morale and cost factors in mind as before, he establishes his null hypothesis as $H_0 : \sigma^2/3{,}500^2 = \sigma^2/12{,}250{,}000 \leq 1.000$. Because this aspect of performance seems to him to have to have a certain importance, due to the immediate concern of "top brass," he decides to use a somewhat higher alpha risk, namely 0.050, to be surer of finding any leads that may emerge. Again making the assumption that the records constitute random samples and are from a normal distribution, his test statistic is $\chi^2/n = s^2/12{,}250{,}000$ and his critical value is $(\chi^2/n)_{0.950,7} = 2.01$. This means that he will call for a review of any salesman showing an s^2 greater than or equal to 24,622,500, or a standard deviation greater than $4,962.

What could result from such a program? Of course, it could detect the salesman who is highly energetic one week and coasts the next. It could also detect, and lead to the correction of, territory and route assignments in which a salesman must cover, in some weeks, areas in which his possible sales are, in fact, relatively small. These results are desirable. But unfortunately it is also quite possible that some of our more wily salesmen who are of the rush-and-loaf persuasion could meet our objective by arranging with some of their customers to enter their orders at delayed dates. Thereby they maintain a satisfactory variance without improving the actual quality of their performance. True, so far as levelling plant production schedules has been concerned, no harm is done, but, so far as the total interests of everyone involved, the best good has not been accomplished.

We bring this idea to your attention to remind you that statistics are not used in a vacuum; they often affect people, and we must always keep in mind the people and how they may react.

C. *Another Aspect of the Weighing Problem.* In our previous chapter we treated the problem of establishing the mean weight delivered by an automatic weighing machine, under the assumption that its variance was known. We found there that, under our assumptions, any machine yielding an $\bar{x}$ for a random sample of $N = 25$ packages of at least 1.0039 pounds would be considered satisfactory. We did, however, mention that controlling the mean was only one aspect of the total problem. To see another aspect, let us suppose that we have two machines, each producing packages with μ (not $\bar{x}$) $= 1.0039$ pounds, and that machine A has $\sigma_A = 0.0075$ pounds, while machine B has $\sigma_B = 0.0100$ pounds. What fraction of the packages from each wlli weigh less than 1.000 pound? At 1.000 pound, for machine A,

$$z_A = \frac{x_A - \mu_A}{\sigma_A} = \frac{1.0000 - 1.0039}{0.0075} = -\frac{0.0039}{0.0075} = -0.520$$

which corresponds to a relative frequency of 0.3016 for smaller values. But for machine B,

$$z_B = \frac{x_B - \mu_B}{\sigma_B} = \frac{1.0000 - 1.0039}{0.0100} = -\frac{0.0039}{0.0100} = -0.390$$

which corresponds to a relative frequency of 0.3483 for smaller values, appreciably larger than the corresponding frequency for machine A.

If it is desirable to insure that the variance does not exceed the value 0.00005625 = 0.0075^2, equivalent to the square of the previously assumed standard deviation, we would take $H_0 : \sigma^2/0.00005625 \geq 1{,}000$, the "undesirable" condition. If we assume a random sample of $N = 25$ from a normal distribution, as we did in testing the hypotheses concerning the mean, and choose the same alpha risk, 0.005, our test statistic becomes $\chi^2/n = s^2/\sigma_0^2 = s^2/0.00005625$ and our critical value is $(\chi^2/n)_{0.005,24} = 0.412$. If when the data are in we observe $s^2 = 0.0015625$, leading to $\chi^2/n = 0.278$, we reject our null hypothesis and consider that the machine is operating with satisfactory uniformity.

9.9 Reconsideration

The procedures for testing hypotheses and computing confidence limits for the variance of a population introduced no fundamentally new idea. We found that it was not immediately obvious how to obtain the best statistic to estimate a population variance, and we saw that a bit of experimenting with synthetic populations could lead us toward the final method. With an estimating statistic, s^2, at hand, we again found that an appropriate test statistic, χ^2/n, was available in well-tabulated form for our use, and that the basic procedures were similar to those we had used for means. This is a pattern that we shall often see from now on.

Specific Problems

1–6. Use the data of Problems 1–6 in Chapter 8 to test the hypotheses that the values there stated for the population variances are true. In each case, use the form of hypothesis and alpha risk ($=$, $\leq$, or $\geq$) previously used in connection with the means.

7–12. Compute confidence limits for the variances according to the instruction given for the means in the previous chapter.

13. An instructor expected that a test he gave would have a population variance of grades equal to 100 units. The grades obtained by one section were

58	56	38
79	69	52
52	45	54
61	73	66
71	46	70
74	56	57
88	58	64
62	46	89
60	72	75
89	67	71

At an alpha risk of 0.100, what decision must be made concerning the instructor's hypothesis? What are 90% confidence limits for his variance of test grades?

14. In a discussion of the uniformity of number of characters per line of typewritten material, Jones advanced the statement that the standard deviation of this number would not exceed two characters per line. Smith doubted his claim. The matter was settled by counting the 16 full lines of typescript for the last section of this chapter. The results were as follows:

53	57	50	53
56	55	53	54
54	53	53	57
57	59	56	56

If Jones' hypothesis were tested at an alpha risk of 0.050, what decision would be made? At alpha risks of 0.100? 0.010?

10

Investigating the Mean of a Population Whose Variance Is Not Known

10.1 Some History

In Chapter 8 we learned how to test hypotheses concerning, or provide confidence limits for, the mean of a population whose variance could be assumed known. While the assumption is often quite valid, as we tried to show you by examples, it is by no means always so, and statistics would be a much less valuable tool if we could not work in the face of unknown variances. The story of how the necessity for the assumption was eliminated is one of the brighter portions of the history of statistics. The method used is so valuable that we are firmly convinced that if, five years from now, you can recall nothing from your study of statistics but this story and its meaning, your time with the subject will have been well spent.

The story begins before the turn of the century. The management of a brewery in Dublin, Ireland, which produces a famous malted beverage known as Guinness', became impressed with the possibility that some of the well-trained young men leaving the great British universities might profitably become part of the Guinness organization. One of their early recruits was a young man who had completed studies roughly equivalent to the course work required for a current American Ph.D. in physical chemistry. This involves a fair command of the ideas of both chemistry and mathematics.

The young man proceeded to become interested in the testing of the raw materials used in the process, of the in-process material, and of the finished product, using the chemical and physical tests known at the time or new ones he may have developed. One of the problems which bothered him was the very question of how sure he could be about population means on the basis of information contained in a sample of a few measurements. He was familiar with the basic statistical methods of his day, which included the methods of our Chapter 8, and he used them. But he soon recognized that the assumption of a known variance was far from justified in many of his problems. He felt that ignorance of the variance ought to mean that he would need a greater difference between $\bar{x}$ and μ_0 to justify rejecting a null hypothesis with a given alpha risk, and that his confidence limits, for a given degree of confidence, should be wider.

He took his concerns to one of the faculty at the University of London, which was then, as now, a center for the study of statistics. He was told, in effect, though surely not in such words (!) to relax and use the procedures as though the variance were known. Everyone else did, and the error would surely not be very great. Fortunately for statistics, the young man was not a relaxer. Although his mathematical abilities did not enable him to solve his problem by mathematical reasoning, he did a most intelligent thing, which could serve as a model to us all: he arranged to make up a population whose characteristics he knew and to draw from it, physically, a series of random samples. With this series, he performed the computations which were traditional and showed that the resulting distribution was not the standard normal, or z, distribution, but one which had more values out in the tails and fewer near the center than did the normal distribution, and that the discrepancy increased as the sample size decreased. He worked out, empirically, a quite good description of the distribution he observed, and returned to London with his results.

This time, the faculty member had the wisdom to recognize the value of the young man's work. He helped the young man master the mathematical skills needed to confirm his findings by formal mathematical analysis of the problem. Finally, the professor encouraged him to publish his results for general use. You might well anticipate that this publication would have marked the beginning of a widespread interest in the use of statistics, and it should have, but you would be wrong.

Possibly there are three reasons for the lack of this happy result. First, the paper appeared under the formal title, "The Probable Error of the Mean," in a journal devoted to biological measurements, and was most unlikely to be read by workers in any other field. The actual reference is *Biometrika*, **6**, 1–25 (1908), and the companion articles deal with a rather unusual human deformity and some discussions of problems in genetics. A second reason is that the author is identified simply by the modest pen name, "Student," and no hint of his interest in "practical" problems of industry is given. A third reason is that neither in discussion nor examples in the article is any indication given of the reasons why the author became interested in the subject nor of the important uses he was making of his results.

Whatever the reasons, the method remained little known until some twenty years later, when another statistician, now Sir Ronald A. Fisher, in his book, *Statistical Methods for Research Workers*, showed the power and usefulness of "Student's" ideas, which have subsequently led to their becoming the basis and core of modern statistical thinking. Actually, "Student" was William Sealy Gossett, and he continued his interest in statistics throughout his life. He is honored by the fact that his publications have been considered so important that they have been republished as a collected volume, an honor which, so far as we know, has been accorded but one other British statistician. All his life he remained in the employ of Guinness', and finally, shortly before his untimely death, he was appointed brewmaster, a most difficult achievement.

10.2 In "Student's" Footsteps

In his attack on the problem "Student" took advantage of the fact that criminal identification in Britain in his time made use of the Bertillon system, which employed a series of measurements of bony portions of the body, notes of deformities, scars, etc. It may interest you to know that the Bertillon system rapidly lost favor after the simultaneous arrest in the United States of two different men for the same murder. They had the same names and Bertillon descriptions! Careful study of past records and appraisal of the probabilities involved indicated that this would not be as rare an occurrence as had been supposed, and the more modern methods have emerged, with heavy reliance on carefully made and classified fingerprints.

But, to return to "Student," he secured the records of Bertillon measurements of some 3,000 British criminals and transcribed two of the measurements for each criminal to a card. He then shuffled the cards well and again transcribed the measurements, now in random order, to a notebook. Thus he had available a random drawing from a population which was essentially normal in form and whose mean and variance he could and did compute. By taking successive groups of any number, N, of these random values, he had a good simulation of random samples from a normal distribution, and he could compare test statistics computed from the samples with their expected behavior.

Actually, it is very easy, today, to prepare an even better set of synthetic random samples than "Student" did from a population whose characteristics are known. Let us do so, then use our result to carry out the same sort of study that he made. Suppose we want a population which will be essentially normal in form with mean $\mu = 50.00$ and variance $\sigma^2 = 25.00$. We add a further requirement that the population is to consist only of integers. We simply consider the integers as class marks and use Appendix II and the methods of Chapter 5 to determine how many of each integer we need. Of course, since we must use only whole numbers of each value, our computed frequencies must be rounded, in consequence of which our variance turns out to be actually $\sigma^2 \doteq 22.44$.

Now we could obtain 100 identical cards, discs, balls or other convenient objects, and number them with the integers in the frequencies indicated by the results of our computations, as shown in Table 10-1. Then we could shuffle

Table 10-1 NEAR-NORMAL POPULATION FOR USE IN SAMPLING EXPERIMENTS

x_i	f_i	Serial Number
39	1	1
40	1	2
41	2	3, 4
42	2	5, 6
43	3	7–9
44	4	10–13
45	5	14–18
46	6	19–24
47	7	25–31
48	7	32–38
49	8	39–46
50	8	47–54
51	8	55–62
52	7	63–69
53	7	64–76
54	6	77–82
55	5	83–87
56	4	88–91
57	3	92–94
58	2	95, 96
59	2	97, 98
60	1	99
61	1	100

$N = 100$ $\mu = 50.00$ $\sigma^2 = 22.44$ $\sigma \doteq 4.73708$

the cards or mix the discs, balls, or other objects and draw one, record its value, return it, remix, redraw, and so on indefinitely. Because no value is permanently removed, we have, in effect, an infinite parent population, and we may draw samples as long as we wish. Of course, we can group our drawings in sets of N to simulate samples of that size.

Even this is a needless effort, however, for if we serially number our values, as we did in Table 10-1, then we can use a table of random numbers to tell us the order in which to write values without ever bothering with the physical

Table 10-2a SAMPLES OF $N = 4$ FROM POPULATION OF TABLE 10-1 USED IN PREPARING TABLE 10-2

1	54 59 52 59	26	58 42 51 45	51	51 57 51 56	76	43 56 42 56
2	47 50 48 51	27	44 47 42 48	52	61 44 49 49	77	46 45 61 51
3	51 49 55 59	28	46 55 60 40	53	50 44 52 51	78	49 53 50 40
4	47 44 50 51	29	45 48 49 47	54	42 57 52 50	79	52 60 53 52
5	47 41 49 52	30	57 46 51 50	55	47 53 44 48	80	49 47 49 48
6	53 47 43 45	31	45 53 45 49	56	53 51 46 52	81	47 44 50 56
7	53 42 58 58	32	56 54 59 47	57	55 58 51 42	82	50 53 50 54
8	51 51 51 54	33	42 47 56 51	58	44 52 56 56	83	56 45 51 47
9	52 47 46 43	34	53 46 49 48	59	51 50 43 48	84	52 46 53 58
10	50 53 52 46	35	49 55 48 44	60	51 48 44 56	85	52 61 47 46
11	40 54 44 51	36	52 58 52 54	61	41 47 55 54	86	50 57 48 52
12	50 42 48 60	37	50 57 47 56	62	49 51 50 43	87	49 55 47 58
13	45 45 50 45	38	51 47 50 52	63	47 44 46 57	88	48 45 52 46
14	53 45 44 46	39	50 41 55 56	64	47 49 52 52	89	49 46 53 56
15	47 49 48 53	40	47 52 56 39	65	50 46 47 51	90	54 40 40 53
16	48 57 56 53	41	56 55 46 53	66	49 46 52 41	91	47 59 47 44
17	50 50 48 51	42	52 53 52 47	67	54 57 55 55	92	47 50 49 61
18	51 56 56 50	43	51 44 55 45	68	44 47 51 47	93	45 51 47 61
19	48 48 56 44	44	53 48 53 45	69	54 52 54 46	94	57 51 49 49
20	49 56 56 47	45	55 43 50 61	70	45 44 50 49	95	42 59 52 43
21	59 48 54 54	46	52 47 48 57	71	55 54 46 52	96	49 53 61 49
22	47 46 47 50	47	44 46 56 39	72	50 52 44 53	97	49 48 55 50
23	47 41 53 53	48	44 55 51 51	73	56 48 47 52	98	58 54 44 46
24	47 47 41 52	49	52 57 50 49	74	46 47 44 55	99	54 52 52 48
25	50 46 46 55	50	45 53 51 41	75	51 53 50 45	100	54 45 43 55

system. We used this procedure to secure 100 random sets of $N = 4$ values recorded in detail in Table 10-2a and 100 random sets of $N = 2$ values recorded in Table 10-3a.

Now suppose that we treat these samples as though we were going to test $H_0 : \mu = 50.00$, but without assuming that we know the population variance. Under such circumstances, we must make an estimate of its value from each sample. That estimate will be s^2, which we know to be an unbiased, efficient, sufficient, and consistent estimate of σ^2. We can use it to compute an estimate of $\sigma_{\bar{x}}^2$ in the form,

$$s_{\bar{x}}^2 = s^2/N \tag{10.2.1a}$$

Table 10-3a SAMPLES OF $N = 2$ FROM POPULATION OF TABLE 10-1 USED IN PREPARING TABLE 10-3

1	41	59	26	55	56	51	48	55	76	59	43
2	52	53	27	47	58	52	44	48	77	49	50
3	59	53	28	46	41	53	53	51	78	49	56
4	57	56	29	48	47	54	51	49	79	49	52
5	44	49	30	51	50	55	54	57	80	45	59
6	53	53	31	50	53	56	56	47	81	54	54
7	51	49	32	43	49	57	43	55	82	47	51
8	47	46	33	53	51	58	54	47	83	59	48
9	48	56	34	53	51	59	50	46	84	51	47
10	46	51	35	55	49	60	50	55	85	52	50
11	48	55	36	53	50	61	46	48	86	58	49
12	50	40	37	53	50	62	46	44	87	53	56
13	58	51	38	43	46	53	54	54	88	59	46
14	58	46	39	42	54	64	50	49	89	48	48
15	46	45	40	50	49	65	43	54	90	51	61
16	55	46	41	46	45	66	53	53	91	54	56
17	56	49	42	54	43	67	42	48	92	53	53
18	42	47	43	45	47	68	59	54	93	53	51
19	43	50	44	44	55	69	55	54	94	48	49
20	47	46	45	52	56	70	39	48	95	46	51
21	57	58	46	45	52	71	59	47	96	49	44
22	51	55	47	52	53	72	51	49	97	46	48
23	47	51	48	47	50	73	53	48	98	43	50
24	57	54	49	44	59	74	48	48	99	56	53
25	49	53	50	55	49	75	44	54	100	41	58

whose square root

$$s_{\bar{x}} = s/\sqrt{N} \tag{10.2.1b}$$

we can use in a formula similar to that of z, but which, because of the substitution, we shall call t as "Student" did:

$$t = (\bar{x} - \mu)/s_{\bar{x}} \tag{10.2.2}$$

These are the values that appear in Tables 10-2 and 10-3, and are summarized in frequency table form in Tables 10-4 and 10-5, together with information to be discussed in the following paragraphs.

Table 10-2 STATISTICS FROM 100 SAMPLES OF $N = 4$ FROM THE NEAR-NORMAL POPULATION OF TABLE 10-1

No.	$\bar{x}$	s^2	$s_{\bar{x}}$	t
1	56.00	12.66666	1.7795	+3.372
2	49.00	3.33333	0.9129	−1.095
3	53.50	19.66666	2.2174	+1.578
4	48.00	10.00000	1.5811	−1.265
5	47.25	22.50000	2.3717	−1.160
6	47.00	18.66666	2.1602	−1.389
7	52.75	56.91666	3.7722	+0.729
8	51.75	2.25000	0.7500	+2.333
9	47.00	14.00000	1.8708	−1.604
10	50.25	9.58333	1.5479	+0.162
11	47.25	23.91666	2.4452	−1.125
12	50.00	56.00000	3.7416	0.000
13	46.25	6.25000	1.2500	−3.000
14	47.00	16.66666	2.0412	−1.470
15	49.25	34.58333	2.9404	−0.255
16	53.75	12.91666	1.7970	+2.087
17	49.75	2.50000	0.7906	−0.316
18	53.25	10.25000	1.6008	+2.030
19	49.00	25.33333	2.5166	−0.397
20	52.00	22.00000	2.3452	+0.853
21	53.75	20.25000	2.2500	+1.667
22	47.50	30.00000	2.7386	−0.913
23	48.50	33.00000	2.8723	−0.522
24	46.75	20.25000	2.2500	−1.444
25	49.25	18.25000	2.1360	−0.351
26	49.00	50.00000	3.5355	−0.283
27	45.25	7.58333	1.3769	−3.450
28	50.25	80.25000	4.4791	+0.056
29	47.25	2.91666	0.8539	−3.221
30	51.00	20.66666	2.2730	+0.440
31	48.00	14.66666	1.9149	−1.044
32	54.00	26.00000	2.5495	+1.569
33	49.00	35.33333	2.9721	−0.336
34	49.00	8.66666	1.4720	−0.679
35	49.00	20.66666	2.2730	−0.440
36	54.00	8.00000	1.4142	+2.828
37	52.50	23.00000	2.3979	+1.043
38	50.00	4.66666	1.0801	0.000
39	50.50	47.00000	3.4278	+0.146
40	48.50	53.66666	3.6629	−0.410
41	52.50	20.33333	2.2546	+1.109
42	51.00	7.33333	1.3540	+0.739
43	48.75	26.91666	2.5903	−0.048
44	49.75	15.58333	1.9378	−0.127
45	52.25	58.25000	3.8161	+0.590

Table 10–2 (*Continued*)

No.	$\bar{x}$	s^2	$s_{\bar{x}}$	t
46	51.00	20.66666	2.2730	+0.440
47	46.25	50.91666	3.5678	−1.051
48	50.25	20.91666	2.2867	+0.109
49	52.00	12.66666	1.7795	+1.124
50	47.50	30.33333	2.7538	−0.908
51	53.75	10.25000	1.8875	+1.987
52	50.75	52.25000	3.6142	+0.208
53	49.25	12.91666	1.7970	−0.417
54	49.75	70.91666	4.2106	−0.059
55	48.00	14.00000	1.8708	−1.069
56	50.50	9.66666	1.5546	+0.322
57	51.50	48.33333	3.4761	+0.432
58	52.00	32.00000	2.8284	+0.707
59	48.00	12.66666	1.7795	−1.124
60	49.75	25.58333	2.5290	−0.099
61	49.25	42.91666	3.2755	−0.229
62	48.25	12.91666	1.7970	−0.974
63	48.50	33.666666	2.9011	−0.517
64	50.00	6.00000	1.2248	0.000
65	48.50	5.66666	1.1902	−1.260
66	47.00	22.00000	2.3452	−1.279
67	55.25	1.58333	0.6292	+8.344
68	47.25	8.25000	1.4361	−1.915
69	51.50	14.33333	1.8930	+0.792
70	47.00	8.66666	1.4720	−2.038
71	51.75	16.25000	2.0156	+0.868
72	49.75	16.25000	2.0156	−0.125
73	50.75	16.91666	2.0565	+0.365
74	48.00	23.33333	2.4152	−0.828
75	49.75	11.5833333	1.9738	−0.127
76	49.25	60.91666	3.9025	−0.192
77	50.75	53.58333	3.6600	+0.205
78	48.00	31.33333	2.7988	−0.715
79	54.25	14.91666	1.9311	+2.201
80	48.25	0.91666	0.4787	−3.656
81	49.25	26.25000	2.5617	−0.293
82	51.75	4.25000	1.0308	+1.698
83	49.75	23.58333	2.4281	−0.103
84	52.25	24.25000	2.4622	+0.914
85	51.50	47.00000	3.4278	+0.438
86	51.75	14.91666	1.9311	+0.906
87	52.25	26.25000	2.5617	+0.878
88	47.75	9.58333	1.5479	−1.454
89	51.00	19.33333	2.9185	+0.455
90	46.75	60.91666	3.9025	−0.833

Table 10-2 (*Continued*)

No.	$\bar{x}$	s^2	$s_{\bar{x}}$	t
91	49.25	44.25000	3.3260	−0.225
92	51.75	39.58333	3.1458	+0.556
93	51.00	50.66666	3.5590	+0.281
94	51.50	14.33333	1.8930	+0.792
95	49.00	64.66666	4.0208	−0.249
96	53.00	32.00000	2.8284	+1.061
97	50.50	9.66666	1.5546	+0.322
98	50.50	43.66666	3.3040	+0.151
99	51.50	6.33333	1.2583	+1.192
100	49.25	37.58333	3.0653	−0.245

Table 10-3 STATISTICS FROM 100 SAMPLES OF $N = 2$ FROM THE NEAR-NORMAL POPULATION OF TABLE 10-1

No.	$\bar{x}$	s^2	$s_{\bar{x}}$	t
1	50.0	162.0	9.0	0.000
2	52.5	0.5	0.5	+5.000
3	56.0	18.0	3.0	+2.000
4	56.5	0.5	0.5	+13.000
5	46.5	12.5	2.5	−1.400
6	53.0	0.0	0.0	$+\infty$
7	50.0	2.0	1.0	0.000
8	46.5	.5	0.5	−7.000
9	52.0	32.0	4.0	+0.5
10	48.5	12.5	2.5	−0.6
11	51.5	24.5	3.5	+0.429
12	45.0	50.0	5.0	−1.000
13	54.5	24.5	3.5	+1.286
14	52.0	72.0	6.0	+0.333
15	45.5	0.5	0.5	−9.000
16	50.5	40.5	4.5	+0.111
17	52.5	24.5	3.5	+0.714
18	44.5	12.5	2.5	−2.200
19	46.5	24.5	3.5	−1.000
20	46.5	0.5	0.5	−7.000
21	57.5	0.50	0.5	+15.000
22	53.0	8.0	2.0	+1.500
23	49.0	8.0	2.0	−0.500
24	55.5	4.5	1.5	+3.666
25	51.0	8.0	2.0	+0.500
26	55.5	0.5	0.5	+11.000
27	52.5	60.5	5.5	+0.455
28	43.5	12.5	2.5	−2.600
29	47.5	0.5	0.5	−5.000
30	50.5	0.5	0.5	+1.000

Table 10-3 (*Continued*)

No.	$\bar{x}$	s^2	$s_{\bar{x}}$	t
31	51.5	4.5	1.5	+1.000
32	46.0	18.0	3.0	−1.333
33	52.0	2.0	1.0	+2.000
34	52.0	2.0	1.0	+2.000
35	52.0	18.0	3.0	+0.667
36	51.5	4.5	1.5	+1.000
37	51.5	4.5	1.5	+1.000
38	44.5	4.5	1.5	−3.667
39	48.0	72.0	6.0	−0.333
40	49.5	0.5	0.5	−1.000
41	45.5	0.5	0.5	−9.000
42	48.5	60.5	5.5	−0.273
43	46.0	2.0	1.0	−4.000
44	49.5	60.5	5.5	−0.091
45	54.0	8.0	2.0	+2.000
46	48.5	24.5	3.5	−0.429
47	52.5	0.5	0.5	+5.000
48	48.5	4.5	1.5	−1.000
49	51.5	112.5	7.5	−0.200
50	52.00	18.0	3.0	+0.667
51	51.5	24.5	3.5	+0.429
52	46.0	8.0	2.0	−2.000
53	52.0	2.0	1.0	+2.000
54	50.0	2.0	1.0	0.000
55	55.5	4.5	1.5	+3.667
56	51.5	40.5	4.5	+0.333
57	49.0	72.0	6.0	−0.167
58	50.5	24.5	3.5	+0.143
59	48.0	8.0	2.0	−1.000
60	52.5	12.5	2.5	+1.000
61	47.0	2.0	1.0	−3.000
62	45.0	2.0	2.0	−5.000
63	54.0	0.0	0.0	$+\infty$
64	49.5	0.5	0.5	−1.000
65	48.5	60.5	5.5	−0.273
66	53.0	0.0	0.0	$+\infty$
67	45.0	18.0	3.0	−1.667
68	56.5	12.5	2.5	+2.667
69	54.5	0.5	0.5	+9.000
70	43.5	40.5	4.5	−1.444
71	53.0	72.0	6.0	+0.500
72	50.0	2.0	1.0	0.000
73	50.5	12.5	2.5	+0.200
74	48.0	0.0	0.0	$-\infty$
75	49.0	50.0	5.0	−0.200

Table 10-3 (*Continued*)

No.	$\bar{x}$	s^2	$s_{\bar{x}}$	t
76	51.0	128.0	8.0	+0.125
77	49.5	0.5	0.5	−1.000
78	52.5	24.5	3.5	+0.714
79	50.5	4.5	1.5	+0.333
80	52.0	98.0	7.0	+0.286
81	54.0	0.0	0.0	$+\infty$
82	49.0	8.0	2.0	−0.500
83	53.5	60.5	5.5	+0.636
84	49.0	8.0	2.0	−0.500
85	51.0	2.0	1.0	+1.000
86	63.5	40.5	4.5	+0.778
87	54.5	4.5	1.5	+3.000
88	52.5	84.5	6.5	+0.385
89	48.0	0.0	0.0	$-\infty$
90	56.0	40.5	4.5	+1.333
91	55.0	2.0	1.0	+5.000
92	53.0	0.0	0.0	$+\infty$
93	52.0	2.0	1.0	+2.000
94	48.5	0.5	0.5	−3.000
95	48.5	12.5	2.5	−0.600
96	46.5	12.5	2.5	−1.400
97	47.0	2.0	1.0	−3.000
98	46.5	24.5	3.5	−1.000
99	54.5	4.5	1.5	+3.000
100	49.5	144.5	8.5	−0.059

Table 10-4 FREQUENCY DISTRIBUTION OF VALUES OF t FOR 100 SAMPLES OF $N = 4$ FROM THE NEAR-NORMAL DISTRIBUTION OF TABLE 10-1, WITH FREQUENCIES COMPUTED FROM THE t- AND z-DISTRIBUTIONS

Class Boundaries		Class Frequencies		
t_L	t_U	f	f_t	f_z
>2.750		2	3.5	0.3
2.250	2.750	1	2.0	0.9
1.750	2.250	4	3.6	2.8
1.250	1.750	4	5.2	6.6
0.750	1.250	12	10.9	12.1
0.250	0.750	15	15.5	17.5
−0.250	+0.250	22	18.6	19.8
−0.750	−0.250	14	15.5	17.5
−1.250	−0.750	12	10.9	12.1
−1.750	−1.250	8	5.2	6.6
−2.250	−1.750	2	3.6	2.8
−2.750	−2.250	0	2.0	0.9
<−2.750		4	3.5	0.3

Table 10-5 FREQUENCY DISTRIBUTION OF VALUES OF t FOR 100 SAMPLES OF $N = 2$ FROM THE NEAR-NORMAL POPULATION OF TABLE 10-1, WITH FREQUENCIES COMPUTED FROM THE t- AND z-DISTRIBUTIONS

Class Boundaries		Class Frequencies		
t_L	t_U	f	f_t	f_z
>5.250		9		
4.750	5.250	3		
4.250	4.750	0 } 16	12.1	0.3
3.750	4.250	0		
3.250	3.750	2		
2.750	3.250	2		
2.250	2.750	2	1.1	0.9
1.750	2.250	5	3.2	2.8
1.250	1.750	4	4.8	6.6
0.750	1.250	6	8.4	12.1
0.250	0.750	16	12.4	17.5
−0.250	+0.250	13	16.0	19.8
−0.750	−0.250	9	12.4	17.5
−1.250	−0.750	8	8.4	12.1
−1.750	−1.250	5	4.8	6.6
−2.250	−1.750	2	3.2	2.8
−2.750	−2.250	1	1.1	0.9
−3.250	−2.750	3		
−3.750	−3.250	1		
−4.250	−3.750	1 } 13	12.1	0.3
−4.750	−4.250	0		
−5.250	−4.750	2		
<5.250		6		

Of course, our whole purpose in this experiment was to determine whether our values of t actually behaved like values of z would have behaved. The final column in Tables 10-4 and 10-5 contains the values for the frequencies, f_z, that would have been observed if this had been true. The discrepancies are appreciable, and are particularly marked for samples of $N = 2$, with fewer values in the classes near the center and far more in the tails for the observed distribution. This was exactly what Student had expected, and he was now faced with the problem of finding an equation for the underlying distribution.

10.3 Student's t-Distribution

His original work, as we said, so impressed the faculty member at the University of London that that professor aided Student to develop the required distribution curves from fundamental mathematical reasoning. The result, which you will not need to use in anything we shall be doing, takes the form,

$$y(t) = \frac{1}{\sqrt{n\pi}} \frac{\Gamma(n+1)/2}{\Gamma(n/2)} \left(1 + \frac{t^2}{n}\right)^{-(n+1)/2} \tag{10.3.1}$$

where use is made of the same gamma-functions that appeared in the χ^2 and χ^2/n distributions. Although you will not need to draw these distribution curves yourselves for this course, the curves for $n = 1$ and $n = 3$ (corresponding to the $N = 2$ and $N = 4$ of our sampling experiment) together with the curve for $n = \infty$ are shown in Fig. 10-1.

Fig. 10-1. The Student's t-distribution for one, three, and infinite degrees of freedom.

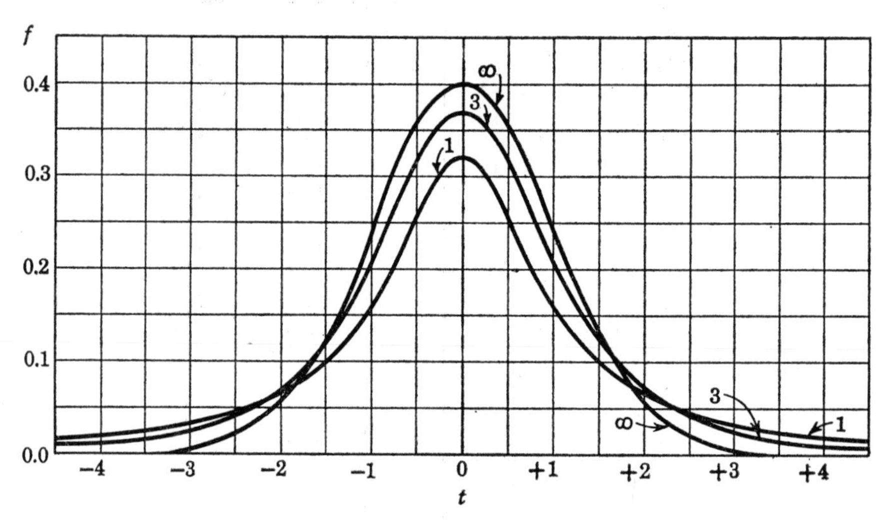

We should again be sure that we understand the idea behind the very convenient symbol, $n = \infty$, which we just employed. On our graph, we showed the curves for $n = 1$ and $n = 3$, which were of immediate interest to us in connection with the sampling experiment we had just performed. There is quite a difference between these two curves, just as there was between the distributions of t in our experiment. If we had conducted further experiments with larger sample sizes, we would have found that the change in form of the distribution for fixed changes in N became smaller and smaller as N itself became larger. Similarly, if we draw the curves for increasing values of n, we shall find that the larger the value of n the less the effect of a given increase in it on the position of the curve, and we shall find that the curves grow progressively closer to that marked "$n = \infty$."

The interesting thing about that curve is that it is exactly the curve for the z-distribution. This is what we should expect, for as we increase the size of our sample, we not only know more about the mean of the population, but also about its variance. So, as our sample size increases indefinitely, it becomes increasingly nearer to true that we do, in fact, know the population variance, and could use the z-distribution. As a matter of fact, it can be shown that the form of the t-distribution equation approaches that of the z-distribution equation as n increases indefinitely. All this is encompassed in our shorthand, $n = \infty$.

As we implied earlier, you will have no need to draw the t-distribution curves (unless you write a text on statistics!) but you will need tables of the areas under the curves, just as you did for the normal and χ^2 or χ^2/n distributions. Because the number of degrees of freedom is a parameter of the t-distribution, these areas must be tabulated for a sufficient number of degrees to cover reasonable needs, as we have done in Appendix VI. If you examine this table, you will see that the final line, for $n = \infty$, gives exactly the values that would have been read from the z-distribution table of Appendix II, which is consistent with our previous considerations. You will also notice that the differences between the values for $n = 20$ or $n = 25$ and $n = \infty$ are very small. It used to be the case that statisticians referred to "small sample theory" and "large sample theory," using the z-distribution for "large" samples, even when the population variance was not known and they were actually computing what we have called t. We now recognize that this is needless, confusing, and actually erroneous. If you cannot assume that the population variance is known, you must use Student's t-distribution, whether you have a "small" or a "large" sample.

10.4 Using the t-Distribution

As our first example of the use of this distribution, consider that we are to test the hypothesis, $H_0 : \mu = 4.00$ with the aid of the data in a random sample of $N = 5$. We must assume not only that the sample is random, but that it comes from a normally distributed population. If this is true, then our test statistic will be $t = (\bar{x} - \mu)/s_{\bar{x}} = (\bar{x} - 4.00)/\sqrt{s^2/5}$ and it will have Student's t-distribution with $n = N - 1 = 5 - 1 = 4$ degrees of freedom. If we choose our alpha risk as 0.050, our critical values become $t_{\alpha/2,n} = t_{0.025,4} = -2.776$ and $t_{1-\alpha/2,n} = t_{0.975,4} = +2.776$. We now obtain our data:

$$5, 4, 5, 6, 5 \qquad \text{(S10.4.1)}$$

and perform the necessary computations:

$$\Sigma x = 25 \qquad s^2 = 0.50$$

$$\Sigma x^2 = 127 \qquad s_{\bar{x}}^2 = 0.10$$

$$\bar{x} = 5.0 \qquad s_{\bar{x}} = 0.32622$$

$$\Sigma (x - \bar{x})^2 = 2.0 \qquad t = 3.162$$

These computations, which you should verify, lead to a value of t in the upper critical region, and we therefore reject our null hypothesis and conclude that $\mu \neq 4.00$.

In testing one-sided hypotheses, we make the usual modifications of procedure to throw our entire critical region into one tail of the distribution, just as we have done in all previous cases. This will be illustrated in detail in the more real problems we shall presently develop.

It will be worth our while to re-examine the data from our experiments in Tables 10-2 and 10-3. Notice that we sometimes had sample means quite remote from our population mean. If these samples had an unusually large value of s^2, then the resulting t was not greatly different from zero, while, if the associated value of s^2 was unusually small, the value of t became very large. Similarly, in cases in which the value of $\bar{x}$ was very close to μ, a very small value of s^2 would still lead to a large value, numerically, for t. It is, of course, the ratio of the difference between $\bar{x}$ and μ to $s_{\bar{x}}$, a quantity dependent on s^2, which determines the value of t. In other words, *t measures the discrepancy between $\bar{x}$ and μ in terms of the estimate of variance and the sample size.* The sampling behavior of both $\bar{x}$ and s^2 contribute to the errors in testing hypotheses. In contrast, when we could assume the variance known, we were only subject to error as a result of the sampling behavior of $\bar{x}$, and this constitutes a fundamental difference between the two situations.

Confidence limits may be assigned as the result of reasoning quite similar to that which we used in the case of the mean with the assumed known variance. The only difference is that we use t instead of z and $s_{\bar{x}}$ in place of $\sigma_{\bar{x}}$, so that our limits are

$$\bar{x} + t_{\alpha/2,n}s_{\bar{x}} \leq \mu \leq \bar{x} + t_{1-\alpha/2,n}s_{\bar{x}} \qquad (10.4.1a)$$

which is equivalent to the convenient computing form:

$$x \pm | t_{\alpha/2,n} | s_{\bar{x}} \qquad (10.4.1b)$$

where, as usual, $\alpha = (100 - P)/100$ for $P\%$ confidence. For our specific problem, 95% confidence limits are

$$5.000 \pm 2.776 \times 0.31662 = 5.000 \pm 0.87894$$
$$= 4.12106 \text{ and } 5.87894$$

10.5 Some Real Problems

A. *Course Test Grades.* There comes a time during the study of statistical methods when it is essential that their use with respect to problems close to our own experience must be considered in order to develop a full understanding of the meaning of some of the ideas involved. Most of us have had a good deal of experience in the taking of tests in various academic courses. We are familiar with the age-old battle between students and instructors as to whether the tests were fair and reasonable, or unfair, unreasonable, and "rugged." In many institutions, there is one or another rule, written or unwritten, concerning what constitutes a test of proper standard.

Let us suppose that, in one such institution, the intent is that tests should be so prepared and graded that the mean grade is 75. In order to give that more than trivial meaning, it must be interpreted as meaning that the mean of an infinite population of grades by comparable students on the test should be 75. How, then, can a given instructor know whether his test is sound? In effect, he should think of each test as an experiment designed to test the hypothesis, $H_0 : \mu = 75.00$.

In order to be able to make a decision concerning that hypothesis after he has given and graded the test, he must make two assumptions. The first is that his class is a random sample from the infinite population of students appropriately taking such tests, and the second is that the test grades for that population would be normally distributed. Under these circumstances, our test statistic becomes

$$t = (\bar{x} - \mu)/s_{\bar{x}}(\bar{x} - 75.00)/s_{\bar{x}} \tag{10.5.1}$$

We must now choose an alpha risk. What that risk should be will depend upon the consequences of the related Type I error, the rejection of a true null hypothesis. If the rejection of the hypothesis that the test was of standard difficulty might simply mean that the next test would be adjusted to be somewhat compensating in its difficulty, an alpha risk of 0.050 might be considered quite appropriate. Under these conditions, and assuming a class of $N = 23$, our critical values become $t_{0.025,22} = -2.074$ and $t_{0.975,22} = +2.074$.

The test is given and graded, and the test results, together with the appropriate calculations thereon, are shown in Table 10-6. The resulting value of

Table 10-6 TEST OF HYPOTHESIS CONCERNING CALCULUS TEST GRADES

1. $H_0 : \mu = 75.00$
2. Assumptions: (a) Sample is random ($N = 23$)
   (b) Parent population is normal
3. Test statistic: $t = (\bar{x} - \mu)/s_{\bar{x}} = (\bar{x} - 75.00)/s_{\bar{x}}$
4. Choose $\alpha = 0.05$
5. Critical values: $t_{0.025,22} = -2.074$
   $t_{0.975,22} = +2.074$
6. Data:

68	64	72	70	76
82	82	76	74	68
60	34	56	73	75
72	92	78	66	
60	68	80	86	

7. Compute observed value of test statistic:

$\Sigma x = 1{,}632$	$s^2 = 138.95256$
$\Sigma x^2 = 118{,}858$	$s_{\bar{x}}^2 = 6.04141$
$\bar{x} = 70.95625$	$s_{\bar{x}} = 2.458$
$\Sigma(x - \bar{x})^2 = 3{,}050.05625$	$t = -1.645$

8. Decision: since t is not in the critical region, do not reject H_0. Act as though $\mu = 75.00$

   The 95% confidence limits are $\mu = 70.95625 \pm 2.074 \times 2.458 = 65.858$ and 76.054, which would be rounded to 65.9 and 76.1 for most presentation purposes

$t = -1.645$, because it is not in the critical region, leads us not to reject H_0 and we conclude that our test met the requirements, and may be considered quite standard.

All this seems quite straightforward, but now let us scrutinize it more closely. Consider our first assumption, that our grades are a random sample: is this true? Perhaps we should tell you that the class in question was one section in a calculus course, taken chiefly by students required to have it. The instructor was not known to the students in advance, and, so far as was known, there were no factors which would have made that section different from others in the same subject, nor were there unusual features of the group of students that particular year which might have affected their grades. So, although the students were not selected by a procedure guaranteed to be random, at least careful thought discloses no evidence of a recognizable bias.

What about the second assumption, that grades on the test would be normally distributed? This sample size, $N = 23$, is too small to permit any effective appraisal from it as to the validity of the assumption. (The methods needed will be discussed in Chapter 13.) However, review of grades on similar tests in the past suggests that this assumption is close to the truth, and is certainly a reasonable one to make.

Because we can find no serious fault with our enabling assumptions, it might seem that we should rest content. However, let us go a step further and compute the 95% confidence limits for μ:

$$\mu = \bar{x} \pm |t_{0.025,22}| s_{\bar{x}} \tag{10.5.2a}$$

$$= 70.956 \pm 2.074 \times 2.458 \tag{10.5.2b}$$

$$= 70.956 \pm 5.098 \tag{10.5.2c}$$

$$= 65.9 \text{ and } 76.1 \tag{10.5.2d}$$

which really tell us that our population mean is not very well located. After all, on the basis of the usual letter equivalents, 65.9 is almost at the center of the range for D, while 76.1 is safely above the range for C, and this difference is important.

Could we make better use of our total information? We could. One plan might take the form of requiring that, if the null hypothesis were rejected with an alpha risk of 0.050, the test should be ignored and a replacement test be made and given, while if the hypothesis could not be rejected at an alpha risk of 0.050, but could be at an alpha risk of 0.100, the test grades should be adjusted according to a predetermined plan. For $\alpha = 0.100$, the critical values are here $t_{0.050,22} = -1.717$ and $t_{0.950,22} = +1.717$. We would still not reject our hypothesis. The 90% confidence limits are

$$\mu = \bar{x} \pm t_{0.050,22} s_{\bar{x}} \tag{10.5.3a}$$

$$= 70.956 \pm 1.717 \times 2.458 \tag{10.5.3b}$$

$$= 70.956 \pm 4.220 \tag{10.5.3c}$$

$$= 66.7 \text{ and } 75.2$$

This brings to our attention the fact that the small size of our sample and large variation in individual grades make it, on the one hand, difficult to support the claim that a particular test is off-standard and, on the other hand, to locate the population mean very exactly. This is exactly what our statistical language has been telling us: here we see its meaning "close to home."

B. *A Different Guarantee Problem.* Because they are quite fragile, sheer full-fashioned nylon stockings are readily damaged by handling in stores. In order to reduce losses by such damage, many manufacturers package their stockings in sealed, transparent packages, with the size, weight, and length clearly marked. In order to maintain customer confidence in the reliability of the package statements, it is essential that they be correct. "Standard" length is 30 in., while other lengths vary by increments of one inch. A store is considering accepting a new brand of stockings and wishes to insure, among other things, that short-length stockings will not be encountered. Suppose that they obtain 10 packages (20 stockings) of the new brand and measure the lengths: how can they use this information effectively?

Since they are primarily interested in protecting their reputation for reliability, they may well test the hypothesis that the stockings are mismarked by one whole size, and are 29 in. or less in length. This means, in other words, that they will test the null hypothesis, $H_0 : \mu \leq 29$ in. If they may assume that the 10 packages they are to test are a random sample from the brand, and that lengths of the brand are normally distributed, their test statistic becomes

$$t = \frac{\bar{x} - \mu}{s_{\bar{x}}} = \frac{\bar{x} - 29}{s_{\bar{x}}}$$

In choosing an alpha risk, they may well recognize the competitive nature of the business and the importance of maintaining their customers' confidence and decline to consider the new brand unless the null hypothesis can be rejected with an alpha risk as small as 0.005. This sets the critical value at $t_{0.995,19} = +2.861$.

The stockings are now measured with the following results:

29.6	30.3	30.5	29.8
30.1	30.0	29.7	30.1
30.3	29.6	30.2	30.0
30.0	30.1	29.7	29.8
30.2	30.0	29.8	29.9

$$\Sigma x = 599.7 \qquad s^2 \doteq 0.0613421$$

$$\Sigma x^2 = 17{,}983.17 \qquad s_{\bar{x}}^2 \doteq 0.003067105$$

$$\bar{x} = 29.985 \qquad s_{\bar{x}} \doteq 0.0554$$

$$\Sigma(x - \bar{x})^2 = 1.1655 \qquad t \doteq 0.985/0.0554 = 17.8$$

The observed value is definitely in the critical region, so that the null hypothesis may be rejected and the stockings considered to be of standard length.

10.6 Closing Comments

You will have noticed, we hope, that the fundamental principles of hypothesis testing and interval estimation have now become so well established in our thinking that there was nothing new for us here, once we had recognized the value of Student's work, except the details of the particular test statistic to be employed. This is one of the comforting features of statistics: we shall not have to learn whole new ways of thinking as we attack more complex problems. Rather, we shall but extend and develop ideas already established.

General Study

1. Now that you are no longer restricted to the assumption that you know the population variance when you must test hypotheses or develop confidence limits concerning a population mean, can you list a number of situations in the field of your particular interest in which it would be quite proper to assume the variance to be known? Can you list other situations in which that assumption is definitely not warranted?

2. Do you know of any advances in your major field which have been made first by empirical methods, later to be refined by more erudite considerations, as was Student's development? What do you know of the character and accomplishments of the empirical workers? Of the refiners?

Specific Problems

1–6. Treat the data of Problems 1–6 in Chapter 8 under the modified assumption that the population variance is not known. In each case in which the conclusion is different from that previously reached, explain why this is so.

7–12. Provide confidence limits as directed in Chapter 8 for these data, but under the modified assumption that the population variance is unknown.

13. In preparing the test discussed in Problem 13 of Chapter 9, the instructor intended that the mean grade would be 75. Test this as an hypothesis with an alpha risk of 0.050 and provide 95% confidence limits for the population mean.

14. In typing the material mentioned in Problem 14 of Chapter 9, the margin stops were adjusted for a line of 57 characters. Test the hypothesis that the mean length is less than or equal to this number with an alpha risk of 0.100 and provide 90% confidence limits for the length.

15. Obtain the most recent academic index data for the student group of which you are a member and make appropriate tests of hypotheses concerning the position of your group with respect to the "norms" to which it is expected to conform. Apply appropriate confidence limits.

16. During one of your rest periods in a snack bar, watch the cash register and record the individual sales during a known period of time. Compute confidence limits for the mean and variance of these sales. Before making the observations, formulate your own estimate of the values, and test the hypotheses that these estimates are correct.

17. Apply these methods, where feasible, to the most recent data you have obtained in any quantitative laboratory course you may be taking.

11

The Variances of Two Populations

11.1 Our Problem and Our Attack

In our work so far we have confined our thinking to single populations. We have learned how to describe them and how to make inferences concerning their parameters on the basis of single samples. As we have seen, it is only within this century that statisticians have acquired the methods by which some of these tasks could be accomplished, but we cannot long remain content with our ability to deal with a single population. We must move ahead to learn how to compare two and more populations. It may seem strange that we begin our attack by considering the variances before we cope with the more familiar means. We could have begun with the means, had we wished, but before the task could be accomplished it would have been necessary for us to investigate the variances, so we may as well begin with them.

Suppose we wish to test the hypothesis that the variances of two populations, which we may designate as σ_A^2 and σ_B^2, are equal. As you may have guessed from our work with single populations, we shall express our hypothesis in the form that the ratio of variances is unity:

$$H_0 : \sigma_A^2/\sigma_B^2 = 1 \quad \text{or} \quad H_0 : \sigma_B^2/\sigma_A^2 = 1 \tag{11.1.1}$$

You properly expect that, in order to have a test statistic, we must make certain assumptions. They will be that the samples are random from each population and that the populations are normally distributed. If our hypothesis is true and our assumptions are valid, then our test statistic, traditionally symbolized by F, will be the ratio of the two sample variances:

$$F = s_A^2/s_B^2 \quad \text{or} \quad F = s_B^2/s_A^2 \tag{11.1.2}$$

Suppose we let the subscript one represent the population whose variance we have happened to place in the numerator in our null hypothesis and test statistic and subscript two denote the population whose variance is in the denominator. We let N and $n = N - 1$ with appropriate subscripts denote the number of observations and number of degrees of freedom, respectively, for the indicated sample variances. The equation for the distribution of F can then be written as

$$f(F) = \frac{\Gamma[(n_1 + n_2)/2]}{\Gamma(n_1/2)\Gamma(n_2/2)} n_1^{1/2n_1} n_2^{1/2n_2} \frac{F^{1/2n_1 - 1}}{(n_2 + n_1F)^{1/2(n_1+n_2)}} \tag{11.1.3}$$

This is, indeed, a complicated equation but, fortunately, we shall have no need to plot its curves. For your interest we show you a few in Fig. 11-1, however.

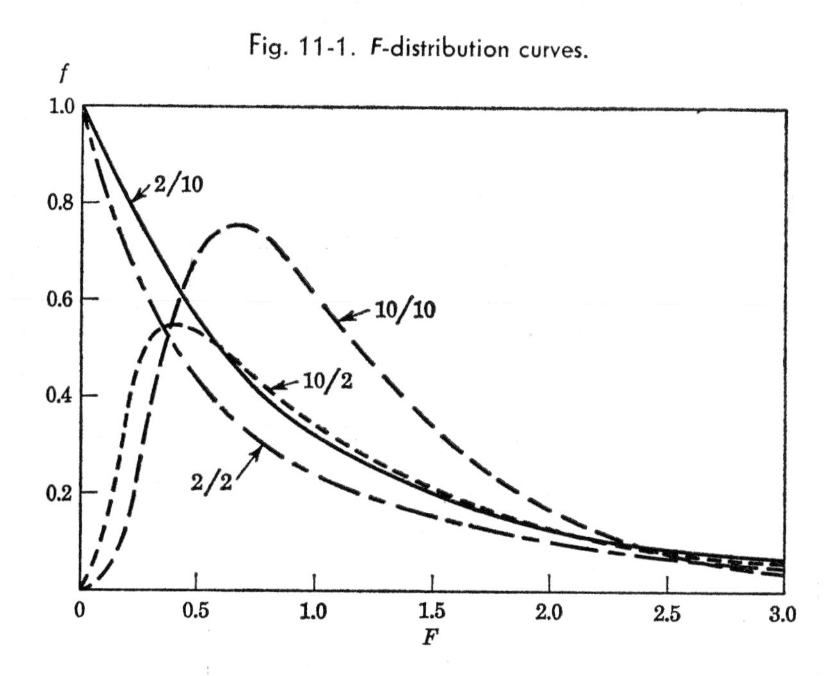

Fig. 11-1. F-distribution curves.

The important thing to notice is that the equation has two parameters, n_1 and n_2, the numbers of degrees of freedom. As usual, we shall need tables of the areas under the curves. Appendix VII provides such a table. We shall use the symbol $F_{p,n_1/n_2}$ to denote the value of F below which a fraction p of the distribution falls when s_1^2 is in the numerator and s_2^2 is in the numerator.

Now let us consider an example involving very simple numbers to see just how the principle works. Suppose that we wish to test our hypothesis of equality with $N_A = 5$ and $N_B = 7$ observations in the samples we intend to secure. Suppose, further, that we stated our hypothesis only in the form:

$$H_{01} : \sigma_A^2/\sigma_B^2 = 1$$

We make the required assumptions that we have random samples from normally distributed populations. Our test statistic is therefore: $F = s_A^2/s_B^2$.

We must now choose our alpha risk, which we shall suppose was set at 0.050. Our critical values then become $F_{\alpha/2,n_A/n_B} = F_{0.025,4/6}$ and $F_{1-\alpha/2,n_A/n_B} = F_{0.975,4/6}$. The latter value we have no difficulty in finding in Appendix VII as 6.23, but we cannot find the value for $F_{0.025,4/6}$. For the present, let's just record that fact as a little worry and continue on to get our sample and carry out the computations, with the results shown in Table 11-1.

Table 11-1 TEST OF HYPOTHESIS OF EQUALITY OF VARIANCES (SYNTHETIC EXAMPLE)

	Group A	*Group B*
	5	4
	6	8
	5	5
	6	2
	5	5
		6
		5
N	5	7
n	4	6
Σx	27	35
Σx^2	147	195
$\bar{x}$	5.4	5.0
$\Sigma(x - \bar{x})^2$	1.2	20.0
s^2	0.30000	3.33333

$$F = s_A^2/s_B^2 = 0.30000/3.33333 = 0.090$$

$$F = s_B^2/s_A^2 = 3.33333/0.30000 = 11.11111$$

Sure enough, we are in trouble! Our value of s_A^2 is much smaller than our value of s_B^2, and our value of F, 0.090, is a fraction, less than unity. We are suspicious that it is, in fact, so much less that we should reject our hypothesis, but where is the critical value? Let's work our way out of the difficulty. We stated, back in Eq. 11.1.1, that our null hypothesis could be written with either variance in the numerator. Suppose, then, that we had chosen the form:

$$H_{02} : \sigma_B^2/\sigma_A^2 = 1$$

This would have made our test statistic $F = s_B^2/s_A^2$ and our critical values would have been $F_{0.025,6/4}$ and $F_{0.975,6/4}$. Again, we can find the upper value from our table as 9.20, but the lower value is missing. But, with the hypothesis in this form, our observed value of F becomes 11.111, which exceeds the upper critical value and leads to the rejection of the null hypothesis.

Now we can work our way out of the difficulty we were in. The two ways of stating the hypothesis are simply reciprocals of each other and lead to test statistics which are also reciprocals of each other. Therefore, the lower critical value for the hypothesis stated one way must be just the reciprocal of the upper critical value when the hypothesis is stated in the other way. In symbols, then,

$$F_{\alpha/2,n_A/n_B} = 1/F_{1-\alpha/2,n_B/n_A} \tag{11.1.4}$$

In other words, the lower critical value is just the reciprocal of the equivalent upper critical value for reversed degrees of freedom.

We can now complete our specification of critical values. For our hypothesis in the first form, $H_{01}: \sigma_A^2/\sigma_B^2 = 1$, the critical values are

$$F_{0.025,4/6} = 1/F_{0.975,6/4} = 1/9.20 = 0.109$$

and

$$F_{0.975,4/6} = 6.23$$

while for the hypothesis in the second form, $H_{02}: \sigma_B^2/\sigma_A^2 = 1$, the critical values are

$$F_{0.025,6/4} = 1/F_{0.975,4/6} = 1/6.23 = 0.161$$

and

$$F_{0.975,6/4} = 9.20$$

For the first form, our observed value, 0.090, is below the lower critical value, which requires us to reject the hypothesis. For the second form, the observed value, 11.1, as we saw, is above the upper critical value, and we, of course, reject the hypothesis.

11.2 A Practical Recommendation

You may well wonder why tables are not commonly printed with the necessary values for both tails of the distribution. The answer is an interesting combination of history and economics. Historically, the purpose for which the F-distribution was developed required only the upper critical values, and it was possible to publish tables in quite compact form by making one page for each needed value of p, with numerator degrees of freedom as column headings and denominator degrees of freedom as row stubs. In fact, a very common form of table showed values for only two values of p, 0.950 and 0.990. The former were often printed in boldface and the latter in italics as two rows to the right of each number of denominator degrees of freedom. Sometimes a third level of p was included by the use of still another type face.

The arrangement we have employed in Appendix VII makes it possible to include a number of upper-tail values for each combination of numbers of degrees of freedom, while still retaining relative compactness and resultant economy by omitting the lower-tail values. Since these lower values are needed less often, it seems quite feasible, in view of the ease with which they may be calculated, to omit them.

We can make our use of the table still more practical. A purist would state his hypothesis in one form and look up both critical values, then proceed to obtain his data, make his computations, reach his decision, and state it. But let us analyze his operations. He must look up the upper critical value for the hypothesis as he stated it and the value that would have been the upper critical value if he had stated the hypothesis in the other form. Then he must take the reciprocal of the latter value. Thus he has a total of three possible ways in making a mistake in finding his critical values, even if he formulates them correctly.

Suppose, instead, we state our hypothesis in both forms and look up the upper-tail value for each form. Then, when the data are in, we simply write F in the form which makes it greater than unity and compare our quotient with the corresponding critical value. Now we have only to look up the two values — two chances for a mistake instead of three. We can go still farther: formulate both critical values but look up only the one our data show we shall need — one chance of a mistake! Yet we have in no way biased our result. We have simply saved ourselves much needless effort, directly reduced our chances to make a mistake, and, by reducing fatigue, increased our chances of remaining clear-headed. This may seem like an inappropriate suggestion in a textbook on elementary statistics. Why, then, is it included? We offer you this book only because we, ourselves, have worked at the serious application of statistics to problems that have been very real and pressing. We believe the methods will be valuable to you, and we know from experience the ever-present danger of slips from fatigue. So we think it most proper to share our experience with you in the form of some of these suggestions. Notice that they are *not* suggesting that you depart from sound principles, but rather that you organize your thinking and work so as to reduce the hazards.

Our suggestion, then, would be that your work might be set up as follows:

$$H_{0_a}: \sigma_A^2/\sigma_B^2 = 1.00 \quad \text{or} \quad H_{0_b}: \sigma_B^2/\sigma_A^2 = 1.00$$

Assumptions:
  Samples are random.
  Parent populations are normally distributed.
Test Statistic:

$$F = s_A^2/s_B^2 \qquad \text{or} \qquad F = s_B^2/s_A^2$$

Alpha Risk:
  Chosen as α.
Critical Values:

$$F_{1-\alpha/2, n_A/n_B} \qquad \text{and} \qquad F_{1-\alpha/2, n_B/n_A}$$

You ought to use this formulation until and unless you become thoroughly accustomed to the thinking.

After you have become thoroughly acquainted with the idea, you might condense your formulation to something like the following:

$H_0 : \sigma_A^2/\sigma_B^2 = 1.00$

Assumptions: R.S., N.D.
Test Statistic: $F = s_1^2/s_2^2$ where $s_1^2 > s_2^2$
Alpha Risk: a
Critical Value: $F_{1-\alpha/2, n_1/n_2}$

11.3 One-sided Hypotheses

Our preceding discussion should make it very clear that whenever we are concerned with a one-sided hypothesis we always state it in the form that the ratio of the two population variances is less than or equal to one. We may have *thought* of our problem originally in the other form, but we *express* it in this form. For instance, if we had thought of the hypothesis as that the variance of B was greater than or equal to the variance of A, we would state it in the form, $H_0 : \sigma_A^2/\sigma_B^2 \leq 1.00$. Our only reason for rejecting the hypothesis would be the observation of a sufficiently large value of $F = s_A^2/s_B^2$, and specifically a value larger than $F_{1-\alpha, n_A/n_B}$. We shall see this idea applied in the problems with real data.

11.4 Combining Information

We shall often find that we have obtained samples from two populations which may well turn out to have, so far as we can determine by our tests above, the same variance. It then becomes very logical to combine, or "pool," the two estimates into a single estimate of the common variance. We might carelessly think that the way to do that would be simply to combine all the observations into a single set and compute a value of s^2 from them, but this would not be sound. The reason is that the two populations might well have different means but the same variance. The data of Table 11-2 will illustrate just such a situation. The two sample variances would lead to the rejection of the hypothesis of equal population variances only at very high alpha risks. If we then pool the observations, as in Part B of the table, we obtain a value of $s^2 = 2.\overline{\dot{6}9}$ which is far larger than either $s_A^2 = 0.3\dot{0}$ or $s_B^2 = 0.\overline{28\dot{5}714}$. Now look at the sample means, 5.4 and $8.\overline{\dot{4}28571}$, respectively. While we can't prove it yet, they certainly suggest that the population means may be different, and that difference is reflected in the s^2 obtained from combining the observations.

But all that we have so far claimed is that the sample *variances* are consistent

Table 11-2 POOLING OF VARIANCE ESTIMATES (SYNTHETIC EXAMPLE)

Part A. Data and Test of Hypothesis of Equality of Variances

	Group A	*Group B*
	5	9
	6	8
	5	9
	6	8
	5	8
		9
		8
N	5	7
n	4	6
Σx	27	59
Σx^2	147	499
$\bar{x}$	5.4	8.42857
$\Sigma(x - \bar{x})^2$	1.2	1.71428
s^2	0.30000	0.28571
	$F = 1.050$	

Part B. Pooling All Observations (Poor Procedure)

N	12
n	11
Σx	86
Σx^2	646
$\bar{x}$	7.16666
$\Sigma(x - \bar{x})^2$	29.66666
s^2	2.69696

Part C. Pooling Estimates

$$s_p^2 = [\Sigma(x - \bar{x})_A^2 + \Sigma(x - \bar{x})_B^2]/(N_A - N_B - 2) = 2.91428/10$$
$$= 0.29143^-$$

with the idea that the population *variances* are the same. What we ought to do, then, is combine the sample variances. It would be quite reasonable to take their mean as a combined estimate, except for the fact that this would give equal importance to the two samples in spite of their difference in size. An improvement would result from multiplying both variances by the number of observations in their samples and dividing by their total number. But we can do better: recall the concept of degrees of freedom. It is the number of degrees of freedom that reflects the real worth of the estimate of variance from each sample, and we therefore compute our pooled estimate as

$$s_p^2 = \frac{n_A s_A^2 + n_B s_B^2}{n_A + n_B} \tag{11.4.1a}$$

$$= \frac{\Sigma(x - \bar{x})_A^2 + \Sigma(x - \bar{x})_B^2}{N_A + N_B - 2} \tag{11.4.1b}$$

In our specific case, the resulting value, $0.29\overline{142857}$ is completely satisfying. In passing, we should note that a mean such as s_p^2, which is obtained by multiplying each element in it by some factor and dividing the sum of the products by the sum of the factors, is called a *weighted mean*, and that the factors are called *weights*. Here, the weights are the numbers of degrees of freedom.

11.5 Confidence Limits

Although it does not seem to be common practice to supply confidence limits for the ratio of population variances, there is no particular difficulty involved. Similar thinking to that used in other instances leads to the fact that $P\%$ confidence limits for σ_1^2/σ_2^2 are given by the formulas,

$$(\sigma_1^2/\sigma_2^2)_L = \frac{(s_1^2/s_2^2)}{F_{(1-\alpha/2)n_1/n_2}} \tag{11.5.1a}$$

and

$$(\sigma_1^2/\sigma_2^2)_U = \frac{(s_1^2/s_2^2)}{F_{\alpha/2,n_1/n_2}}$$

$$= (s_1^2/s_2^2) \times F_{(1-\alpha/2)n_2/n_1} \tag{11.5.1b}$$

For the example we used in connection with testing the hypothesis, H_{0_a}: $\sigma_A^2/\sigma_B^2 = 1.00$, the 95% confidence limits for σ_A^2/σ_B^2 are thus:

$$(\sigma_A^2/\sigma_B^2)_L = \frac{(s_A^2/s_B^2)}{F_{0.975,4,6}}$$

$$= 0.090/6.23 = 0.0144$$

$$(\sigma_A^2/\sigma_B^2)_U = (s_A^2/s_B^2) \times F_{0.975,6/4}$$

$$= 0.090 \times 9.20 = 0.828$$

Of course, if we had happened to express the relation in terms of σ_B^2/σ_A^2, we should have had the reciprocals of the limits, or $1/0.828 = 1.21$ and $1/0.0144 = 69.4$. Perhaps the fact that the results are expressible only in terms of the ratio is one of the reasons why the confidence limits are not as often quoted for this type of problem as for many others.

11.6 Real Problems

A. *A Problem in Test Variances.* Two sections in the same subject in a certain semester were given different tests on the same portion of the course. It was a matter of concern whether the variance of test grades for the two sections was the same. Suppose the two sections are designated as P and Q. We shall test the hypothesis,

$$H_{0a}: \sigma_P^2/\sigma_Q^2 = 1.00 \qquad \text{or} \qquad H_{0b}: \sigma_Q^2/\sigma_P^2 = 1.00$$

and shall make the assumption that the sections constitute a random sample of students qualified to take the test and that the distribution of the test grades in that population would be normal. Our usual reasoning about the consequences of error relative to the nature of test grade data may lead us to choose an alpha risk of 0.050. If $N_P = 32$ and $N_Q = 28$, our critical values of our test statistic, under our rational system, become

$$F_{0.975,31/27} \quad \text{and} \quad F_{0.975,27/31}$$

The data, in Table 11-3, lead to $s_P^2 > s_Q^2$, so we adopt the first form of our hypothesis, for which the observed value of $F = 193.80645/95.20105 = 2.035$.

Table 11-3 Grades of Two Sections of Same Course on Similar Tests

	Section P		*Section Q*	
	82	58	84	88
	98	58	73	69
	89	94	64	73
	67	73	72	89
	88	41	61	60
	81	72	80	79
	91	74	64	68
	83	76	80	86
	66	75	65	86
	86	68	75	78
	59	78	85	82
	86	55	69	78
	84	71	56	95
	77	48	71	
	63	56	73	
	74			
	57			
N	32		28	
n	31		27	
Σx	2,328		2,082	
Σx^2	175,370		157,382	
$\bar{x}$	72.75000		75.35714	
$\Sigma(x - \bar{x})^2$	6,008.00000		2,570.42857	
s^2	193.80645		95.20150	

$$F = 2.035$$

$$F_{0.975,31,27} = 2.13$$

Using the interpolation procedures given in Appendix XIII, we find $F_{0.975,31,27} = 2.13$. Our observed value is not in the critical region, and we do not reject the null hypothesis. We conclude that the population variances are equal.

We may reasonably pool the two variances to obtain

$$s_p^2 = \frac{\Sigma(x - \bar{x})_P^2 + \Sigma(x - \bar{x})_Q^2}{N_P + N_Q - 2}$$

$$= \frac{6008.00000 + 2570.42857}{32 + 28 - 2}$$

$$= \frac{8578.42857}{58} = 147.90394$$

B. *A One-sided Hypothesis Concerning Course Grades.* A certain section of one course was composed partly of students who, during the preceding semester, had taken a course designed to make up certain deficiencies in their prior training in preparation for the current course. These students constituted group A. Another portion of the class, group B, comprised students who were repeating the course because they had failed or achieved a low passing grade the previous semester. One faculty member advanced the theory that the grades of group A would be more uniform than those of group B.

This can be stated as an hypothesis:

$$H_0 : \sigma_A^2/\sigma_B^2 \leq 1.00$$

and, under the assumption that the students actually in the two groups are a random sample of similar students and that the distribution of their grades would be normal, our test statistic is

$$F = s_A^2/s_B^2$$

Because the particular theory being tested bore on an important aspect of advising future students, it was decided to adopt a higher than usual alpha risk, namely 0.100, to make the test sensitive to any departure from the proposed theory. The numbers in the groups were $N_A = 12$ and $N_B = 6$, so the critical value became

$$F_{0.900,11/5} = 3.91$$

The data, in Table 11-4, led to an observed value $F = 6.04$, so that the null hypothesis must be rejected, and we must conclude that the "repeaters" have more uniform grades than the "prepared" students.

Table 11-4 GRADES OF TWO GROUPS OF STUDENTS IN SAME COURSE

Group A had taken preparatory course the previous semester. Group B were repeating the course after receiving low or failing grade the previous semester. Source: Instructor

	Group A		*Group B*
	63	40	78
	82	86	84
	82	65	72
	63	72	77
	89	68	73
	73	83	61
N	12		6
n	11		5
Σx	866		445
Σx^2	64,554		33,159
$\bar{x}$	72.16666		74.16666
$\Sigma(x - \bar{x})^2$	2,057.66666		154.83333
s^2	187.06060		30.96666
	$F = 6.041$		

General Study

1. There seems to be a general reluctance to come to grips with problems involving comparisons of uniformity or variability for two groups. Is there any real reason for this reluctance? Is the reason excusable?

2. Consider the problems of your major field. In how many of them could it well be that variability is of more concern than mean?

3. Of the various factors affecting your daily life, how many can you think of whose variability is at least as much a matter of concern as their mean level? Consider, among other factors: temperature, humidity, work assignments, available income.

Specific Problems

1. Compare your test grades in two courses from the standpoint of equality of variance.

2. A certain plant operates two shifts. The variances of daily production figures for the 20 workers on each shift were 18.3 and 45.7. At an appropriate alpha risk, determine whether the two shifts have equal variability. Discuss why this would be a matter of concern to the plant.

3. A manufacturer was receiving complaints that his product, a plastic tape, was too irregular in width. At the time the standard deviation of widths, determined on a sample of 50 rolls of tape, was found to be 0.0020 in. After a program of maintenance and adjustment of his machines, the standard deviation of width on 25 new rolls was found to be 0.0015 in. Has an improvement really been made?

(Note that the information and question are in terms of standard deviations, *not* variances. What must you do?)

12

Inferences Concerning the Means of Two Populations

12.1 Analysis of the Problem

When we are involved in making inferences from two samples as to the size of the means of the populations from which they came, we may be interested in testing a hypothesis about the differences of the means, or we may wish to establish confidence limits for the difference. From what we have already learned, we rightly suspect that the techniques we employ when we do know the population variances will be different from those we employ when we do not know them. In order to achieve our results, we must know how the means of samples from two populations behave. With this information at our command, it should not be difficult to establish the actual techniques we shall need.

12.2 Behavior of Sample Means When Population Variances Are Known

Suppose that we have two infinite normal populations, designated as population 1 and population 2, with means μ_1 and μ_2 and variances σ_1^2 and σ_2^2, respectively. We draw from these populations random samples of N_1 and N_2, respectively. If we continue to draw such samples indefinitely and record our findings, we already know that the means, $\bar{x}_1$, of the samples from population 1 will be normally distributed with mean $\mu_{\bar{x}_1} = \mu_1$ and variance $\sigma_{\bar{x}_1}{}^2 = \sigma_1^2/N_1$. Similar statements can be made concerning the samples from population 2.

Now let us suppose that, after each drawing, we calculate the difference between the two sample means. It will prove convenient to have a new symbol, Δ, the upper case Greek D, delta, to indicate a difference, just as we found it convenient to let Σ denote a sum. Under this plan, if we let $\Delta\mu = \mu_1 - \mu_2$, then we must let $\Delta\bar{x} = \bar{x}_1 - \bar{x}_2$, being careful to keep the order of subtraction the same in all related differences. If we record the values of our $\Delta\bar{x}$'s for an indefinitely large number of pairs of samples, we shall find the following:

1. The values of $\Delta\bar{x}$ will be normally distributed.

2. The mean of this distribution will be

$$\mu_{\Delta\bar{x}} = \Delta\mu \tag{12.1.1}$$

that is, the mean difference is the difference of the means of the parent populations.

3. The variance of this distribution will be

$$\sigma_{\Delta\bar{x}}^2 = \sigma_{\bar{x}_1}^2 + \sigma_{\bar{x}_2}^2 = \Sigma\sigma_{\bar{x}}^2 \tag{12.2.2a}$$

that is, the variance of the difference of the means is the sum of the variances of the means. Another equivalent form of 12.2.2a is

$$\sigma_{\Delta\bar{x}}^2 = \sigma_1^2/N_1 + \sigma_2^2/N_2 \tag{12.2.2b}$$

Quite likely this is not very surprising insofar as the first two statements are concerned, but the third statement, concerning variances, may be. This is just a consequence of the peculiarities of language: the words "difference" and "sum" happen to occur near enough together in the same sentence so that we have an unjustified feeling that they are contradictory. A little reference to everyday experience will show that we intuitively appreciate the fact that the variance should behave as we stated.

If you go to a hardware store and examine the various devices for measuring length, you will notice a common feature of many of them. The convenient six-foot steel tapes have a small projection, or hook, at right angles to the length of the tape at its zero point. Many of the folding two-foot rules used by carpenters have a similar, but more sturdy, hook at their zero. The finely graduated six-inch steel rules often used by machinists have a similar hook. They are all used for the same purpose. In measuring a length, say of a bar, the hook is placed against one end of the bar and the length is read or the required length marked at the appropriate point on the rule. True, if a series of bars is marked to a stated length in this way and the bars then cut, there will be some variation in the length of the bars. But if the bars have to be marked without the hook at zero, the variation will be greater because of the added uncertainty in the location of the zero point. Of course, we could make ourselves still more confident that the mathematician is correct in his statement that the variances add by doing an experiment with artificial samples such as we used in gaining confidence about Student's t-distribution.

12.3 Testing Hypotheses About Differences of Means When Population Variances Are Known

Now we can put this information to work to permit us to test hypotheses. Suppose that we have two populations whose variances are known to be $\sigma_1^2 = 16$ and $\sigma_2^2 = 25$ from which we propose to draw samples of $N_1 = 4$ and $N_2 = 5$, respectively. From these samples, we wish to obtain a test of the hypothesis,

$$H_0 : \Delta\mu = \mu_1 - \mu_2 = 5.00$$

We make the required assumptions: (1) that our samples are random, (2) that the parent populations are normally distributed, and (3) that the variances are, as stated, known. If these assumptions are valid and our hypothesis is true, then our test statistic will be

$$z = \frac{\Delta\bar{x} - \Delta\mu}{\sigma_{\Delta\bar{x}}} \tag{12.3.1a}$$

$$= \frac{(\bar{x}_1 - \bar{x}_2) - (\mu_1 - \mu_2)}{\sqrt{\sigma_1^2/N_1 + \sigma_2^2/N_2}} \tag{12.3.1b}$$

$$= \frac{\Delta\bar{x} - 5.00}{\sqrt{16/4 + 25/5}} \tag{12.3.1c}$$

$$= \frac{\Delta\bar{x} - 5.00}{\sqrt{4 + 5}} \tag{12.3.1d}$$

$$= \frac{\Delta\bar{x} - 5.00}{\sqrt{9}} = \frac{\Delta\bar{x} - 5.00}{3} \tag{12.3.1e}$$

which will have the standard normal distribution. If we choose an alpha risk of 0.100, that fixes our critical values as $z_{\alpha/2} = z_{0.050} = -1.645$ and $z_{1-\alpha/2} = z_{0.975} = +1.645$. If we then obtain data such as those in Table 12-1 and carry out

Table 12-1 SYNTHETIC DATA TO ILLUSTRATE TEST OF HYPOTHESIS AND COMPUTATION OF CONFIDENCE LIMITS FOR THE DIFFERENCE OF TWO POPULATION MEANS

	Sample 1	*Sample 2*
	22	25
	25	16
	30	19
	23	11
		4
N	4	5
ΣX	100	75
$\bar{X}$	25	15
$\Delta\bar{X}$	10	
z	$(10 - 5)/3 = 1.\dot{6}$	

the computations there shown, we shall obtain as our observed value $z = 1.666$. This value is in our upper critical region, so that we must reject our null hypothesis and consider our difference of population means to be something other than 5.00.

The modifications of the test procedure for one-sided hypotheses are just as you would expect. For the hypothesis, $H_0 : \Delta\mu \leq A$, the critical value is $z_{1-1/2\alpha}$, while for the hypothesis $H_0 : \Delta\mu \geq A$, the critical value is $z_{1/2\alpha}$. The details will be illustrated in the examples dealing with real data. Of course, quite often we shall be testing hypotheses that $\Delta\mu = 0$, $\Delta\mu \geq 0$, or $\Delta\mu \leq 0$, and we shall find ourselves, in practice, not bothering to write this zero into our formulations. In a busy world this is understandable but not always totally wise, for it causes us to forget that our test statistic is comparing our observed difference of means with a hypothetical difference in terms of the known standard deviation of such differences. We urge you to write in the hypothetical value of $\Delta\mu$, even when it is zero, until you are thoroughly familiar with the principle.

12.4 Confidence Limits for the Difference of Two Population Means

Whenever we have found a test statistic for use in testing an hypothesis, we have always found that it could be used to provide confidence limits for the parameter concerned. The present case is no exception, and the thinking we have used before will establish $P\%$ confidence limits for $\Delta\mu$ as

$$\Delta\mu = \Delta\bar{x} \pm \left| z_{1/2\alpha} \right| \sigma_{\Delta\bar{x}} \tag{12.4.1}$$

where $\alpha = (100 - P)/100$ is the related alpha risk as usual.

In the problem above, 90% confidence limits would be

$$\begin{aligned} \Delta\mu &= 10.0 \pm 1.645 \times 3 = 10.0 \pm 4.935 \\ &= 5.065 \text{ and } 14.935 \end{aligned}$$

12.5 Testing Hypotheses Concerning Differences of Means When Population Variances Are Unknown

When we do not know the population variances, we may sometimes know that the two variances are equal. In still other situations, we may not even have that knowledge. How could this happen? Consider a comparison of grades of two different sections of the same course taking the same final examination simultaneously. Because the examination is a new examination, and because some new ideas may have been used in teaching the course this semester, we may quite properly be uncertain as to what the variance of examination grades will be, yet we may reasonably expect that the same factors will cause variations in both sections and that the populations from which they may be considered samples will have the same variances. If, however, the two sections take different final examinations, but take them simultaneously, we may well be uncertain that the variances will even be equal, to say nothing of known.

In a great many situations, fortunately, we may be able to claim with legitimate assurance that the variances of the two populations will be the same, because they are the result of the operation of the same set of causes, even though we may not be able to claim knowledge, in advance, of what that variance will be. The fact that our statistical path will be much smoother when we can make this assumption will place us under considerable temptation to make it when it is not warranted. This we must constantly guard against, for no statistical treatment is more valid than its assumptions.

When, however, we can legitimately assume that the variances, though unknown, are equal, we recognize that we shall be in a position to estimate this common value from the data in each of our samples through the sample variances, s_1^2 and s_2^2, and we might expect to divide these estimates by the sizes of their respective samples to obtain estimates of the variances of the sample means, and so on. But the path we actually follow is a bit different. We have assumed the population variances to be equal, so we combine our sample variance to form an estimate of the common variance as we did in Chapter 11:

$$s_p^2 = \frac{\Sigma(x_1 - \bar{x}_1)^2 + \Sigma(x_2 - \bar{x}_2)^2}{N_1 + N_2 - 2} \tag{12.5.1}$$

Incidentally, now you see one reason for considering two variances before we considered two means.

Now we use this pooled estimate to construct estimates of the variance of the sample means:

$$s_{\bar{x}_1}^2 = s_p^2/N_1 \text{ and } s_{\bar{x}_2} = s_p^2/N_2 \tag{12.5.2}$$

Then we can state that

$$s_{\Delta\bar{x}}^2 = s_{\bar{x}_1}^2 + s_{\bar{x}_2}^2 \tag{12.5.3a}$$

$$= s_p^2/N_1 + s_p^2/N_2 \tag{12.5.3b}$$

$$= s_p^2(1N_1 + 1/N_2) \tag{12.5.3c}$$

which a little more algebra reduces to

$$s_{\Delta\bar{x}}^2 = s_p^2(N_1 + N_2)/N_1N_2 \tag{12.5.3d}$$

In our development, we have been writing down our thoughts as they emerged, but we may now combine equations 12.5.1 and 12.5.3c to obtain:

$$s_{\Delta\bar{x}}^2 = \left(\frac{\Sigma(x_1 - \bar{x}_1)^2 + \Sigma(x_2 - \bar{x}_2)^2}{N_1 + N_2 - 2}\right)\left(\frac{N_1 + N_2}{N_1N_2}\right) \tag{12.5.3e}$$

This is a very convenient formula for computation. Of course, the sums of squared differences from the means will, themselves, be computed by the use of the appropriate working formula.

It can be shown by mathematical reasoning and confirmed by sampling experiments of the type we have been using before, that

$$t = (\Delta\bar{x} - \Delta\mu)/s_{\Delta\bar{x}} \tag{12.5.4}$$

will have Student's t-distribution with $n = N_1 + N_2 - 2$ degrees of freedom.

Now, of course, we are in a position to test the hypothesis that $\Delta\mu$ has any stated value. If we can make the three assumptions that

1. the samples are random,
2. the parent populations are normally distributed,
3. the variances of the populations, though unknown, are equal,

then our test statistic is simply t as defined by equation 12.5.2 and our critical values are $t_{1/2\alpha,n}$ and $t_{1-1/2\alpha,n}$. Let us, as usual, see how this works on a simple synthetic sample. Suppose we wish to test

$$H_0 : \Delta\mu = \mu_1 - \mu_2 = 3.00$$

on the basis of samples of $N_1 = 5$ and $N_2 = 7$. If we make the assumptions just stated, our test statistic becomes

$$\begin{aligned} t &= (\Delta\bar{x} - \Delta\mu)/s_{\Delta\bar{x}} \\ &= \frac{\Delta\bar{x} - 3.00}{\left(\frac{\Sigma(x - \bar{x})_1^2 + \Sigma(x - \bar{x})_2^2}{5 + 7 - 2}\right)\left(\frac{5+7}{5 \times 7}\right)} \\ &= \frac{\Delta\bar{x} - 3.00}{\left(\frac{\Sigma(x - \bar{x})_1^2 + \Sigma(x - \bar{x})_2^2}{10}\right)\left(\frac{12}{35}\right)} \end{aligned}$$

If we choose an alpha risk (for reasons of the kind previously considered) of 0.010, our critical values will be $t_{0.005,10}$ and $t_{0.995,10}$, which are ± 3.169. We now obtain our data and perform the calculations as shown in Table 12-2. We find that $t = -4.657$, which is in our lower critical region, so that we reject our hypothesis and consider the populations differing in mean by some amount other than 3.00.

Modifications for one-sided hypotheses should be evident to you and will be illustrated by means of the real examples to follow.

Table 12-2 SYNTHETIC DATA AND COMPUTATIONS FOR TEST OF HYPOTHESIS CONCERNING DIFFERENCE OF TWO MEANS WHEN POPULATION VARIANCES, THOUGH UNKNOWN, ARE ASSUMED EQUAL. SOURCE: SYNTHETIC

	Sample 1	*Sample 2*
	5	7 9
	7	7 8
	2	5 4
	2	8
	6	
N	5	7
$1/N$	0.2	0.142857 (unwieldy)
ΣX	22	48
ΣX^2	118	348
$\overline{X}$	4.40000	6.85714+
$\Sigma(X - \overline{X})^2$	21.20000	18.85714+
$\Sigma[\Sigma(X - \overline{X})^2]$	40.05714+	
$N_1 + N_2$	12	
$N_1 + N_2 - 2$	10	
$N_1 N_2$	35	
$s_{\Delta \bar{x}}^2$	$(40.05714/10)(12/35) = 1.37338$	
$s_{\Delta \bar{x}}$	1.17191	
$\Delta_{\bar{x}}$	−2.45714	
t	$(-2.45714 - 3.00000)/1.17191 = -4.657$	

Test of Auxiliary $H_0 : \sigma_1^2/\sigma_2^2 = 1.00$ or $\sigma_2^2 / \sigma_1^2 = 1.00$
Alpha risk taken as 0.100 because risk for main H_0 was taken as 0.010
Critical value actually needed is $F_{0.950,4/6} = 4.53$
Observed $F = (21.2/4)/(18.85714/6) = 1.686$
Auxiliary H_0 is not rejected and main H_0 is legitimately tested.

12.6 A Prudent Precaution: Auxiliary Test

In testing our hypothesis of equality of means, we assumed that the population variances were equal. But the same data that were to provide us information about the means and our estimates of variances would, of course, permit us to test the hypothesis that the variances are, in fact, equal. It would seem most prudent to make this test before taking the results of the test of the hypotheses concerning means as face value. (This is another reason why we discussed two variances before discussing two means.)

We already have the test method from Chapter 11. Our only problem, then, is to select an appropriate alpha risk. In order to determine the proper risk on a strictly logical basis, we would really have to know about the effect of inequalities in variance upon the form of the test statistic which should be used and the discrepancies between the results of using t when it should not be used and the proper results. Unfortunately, this information has not yet been completely developed, but we do know that the effects become more severe as the alpha risk used in connection with the hypothesis concerning the means becomes smaller. Strictly as a rule of thumb, we offer the following suggestions:

α for Hypothesis Concerning

$\Delta\mu$	$\sigma_1^2/\sigma_2^2 = 1$
≥ 0.100	0.010
0.050	0.050
≤ 0.010	0.100

If we apply this test in the case of our problem in the previous section, the results are shown in Table 12-2, and we find that we need not reject the hypothesis of equal variances and may consider our results on the test concerning the means as valid.

12.7 Confidence Limits

The computation of confidence limits requires formulas which result from the same kind of thinking we have done in other cases. For $P\%$ confidence limits, the values are

$$\Delta\mu = \Delta\bar{x} \pm | t_{\alpha/2,n} | s_{\Delta\bar{x}} \tag{12.7.1}$$

In the case of our illustrative example, 99% confidence limits are

$$\begin{aligned} \Delta\mu &= 1.00 \pm 3.169 \times 0.45355 \\ &= 1.00 \pm 1.437 = -0.437 \text{ and } +2.437 \end{aligned}$$

12.8 When the Two Population Variances Are Unequal

When prior knowledge assures us that the population variances are not equal, or when the auxiliary test leads to a rejection of the hypothesis that they are, then we can no longer use the methods just discussed for making inferences concerning the means. Under such circumstances, it is very wise to reconsider our total problem to determine whether we are still interested in the means.

Often it will turn out that the means no longer concern us, because our ultimate interest was in knowing whether the two populations were, in fact, identical. For example, we may be preparing a number of tests to be used in the appraisal of the learning progress of students in a given school system. Because the tests must be given over a period of several days, we may decide that we should have several different forms of each test so that test scores will not be affected by discussions between students who have already taken the test and those who have yet to take it. If, on pretesting with small groups, we have two forms with markedly different variances, we shall either wish to eliminate one or both tests or modify the scoring procedures. If, in studying the output per man-hour for two similar plants of the same company, we find the variances of the daily figures much greater for one plant than for the other, we shall surely wish to determine the causes of the difference. Experience has shown that very often when these causes have been found and corrected, the means come together in consequence.

Sometimes, however, we still legitimately want to know about differences in means in spite of differences in variance. Under such circumstances, it is sometimes possible to arrange to obtain new data taken under conditions that produce what are sometimes called "paired observations." What this means can probably best be made clear by an actual example, using the problem of preparing two comparable learning progress examinations. Suppose that we had prepared two forms of one of the tests and had pretested them by giving Form A to one random sample of $N_A = 20$ students and Form B to another random sample of $N_B = 20$ students. The results, shown in Table 12-3, were to be used

Table 12-3 COMPARISON OF GRADES ON TWO FORMS OF TESTS INTENDED TO BE EQUIVALENT

Separate random samples of $N = 20$ used on each test. Source: Test record

	Form A	*Form B*
	57	53
	90	79
	77	73
	63	49
	63	86
	72	48
	76	70
	82	58
	65	86
	67	71
	69	66
	85	30
	75	88
	66	79
	67	95
	63	68
	74	70
	75	73
	74	68
	80	86
Σx	1,440	1,396
Σx^2	105,016	102,320
$\bar{x}$	72.00	69.80
$\Sigma(x - \bar{x})^2$	4,879.2	1.336.0
s^2	256.800000	70.31578

$F = s_A^2/s_B^2 = 3.652$ $\qquad F_{0.975,19,19} = 2.13$

$H_0 : \sigma_A^2/\sigma_B^2 = 1.00$ must be rejected if $\alpha = 0.050$

to test the hypothesis that the two means were identical, using an alpha risk of 0.050. The auxiliary test of the hypothesis that the population variances were equal forced us to reject the hypothesis and, therefore, to abandon further use of the data. A new sample of $N = 20$ students was obtained, and each was given both forms. Random numbers were used to select which 10 students took the Form A test first.

The resulting data, with the two scores, x_A and x_B, associated with each student kept together, are shown in Table 12-4. First the differences, $x =$

Table 12-4 COMPARISON OF GRADES ON TWO FORMS OF TESTS INTENDED TO BE EQUIVALENT, USING PAIRED OBSERVATIONS. SOURCE: TEST RECORD

Student	x_A	x_B	x
1	69	58	11
2	85	78	7
3	72	90	−18
4	71	71	0
5	73	46	27
6	76	74	2
7	82	84	−2
8	75	70	5
9	72	59	13
10	47	34	13
11	88	83	5
12	77	44	33
13	85	86	−2
14	74	71	3
15	75	57	18
16	72	71	1
17	69	56	13
18	62	51	11
19	56	31	25
20	71	56	15
Σx	1,450	1,270	180
Σx^2	106,854	86,160	4,186
$\bar{x}$	72.5	63.5	9.0
$\Sigma_2(x - \bar{x})^2$	1,729.0	5,515.0	2,566.0
s	91.00000	290.26315	135.05263

$F = s_B^2/s_A^2 = 290.26315/91.00000$
$= 3.190$
$F_{0.975,19,19} = 2.53$
Reject $H_0 : \sigma_B^2/\sigma_A^2 = 1.0$
$s_{\bar{x}}^2 = 6.75263^+$
$s_{\bar{x}} = 2.59858$

$t = (\bar{x} - 0)/s_{\bar{x}}$
$= 9.0/2.59863$
$= 3.463$
$t_{0.975,19} = 2.093$
Reject $H_0 : \mu_x = 0$

$x_A - x_B$, were calculated and these 20 values were then used as a random sample of $N = 20$ values to test the hypothesis, $H_0 : \mu_x = 0$, that the mean difference in scores is zero. The results clearly lead to a rejection of the hypothesis. The individual values of x_A and x_B can now be used to test the hypothesis that the variances of the populations of scores on the two tests are identical, that is, $H_0 : \sigma_A^2/\sigma_B^2 = 1.00$, which must again be rejected.

Notice what we have gained by the paired comparison. We were able to examine the difference in scores by a procedure that did not demand the assumption that the variances of the two populations be identical. Furthermore, in examining the difference in this way, we were a lot more certain that the difference was a result of differences in the tests, rather than in the students. Finally, when we used these data to examine the difference in variance, we again had the assurance that the difference was due to the tests, not the students. For our specific example, we are now well assured that our two test forms do, indeed, differ in both mean and variance.

What can we do when we cannot make such paired comparisons? We might, for example, be interested in the effect of two different methods for training new employees, and we might discover that the variances of first-week production figures for trainees from the two methods were different. Here, obviously, we cannot use a paired comparison, for once an employee has been trained by either method he is no longer a new, untrained employee. This situation requires careful thought. Let us reconsider it.

First of all, if we knew the mean and variance of both populations, we could determine whether, for some value, x_c, the value of z would be the same for both populations. This can be determined by solving the right-hand equation below for x_c:

$$z = \frac{x_c - \mu_A}{\sigma_A} = \frac{x_c - \mu_B}{\sigma_B} \tag{12.8.1}$$

However, because we do not know the parameters, but have only estimates of them, we may work with an equation in which the parameters are replaced by their estimating statistics. We may symbolize the ratio at x_c by k, so that

$$k = \frac{x_c - \bar{x}_A}{s_A} = \frac{x_c - \bar{x}_B}{s_B} \tag{12.8.2a}$$

from which

$$x_c = \frac{s_B\bar{x}_A - s_A\bar{x}_B}{s_B - s_A} \tag{12.8.2b}$$

The k of equation 12.8.2a is a rather interesting quantity in its own right. With the aid of appropriate tables, we can state that specified fractions of the populations will lie between the values $\bar{x} \pm ks$ but, because we are dealing with statistics, not parameters, we have to attach a statement about our degree of confidence when we state these values. Thus we can state that we are $P\%$ certain that a fraction γ of our population is beyond the stated limits. Such limits are known as *tolerance limits*. Tables for their computation and a more complete discussion of them will be found in the following references for those of you may find need for such limits:

EISENHART, C., HASTAY, M. W., and WALLIS, W. A., *Techniques of Statistical Analysis*, McGraw-Hill Book Company, Inc., New York, 1947.
DIXON, W. J., and MASSEY, F. J., JR., *Introduction to Statistical Analysis*, McGraw-Hill Book Company, Inc., New York, Second Edition, 1957.

Returning to our main problem, suppose that we call x_c the *crossover point*, for reasons soon to become apparent. Without loss of generality, suppose we designate as population B that with the larger sample variance (and hence, standard deviation). Now let us ask under what conditions the crossover point will be below $\bar{x}_A$. This merely requires that we solve the inequality,

$$x_c = \frac{s_B\bar{x}_A - s_A\bar{x}_B}{s_B - s_A} < \bar{x}_A \tag{12.8.3a}$$

whence

$$s_B\bar{x}_A - s_A\bar{x}_B < s_B\bar{x}_A - s_A\bar{x}_A \tag{12.8.3b}$$

$$-s_A\bar{x}_B < -s_A\bar{x}_A \tag{12.8.3c}$$

and

$$\bar{x}_B > \bar{x}_A \qquad \text{or} \qquad \bar{x}_A < \bar{x}_B \tag{12.8.3d}$$

Similarly, the crossover point will be above $\bar{x}_A$ if

$$\bar{x}_B < \bar{x}_A \qquad \text{or} \qquad \bar{x}_A > \bar{x}_B \tag{12.8.3e}$$

as can be shown by similar algebraic steps starting from the reverse inequality. Finally, similar reasoning shows that the crossover point will be at $\bar{x}_A$ if and only if $\bar{x}_A = \bar{x}_B$. All this can be stated in English as follows:

If two populations have different variances, the estimated crossover point will be below both means if the lower mean is associated with the lower variance, above both means if the lower mean is associated with the higher variance, and at the common mean when the means are equal. It is understood that "mean" and "variance" refer to the sample estimates.

By some further tedious algebra, it can be shown that in case 1, where the crossover point is below both means, for all values of x below x_c the fraction of the population below x will be greater for the population with the higher mean and variance. Similarly, for case 2, where the crossover point is above both means, it can be shown that, for values of x above x_c, the fraction of the population above x will be greater for the population with the lower mean and higher variance. Thus, in both cases, the variance is the controlling characteristic in determining the proportion of the distributions more remote from the mean than the crossover point. For this reason, then, we may often cease to be much interested in differences in means when the differences in the associated variances are real. In a training program, for example, a method which produces a higher mean production may produce a variance sufficiently larger than that of a program with a lower mean so that the fraction of newly trained employees with unsatisfactorily low production rates will be serious.

If, after careful consideration, it is still desired to determine whether the means are really different, there is an approximate procedure in which the test statistic becomes what we shall designate as

$$t' = \frac{\Delta\bar{x} - \Delta\mu}{\sqrt{s_A^2/N_A + s_B^2/N_B}} \qquad (12.8.4)$$

The modification consists, as you see, in the computation of an estimate of $s_{\Delta\bar{x}}^2$ by adding the separate estimates of $s_{\bar{x}}^2$ instead of pooling the estimates of s^2, then using it to estimate the required $s_{\Delta\bar{x}}^2$. Instead of using two less than the total number of observations as the number of degress of freedom, we use an artificial value:

$$n' = \frac{(N_A + 1)(N_B + 1)(N_B s_A^2 + N_A s_B^2)^2}{N_B^2(N_B + 1)(s_A^2)^2 + N_A^2(N_A + 1)(s_B^2)^2} - 2 \qquad (12.8.5)$$

This formula often results in fractional values for n' but, because we are already dealing with an approximate method, it suffices to use table values corresponding to the nearest integral number of degrees of freedom. As we have implied, we doubt that you will often use this method.

In this section, we have had to deal with rather a welter of details, so perhaps we should summarize our principal findings. We may say that when we are primarily interested, at the start of an investigation, in the means of two populations whose variances are unknown and which the auxiliary test shows to be unequal, we should consider the possibility of taking new data under such conditions that paired comparisons may be made. If this is not feasible (for physical, time, or economic reasons) we should give careful consideration to the behavior of frequencies in the extremes of the populations to see whether the advantage of the indicated levels of the means may be offset by the variance difference. If we still must consider the hypothesis concerning the means, we may use the approximate method just discussed.

General Study

1. Consider several problems in your field of major interest which involve two population means. Determine the class to which they belong in the list below.

   I. Population variances are known.
   II. Population variances are unknown but are quite certainly equal.
   III. Population variances are unknown and, if they prove to be unequal, the cross-over point will be more important than differences between the means.
   IV. Population variances are unknown and differences between the means will be important regardless of any differences between variances.

2. In any of the foregoing cases would the normality of distribution of the populations be open to serious doubt? If so, have you a suggestion for an appropriate transformation?

Specific Problems

1–6. The first six problems will be simply for experience in the use of the formulas with simple calculations. Test the hypotheses stated at the alpha risks given in the light of the stated information. In all cases, state your assumption, show the formulas used, and your final conclusion.

No.	H_0	α	σ_A^2	σ_B^2	$\bar{x}_A$	$\bar{x}_B$	s_A^2	s_B^2	N_A	N_B
1	$\mu_A = \mu_B$	0.100	18	64	25	30	—	—	2	4
2	$\mu_A \geq \mu_B$	.050	20	24	10	7	—	—	5	6
3	$\mu_A \leq \mu_B$	.010	0.40	2.10	50.6	51.6	—	—	20	30
4	$\mu_A = \mu_B$	.010	—	—	40	44	144	196	3	11
5	$\mu_A \geq \mu_B$	.100	—	—	1.40	1.45	0.15	0.30	5	5
6	$\mu_A \leq \mu_B$	.050	—	—	150	140	120	100	20	10

7. In reviewing maintenance costs, a plant manager noticed that the costs, as a percentage of total costs, for two departments for the past ten months had been as shown.

Department A		*Department B*	
6.1	5.8	5.9	6.1
7.0	6.1	5.7	5.8
5.8	6.4	5.9	5.6
6.1	6.0	5.7	5.6
5.9	5.8	5.9	5.6

Test the hypotheses that the means and variances of maintenance costs for the two departments are equal. Choose an alpha risk that seems appropriate and explain your choice. Provide appropriate confidence limits.

8. The scholastic officer on a certain campus reviews the academic indexes of two residence groups for the past five semesters. State hypotheses in which he should be interested and select appropriate alpha risks for testing them. What would be the consequences of using larger alpha risks? Smaller alpha risks? State the assumptions made in preparing your plan of analysis and discuss their validity. The data were as follows:

Group P	*Group Q*
2.66	2.26
2.24	2.33
2.39	2.35
2.35	2.44
2.42	2.43

13

Dealing with Samples from More Than Two Populations

13.1 Some Preliminary Thinking

So far, we have learned to make inferences about the mean and variance of one population and of two populations from samples obtained from them. This might lead us to fear that we might have to develop detailed methods for dealing with three populations, then four, and so on. Happily, this is not the case: when we learn how to deal with more than two populations, the basic procedure will be the same, regardless of the number of populations. We are a little like the primitive tribes which can only count "one," "two," and "many"! As a matter of fact, we shall presently find that our procedures for dealing with two populations are just an algebraic modification of those we shall develop for many.

It will probably help us to do our thinking in relation to a set of synthetic data such as we have used before. Suppose we have samples, each comprising five observations, from four populations. It will be convenient, in view of possible complexities in keeping track of what we are doing, to agree upon some notations. We shall designate any observation by X_{ij} where the subscript i will indicate the sample and the subscript j will indicate the serial number of the observation in that sample. Thus X_{23} will indicate that the value is from sample No. 2 and is the third observation in that sample.

We shall find we need a designation for the number of observations in each sample, and shall use $N_{i \cdot}$. Unless we specifically state otherwise, we shall assume that all values of N_i are equal, that is, that all samples have the same number of observations. We shall designate the number of samples by k and the total number of observations by N. Of course, $N = kN_{i \cdot}$. We shall find that we need subtotals for the individual samples, as well as the grand total, and our sigma notation for sums, convenient though it has been, will now prove a little cumbersome. So we shall designate the subtotal of the i-th sample by

$$T_{i+} = \sum_{j=1}^{N_i} X_{ij} \tag{13.1.1}$$

The grand total, which may be thought of as the sum of the subtotals, we shall designate by

$$T_{++} = \sum_{i=1}^{k} T_{i+} = \sum_{i=1}^{k} \sum_{j=1}^{N_i} X_{ij} \tag{13.1.2}$$

We shall similarly designate sample means as $\overline{X}_{i+}$ and the grand mean as $\overline{X}_{++}$. The code is simple: when a set of values has been added, replace their subscript by a subscript plus sign.

The synthetic samples we shall consider, together with some calculations we shall be making on them, are shown in Table 13-1. We might consider

Table 13-1 SYNTHETIC DATA TO ILLUSTRATE TREATMENT OF SEVERAL SAMPLES

Population, i:	1	2	3	4
	2	3	8	9
	1	4	7	8
	2	3	6	8
	3	2	7	7
	2	3	7	8
T_{i+}	10	15	35	40
ΣX_{ij}^2	22	47	247	322
$\overline{X}_{i+}$	2	3	7	8
$\Sigma(X_{ij} - \overline{X}_{i+})^2$	2	2	2	2

$T_{++} = 100$ $\qquad$ $T_{++}^2/N = 500$

$\Sigma X_{ij}^2 = 638$ $\qquad$ $\Sigma T_{ij}^2/N_i = 630$

$\overline{X}_{++} = 5$

$\Sigma(X_{ij} - \overline{X}_{++})^2 = 138$

attacking these data by using the methods of the preceding chapter to test the hypothesis, $H_0: \mu_1 - \mu_2 = 0$, that is, that the means of populations Nos. 1 and 2 are identical. We would assume that we had random samples, that the parent populations were normally distributed, and that their variances were equal. This would permit us to use our established procedures, involving Student's t-distribution.

Then, continuing in the same vein of thought, we might go on to test other hypotheses concerning equality of pairs of means as follows:

$$\mu_1 - \mu_3 = 0 \qquad \mu_2 - \mu_3 = 0 \qquad \mu_3 - \mu_4 = 0$$

$$\mu_1 - \mu_4 = 0 \qquad \mu_2 - \mu_4 = 0$$

In this way we would test the equality of all possible pairs of two means from our set of four and would be using our newly acquired statistical knowledge.

But there are some faults with this proposal. As we made test after test, we would ultimately have assumed that all four of the population variances were equal. That being the case, couldn't we somehow use the information contained in all four samples in testing each hypothesis? Wouldn't we be surer of the value of this common variance by using all available information concerning it? We can and shall do just this in the method we are about to employ.

Another fault should become apparent with a little more thought. When we test each hypothesis, we know that we are subject to error. In testing the equality of μ_1 and μ_2, for instance, the error may arise from a misestimate of μ_1, a misestimate of μ_2, a misestimate of the common variance, or any combination of these errors. Suppose there was, in fact, a misestimate of μ_2. This same misestimate will apply to the tests of all other hypotheses involving μ_2, and our errors will have a disturbing tendency to accumulate.

Still another fault is inherent in our proposed plan. Suppose we have tested the equality of μ_1 and μ_2, of μ_2 and μ_3, and of μ_3 and μ_4, and that we have, in fact, concluded that all four means are equal. Then the other three tests we had proposed are, actually, redundant and represent wasted effort. Other objections to our proposed plan can be raised, but these alone are sufficient to cause us to look for a better plan.

13.2 A Sounder Attack, in Elemental Form

Suppose we pick up two of the ideas we just discovered and see what we can do with them. Since, in effect, the hypotheses we originally proposed were equivalent to the hypothesis, $H_0: \mu_1 = \mu_2 = \mu_3 = \mu_4 = \mu$, that the four means are equal to each other and, hence, to a common value, why not try to test that hypothesis immediately? We may quite properly assume that we have random samples, that they come from normally distributed populations, and that the variances of these populations are all equal, that is, that $\sigma_1^2 = \sigma_2^2 = \sigma_3^2 = \sigma_4^2 = \sigma^2$. Although we are interested in testing the hypothesis about means, we shall actually do so through the use of different estimates of the assumed common variance. Let's see how it is done.

If our hypothesis is true and our assumptions are valid, then only some characteristic other than the kinds of observed values comprising our samples distinguishes the different populations. Under those circumstances, we might combine all values into a single total set, and estimate the variance from it as we would from any single sample. It will prove convenient to compute our sum of squares and degrees of freedom separately, then divide the former by the latter to obtain our estimate of variance. It will also be desirable to use ss as shorthand for "sum of squares" and df for "degrees of freedom," together with a subscript t to indicate that the estimates are derived from the set considered as a totality.

A. *The "Total" Estimate.* Our formulas take account, initially, of the fact that we may develop our totals from subtotals:

$$\text{ss}_t = \sum_{i=1}^{k} \sum_{j=1}^{N_i} (X_{ij} - \overline{X}_{++})^2 \qquad (13.2.1a)$$

We recognize, of course, that we shall not calculate the value by this formula if we have a calculator available, but shall take advantage of the kind of algebra we have previously employed to obtain a simpler formula. Recall that, when we were dealing with a single sample, we found that

$$\text{ss} = \Sigma(X - \overline{X})^2 = \Sigma X^2 - \Sigma \overline{X} X = \frac{N\Sigma X^2 - (\Sigma X)^2}{N}$$

and we could have converted the last form to

$$\text{ss} = \Sigma X^2 - \frac{(\Sigma X)^2}{N}$$

although we did not do so then because, for estimating a single variance, that formula is not convenient. However, for what we are going to be doing, it has merits that warrant its use. The kind of algebra that was used above would convert equation 13.2.1a to the form:

$$\text{ss}_t = \sum_{i=1}^{k} \sum_{j=1}^{N_i} X_{ij}^2 - \frac{T_{++}^2}{N} \qquad (13.2.1b)$$

For our data, $\text{ss}_t = 638 - 500 = 138$. The degrees of freedom are simply

$$\text{df}_t = N - 1 = 20 - 1 = 19 \qquad (13.2.2)$$

so that the estimate of variance is

$$s_t^2 = \text{ss}_t/\text{df}_t = 138/19 \doteq 6.84210$$

B. *The "Within" Estimate.* But suppose that our hypothesis is false: we can still obtain an estimate of the common variance by combining (or "pooling") the estimates from our four samples. By an extension of the idea we used to combine two estimates, the sum of squares will simply be the sum of the sums of squares for the individual samples. Using a subscript w to indicate that this estimate is developed from the estimates made from variations *within* the samples, we have:

$$\text{ss}_w = \sum_{i=1}^{k} \sum_{j=1}^{N_i} (X_{ij} - \overline{X}_{i+})^2 \qquad (13.2.3a)$$

Algebra similar to that we have previously employed will develop the convenient computing formula:

$$\mathrm{ss}_w = \sum_{i=1}^{k} \sum_{j=1}^{N_i} X_{ij}^2 - \sum_{i=1}^{k} \frac{T_{i+}^2}{N_i} \tag{13.2.3b}$$

from which our numerical value will be

$$\mathrm{ss}_w = 638 - 630 = 8$$

Our degrees of freedom will be our total number of observations minus the number of sample means:

$$\mathrm{df}_w = N - k \tag{13.2.4}$$

for which our numerical value is

$$\mathrm{df}_w = 20 - 4 = 16$$

and

$$s_w^2 = \mathrm{ss}_w/\mathrm{df}_w = 8/16 = 0.5$$

We seem to have a tremendous discrepancy between these two estimates of our common variance.

C. *The "Among" Estimate.* There is yet a third method by which we can estimate that variance: suppose we employ it and see whether it throws light on the subject. When we used Student's t-distribution for testing hypotheses concerning a single mean, we estimated the variance of sample means by the aid of the formula:

$$s_{\bar{x}}^2 = s^2/N$$

In that situation, we obtained our value of s^2 from our sample data, then divided it by N to obtain our value for $s_{\bar{x}}^2$. In the present situation, we have $k = 4$ sample means, $\overline{X}_{i+}$. Could we not consider these means as a sample of four means from an infinite population of such means, each calculated from the data in a random sample of N_i observations from a normal population with our hypothetical mean, μ, and our assumed common variance, σ^2?

Under those conditions, we would have

$$s_{\bar{x}}^2 = \sum_{i=1}^{k} \frac{(\overline{X}_{i+} - \overline{X}_{++})^2}{k - 1} \tag{13.2.5a}$$

whence

$$s^2 = N_i s_{\bar{x}}^2 = N_i \sum_{i=1}^{k} \frac{(\overline{X}_{i+} - \overline{X}_{++})^2}{k - 1} \tag{13.2.5b}$$

Again we recognize the fact that the variance involves a sum of squares as its numerator and a number of degrees of freedom as its denominator. This variance was estimated from the variations *among* the sample means, so, with the aid of more algebra, we find that

$$\text{ss}_a = N_i \sum_{i=1}^{k} (\overline{X}_{i+} - \overline{X}_{++})^2 \tag{13.2.6a}$$

$$= \sum_{i=1}^{k} \frac{T_{i+}^2}{N_i} - \frac{T_{++}^2}{N} \tag{13.2.6b}$$

which for our particular data yields the numerical value

$$\text{ss}_a = 630 - 500 = 130$$

Our number of degrees of freedom is

$$\text{df}_a = k - 1 = 4 - 1 = 3 \tag{13.2.7}$$

so that our value of $s_a^2 = 130/3 \doteq 43.33333$.

D. *Using the Estimates.* Now we have three different estimates of the common variance! This seems disturbing, but notice how they were derived. Our estimate, s_w^2, based on a combination of the four estimates made on the individual samples, is not affected by variations among the population means. Therefore, regardless of the truth or falsity of our hypothesis about the means, it should be a valid estimate of the assumed common variance. Our estimate, s_a^2, derived from the variation among our sample means would, as we said when we developed its formula, be a valid estimate of the common variance *if* the hypothesis were true, for then the only variations in the $\overline{X}_{i+}$ values would be those resulting from random sampling from a population having the common variance. But, if the hypothesis is not true, then the population means are not all alike, and their differences will be reflected in $s_{\bar{x}}^2$ and hence in s_a^2.

How could we determine whether the population means are different? If they were not, we should expect both s_a^2 and s_w^2 to behave like variance estimates from two random samples. We might consider their ratio as

$$F = s_a^2/s_w^2 \tag{13.2.8}$$

which we are assured by mathematicians does have the F-distribution with $(k - 1)$ and $(N - k)$ numerator and denominator degrees of freedom, respectively. If the observed F-value exceeds $F_{1-a,(k-1)/(N-k)}$, we may then reject our hypothesis that all the population means are equal.

13.3 Some Convenient Order: The Analysis of Variance Table

It will pay us to examine what we have done more thoughtfully. Suppose we tabulate the values of ss and df for our three different estimates of the common variance, indicating, in our previously used terms, the source of the estimates:

Source	*ss*	*df*
Total	138	19
Among	130	3
Within	8	16

This brings out the fact that we have analyzed (that is, usefully broken up) the total sum of squares, ss_t, into two parts, one of which, ss_a, reflects the variation among means as well as the variation of individual values, while the other, ss_w, reflects only variations of individual values within the sample. We have similarly analyzed the degrees of freedom. This enables us to make two useful estimates of variance which lead to our test of the hypothesis that all means are equal.

It really should seem quite amazing to you that, by forming these three estimates of the common variance, each estimate arising from a different line of reasoning, we should have accomplished this analysis of the sum of squares for the total set into two parts which exactly add to the original value, and should similarly have analyzed the total degrees of freedom. A little algebra will show why this is so. For simplicity, we shall examine the degrees of freedom first. The total degrees of freedom was simply $N - 1$. If, to $N - 1$, we add and subtract k, we shall not affect the value. But then we may group the numbers involved in any way we choose, thus:

$$\begin{aligned} df_t &= N - 1 = N + k - k - 1 \\ &= (N - k) + (k - 1) \\ &= df_a + df_w \end{aligned} \tag{13.3.1}$$

We can similarly subtract $\overline{X}_{i+}$ inside our parentheses in the formula for the total sum of squares and carry out the indicated algebra:

$$ss_t = \sum_{i=1}^{k} \sum_{j=1}^{N_i} (X_{ij} - \overline{X}_{++})^2 \tag{13.3.2a}$$

$$= \sum_{i=1}^{k} \sum_{j=1}^{N_i} [(X_{ij} - \overline{X}_{i+}) + (\overline{X}_{i+} - \overline{X}_{++})]^2 \tag{13.3.2b}$$

$$= \sum_{i=1}^{k} \sum_{j=1}^{N_i} [(X_{ij} - \overline{X}_{i+})^2 + 2(X_{ij} - \overline{X}_{i+})(\overline{X}_{i+} - \overline{X}_{++}) + (\overline{X}_{i+} - \overline{X}_{++})^2] \tag{13.3.2c}$$

This sum can then be expressed as the sum of three subtotals, thus:

$$\begin{aligned} ss_t = & \sum_{i=1}^{k} \sum_{j=1}^{Ni} (X_{ij} - \overline{X}_{i+})^2 \\ & + 2\sum_{i=1}^{k} \sum_{j=1}^{Ni} (X_{ij} - \overline{X}_{i+})(\overline{X}_{i+} - \overline{X}_{++}) \\ & + \sum_{i=1}^{k} \sum_{j=1}^{Ni} (\overline{X}_{i+} - \overline{X}_{++})^2 \end{aligned} \tag{13.3.2d}$$

The first subtotal we recognize as our ss_a and the last as ss_w. What about the second subtotal? Read this formula carefully and you will see that it instructs you to take each observation in group 1 and subtract its value from the mean of group 1, then multiply that difference by the difference between the mean of group 1 and the grand mean and add the resulting products. But in each product the difference between the group mean and grand mean is a common factor, so that the sum of the products would be this factor times the sum of the differences between the individual values and the group mean. Now we learned long ago that the sum of differences between a set of values and their mean is zero so, for the first group, the sum of products is zero. The same thing happens for all the other groups, hence the entire "cross-product" sum, as it is sometimes called, is just zero. It is indeed comforting to find that we can approach a problem from different viewpoints and yet achieve the same results, with each viewpoint strengthening our confidence in the validity of our results.

The method is known as the *analysis of variance*. Some years ago, Sir Ronald A. Fisher laid the basis of a convenient method for tabulating the values involved, known as an "analysis of variance table," which we commonly (though not necessarily happily!) abbreviate to "anov table." Such a table, in expanded form, is shown as Table 13-2. The first column gives the abbreviated identification of the source of the figures used in forming the estimates. The second column shows the exact, defining formula for the sum of squares, while in the third column a highly coded representation of this form is given. Notice that, in the coded form, only single summations are indicated and all indexes are omitted from the sigmas. This is confusing, at first, but you are supposed to recognize that, when such a formula appears in an anov table, the extreme coding has been employed. In the fourth column we show the actual formulas used for computation, while we show the numerical values resulting in the fifth column. The sixth column shows the formula and the seventh column shows the numerical values for the degrees of freedom. The various estimates of variance are traditionally known as mean squares, and their values are shown in the eighth column. Actually, of course, these are unbiased estimates of mean squares, not actually mean squares. The remaining columns show, in order, the observed and critical values of F and our decision concerning the null hypothesis being tested.

Table 13-2 DETAILED ANALYSIS OF VARIANCE (ANOV) TABLE FOR DATA OF TABLE 13-1

(1)	(2)	(3)	(4)	(5)
Source	Sum of Squares (ss)			
	Complete	*Coded*	*Computing*	*Numerical*
Total	$\sum_{i=1}^{k}\sum_{j=1}^{N_i}(X_{ij} - \overline{X}_{++})^2$	$\Sigma(X_{ij} - {}_{++}\overline{X})^2$	$\Sigma X_{ij}^2 - T_{++}^2/N$	$638 - 500 = 138$
Among	$N_i \sum_{i=1}^{k}(\overline{X}_{i+} - \overline{X}_{++})^2$	$\Sigma(\overline{X}_{i+} - \overline{X}_{++})^2$	$\Sigma T_{i+}^2/N_i - T_{++}^2/N$	$630 - 500 = 130$
Within	$\sum_{i=1}^{k}\sum_{j=1}^{N_i}(X_{ij} - \overline{X}_{i+})^2$	$\Sigma(X_{ij} - X_{i+})^2$	$\Sigma X_{ij}^2 - \Sigma T_{i+}^2/N_i$	$638 - 630 = 8$

	(6)	(7)	(8)	(9)	(10)	(11)
	Degrees of Freedom (df)		*Mean Square*	F	F_{cr}	*Decision*
	Formula	*Numerical*	(ms)			
Total	$N - 1$	$20 - 1 = 19$	—	—	—	—
Among	$k - 1$	$4 - 1 = 3$	43.33333	86.67	3.24	Reject
Within	$N - k$	$20 - 4 = 16$	.50000	—		

Using $\alpha = 0.050$, $F_{cr} = F_{0.950,3/16}$

We should make two comments here. First, the traditional anov table places the total at the bottom. This is reasonable in view of the fact that the total normally appears at the bottom of a column of figures to be added. But, in a very real sense, in an analysis of variance, we *start* with the total and *analyze* it into pieces which have meaning for us. It seems to us that our order bears a more logical relation to our task, and we therefore commend it to you. Our second comment is that, once you have become familiar with analysis of variance, you will probably employ only columns 1, 5, 7, 8, 9, and 10. You will probably follow the custom of indicating by an asterisk those observed values of F which exceed the critical values and so lead to rejection of the null hypotheses.

13.4 A More Specific Hypothesis

In opening this chapter, we suggested the possibility of testing more specific hypotheses, such as $H_0 : \mu_1 - \mu_2 = 0$, but we saw certain difficulties involved. We suggested that, in testing such hypotheses, it would be desirable to take advantage of the information about the common variance contained in all the samples. We further recognized that the hypotheses we then considered were by no means unrelated, but that errors had a tendency to accumulate, and that some of our proposed hypotheses were redundant.

Suppose we return to our problem and plan a test of the first hypothesis, $\Delta\mu = \mu_1 - \mu_2 = 0$. Under the assumption that we have random samples from normal populations with equal variances, our s_w^2 from our analysis of variance table is an estimate of the common variance. It has $N - k$ associated degrees of freedom, and is a valid estimate if the assumptions are warranted, whether the hypothesis is true or not. We might therefore presume that an appropriate test statistic would be

$$t = (\Delta\overline{X} - \Delta\mu)/s_{\Delta\bar{x}} \tag{13.4.1}$$

which would have Student's t-distribution with $N - k$ degrees of freedom. It can be shown mathematically that this is true if $s_{\Delta\bar{x}}$ is calculated from the formula,

$$s_{\Delta\bar{x}} = \sqrt{s_w^2[(1/N_i) + (1/N_i)]} = \sqrt{s_w^2(2/N_i)} \tag{13.4.2}$$

which, aside from the replacement of s_p^2 by s_w^2 is quite consistent with the corresponding equation 12.5.1c in our original treatment of the means of two populations.

Now let us try something. Very early in our study, we recognized that, by using the variance instead of the standard deviation as a measure of dispersion, we avoided the necessity for taking square roots. Suppose we just square our test statistic from equation 13.4.1 and obtain

$$t^2 = (\Delta\overline{X} - \Delta\mu)^2/s_{\Delta\bar{x}}^2 \tag{13.4.3a}$$

Then we note that $\Delta\mu = 0$ by hypothesis and that

$$\Delta\overline{X} = \overline{X}_1 - \overline{X}_2 = (T_{1+}/N_i) - (T_{2+}/N_i) = (1/N_i)(T_{1+} - T_{2+})$$

and make these substitutions to obtain

$$t^2 = \frac{(1/N_i^2)(T_{1+} - T_{2+})^2}{s_w^2\,(2/N_i)} \tag{13.4.3b}$$

Multiplication of the numerator and denominator of this expression by $N_i/2$ produces the result,

$$t^2 = \frac{(T_{1+} - T_{2+})^2/2N_i}{s_w^2} \tag{13.4.3c}$$

This result should be challenging: notice that the denominator is a variance estimate, and that the numerator involves the kinds of elements that went into s_a^2 in the previous section. We certainly could suspect that this t^2 would be a variance ratio, or F. What about the number of degrees of freedom for the numerator? Notice that it involves two sample means, and that what we are, in fact, doing is using these two means to estimate the variance of sample means, and from that estimate, under our hypothesis, the common variance. Thus we might expect to have $2 - 1 = 1$ degrees of freedom just as, in the previous section, the similar use of k means gave us $k - 1$ degrees of freedom. All this is true and can be demonstrated by rigorous mathematics. Thus our critical values for our proposed t-test would be $t_{1/2\alpha,(N-k)}$ and $t_{(1-1/2\alpha),(N-k)}$, which have the same absolute value, namely, $t_{(1-1/2\alpha),(N-k)}$. The square of this value must be and is

$$t_{(1-1/2\alpha),(n-k)}{}^2 = F_{(1-\alpha),1/(N-k)} \tag{13.4.4}$$

Suppose that we look at the numerical values for our specific problem:

$$F = \frac{(10 - 15)^2/(2 \times 5)}{0.5} = \frac{(-5)^2/10}{0.5} = \frac{2.5}{0.5} = 5.0$$

If we used an alpha risk of 0.050, our critical value would have been $F_{0.950,1/16} = 4.49$ and we would reject our null hypothesis. Had we taken the trouble to take square roots and use the t-test, our values would have been

$$t = \frac{2.0 - 3.0}{\sqrt{0.5(2/5)}} = \frac{-1.0}{0.44721} = -2.236$$

and the critical values would have been $\pm t_{0.975,16} = \pm 2.120$. Notice that $(-2.236)^2 \doteq 5.000$ and $2.120^2 \doteq 4.49$ which agree within rounding errors with the corresponding F values.

13.5 Another Specific Hypothesis

We might proceed in an exactly similar way to test another hypothesis, namely, $H_0: \mu_3 - \mu_4 = 0$. In our specific example, we would obtain

$$F = \frac{(T_{3+} - T_{4+})^2/2N_i}{s_w^2} = \frac{(35 - 40)^2/(2 \times 5)}{0.5} = 5.0$$

and the same critical value would be used as before, again leading to rejection of the null hypothesis.

13.6 A Third Hypothesis and a Mistake

Now let us do something *that we shall find is wrong;* doing it will help us to recognize, in fact, why it was wrong and to seek means of protection from such mistakes. We shall test as a third hypothesis $H_0: \mu_2 - \mu_3 = 0$, for which

$$F = \frac{(T_{2+} - T_{3+})^2/2N_i}{s_w^2} = \frac{(15 - 35)^2/(2 \times 5)}{0.5} = \frac{(-20)^2/10}{0.5}$$
$$= 40/0.5 = 80$$

Again we would have one degree of freedom for the numerator and would use the same critical F value. But notice that in our original analysis of variance we had three degrees of freedom associated with our "among" estimate and a sum of squares equal to 130. In these three tests we have just made, we have had one numerator degree of freedom for each. Thus we have broken down or analyzed our three "among" degrees of freedom into three individual degrees of freedom. Since the numerator of each F had one degree of freedom, it was, in fact, both a mean square and a sum of squares. Therefore, we would expect that these three sums of squares, 2.5 + 2.5 + 40.0, would total the previous "among" sum of squares, 130.0. But their actual total is only 45.0: something must be wrong. There is no algebraic nor arithmetic error, so our thinking must be wrong, and it is.

13.7 Correcting the Mistake

To find the error recall that, in opening our discussion of our problem, we suggested that if we misestimated μ_2 in connection with testing $H_0: \mu_1 - \mu_2 = 0$ and misestimated μ_3 in connection with testing $H_0: \mu_3 - \mu_4 = 0$, then these errors could affect our conclusion with respect to $H_0: \mu_2 - \mu_3 = 0$. Let us try a different hypothesis as our third one, namely, $H_0: (\mu_1 + \mu_2)/2 - (\mu_3 + \mu_4)/2 = 0$, that is, that the mean of the means of the first two populations is equal to the mean of the means of the last two. From experience, we could guess that the numerator of our test statistic, t, would be $(\overline{X}_{1+} + \overline{X}_{2+})/2 - (\overline{X}_{3+} + \overline{X}_{4+})/2$, and we would be faced with the problem of finding an estimate of the variance of such a combination of means. It is a fact, as can be shown mathematically and confirmed by experience, that whenever we combine m means from populations having equal variances, each mean being based on N_i

observations, the combined mean has a variance $1/(mN_i)$ times that of the parent populations. Thus our variance for the combination above will be $s_w^2[1/(2N_i) + 1/(2N_i)] = s_w^2/N_i$.

We could now set up our test statistic as before:

$$F = t^2 = \frac{\left(\frac{\overline{X}_{1+} + \overline{X}_{2+}}{2} - \frac{\overline{X}_{3+} + \overline{X}_{4+}}{2}\right)^2}{s_w^2/N_i}$$

$$= \frac{\frac{(T_{1+} + T_{2+} - T_{3+} - T_{4+})^2}{4N_i^2}}{s_w^2/N_i}$$

$$= \frac{\frac{(T_{1+} + T_{2+} - T_{3+} - T_{4+})^2}{4N_i}}{s_w^2}$$

which, for our specific problem, becomes

$$F = \frac{(10 + 15 - 35 - 40)^2/(4 \times 5)}{0.5}$$

$$= \frac{(-50)^2/20}{0.5} = \frac{2500/20}{0.5} = \frac{125.0}{0.5} = 250.0$$

Notice that now our three sums of squares do, indeed, exactly add up to the "among" sum of squares: $2.5 + 2.5 + 125.0 = 130.0$.

Another set of hypotheses we might have tested is the following, in which we use subscripts a, b, and c for convenience in identifying the three:

$$H_{0a} : \mu_1 - \mu_2 = 0.$$

$$H_{0b} : (\mu_1 + \mu_2)/2 - \mu_3 = 0.$$

$$H_{0c} : (\mu_1 + \mu_2 + \mu_3)/3 - \mu_4 = 0.$$

We have already shown the details of the test of H_{0a}. For H_{0b}, our preceding principles lead to the formulation and values,

$$F = t^2 = \frac{\left(\frac{\overline{X}_{1+} + \overline{X}_2}{2} - \overline{X}_{3+}\right)^2}{s_w^2[1/(2N_i) + 1/N_i]}$$

$$= \frac{\frac{(T_{1+} + T_{2+} - 2T_{3+})^2}{6N_i}}{s_w^2}$$

$$= \frac{\frac{[10 + 15 - (2 \times 35)]^2}{6 \times 5}}{0.5} = \frac{(-45)^2/30}{0.5}$$

$$= \frac{2025/30}{0.5} = 67.5/0.5 = 135$$

and for H_{0c}:

$$F = t^2 = \frac{\left(\frac{\bar{X}_{1+} + \bar{X}_{2+} + \bar{X}_{3+}}{3} - \bar{X}_{4+}\right)^2}{s_w^2[1/(3N_i) + 1/N_i]}$$

$$= \frac{\frac{(T_{1+} + T_{2+} + T_{3+} - 3T_{4+})^2}{12N_i}}{s_w^2}$$

$$= \frac{\frac{[10 + 15 + 35 - (3 \times 40)]^2}{12 \times 5}}{0.5}$$

$$= \frac{(-60)^2/60}{0.5} = 60/0.5 = 120$$

Notice that, for this set of hypotheses also, the sums of squares for the three tests, $2.5 + 67.5 + 60 = 130$, add to the "among" sum of squares. How can we be sure that we have a set of hypotheses whose sums of squares will be an exact analysis of the "among" sum of squares? It happens that the answer to this question also leads to a very simple computing procedure for each of the sums of squares involved, so let's establish the idea.

13.8 A General Plan: Orthogonal Linear Contrasts

Any of the hypotheses we have been considering above is a statement that a sum of terms, each involving one of the population means multiplied by some coefficient, is zero. Such a statement is said to be a *linear contrast* (or *comparison*) among the means. As we formulated our contrasts, the coefficients were fractions. However, by multiplying both sides of the equation stating any hypothesis by its least common denominator, we can eliminate the fractions. In this form, our first acceptable set of hypotheses could be stated as

$$H_{0d}: 1\mu_1 - 1\mu_2 + 0\mu_3 + 0\mu_4 = 0$$

$$H_{0e}: 0\mu_1 + 0\mu_2 + 1\mu_3 - 1\mu_4 = 0$$

$$H_{0f}: 1\mu_1 + 1\mu_2 - 1\mu_3 - 1\mu_4 = 0$$

while the second set could be stated in the form,

$$H_{0a}: 1\mu_1 - 1\mu_2 + 0\mu_3 + 0\mu_4 = 0$$

$$H_{0b}: 1\mu_1 + 1\mu_2 - 2\mu_3 + 0\mu_4 = 0$$

$$H_{0c}: 1\mu_1 + 1\mu_2 + 1\mu_3 - 3\mu_4 = 0$$

and the *unacceptable* set could be written in the form,

$$H_{0q}: 1\mu_1 - 1\mu_2 + 0\mu_3 + 0\mu_4 = 0$$

$$H_{0r}: 0\mu_1 + 0\mu_2 + 1\mu_3 - 1\mu_4 = 0$$

$$H_{0s}: 0\mu_1 + 1\mu_2 - 1\mu_3 + 0\mu_4 = 0$$

Let us now denote the coefficient used with μ_i in contrast m as l_{im}. A little study will show that the following statements are true:

1. For any linear contrast, $\sum_{i=1}^{k} l_{im} = 0$.

2. The sum of squares associated with the contrast may be computed by the formula,

$$\mathrm{SS}_m = \frac{(\Sigma l_{im} T_{i+})^2}{N_i \Sigma l_{im}^2}$$

3. In all the sets that we found made an acceptable analysis of our "among" sum of squares, for each pair of contrasts, say the mth and n^{th},

$$\Sigma l_{im} l_{in} = 0$$

that is, the sum of the products of the coefficients applied to corresponding totals must be zero. (Notice that in the unacceptable set, $\Sigma l_{iq} l_{is} = -1$ and $\Sigma l_{ir} l_{is} = -1$.)

Any set of linear contrasts which meets the third requirement is said to be an *orthogonal set* of *linear contrasts*, and any set involving k such contrasts will be found exactly to break up, or analyze, the "among" sum of squares into k parts, each associated with one of the k degrees of freedom related to the "among" estimate in the analysis of variance.

A convenient way of displaying the coefficients is to place them in rows under the respective totals, then to place the needed sums of products to the right. It is also convenient to code the contrasts by putting in one group the i's designating the means having positive coefficients and in another those having negative coefficients, separating the groups by a "v" for "versus." Thus contrasts for hypotheses a, b, and c would be: 1 v 2, 12 v 3, and 123 v 4.

Table 13-3 Computations for Orthogonal Linear Contrasts for Data of Table 13-1

Population, i:	1	2	3	4	$\Sigma l_i T_{i+}$	$(\Sigma l_i T_{i+})^2$	Σl_i^2	$\Sigma N_i l_i^2$
T_{i+}	10	15	35	40				
Contrast								
1 v 2	+1	−1	0	0	− 5	25	2	10
12 v 3	+1	+1	−2	0	−45	2025	6	30
123 v 4	+1	+1	+1	−3	−60	3600	12	60

A table in such form for these contrasts is shown as Table 13-3, while a condensed form of anov table including these tests is shown as Table 13-4.

Table 13-4 ANOV FOR DATA OF TABLE 13-1, SHOWING ORTHOGONAL LINEAR CONTRASTS WITH INDIVIDUAL DEGREES OF FREEDOM

Source	*ss*	*df*	*ms*	*F*	F_{cr}	*Decision*
Total	138	19	—			
Among	130	3	43.33333	86.67	3.24	Reject
1 v 2	2.5	1	2.5	5.00	4.49	Reject
12 v 3	67.5	1	67.5	135.00	4.49	Reject
12 v 3	60.0	1	60.0	120.00	4.49	Reject
Within	8.0	16	0.50000	—		

13.9 Which Set of Hypotheses Should Be Tested?

Because it seems to be desirable to learn how to perform statistical analyses before attempting to learn very much about how to plan experiments and surveys, it is somewhat troublesome to a student to be confronted by the fact that, with several samples, there are many different sets of orthogonal linear contrasts that could be studied. It seems to be a problem to decide which set should be tested. But in actual use the data normally would have been costly to obtain, and one does not prudently obtain data without having a purpose in mind. That purpose will be to test a specific group of hypotheses around which the procurement of the data was planned. In the planning, the orthogonality of the contrasts should have been tested, and the volume of data to be obtained planned to insure that the effects sought, if present, would be detected with the appropriate risks of error. The details of such planning are beyond the scope of this text, but it should be borne in mind that the contrasts to be considered are part of the plan and purpose behind the taking of the data, not something resolved by occult processes later.

13.10 A More Complicated Set of Data

In the situation we have just considered, we recognized that there was some characteristic other than the observed numerical values which served to distinguish one population from another, and which it was suspected might be associated with differences among the population means. Such a characteristic, associated with possible differences in the measurements under consideration, we shall refer to as a *factor*, and the differing specific categories with respect to this characteristic as *levels* of this factor. Thus, if we were studying academic indexes of students, their majors might represent one factor, with English, History, Modern Languages, Business Administration, Psychology, Sociology, and so on constituting levels of that factor. But students are also in different academic years, another factor, with freshman, sophomore, junior, and senior constituting its four levels. Thus each student can be classified in two ways, with respect to major and year, and his academic index will have two associated factors.

We could recognize still other factors: sex, age, campus residence, socio-economic status, and so on, so that the identification of the population from which an observation came could become quite complex. For the present, suppose we consider only two factors, a situation which we express by saying that we are dealing with a *two-way classification.* We can use one factor as the row designation and the other as the column designation in a tabular layout in which our future data may be entered. We might use a numerical subscript, i, to denote the levels of the first factor, followed by a second subscript, j, to denote the levels of the second factor. A third subscript, k, could designate the serial number of a particular observation from the group made at its specific combination of conditions. Quite often the term *treatment*, borrowed from agricultural experimentation, will designate a specific combination of levels of the different factors. Such an arrangment, for five different majors (first factor) and four different classes (second factor), with five observations per treatment, would, according to this plan, be set up as in Table 13-5, Part A.

Table 13-5 Plans for Tabulating Observations for a Two-Way Classification of Academic Indexes by Major and Year

Part A. Using Rows and Columns

Major, i	*Year, j*			
	1	2	3	4
1	X_{111}	X_{121}	X_{131}	X_{141}
	. . .	. . .	. . .	. . .
	X_{115}	X_{125}	X_{135}	X_{145}
2	X_{211}	X_{221}	X_{231}	X_{241}
	. . .	. . .	. . .	. . .
	X_{215}	X_{225}	X_{235}	X_{245}
3	X_{311}	X_{321}	X_{331}	X_{341}
	. . .	. . .	. . .	. . .
	X_{315}	X_{325}	X_{335}	X_{345}
4	X_{411}	X_{421}	X_{431}	X_{441}
	. . .	. . .	. . .	. . .
	X_{415}	X_{425}	X_{435}	X_{445}
5	X_{511}	X_{521}	X_{531}	X_{541}
	. . .	. . .	. . .	. . .
	X_{515}	X_{525}	X_{535}	X_{545}

Part B. Using Dual Headings

Major, i	1	1	1	1	2	2	2	. . .	5	5
Year, j	1	2	3	4	1	2	3	. . .	3	4
	X_{111}	X_{121}	X_{131}	X_{141}	X_{211}	X_{221}	X_{231}	. . .	X_{531}	X_{541}
	. . .	. . .	. . .	. . .	. . .	. . .	. . .	. . .	. . .	. . .
	X_{115}	X_{125}	X_{135}	X_{145}	X_{215}	X_{225}	X_{235}	. . .	X_{535}	X_{545}

Another plan, which has certain advantages when we come to make our final analysis, simply lists the levels of the first factor as the upper heading and those of the second factor as the lower heading of the required number of columns. Such a plan is shown in Table 13-5B. For most purposes, the second plan will prove convenient, partly because of the accessibility of all subtotals and partly because of the ease with which the plan can be extended to more complicated sets of data.

In order to have some specific figures let us, as we have done before, use some highly simplified "data" as shown in Table 13-6. We can imagine that

Table 13-6 UNITS OVER QUOTA SOLD BY FIVE SALESMEN IN EACH OF FIVE REGIONS (i) FOR EACH OF FOUR WEEKS (j). SOURCE: SYNTHETIC

Region, i	1	1	1	1	2	2	2	2	3	3	3	3	4	4	4	4	5	5	5	5
Week, j	1	2	3	4	1	2	3	4	1	2	3	4	1	2	3	4	1	2	3	4
	0	3	5	6	5	6	10	9	5	4	2	1	8	7	4	2	3	11	6	2
	1	2	4	4	6	8	9	10	5	4	2	2	8	7	6	4	5	11	5	1
	1	2	4	4	6	8	9	10	5	4	2	2	8	7	6	4	5	11	5	1
	2	2	4	5	7	6	8	9	5	4	2	0	9	8	6	2	4	10	5	0
	1	2	4	5	6	7	9	11	4	3	3	0	10	6	4	3	4	9	5	1
	1	1	3	5	6	8	9	11	6	5	1	2	10	7	5	4	4	9	4	1
T_{ij+}	5	10	20	25	30	35	45	50	25	20	10	5	45	35	25	15	20	50	25	5

T_{1++}	60	T_{+1+}	125	T_{+++}	500
T_{2++}	160	T_{+2+}	150		
T_{3++}	60	T_{+3+}	125	T_{+++}^2/N	$= 2500$
T_{4++}	120	T_{+4+}	100		
T_{5++}	100			T_{ij+}^2/N_{ij}	$= 3320$

$T_{i++}^2/N_i = 2860$ $\qquad$ $T_{+j+}^2/N_j = 2550$

the data will comprise the number of units above quota sold by salesmen for a certain company. The first factor will denote the sales region, while the second will denote the week. The individual values will be listed simply in the order reported, and will not be identified in terms of the individual salesmen. The table presents the data according to our second layout plan, and includes certain preliminary computations we shall soon need. By an extension of our previous scheme, T_{ij+} will represent the total of the five observations from treatment ij, and $N_{ij} = 5$ will represent the number of those observations. T_{i++} and N_i will represent the total and number of observations for level i of the first factor, while T_{+j+} and N_j will similarly represent the total and number for level j of the second factor. T_{+++} and N will represent the grand total and total number of observations. It will be convenient to denote the number of levels of our first factor by r (reminiscent of the rows in two-way table) and the number of levels of the second factor by c (for columns).

13.11 Analysis of the Two-way Classification

A. *First Stage.* We might start our attack on these data by recognizing that we have, in fact, $r \times c = 5 \times 4 = 20$ different treatments, and we might analyze our total sum of squares and degrees of freedom into an among and within portion, just as we did in our one-way classification. The needed formulas in coded and computing form are

Total

$$\text{ss}_t = \Sigma(X_{ijk} - \overline{X}_{+++})^2 = \Sigma X_{ijk}^2 - T_{+++}^2/N$$

$$= 3374 - 2500 = 874 \quad (13.11.1)$$

$$\text{df}_t = N - 1 = 100 - 1 = 99 \quad (13.11.2)$$

Among

$$\text{ss}_a = \Sigma(\overline{X}_{ij+} - \overline{X}_{+++})^2 = \Sigma T_{ij+}^2/N_{ij} - T_{+++}^2/N$$

$$= 3320 - 2500 = 820 \quad (13.11.3)$$

$$\text{df}_a = rc - 1 = (5 \times 4) - 1 = 20 - 1 = 19 \quad (13.11.4)$$

Within

$$\text{ss}_w = \Sigma(X_{ijk} - \overline{X}_{+++})^2 = \Sigma X_{ijk}^2 - \Sigma T_{ij+}^2/N_{ij}$$

$$= 3374 - 3320 = 54 \quad (13.11.5)$$

$$\text{df}_w = N - rc = 100 - 20 = 80 \quad (13.11.6)$$

These results may be conveniently entered in an anov table, such as Table 13-7, Part A, which includes some additional entries to be explained presently. Notice that, as with the simpler one-way sets of data, the among and within sums of squares and degrees of freedom add to the total values. At this stage, we may test the hypothesis that all population means have the same value. The appropriate test statistic is

$$F = s_a^2/s_w^2 \quad (13.11.7)$$

which has the F distribution with df_a/df_w degrees of freedom. For illustration, we used an alpha risk of 0.050 and thus rejected our hypothesis.

B. *Second Stage.* Our experience with the one-way classification will make us unhappy to leave our data with this rather coarse analysis. It will occur to us to determine whether there were differences among the different regions, for example. For this purpose, we might combine our treatment totals by regions. Each of these intermediate totals, T_{i++}, will have one subtotal from each of the four months in it, and we may thus think of any effect of months as being "balanced out." We could, following our pattern of thinking, compute a sum of squares and degrees of freedom for the effect of regions thus:

Among Regions (First Factor)

$$\text{ss}_r = \Sigma(\overline{X}_{i++} - \overline{X}_{+++})^2 = \Sigma T_{i++}^2/N_i - T_{+++}^2/N$$

$$= 2860 - 2500 = 360 \qquad (13.11.8)$$

$$\text{df}_r = r - 1 = 5 - 1 = 4 \qquad (13.11.9)$$

In a quite similar way, we might combine the treatment subtotals by months, "balancing out" the effect of regions, thus:

Among Months (Second Factor)

$$\text{ss}_c = \Sigma(\overline{X}_{+j+} - \overline{X}_{+++})^2 = \Sigma T_{+j+}^2/N_j - T_{+++}^2/N$$

$$= 2550 - 2500 = 50 \qquad (13.11.10)$$

$$\text{df}_c = c - 1 = 4 - 1 = 3 \qquad (13.11.11)$$

Now it seems evident that differences among means associated with the first factor and those associated with the second factor must be at least part of the differences among the treatment means. But these two sums of squares, $360 + 50 = 410$, do not account for 820, the among sum of squares, nor do the degrees of freedom, $4 + 3 = 7$, account for the 19 among degrees of freedom. There must be some other cause of variation among the 20 populations to account for the remainders of 410 for the sum of squares and 12 for the degrees of freedom. Some thought will suggest the possibility that the variation from month to month may not be the same for all regions or, to state the same fact in a different way, the difference from region to region may not be the same every month. Such a difference in response to one factor at different levels of another is termed *interaction.*

C. *Interaction: Its Measurement.* To see how we may arrive at a measure of the amount of interaction, let us recall that, in our one-way classification problem, we found that we could add and subtract the sample means inside the parentheses in our expression for the total sum of squares without changing the value of the expression. We then found that upon expanding the elaborated expression and performing the necessary summations, we showed that the total sum of squares could, indeed, be broken into two parts, the among and within sums of squares, and that the "cross-product" sum was zero. Suppose we try the plan in extended form here, adding and subtracting the necessary elements to form the sums of squares we have already considered and such other elements as may be necessary to keep the value of the expression unchanged. This time, we had better write out our summations completely:

$$\text{ss}_t = \sum_{i=1}^{r} \sum_{j=1}^{c} \sum_{k=1}^{N_{ij}} (X_{ijk} - \overline{X}_{+++})^2$$

$$= \sum_{i=1}^{r} \sum_{j=1}^{c} \sum_{k=1}^{N_{ij}} [X_{ijk} + (\overline{X}_{i++} - \overline{X}_{i++}) + (\overline{X}_{+j+} - \overline{X}_{+j+}) \qquad (13.11.12a)$$

$$+ (\overline{X}_{ij+} - \overline{X}_{ij+}) + (\overline{X}_{+++} - \overline{X}_{+++}) - \overline{X}_{+++}]^2 \qquad (13.11.12b)$$

In its present form, this expression looks pretty uninformative, to say the least, but let us do a little rearranging:

$$\text{ss}_t = \sum_{i=1}^{r}\sum_{j=1}^{c}\sum_{k=1}^{N_{ij}}[(\overline{X}_{i++} - \overline{X}_{+++}) + (\overline{X}_{+j+} - \overline{X}_{+++}) + (\overline{X}_{ij+} - \overline{X}_{i++} - \overline{X}_{+j+} + \overline{X}_{+++}) + (X_{ijk} - \overline{X}_{ij+})]^2 \tag{13.11.12c}$$

Now, if we were to expand this square and perform the additions, we should find, after some very tiresome algebra, that again all the "cross-product" terms disappear, since their sums are each zero, and we would have left only

$$\begin{aligned}\text{ss}_t &= \sum_{i=1}^{r}\sum_{j=1}^{c}\sum_{k=1}^{N_{ij}}(X_{ijk} - \overline{X}_{+++})^2 \\ &= \sum_{i=1}^{r}\sum_{j=1}^{c}\sum_{k=1}^{N_{ij}}(\overline{X}_{i++} - \overline{X}_{+++})^2 \\ &\quad + \sum_{i=1}^{r}\sum_{j=1}^{c}\sum_{k=1}^{N_{ij}}(\overline{X}_{+j+} - \overline{X}_{+++})^2 \\ &\quad + \sum_{i=1}^{r}\sum_{j=1}^{c}\sum_{k=1}^{N_{ij}}(\overline{X}_{ij+} - \overline{X}_{i++} - \overline{X}_{+j+} + \overline{X}_{+++})^2 \\ &\quad + \sum_{i=1}^{r}\sum_{j=1}^{c}\sum_{k=1}^{N_{ij}}(X_{ijk} - \overline{X}_{ij+})^2 \end{aligned} \tag{13.11.12d}$$

In the final form, the first two terms and the last are, respectively, the first factor, second factor, and within sums of squares which we have previously considered in coded and computing forms. The remaining term is our interaction sum of squares. As usual, it can be shown that it may be more conveniently computed from the totals because of the fact that

$$\begin{aligned}&\sum_{i=1}^{r}\sum_{j=1}^{c}\sum_{k=1}^{N_{ij}}(\overline{X}_{ij+} - \overline{X}_{i++} - \overline{X}_{+j+} + \overline{X}_{+++})^2 \\ &= \sum_{i=1}^{r}\sum_{j=1}^{c} T_{ij+}^2/N_{ij} - \sum_{i=1}^{r} T_{i++}^2/N_i \\ &\quad - \sum_{j=1}^{c} T_{+j+}^2/N_j + T_{+++}^2/N \end{aligned} \tag{13.11.13a}$$

or, omitting multiple summation signs and indexes, to reach the coded form,

$$\begin{aligned}\text{ss}_i &= \Sigma(\overline{X}_{ij+} - \overline{X}_{i++} - \overline{X}_{+j+} + \overline{X}_{+++})^2 \\ &= \Sigma T_{ij+}^2/N_{ij} - \Sigma T_{i++}^2/N_i - \Sigma T_{+j+}^2/N_j + T_{+++}^2/N \end{aligned} \tag{13.11.13b}$$

For our data, the numerical value becomes

$$\text{ss}_i = 3320 - 2860 - 2550 + 2500 = 410$$

The related degrees of freedom may be shown to be

$$df_i = df_t - df_r - df_c - df_w \qquad (13.11.14a)$$

$$= (N - 1) - (r - 1) - (c - 1) - (N - rc) \qquad (13.11.14b)$$

$$= rc - r - c + 1 = (r - 1)(c - 1)$$

$$= (5 - 1)(4 - 1) = 4 \times 3 = 12 \qquad (13.11.14c)$$

This is a general result: the number of degrees of freedom for any interaction is the product of the numbers of degrees of freedom associated with the interacting factors.

Thus we are able to complete our second stage of our analysis of variance by breaking down our "among" component from the first stage into parts associated with the effects of each factor and with their interaction. Perhaps it will help us to gain a little insight into the meaning of this interaction idea if we consider two summary tables of highly simplified values. Imagine that we have three levels of each of the two factors, and that we display the sample means as follows:

Set No. 1					Set No. 2				
i	j			$\bar{X}_{i++}$	i	j			$\bar{X}_{i++}$
	1	2	3			1	2	3	
1	2	4	6	4	1	2	4	6	4
2	3	5	7	5	2	3	9	3	5
3	7	9	11	9	3	7	5	15	9
$\bar{X}_{+j+}$	4	6	8	$6 = \bar{X}_{+++}$	$\bar{X}_{+j+}$	4	6	8	$6 = \bar{X}_{+++}$

Notice that the grand mean and the corresponding row and column means are alike in both sets. The differences lie in the individual treatment means. In the first set, the differences among the row means in each column are the same in all columns and are therefore the same as the differences among the row means themselves. A similar statement applies to column means. Thus any treatment mean could be estimated by starting with the grand mean, then adding the difference between the column mean and grand mean and the difference between the row mean and the grand mean for the column and row in which the treatment occurs.

In the second set, this is not the case. There is a further effect associated with the particular row and column that must be taken into account to arrive at the treatment mean. The first set has no interaction, whereas the second set shows interaction to a marked degree. We can examine a third set in which there are no differences among row and column means, and all treatment differences are associated with the interactions as follows:

Set No. 3				
i	j			$\overline{X}_{i++}$
	1	2	3	
1	2	6	10	6
2	7	6	5	6
3	9	6	3	6
$\overline{X}_{+j+}$	6	6	6	$6 = \overline{X}_{+++}$

Thus we can have, in fact, all combinations of presence and absence of row and column effects, with and without interactions.

D. *Third Stage: Orthogonal Linear Comparisons.* In our one-way classification problem, we recognized that the whole purpose of obtaining our data was to enable us to answer specific questions about differences among our means. These questions, we found, could be phrased as linear comparisons, and, provided the comparisons were orthogonal, we found that a set of comparisons was very readily made with the aid of the appropriate coefficients.

It will be a relief to find that exactly the same principles apply to our more complicated problems. If we think about the comparisons of interest to us concerning the first factor, we can develop an orthogonal set comprising as many comparisons as there are degrees of freedom associated with that factor. The same thing applies to the second factor. Now it might seem that one would have to use the T_{i++} values in arriving at the needed sums of squares for comparisons related to the first factor and the T_{+j+} values for those related to the second factor, but this is not necessary. All that we need to do is to develop the coefficients as though we were going to use these totals, but then apply the coefficient that would have been applied to each T_{i++} to each T_{ij+} involving the same i-value. We act similarly with the comparisons involving T_{+j+} values.

This has the further merit that the coefficients needed for the related interaction are simply the products of the coefficients for the two comparisons involved. We are assured that if the comparisons selected for the first factor are orthogonal among themselves and those for the second factor are similarly orthogonal, then the interactions will be orthogonal as will the entire set.

Suppose we see how this works out for our specific set of data. Let us imagine that Regions 1 and 2 are, respectively, the northern and southern regions of the eastern part of the country, while Regions 3, 4, and 5 are, respectively, the northern, central, and southern regions of the central part of the country. Comparisons which could reasonably be of interest might be as indicated below, where each is given a single code to identify it:

Code	*Comparison*
A	1 v 2
B	3 v 4
C	34 v 5
D	12 v 345

If the months are simply the four most recent months for which reports are available, it might be appropriate to make the following comparisons:

E	1 v 2
F	3 v 4
G	12 v 34

The appropriate interactions would then be as shown below, where the × traditionally indicates the two comparisons whose interaction is considered:

$A \times E$ $B \times E$ $C \times E$ $D \times E$

$A \times F$ $B \times F$ $C \times F$ $D \times F$

$A \times G$ $B \times G$ $C \times G$ $D \times G$

The required coefficients and resulting coefficients are shown as Table 13-7, Part B.

Table 13-7 ANALYSIS OF DATA ON SALESMEN'S PERFORMANCE FROM TABLE 13-6

Part A. First Two Stages

Source	*ss*	*df*	*ms*	*F*	F_{cr}
Total	874	99	—	—	—
Among	820	19	43.158⁻	63.94	1.72
Regions	360	4	90.000	133.33	3.57
Weeks	50	3	16.667⁻	24.69	4.04
Interaction	410	12	34.167⁻	50.62	2.42
Within	54	80	0.675		

Alpha Risk: 0.050

Part B. Orthogonal Linear Coefficients for Making the Comparisons Discussed in the Text on the Data of Table 13-6

Region, i	1	1	1	1	2	2	2	2	3	3	3	3	4	4	4	4	5	5	5	5
Week, j	1	2	3	4	1	2	3	4	1	2	3	4	1	2	3	4	1	2	3	4
T_{ij+}	5	10	20	25	30	35	45	50	25	20	10	5	45	35	25	15	20	50	25	5
Comp.																				
A	+	+	+	+	−	−	−	−	0	0	0	0	0	0	0	0	0	0	0	0
B	0	0	0	0	0	0	0	0	+	+	+	+	−	−	−	−	0	0	0	0
C	0	0	0	0	0	0	0	0	+	+	+	+	+	+	+	+	−2	−2	−2	−2
D	+3	+3	+3	+3	+3	+3	+3	+3	−2	−2	−2	−2	−2	−2	−2	−2	−2	−2	−2	−2
E	+	−	0	0	+	−	0	0	+	−	0	0	+	−	0	0	+	−	0	0
F	0	0	+	−	0	0	+	−	0	0	+	−	0	0	+	−	0	0	+	−
G	+	+	−	−	+	+	−	−	+	+	−	−	+	+	−	−	+	+	−	−
$A \times E$	+	−	0	0	−	+	0	0	0	0	0	0	0	0	0	0	0	0	0	0
$A \times F$	0	0	+	−	0	0	−	+	0	0	0	0	0	0	0	0	0	0	0	0
$A \times G$	+	+	−	−	−	−	−	+	+	0	0	0	0	0	0	0	0	0	0	0
$B \times E$	0	0	0	0	0	0	0	0	+	−	0	0	−	+	0	0	0	0	0	0
$B \times F$	0	0	0	0	0	0	0	0	0	0	+	−	0	0	−	+	0	0	0	0
$B \times G$	0	0	0	0	0	0	0	0	+	+	−	−	−	−	+	+	0	0	0	0
$C \times E$	0	0	0	0	0	0	0	0	+	−	0	0	+	−	0	0	−2	+2	0	0
$C \times F$	0	0	0	0	0	0	0	0	0	0	+	−	0	0	+	−	0	0	−2	+2
$C \times G$	0	0	0	0	0	0	0	0	+	+	−	−	+	+	−	−	−2	−2	+2	+2
$D \times E$	+3	−3	0	0	+3	−3	0	0	−2	+2	0	0	−2	+2	0	0	−2	+2	0	0
$D \times F$	0	0	+3	−3	0	0	+3	−3	0	0	−2	+2	0	0	−2	+2	0	0	−2	+2
$D \times G$	+3	+3	−3	−3	+3	+3	−3	−3	−2	−2	+2	+2	−2	−2	+2	+2	−2	−2	+2	+2

Part C. Computations Using the Coefficients, and F-values

Comp.	$\Sigma l_i T_{ij+}$	$(\Sigma l_i T_{ij+})^2$	$N_{ij} \Sigma l_i^2$	$ss = ms$	F
A	-100	10,000	40	250.000	370.37*
B	-60	3,600	40	90.000	133.33*
C	-20	400	120	3.333	4.94
D	$+100$	100,100	600	16.666	24.69*
E	-25	625	50	12.500	18.52*
F	$+25$	625	50	12.500	18.52*
G	$+50$	2,500	100	25.000	37.04*
$A \times E$	0	0	20	0.000	0.000
$A \times F$	0	0	20	0.000	0.000
$A \times G$	0	0	40	0.000	0.000
$B \times E$	-5	25	20	1.250	1.85
$B \times F$	-5	25	20	1.250	1.85
$B \times G$	-10	100	40	2.500	3.70
$C \times E$	$+75$	5,625	60	93.750	138.89*
$C \times F$	-25	625	60	10.416	15.43*
$C \times G$	-10	100	120	0.833	1.23
$D \times E$	-100	0	300	0.000	0.00
$D \times F$	-100	10,000	300	33.333	49.38*
$D \times G$	-400	160,000	600	266.666	395.06*

$ms_w = 0.675$ from Table 13-7a. $\quad F_{cr} = F_{0.950,1/80} = 6.97.$

Observed F-values exceeding F_{cr} and thus leading to rejection of the hypothesis that the effect being considered is nonexistent are marked *.

E. *Interpretation.* We have now completed the formal analysis and must determine what it means. It will help to realize that our three-stage analysis was so developed primarily to help guide our thinking toward the ultimate stage. Secondarily, the intermediate stages do provide some checks on our computations. But the fact is that our goal was, all along, the ultimate orthogonal set of linear comparisons. Now, when we come to interpret our results, we appear to work backward: first we must consider the interactions!

Why should this be so? A little thought will remind us that, if we must accept the idea that an interaction exists, then we must recognize, first, that there are differences among the means involved and, second, that the differences among one set of the means depends on the levels of the other set involved in the interaction. This means that, when an interaction is found, we must immediately recognize the existence of these differences and must further recognize that the hypotheses concerning the individual factors involved are no longer pertinent. When, however, an interaction is rejected, then we examine the effect of the factors individually.

Let us work through our comparisons systematically with these ideas in mind. Consider first Comparison A (Region 1 vs. Region 2). None of its interactions was significant, but its direct effect was significant, with Region 2 showing the higher level.

Comparison B (Region 3 vs. Region 4) showed no significant interactions, but its direct effect was significant, with Region 4 showing the higher level.

Comparison C (The combined levels of Regions 3 and 4 vs. Region 5) showed significant interactions with Comparison E (the first vs. the second week) and with Comparison F (the third vs. the fourth week), but not with Comparison G (the combined first two weeks vs. the combined last two weeks. In order to be in a position to make clear statements about this finding, it will help to display the means involved in a supplementary table:

Week	Region	
	3 + 4	5
1	7.0	4.0
2	5.5	5.0
3	3.5	5.0
4	2.0	1.0
1 + 2	6.25	4.50
3 + 4	2.75	3.00

The table makes it possible to see that the interactions resulted from the fact that the combined means for Regions 3 and 4 were much more above the mean for Region 5 during the first week than during the second, and that the combined Regions 3 and 4 were below Region 5 during the third week but above it during the fourth week. This, then, makes it clear that the week-to-week variations do indeed affect the region-to-region variations in sales performance within the central states regions.

Comparison D (Regions 1 and 2, the eastern area, vs. Regions 3, 4, and 5, the central area) showed no interaction with Comparison E but did with Comparisons F and G. Again, a supplementary table will help:

Week	Region	
	1 + 2	3, 4, + 5
1	3.5	6.0
2	4.5	7.0
3	6.5	4.0
4	7.5	1.6
1 + 2	4.0	6.5
3 + 4	7.0	2.83

It is now clear that, although the central region was the same amount above the eastern region during each of the first two weeks (as shown by the absence of the $D \times E$ interaction) the eastern region was somewhat higher in the third week and much higher in the fourth week (indicated by the existence of the $D \times F$ interaction). Furthermore, the reversal of the leading region is clearly evident in the final part of the table, consistent with the existence of the $D \times G$ interaction.

F. *Plan and Interpretation.* You will agree, we believe, that it requires considerable persistence to keep the factors involved in such a set of data clearly in mind during the interpretation of the results of the analysis. Herein lies a rather serious pitfall for the thoughtless user of statistical methods. It is often possible to obtain sets of data involving several levels of each of a number of different categories, and to perform the analysis of variance by quite straightforward procedures that are, at their worst, tedious. But, to make a clear interpretation of the results in terms of statements which can guide future thought and action is, as you can see from our quite simple example, likely to prove quite a task. Perhaps this is one of the greater, though less often recognized, benefits of statistical methods: they force us to ask ourselves just what we want to know and what we propose to do with the information when we get it! While this can be rather humbling, it can also lead us to make our efforts more productive because we ask ourselves these questions *before* we obtain the data.

For your encouragement, may we say that, as you become more familiar with your principal professional field, you will become able to grasp more complex ideas concerning it, and to take advantage of the statistical treatment (after statistical planning) of more complicated sets of data. It is also true that some understanding of these statistical ideas will help you better to grasp the ideas of your main field. From a practical standpoint, then, your statistical knowledge and your knowledge of your subject area should be partners.

13.12 Applications

We have just suggested that there is a close connection between the command of the subject matter of the field under study and the effective use of the ideas we have just been considering. Therefore, rather than including in our text examples from a variety of fields, we are suggesting in our problem section ways in which you can develop your understanding and confidence by working with data with which you have some real association of interest. We urge you to work through appropriate problems of this sort, for only in this way will the ideas become truly yours.

General Study

1. A number of algebraic details were omitted in the text in the development of the working formulas. By use of the ideas suggested, fill in the details for your own satisfaction.

2. Try your hand at making up illustrative tables by developing a table of means for two levels of the row factor and three of the column factor showing each of the following situations:
a. Only row effects.
b. Only column effects.
c. Only interactions.
d. Column and interaction effects, but no row effects.
e. Row and column effects, but no interactions.

Specific Problems

Note: In developing class problems, subjects of general interest may be found in such areas as the following:
a. Academic index of groups on the campus.
b. Stock market prices.
c. Climatological data for regions of interest.
In some schools, it will prove feasible to use data from laboratory courses in other subjects for material for groups.

1.* Consider a set of data involving a one-way classification. Formulate the hypotheses to be tested, and state clearly the reasons why each hypothesis is of real interest. Then plan a table in which the data may be entered and analyzed conveniently. Obtain the data, perform the analysis, and state your conclusions clearly.

2.* Similarly treat a set of data involving a two-way classification with at least three levels of at least one of the factors.

3.* Similarly treat a set of data involving at least three factors, though not necessarily at more than two levels each.

4. From journals in the field of interest to you, study the results of analyses of variance there reported. Did the worker make a complete analysis? Did you consider his selection of comparisons to be made sound? If you would have made a different set. reanalyze the data and state your conclusions.

*In each problem you will find it instructive to attempt to state your conclusions from a nonstatistical perusal of the data, then to analyze them properly and compare your conclusions after this analysis with your earlier statements.

14

Relationships Between Variables

14.1 The Nature of the Problem

In all of our problems so far, we have been able to center our attention upon a single variable, the result of measurement of one property of the individuals in the populations of interest to us. True, in the analysis of variance, we sometimes had other measured and numerically expressed characteristics of the individuals, but they were used simply as "tags" to identify the particular populations from which the individuals came. Now we must face the fact that we must often deal with two variables, say Y and X, which result from the measurement of two properties of each individual, and that we shall be interested in the relationship between these two variables.

We shall think of one variable being a function of the other, say $Y = f(X)$, and we shall be seeking the form of the equation which represents the relationship, the particular values of its parameters, and some measure of how much of the variation in the values of Y is attributable to this relationship and the variation in X. Our reasons for this interest may be any of several. In some cases we may hope that investigation of the relationship may aid our understanding of some underlying principle in a field of interest to us. In others, it may be that the measurement of X is rapid, simple, and inexpensive, while the measurement of Y is slow, difficult, and costly: by measuring only X in the future, and calculating the related values of Y, we shall save considerable time and expense. In yet other cases, there may be a considerable difference between the time at which X becomes available for measurement and the time at which Y develops, and we may wish to make a measurement of X to aid us in predicting our future Y's.

The following list of pairs of variables will suggest some of these situations.

X	Y
Hour test grades	Final exam grades
Annual income	Annual savings
Years of schooling	Life income
High school index	College index
Size of family	Amount of delinquency
Prices of selected stocks	Total market prices
Amount of street lighting	Amount of crime
Speed limit	Accident rate

They should suggest to you others with which you are already acquainted or in which you will become interested.

By now you are well prepared to recognize that, in order to be able to analyze our data, we must make assumptions about their general nature. These assumptions will control the appropriate test statistics to be used in hypothesis testing and confidence interval estimation. In problems involving relationships, we shall find that there are two broad types of situation we may encounter, and that they lead, through different assumptions, to different statistical methods. We propose to consider these situations, to discuss the appropriate methods, and to draw your attention to some very useful connections between them.

14.2 The Regression Problem

Suppose that we may assume that we are able to select the levels of one variable, say X, at will and measure them exactly. Then suppose that we may assume that at each level of X there is a subpopulation of values of Y and that these subpopulations have the following characteristics:

1. Each is a normal distribution, with mean and variance designated as $\mu_{Y.X}$ and $\sigma_{Y.X}^2$, respectively.

2. The values of $\mu_{Y.X}$ are functions of X, that is, $\mu_{Y.X} = f(X)$. In this chapter, we shall confine our consideration to linear functions, $f(X) = A + BX$.

3. The values of the variance, $\sigma_{Y.X}^2$, are the same for all subpopulations.

The representation, pictorially, of the complete distribution requires a three-dimensional coordinate system. This we might construct by making the X-axis horizontal and positive to the right, the Y-axis horizontal and positive away from us, and the Z-axis, along which the ordinates of the distributions are plotted, vertical and positive upward. The distribution will be represented by a surface that we could visualize as resulting from constructing each of the distribution curves for the subpopulations on a thin sheet of material and placing it at the appropriate place on the coordinate system. Each base would be in the XY-plane, with $\mu_{Y.X}$ lying on the curve representing the relation between $\mu_{Y.X}$ and X, and with the base parallel to the Y-axis. For the case of particular interest at present, where $\mu_{Y.X} = f(X) = A + BX$, that is, where the relationship is linear, the surface would appear as in Fig. 14-1.

Fig. 14-1. Schematic Representation of a Typical Regression Surface.

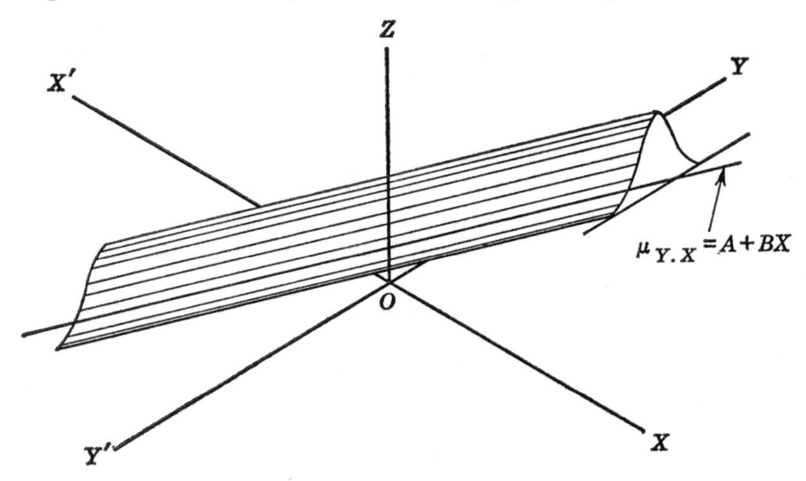

Now suppose that we may assume that our data consist of random samples from the subpopulations of Y's at each of several selected levels of X. We could visualize that each Y-value was formed by the addition to the value of $\mu_{Y.X}$, associated with its particular value of X, of a random value from a normal distribution with mean zero and variance $\sigma_{Y.X}^2$. Suppose we represent such a random value by the symbol $\epsilon(0,\sigma_{Y.X}^2)$, so that we can describe the individual Y-values by the equation,

$$Y = \mu_{Y.X} + \epsilon(0,\sigma_{Y.X}^2) = f(X) + \epsilon(0,\sigma_{Y.X}^2) \qquad (14.2.1)$$

When all these assumptions are acceptable, we are involved in a *regression problem*, and equation 14.2.1, which describes the situation, is known as the *regression model*. We may state our assumptions compactly by stating that our data conform to a regression model.

As we mentioned earlier, one of the cases of great concern to us is that in which the underlying relationship is linear, that is, in which $\mu_{Y.X} = f(X) = A + BX$ so that $Y = A + BX + \epsilon(0,\sigma_{Y.X}^2)$. This case is important to us for several reasons. First, it often does express the true state of affairs. Second, even when the functional relationship is not linear, the use of the simpler linear relationship may be adequate for all our needs and far more convenient. Third, in learning how to deal with this form of the regression problem, we prepare our way to deal with more complex problems.

In dealing with linear regression, we sense that we may be interested in testing hypotheses concerning A, B, and $\sigma_{Y.X}^2$, or in providing confidence limits for them. Therefore, we shall require statistics, which we shall designate by a, b, and $s_{Y.X}^2$, respectively, to estimate the parameters, and we must know the related test statistics.

14.3 The Correlation Problem

Quite possibly you have already realized that data involving relationships will not always conform to the regression model. We may not be able to select our values of X at will. Or we may be subject to errors of measurement in them, so that we cannot claim to know them exactly. Perhaps it would appear that all we have is a random sample of individuals on each of which we have observed a value of Y and a value of X. This might seem rather hopeless, but, with the aid of a few more assumptions, there is a quite effective attack available.

In order to help ourselves grasp the new idea, let us recall some ideas connected with the normal distribution curve. You remember that if we had plotted a histogram for N observations of X, using a class interval, i, the equation of the normal curve which fitted the histogram was given as equation 5.4.1b, which had the form,

$$Y = \left(\frac{Ni}{\sigma}\right)\frac{1}{\sqrt{2\pi}}e^{-1/2[(X-\mu)/\sigma]^2}$$

If, however, our histogram was plotted in relative frequencies and if the class interval was made one standard deviation, that is, $i = \sigma$, and if we made the scale change resulting from letting $z = (X - \mu)/\sigma$, the equation became much simpler in appearance:

$$y = Y/N = \frac{1}{\sqrt{2\pi}}e^{-1/2z^2}$$

which is the standard normal curve. In what we are about to do, the exponents on e will become much more extensive, and it will be convenient to adopt a newer mathematical notation in which $\exp(k)$ means e^k. In this notation, then the standard normal curve would be written:

$$y = \frac{1}{\sqrt{2\pi}}\exp\left(-\frac{1}{2}z^2\right)$$

Now let us imagine that we have an extensive set of pairs of X and Y values of the kind we are now considering. We could use the three-dimensional coordinate system we described in connection with our regression problem to construct a "histogram" representing them. We could lay off classes of interval i along the X-axis and draw horizontal lines perpendicular to the X-axis at each division point. In a similar way, we could lay off classes of interval j along the Y-axis and draw horizontal lines perpendicular to the Y-axis at each division point. This grid of lines will divide the XY-plane into equal rectangular cells. Using each cell as a base, we can form a prism over it whose height is proportional to the number of pairs of values falling within the boundaries of the cell.

The result would appear as a somewhat "jagged" surface, just as our histograms for one variable were "jagged." But just as experience suggested to mathematicians that the normal curve bore a reasonable relation to many of these histograms, so has experience suggested a similar equation representing a smooth surface which "fits" these three-dimensional histograms. This equation takes the rather frightening form,

$$Z = \frac{Nij}{2\pi\sigma_X\sigma_Y\sqrt{1-\rho^2}} \exp\left[-\frac{1}{2\sqrt{1-\rho^2}}(x^2 - 2\rho xy + y^2)\right] \tag{14.3.1}$$

where

$$x = (X - \mu_X)/\sigma_X$$

and

$$y = (Y - \mu_Y)/\sigma_Y$$

If we had chosen to make $i = \sigma_X$ and $j = \sigma_Y$, and to use relative frequencies, the equation would take the form,

$$z = \frac{Z}{N} = \frac{1}{2\pi\sqrt{1-\rho^2}} \exp\left[-\frac{1}{2\sqrt{1-\rho^2}}(x^2 - 2\rho xy + y^2)\right] \tag{14.3.2}$$

While we would hardly attempt to persuade you that this is a simple equation, it serves a valuable purpose. It is known as the *bivariate normal distribution* in *standard form*. Fortunately, we have no need to calculate any values from it ourselves, but we do need to gain some understanding of its meaning, just as we had to do with the normal distribution equation.

To gain this understanding, let us for the present not explain what the ρ (lower case Greek r, rho) in the equation means, but see what would happen if $\rho = 0$. Under this condition, equation 14.3.2 would become

$$z = \frac{1}{2\pi} \exp\left[-\frac{1}{2}(x^2 + y^2)\right] \tag{14.3.3}$$

This is certainly simpler. Now suppose we hold y constant at $y = 0$. The equation then becomes

$$z = \frac{1}{2\pi} \exp\left(-\frac{1}{2}x^2\right) \tag{14.3.4}$$

The right side of this equation is exactly $(1/\sqrt{2\pi})$ times the right side of the standard normal equation, 14.3.0. To people used to working with equations, this is the equation of the curve representing the intersection of the XZ-plane (whose equation is $y = 0$) with the surface of equation 14.3.3, and is like the standard normal curve, except that its ordinates are only $(1/\sqrt{2\pi})$ times as high. Similarly, if we let y vary but hold x constant at $x = 0$, equation 14.3.3 becomes

$$z = \frac{1}{2\pi}\exp\left(-\frac{1}{2}y^2\right) \tag{14.3.5}$$

and we have the same sort of curve. If we hold y fixed at some value other than zero, say at $y = k$, and let x vary, we find that

$$\begin{aligned} z &= \frac{1}{2\pi}\exp\left[-\frac{1}{2}(x^2 + k^2)\right] \\ &= \frac{1}{2\pi}\left[\exp\left(-\frac{1}{2}k^2\right)\right]\left[\exp\left(-\frac{1}{2}x^2\right)\right] \end{aligned} \tag{14.3.6}$$

But $\exp(-\frac{1}{2}k^2)$ is a fraction having the same value at $+|k|$ and $-|k|$ and becoming smaller as $|k|$ becomes larger. Thus, as we move away from the X-axis and cut our surface by planes parallel to the XZ-plane, the curves of intersection are all similar to normal curves, but with progressively lower ordinates. A similar condition prevails if we let x remain fixed at $x = k$ and let y vary.

Finally, suppose we hold z at some fixed value, h, letting x and y vary. This permits us to determine the equation of the curve of intersection of a plane parallel to the XY-plane at height h with our surface. The result, which takes a little more mathematics than you may have at present, is that for all values for h between 0 and $1/(2\pi)$, the equations represent circles centered on the Z-axis with radii which decrease to zero as h increases to $1/(2\pi)$. The surface, Fig. 14-2a and Fig. 14-3a, somewhat resembles a "sugar-loaf" mountain.

Now let's consider ρ. As it increases in value toward $+1$, the following changes in character of the surface represented occur:

1. The curves at $x = 0$ and $y = 0$ have increasing ordinates.
2. The curves at $z = k$ become ellipses with their major axis (i.e., long axis) over the line $y = x$.
3. The ellipses become longer and narrower as k increases.
4. The curves at $y = k$ and at $x = k$ remain similar in form to normal curves, but their peaks lie over the line $y = x$.

Finally, when $\rho = 1$, the surface collapses, and the only values of y at any value of x are $y = x$ itself. If ρ decreases toward -1, a similar sequence of changes occurs, except that the major axes of the ellipses lie along the line $y = -x$.

We might visualize the result of these changes by imagining that our "sugar loaf" corresponding to $\rho = 0$ had been modelled in clay. As we changed ρ toward $+1$, we would have to push our clay up at the center, stretch it out along the region over the line $y = x$, and compact it along lines perpendicular to that line. The change toward $\rho = -1$ would make the changes with respect to $y = -x$. Some of the surfaces are shown in Fig. 14-2 and Fig. 14-3.

It thus appears that the parameter ρ measures the extent to which the values in our distribution will conform to the linear relationship $y = +x$ or $y = -x$, or the equivalent relationship $Y = A + BX$. It is for this reason that ρ is called the *correlation coefficient.* In many respects it is more convenient to deal with its square, ρ^2, which is known as the *coefficient of determination.* It is also convenient, sometimes, to work with $1 - \rho^2$, which is called the *coefficient of alienation.* We shall be concerned with testing hypotheses concerning ρ and ρ^2, and shall require statistics, r and r^2, to estimate them.

14.4 The Linear Regression Problem in Detail

A. *Estimating the Parameters.* Let us now return to a consideration of the linear regression problem. You will recall that our model involved the linear relationship $\mu_{Y.X} = A + BX$. We wish to obtain statistics, a and b, estimating A and B, respectively, so that we can use the equation,

$$Y_L = a + bX \tag{14.4.1}$$

with justified confidence that it will be the best approximation we can make to the true equation. Here again we are in the position of wanting a and b to be the "best" statistics, but we haven't yet established a criterion of goodness.

Suppose that we had a set of data, such as those in Table 14-1, which we could assume conformed to our linear regression model. In the table we have

Table 14-1 SYNTHETIC DATA TO ILLUSTRATE REGRESSION ANALYSIS

X_i	1	4	7	10	13
Y_{ij}	6	1	9	11	16
	0	5	7	7	18
	2	9	13	11	12
	4	5	15	15	14
T_{i+}	12	20	44	44	60

$N = 20$ $\quad 1/N = 0.05$

ΣX	140	ΣY	180	ΣXY	1620
ΣX^2	1340	ΣY^2	2148	$\Sigma(X - \overline{X})(Y - \overline{Y})$	360
$\overline{X}$	7	$\overline{Y}$	9		
$\Sigma(X - \overline{X})^2$	360	$\Sigma(Y - \overline{Y})^2$	528		

$b = [\Sigma(X - \overline{X})(Y - \overline{Y})]/\Sigma(X - \overline{X})^2 = 360/360 = 1.00000$

$a = \overline{Y} - b\overline{X} = 9 - 1 \times 7 = 9 - 7 = 2.00000$

$\Sigma(Y - Y_L)^2 = \Sigma Y^2 - a\Sigma Y - b\Sigma XY = 2148 - (2 \times 180) - (1 \times 1620) = 168$

$s_{Y.X}{}^2 = \Sigma(Y - Y_L)^2/(N - 2) = 168/18 = 9.\dot{3}$

$s_{Y.X} = 3.05_{505}$

Fig. 14-2. Schematic Representation of Bivariate Normal Distribution with Various ρ.

Traces of the horizontal planes at 0.02 Increments of z and of the planes $X = 0$ and $Y = 0$ are shown.

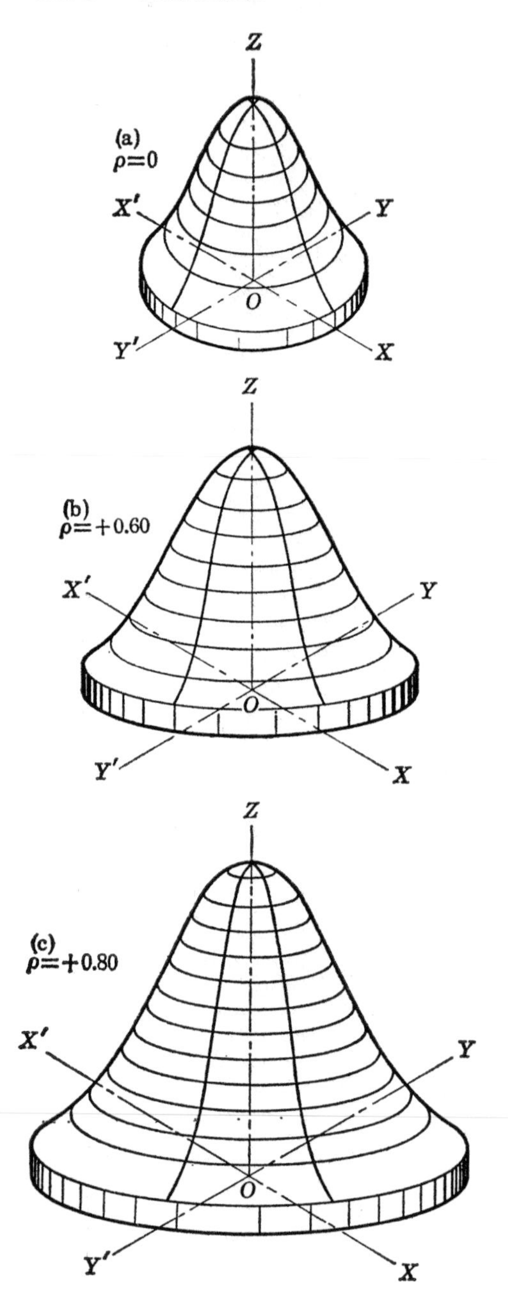

Fig. 14-3. Contour Lines of the Bivariate Normal Distribution with Various ρ.

Drawn at 0.02 Increments of z.

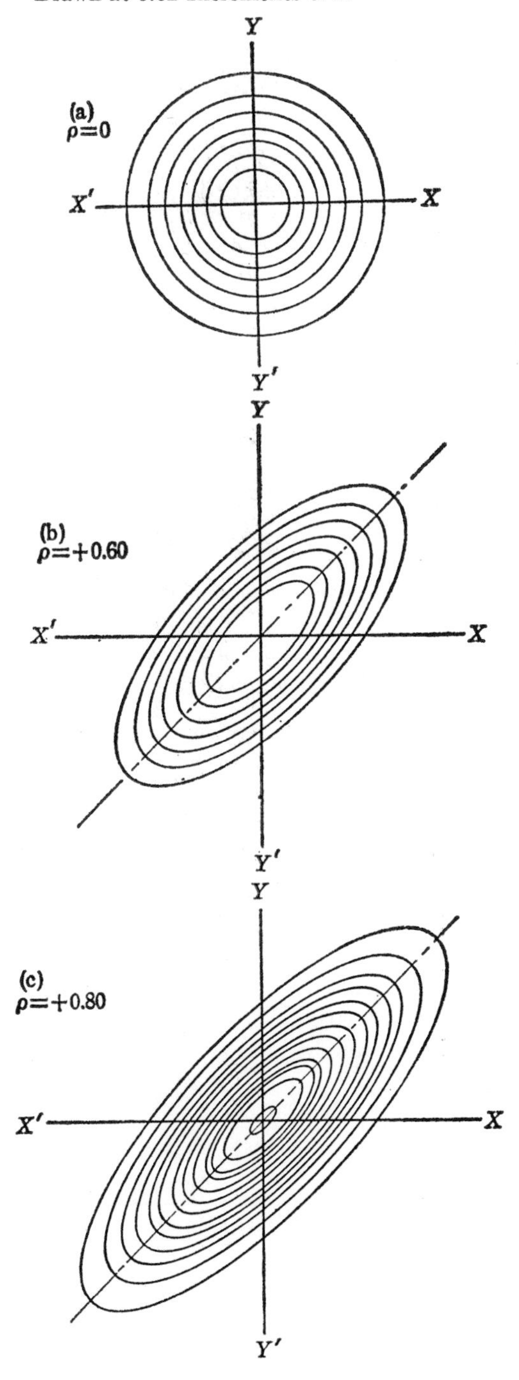

four values of Y at each of five equally spaced levels of X. So far as linear regression is concerned, it is not essential that we have the same number of values at each level, nor that the levels be equally spaced, nor even that we have more than one value at each level of X. Later, however, we plan to analyze these same data more extensively, and shall want these conditions, so we use them here.

Now recall that in our model the Y's at each X were normally distributed with variance $\sigma_{Y.X}^2$. Presumably we shall need an estimate of that parameter, and will have to approach it through a measurement of the scattering of our observed Y's about the calculated values, the Y_L's of equation (14.4.1). It would therefore seem reasonable to require that our values of a and b be those which make $\Sigma(Y - Y_L)^2$ a minimum. This again involves the method of least squares, and it would take a bit of calculus to prove that the required values are those obtained as the solution of a pair of equations known as the normal equations:

$$\begin{cases} aN + b\Sigma X = \Sigma Y \\ a\Sigma X + b\Sigma X^2 = \Sigma XY \end{cases} \tag{14.4.2}$$

This solution results in the formulas,

$$b = \frac{\Sigma XY - \overline{X}\Sigma Y}{\Sigma X^2 - \overline{X}\Sigma X} \tag{14.4.3a}$$

$$= \frac{N\Sigma XY - \Sigma X\Sigma Y}{N\Sigma X^2 - (\Sigma X)^2} \tag{14.4.3b}$$

where the first form, you should recognize, is better when N has a wieldy reciprocal and the second is better otherwise. In either case,

$$a = \overline{Y} - b\overline{X} \tag{14.4.4}$$

Look more closely at the denominators in equation 14.4.3a and b and you will see that they are just our usual computing formulas for $\Sigma(X - \overline{X})^2$. Let us pursue the idea further. It is true that $\Sigma(X - \overline{X})^2 = \Sigma(X - \overline{X})(X - \overline{X})$ and this suggests that the numerators of equation 14.4.3a and b may be another way of expressing $\Sigma(X - \overline{X})(Y - \overline{Y})$. The same sort of algebra that we used long ago in working with $\Sigma(X - \overline{X})^2$ will show that this is the case, and we urge you to work through the process for yourself. So we can add a third form of 14.4.3:

$$b = \frac{\Sigma(X - \overline{X})(Y - \overline{Y})}{\Sigma(X - \overline{X})^2} \tag{14.4.3c}$$

Application of these formulas, by way of the intermediate values shown in the table, leads to the values $b = 1.00000$ and $a = 2.00000$ for the data of Table 14-1.

Now we must see how to estimate $\sigma_{Y.X}^2$. To approach that problem, let us see first how we would calculate $\sigma_{Y.X}^2$ if we had a complete, finite population comprising ν_i values of Y at the ith level of X and κ levels of X, for a total of $\nu = \kappa\nu_i$ values. At any level of X,

$$\sigma_{Y.X_i}^2 = \sum_{j=1}^{\nu_i} \frac{(Y_{ij} - \mu_{Y.X_i})^2}{\nu_i}$$

and, because all $\sigma_{Y.X_i}^2$ are assumed equal, we simply pool the estimates from all the subpopulations, using the values of ν_i as weights. The result is

$$\sigma_{Y.X}^2 = \sum_{i=1}^{\kappa} \sum_{j=1}^{\nu_i} \frac{(Y_{ij} - \mu_{Y.X_i})^2}{\nu}$$

$$= \sum_{i=1}^{\kappa} \sum_{j=1}^{\nu_i} \frac{(Y_{ij} - A - BX_i)^2}{\nu}$$

Of course, as in the case of a single population, if $\nu = \infty$, we must use a limiting process to reach our value of $\sigma_{Y.X}^2$.

In our actual data, we have k levels of X, with N_i values of Y at the ith level for a total of $N = kN_i$ values. Because we do not know A and B, we sensibly employ their estimates, a and b. We realize that, in consequence, we must use degrees of freedom instead of numbers of observations, and the question arises as to what is that number. We previously stated the principle that the number of degrees of freedom associated with a statistic was the number of observations from which it was computed less the number of statistics which had to be computed from the data before it could be computed. In the present situation, we have N values of Y from which we have previously computed $\bar{Y}$ and $b_{Y.X}$, so that our number of degrees of freedom is $n = N - 2$. You may wonder why we didn't count a as a statistic. The answer is that a does not involve a *new* estimate, but is just a simple combination of $\bar{Y}$ and b: $a = \bar{Y} - b\bar{X}$. So our formula for the required estimate is

$$s_{Y.X}^2 = \sum_{i=1}^{k} \sum_{j=1}^{N_i} \frac{(Y_{ij} - a - bX_i)^2}{N - 2} \quad (14.4.5a)$$

which we shall usually write in condensed notation as

$$s_{Y.X}^2 = \frac{\Sigma(Y - a - bX)^2}{N - 2} \quad (14.4.5b)$$

Careful application of some algebra will develop this into a very convenient computing form:

$$s_{Y.X}^2 = \frac{\Sigma Y^2 - a\Sigma Y - b\Sigma XY}{N - 2} \quad (14.4.5c)$$

For our data in Table 14-1, the numerical value turns out to be 9.3, as developed in the table.

B. *Testing Hypotheses Concerning B.* The coefficient, B, often called the *regression coefficient*, is often of particular importance because it reflects the change in Y per unit change in X. For example, it may be that, unless B has at least some minimum value, the relation between Y and X will be of no further interest to us. Or it may be that our thinking about the fundamentals involved suggests that B ought to have a specified value. If the data make this idea untenable, then we must study our subject further. To see how we can test hypotheses, let us suppose that we obtained the data of Table 14-1 to enable us to test $H_0: B = B_0 = 1.35000$, or $H_0: B - B_0 = B - 1.35000$

Fig. 14-4. Plot of Synthetic Regression Data of Table 14.1.

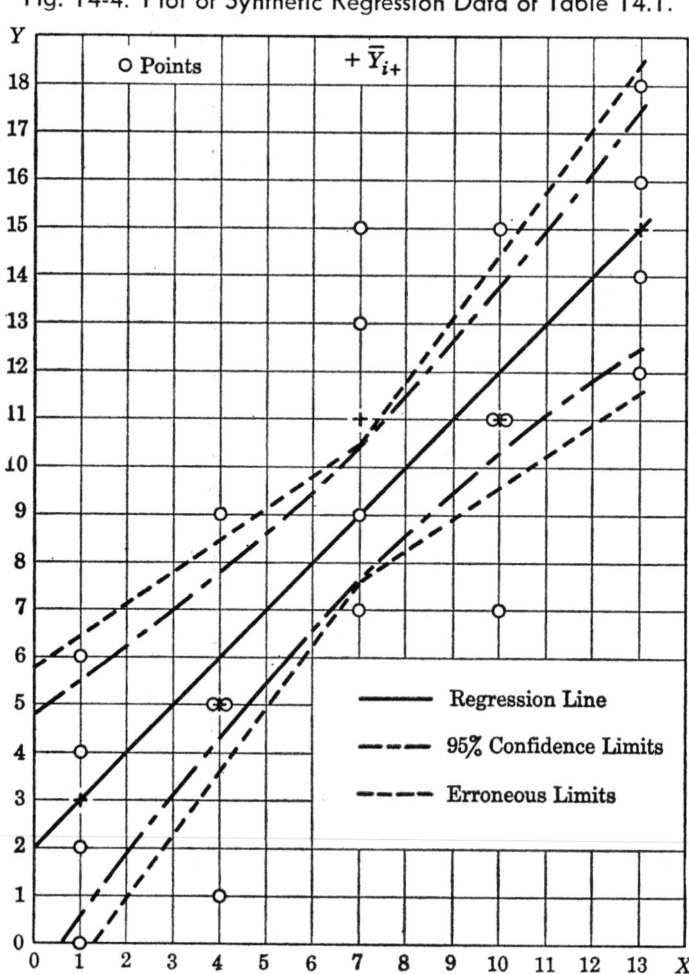

$= 0$. We have assumed the regression model. Under these circumstances, it can be shown that the ratio,

$$t = \frac{b - B_0}{s_b} \tag{14.4.6}$$

where

$$s_b = \sqrt{s_b^2} = \sqrt{s_{Y.X}^2/\Sigma(X - \overline{X})^2} \tag{14.4.7}$$

will have Student's t-distribution with $n = N - 2$ degrees of freedom if the null hypothesis is true. Of course, the two formulas can be combined to yield

$$t = \frac{b - B_0}{\sqrt{s_{Y.X}^2/\Sigma(X - \overline{X})^2}} \tag{14.4.8a}$$

$$= \frac{(b - B_0)\sqrt{\Sigma(X - \overline{X})^2}}{s_{Y.X}} \tag{14.4.8b}$$

We must choose an alpha risk. Let us again take 0.050, which leads to the critical values $\pm t_{1-\alpha/2,n} = \pm t_{0.975,18} = \pm 2.101$. Our observed value is, as shown in the table, -2.174, so that we must reject the null hypothesis and consider $B \neq 1.35$.

Your previous experience would suggest that we might have stated our hypothesis in the form $H_0 : (B - B_0)^2 = 0$ and so have used as our test statistic

$$F = t^2 = \frac{(b - B_0)^2}{s_b^2} \tag{14.4.9a}$$

$$= \frac{(b - B_0)^2\Sigma(X - \overline{X})^2}{s_{Y.X}^2} \tag{14.4.9b}$$

which should have the F-distribution with 1 numerator and $n = N - 2$ denominator degrees of freedom. This is correct, and its use saves the necessity for taking the square roots required for the use of t. Our critical value would be $F_{1-\alpha,1/n} = F_{0.950,1/18} = 4.41$, while our observed value would be 4.72, which, of course, requires the rejection of the null hypothesis.

Very often we shall be concerned with the hypothesis $H_0 : B - 0 = 0$ or $H_0 : (B - 0)^2 = 0$. This is equivalent to the hypothesis that there is no real linear relationship between Y and X. Of course, this makes the numerators of t and F simply b and b^2, respectively. We believe you will be most prudent not to think of this as a special formula, however, but rather as the simple result of the substitution of 0 for B_0 in the general formula. It should also be clear from past experience that if you wish to test the one-sided hypothesis $H_0 : B - B_0 \leq 0$, the critical value becomes $t_{1-\alpha,n}$, while the one-sided hypothesis $H_0 : B - B_0 \geq 0$ requires the critical value $t_{\alpha,n}$. If such hypotheses are tested using F as the test statistic, the critical value becomes $F_{1-2\alpha,1/n}$ in either case, and the hypothesis is rejected only when the sign of $b - B_0$ is opposite to that stated by the hypothesis.

C. *Confidence Limits for Parameters.* Your previous experience will suggest that we can immediately establish confidence limits for B and $\sigma_{Y.X}^2$ by using the principles we have previously employed. As in the past, $P\%$ confidence limits lead to related values of $\alpha = (100 - P)/100$, and the limits for B become

$$B = b \pm t_{1/2\alpha, n} s_b \tag{14.4.10}$$

where $n = N - 2$ and s_b is calculated from equation 14.4.7. For our example, 95% confidence limits for B are

$$B = 1.00000 \pm 2.101 \times 0.16101$$
$$= 1.00000 \pm 0.338 \doteq 1.34 \text{ and } 0.66$$

For $\sigma_{Y.X}^2$, the limits are

$$\sigma_{Y.X}^2 = \frac{s_{Y.X}^2}{(\chi^2/n)_{1/2\alpha, n}} \tag{14.4.11a}$$

and

$$\sigma_{Y.X}^2 = \frac{s_{Y.X}^2}{(\chi^2/n)_{1-1/2\alpha, n}} \tag{14.4.11b}$$

For our data, 95% confidence limits are thence

$$\sigma_{Y.X}^2 = \frac{9.333}{0.457} \doteq 20.42$$

and

$$\sigma_{Y.X}^2 = \frac{9.333}{1.75} \doteq 5.33$$

14.5 Confidence Intervals for Lines

In the previous section, we have discussed the details of the computation of a, b, and $s_{Y.X}^2$ and their use in testing hypotheses concerning B and $\sigma_{Y.X}^2$ and in providing confidence intervals for those two parameters. Why, you may properly wonder, was A not discussed in terms of hypotheses and confidence limits? It could have been, but we think you will find it more revealing to consider the problem of placing a confidence interval about the line first.

We have the line $Y_L = a + bX$ as our best line, in the sense that the sum of squared deviations of the Y-values from it is less than for any other line. But we recognize that resampling from the same population might well lead us to slightly different values for a, for b, or for both, and thus to different lines. Can we somehow provide a band about our line and assert with $P\%$ confidence that this band includes the values of $\mu_{Y.X}$? We can do so, though the task is not quite as simple as we might think.

Let us approach it by recognizing that we already have confidence limits for B. If, in the equation of the line, we replace a by its equivalent, $\bar{Y} - b\bar{X}$, and carry out a little algebra, we shall have

$$Y_L = a + bX = \bar{Y} - b\bar{X} + bX$$
$$= \bar{Y} + b(X - \bar{X}) \qquad (14.5.1)$$

While this is not a convenient form for most uses, it will prove valuable for our present purpose. Notice that it immediately shows us that $Y = \bar{Y}$ when $X = \bar{X}$, so that our line must pass through the point $(\bar{X},\bar{Y})$.

Now let us consider an attack on our confidence limits which is attractive, but has some flaws, then discover and correct the flaws. We might provide confidence limits for $\bar{Y}$, say $\bar{Y}_u$ and $\bar{Y}_l$, and plot the points $(\bar{X},\bar{Y}_u)$ and $(\bar{X},\bar{Y}_l)$ above and below $(\bar{X},\bar{Y})$. Then, through each of these points, we might pass two lines, one with slope B_u and the other with slope B_l. We might then regard the outlying line segments in each region as our confidence interval about our line. In effect, this recognizes that the line is subject to misplacement in both its height and its slope, and we have combined our estimates of both effects. This is good, but not quite good enough, for we failed to recognize that it is unlikely that, in sampling, we should obtain values leading to both a very poor estimate of A and a very poor estimate of B. Somehow, we must find a band that recognizes this fact.

Let us start by finding the actual limits for $\bar{Y}$. Actually, our use of the symbol $\bar{Y}$, while it correctly designates the numerical value and part of the facts, sacrifices some of the information for the sake of compactness. Recall that $Y_L = f(X) = a + bX$ and you will be reminded that the value we designate as $\bar{Y}$ is $f(\bar{X})$. This would suggest that in establishing confidence limits for it we should take into account not merely the variation in Y alone, but rather that variation in relation to X. This has led mathematicians to recognize that the standard deviation of $\bar{Y}$ in such cases is not $s_Y\sqrt{1/N}$ but $s_{Y.X}\sqrt{1/N}$. Thus our $P\%$ confidence limits for $\bar{Y}$ on our regression line become

$$\mu_{Y.\bar{X}} = \bar{Y} \pm t_{1/2\alpha,n}s_{Y.X}\sqrt{1/N} \qquad (14.5.2)$$

which yield 95% confidence limits for our data as

$$\mu_{Y.\bar{X}} = 9.00000 \pm 2.101 \times 3.05505\sqrt{0.05000}$$
$$= 9.00000 \pm 1.435 \doteq 10.4 \text{ and } 7.6$$

Now how can we avoid the extremes we discussed above in providing confidence limits for the rest of the line? While it is beyond our scope to trace the details, the mathematical statisticians have found that these limits are given by the not too difficult formula,

$$\mu_{Y.\bar{X}} = Y_L \pm t_{1/2\alpha,n}s_{Y.X}\sqrt{(1/N) + (X - \bar{X})^2/\Sigma(X - \bar{X})^2} \qquad (14.5.3)$$

In fact, then, all we do is add to $1/N$ under the radical the ratio of the squared deviation of the value of X at which we wish our limits to the sum of the squared deviations of all X's. This is a most interesting formula. Notice that it immediately reduces to equation 14.5.1 when $X = \bar{X}$, as it should. Notice, further, that the larger the value of $\Sigma(X - \bar{X})^2$, the smaller the increase in the confidence interval for any value of X other than $\bar{X}$. This is quite proper, for the sum can be increased by increasing either the number of observations or the range of X or both, which should increase our certainty that we are close to the true line with our actual line.

It is convenient to use a form like Table 14-2 in computing confidence limits for lines. We have plotted our line with its confidence limits in Fig. 14-4. Notice that the limits flare away from the line in a form somewhat like the bell on a clarinet.

Now, of course, we are in a position to compute confidence limits about $a = f(0)$, which may be considered as confidence limits for A. These limits have been included in Table 14-2.

Table 14-2 COMPUTATION OF CONFIDENCE LIMITS FOR REGRESSION LINE OF TABLE 14-1

X	$\Delta X = X - \bar{X}$	$(\Delta X)^2$	$\dfrac{(\Delta X)^2}{\Sigma(\Delta X)^2} = C$	$1/N + C = D^2$
0	−7	49	0.13611	0.18611
1	−6	36	0.10000	0.15000
4	−3	9	0.02500	0.07500
7	0	0	0.00000	0.05000
10	+3	9	0.02500	0.07500
13	+6	36	0.10000	0.15000

X	D	KD	Y_L	Y_u	Y_l
0	0.43140	2.769	2.0	4.8	−0.8
1	0.38729	2.486	3.0	5.5	+0.5
4	0.27386	1.758	6.0	7.8	4.2
7	0.22360	1.435	9.0	10.4	7.6
10	0.27386	1.758	12.0	13.8	10.2
13	0.38729	2.486	15.0	17.5	12.5

$t_{0.975,18} = 2.101 \qquad s_{Y.X} = 3.05505 \qquad K = t_{0.975,18}s_{Y.X} = 6.41866$

Of course, this suggests an idea which is true, namely, that

$$s_a = s_{Y.X}\sqrt{(1/N) + (0 - \bar{X})^2/\Sigma(X - \bar{X})^2} \qquad (14.5.4a)$$

$$= s_{Y.X}\sqrt{(1/N) + \bar{X}^2/\Sigma(X - \bar{X})^2} \qquad (14.5.4b)$$

and that appropriate statistics for testing $H_0 : A - A_0 = 0$ are

$$t = \frac{a - A_0}{s_a} \tag{14.5.5}$$

and

$$F = \frac{(a - A_0)^2}{s_a{}^2} \tag{14.5.6}$$

which have Student's t-distribution with $n = N - 2$ degrees of freedom and the F-distribution the 1 numerator and n denominator degrees of freedom, respectively.

14.6 Measuring Correlation

Now that we have learned something of how to treat linear regression problems, let us consider the correlation problem in more detail. We have previously stated some of the properties of the correlation coefficient, ρ, and of its square, ρ^2, the coefficient of determination, which appear in the equation of the bivariate normal distribution. We have, however, given no indication of how we might obtain from a sample the necessary statistics, which we shall symbolize as r and r^2, respectively, to estimate these parameters. We must now do so.

Suppose that we have a set of pairs of values of X and Y which are exactly represented by the equation $Y = A + BX$. From our work with regression, we know that $\overline{Y} = A + B\overline{X}$, so we know that

$$Y - \overline{Y} = B(X - \overline{X}) \tag{14.6.1}$$

$$(Y - \overline{Y})^2 = B^2(X - \overline{X})^2 \tag{14.6.2}$$

and

$$\Sigma(Y - \overline{Y})^2 = B^2\Sigma(X - \overline{X})^2 \tag{14.6.3}$$

If, instead of squaring 14.6.1, we multiply both sides by $(X - \overline{X})$, we have

$$\begin{aligned}(X - \overline{X})(Y - \overline{Y}) &= B(X - \overline{X})(X - \overline{X}) \\ &= B(X - \overline{X})^2\end{aligned}$$

and

$$\Sigma(X - \overline{X})(Y - \overline{Y}) = B\Sigma(X - \overline{X})^2 \tag{14.6.5}$$

The statistics we are seeking are defined by the formulas,

$$r = \frac{\Sigma(X - \overline{X})(Y - \overline{Y})}{\sqrt{\Sigma(X - \overline{X})^2\Sigma(Y - \overline{Y})^2}} \tag{14.6.6}$$

and

$$r^2 = \frac{[\Sigma(X - \overline{X})(Y - \overline{Y})]^2}{\Sigma(X - \overline{X})^2\Sigma(Y - \overline{Y})^2} \tag{14.6.7}$$

In order to understand why these formulas are sensible, let us apply 14.6.7 to a set of data such as we discussed in the preceding paragraph. Substituting equivalents from 14.6.5 into the numerator and from 14.6.3 into the denominator of 14.6.7, we have:

$$r^2 = \frac{[B\Sigma(X - \overline{X})^2]^2}{[\Sigma(X - \overline{X})^2]B^2\Sigma(X - \overline{X})^2} = 1 \tag{14.6.8}$$

Thus it is evident that we have a quantity which, whenever the related points fall exactly on a straight line, has exactly the value unity. Under the same circumstances $|r| = 1$, and the sign will be the same as that of B.

Strictly, there are two exceptions to this statement. Whenever the line is vertical, $\Sigma(X - \overline{X})^2 = 0$, and r^2 is not defined. Similarly, when $B = 0$ and $\Sigma(Y - \overline{Y})^2 = 0$, r^2 is also not defined. This will not trouble us, however, because in neither case is Y a function of X. So far, then, the statistics are sound.

Now let us examine the numerator of r and r^2 in a different light. Suppose that B is positive, so that for all values of X greater than $\overline{X}$ the related values of Y will be greater than $\overline{Y}$, as long as the points fall perfectly along the line. For all such points, $(X - \overline{X})$ and $(Y - \overline{Y})$ will both be positive, as will their product. For all values below the means, $(X - \overline{X})$ and $(Y - \overline{Y})$ will both be negative, but their product will again be positive, so that all points except $(\overline{X},\overline{Y})$ will contribute to an increase of $\Sigma(X - \overline{X})(Y - \overline{Y})$ and thus to an increase in the numerators or r and r^2. If B is negative, similar considerations show that each product will be negative, save that for the point $(\overline{X},\overline{Y})$ since $(X - \overline{X})$ and $(Y - \overline{Y})$ have opposite signs and the product is negative. Thus these points contribute to an increase in the numerical value of r and the actual value of r^2. As we have seen, the numerical values are all unity.

But suppose that we had the same values of X and Y as above, but that we interchanged the values of Y associated with two of the values of X, which we may designate as X_1 and X_2 where $X_1 < X_2$. Before the shift, the points (X_1,Y_1) and (X_2,Y_2) fell exactly on the line $Y = A + BX$, but after the shift, the new points, (X_1,Y_2) and (X_2,Y_1) will be off the line on opposite sides of it. Let us see what happens to $\Sigma(X - \overline{X})(Y - \overline{Y})$ as a result of the shift.

Recall that

$$\Sigma(X - \overline{X})(Y - \overline{Y}) = \Sigma XY - \overline{X}\Sigma Y$$

and that, because we retained the same values of X and Y, but simply changed "partners" in two pairs, $\bar{X}$ and ΣY remain unchanged. Therefore, any effect must result from a change in ΣXY associated with the change in pairs. Before the shift, the contribution of the two points in question was

$$\begin{aligned} X_1Y_1 + X_2Y_2 &= X_1(A + BX_1) + X_2(A + BX_2) \\ &= AX_1 + BX_1^2 + AX_2 + BX_2^2 \\ &= A(X_1 + X_2) + B(X_1^2 + X_2^2) \end{aligned}$$

After the shift, their contribution was

$$\begin{aligned} X_1Y_2 + X_2Y_1 &= X_1(A + BX_2) + X_2(A + BX_1) \\ &= AX_1 + BX_1X_2 + AX_2 + BX_1X_2 \\ &= A(X_1 + X_2) + 2BX_1X_2 \end{aligned}$$

The difference, expressed as the value after the change minus the value before, is, consequently,

$$\begin{aligned} (X_1Y_2 + X_2Y_1) - (X_1Y_1 + X_2Y_2) &= 2BX_1Y_2 - B(X_1^2 + X_2^2) \\ &= -B(X_1^2 - 2X_1X_2 + X_2^2) \\ &= -B(X_1 - X_2)^2 \end{aligned}$$

Thus, since $(X_1 - X_2)^2$ must be positive, we have the result that the change must be opposite in sign to B.

This means that if B was positive, ΣXY and hence $\Sigma(X - \overline{X})(Y - \overline{Y})$ must be reduced. Otherwise, both quantities must be algebraically increased. Suppose there had been only these two points. We know that the interchange of pairs would simply have reversed the sign of B, and thus of r, but that in consequence of the fact that two points have to be on a line, $|r|$ and r^2 will both remain 1. In all other cases, then, after the shift,

$$-1 < r < +1 \qquad \text{and} \qquad 0 < r^2 < +1$$

By an extension of this thinking, it can be demonstrated that no matter what shifts in pairings are made,

$$-1 \leq r \leq +1 \qquad \text{and} \qquad 0 \leq r^2 \leq +1$$

But these same restrictions applied to ρ and ρ^2, and it would therefore seem that the selection of r and r^2 as their estimating statistics was sensible. Formal mathematical treatment can show that r^2 is, in fact, our best estimator of ρ^2, just as s^2 was of σ^2, while an element of bias enters in the use of r as an estimate of ρ just as it did in the use of s as an estimate of σ. However, the methods we shall employ will avoid the consequences of that bias, just as they have in the past.

14.7 Correlation and Regression

We suspect that while the preceding discussion has presented you with the formulas for r and r^2, and has made you somewhat acquainted with the bivariate normal distribution, it has given you little real feeling for the meaning of correlation with actual data. To help develop that feeling, we have prepared two tables and related graphs. In the first table, we have synthesized a simple set of data which could have been obtained under the correlation model. They are shown as set *a* in Table 14-3. They are a bit special, actually,

Table 14-3 SYNTHETIC DATA TO ILLUSTRATE CORRELATION PROBLEMS, WITH COMPUTATIONS THEREON

Variable	X	Y	Y	Y	Y	Y	Y	Y	Y	Y	Y	Y
Set	*All*	*a*	*b*	*c*	*d*	*e*	*f*	*g*	*h*	*i*	*j*	*k*
	9	10	10	10	10	10	1	−2	−8	−8	−8	−8
	7	7	7	4	4	1	4	7	−2	−2	−5	−5
	7	7	4	1	−2	−5	−2	−5	4	1	−2	−5
	5	4	1	−5	7	4	7	4	−5	7	1	−2
	5	4	−2	7	1	−2	−5	−8	1	−5	4	−2
	3	1	−5	4	−5	7	10	1	7	−2	7	1
	3	1	7	−2	7	1	−8	7	−5	4	−5	1
	1	−2	4	−5	1	−8	7	−2	1	7	−2	4
	1	−2	1	7	−5	4	−5	4	7	−5	1	4
	−1	−5	−2	1	4	−5	4	−5	−2	1	4	7
	−1	−5	−5	−2	−2	7	−2	1	4	4	7	7
	−3	−8	−8	−8	−8	−2	1	10	10	10	10	10
ΣX	36			ΣY	12					$\Sigma(X - X(^2\Sigma(Y - Y)^2$		51,984
ΣX^2	260			ΣY^2	354							
$\overline{X}$	3			$\overline{Y}$	1					$\sqrt{\Sigma(X-\overline{X})^2\Sigma(Y-\overline{Y})^2}$		228
$\Sigma(X - \overline{X})^2$	152			$\Sigma(Y - Y)^2$	342							
ΣXY		264	204	168	168	96	0	−24	−96	−96	−132	−192
$\Sigma(X-\overline{X})(Y-\overline{Y})$		228	168	132	132	60	0	−60	−132	−132	−168	−228
r		1.00000	0.73684	0.57894	0.57894	0.26315	0.00000	−0.26315	−0.57894	−0.57894	−0.73684	−1.00000
$[\Sigma(X-\overline{X})(Y-\overline{Y})]^2$		51984	28224	17424	17424	3600	0	3600	17424	17424	28824	51984
r^2		1.00000	0.54293	0.33518	0.33518	0.06925	0.00000	0.06925	0.33518	0.33518	0.54293	1.00000
$b_{Y.X}$		1.50000	1.10526	0.86842	0.86842	0.39473	0.00000	−0.39473	−0.86842	−0.86842	−1.10526	−1.50000
$a_{Y.X}$		−3.50000	−2.31578	−1.60526	−1.60526	−0.18419	1.00000	2.18419	3.60526	3.60526	4.31578	5.50000
$b_{X.Y}$		0.66666	0.49122	0.38596	0.38596	0.17543	0.00000	−0.17543	−0.38590	−0.38596	−0.49122	−0.66666
$a_{X.Y}$		2.33333	2.50878	2.61404	2.61404	2.82457	3.00000	3.17453	3.38596	3.38596	3.49122	3.66666

Fig. 14-5. Plot of data from Table 14-3 to illustrate meaning of correlation.

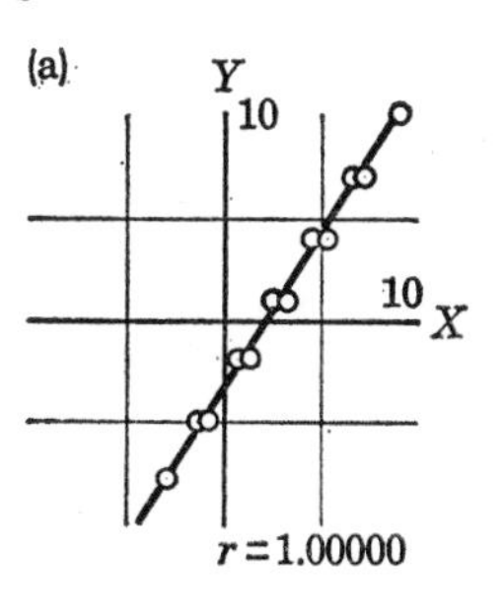

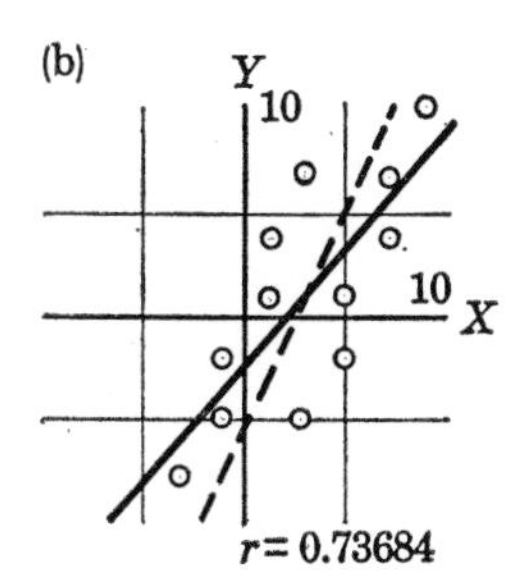

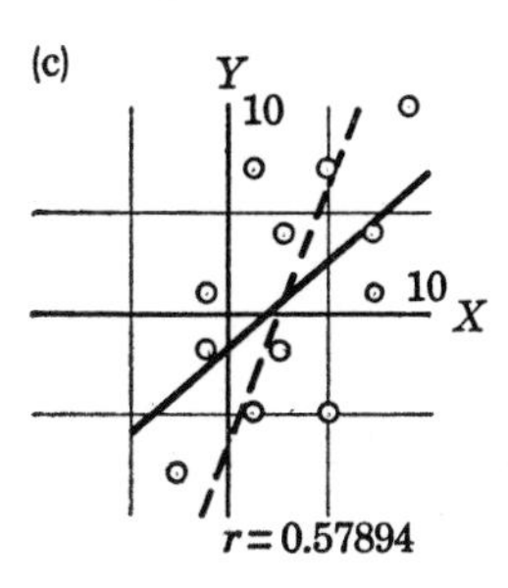

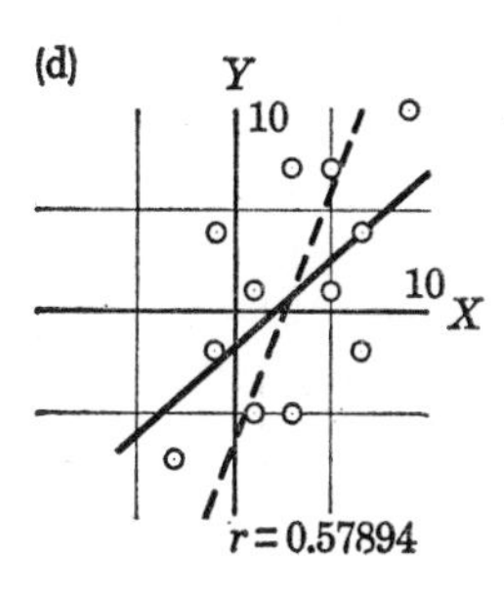

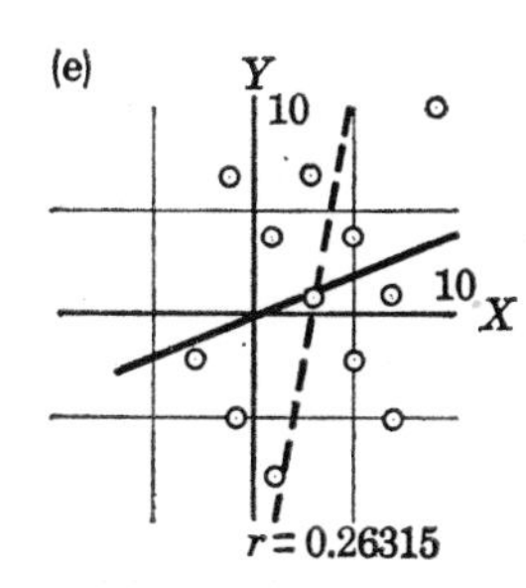

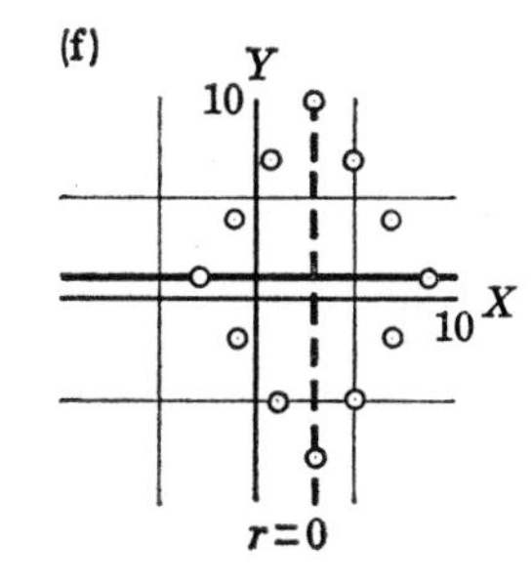

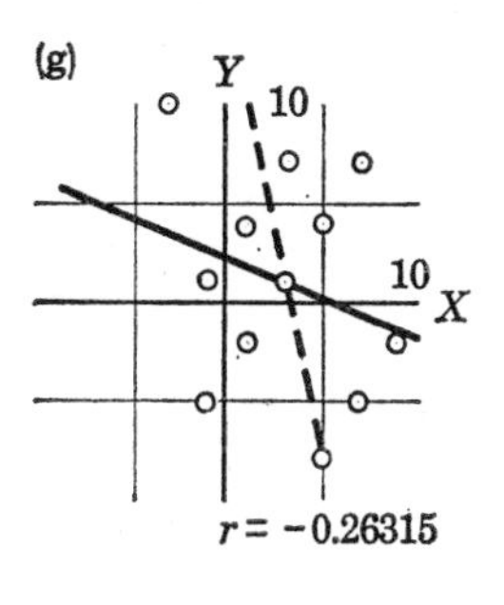

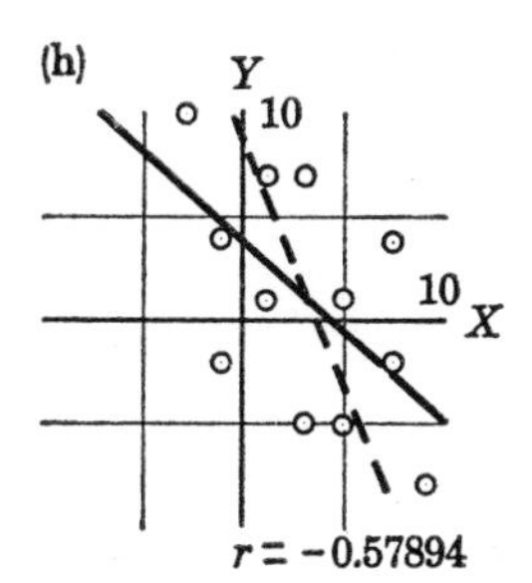

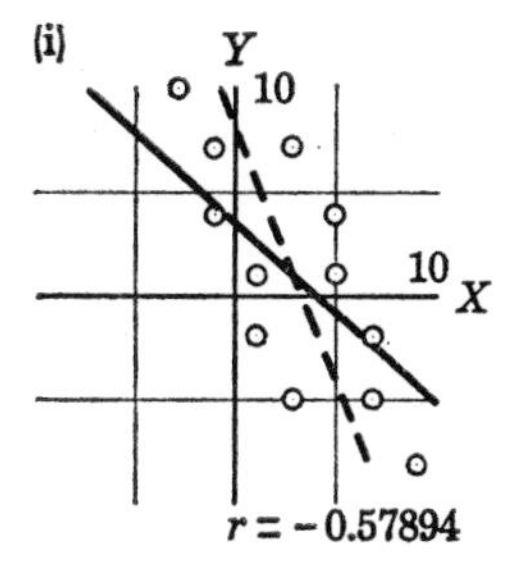

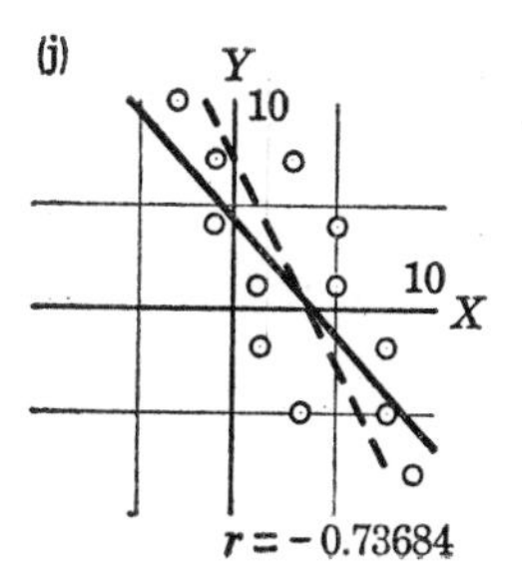

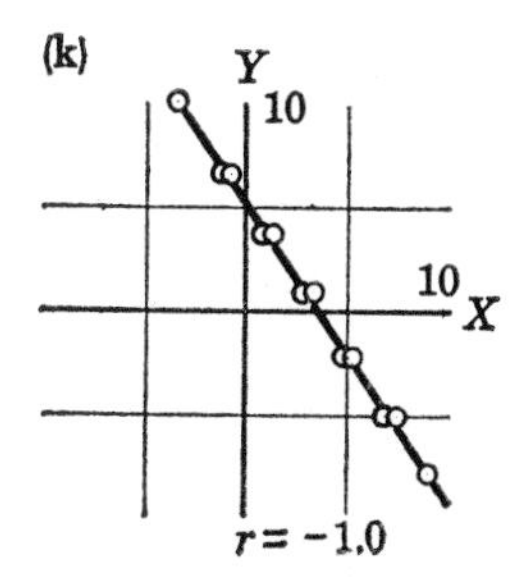

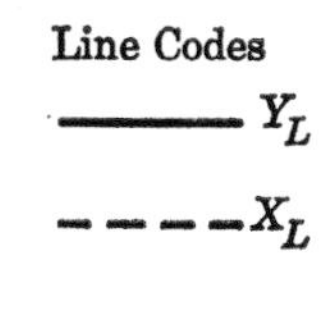

in two respects. First, the points fall exactly along the line $Y = -3.5 + 1.5X$. Second, the values of X and of Y are each symmetrically distributed about their respective means, $\overline{X} = 3$ and $\overline{Y} = 1$.

In the rest of the table, all sets comprise the same values of X and of Y as did set a, but the pairings have been altered. For each set we have calculated r and r^2, and have arranged the sets in the order of decreasing values of r. Notice that, in set f, r has become exactly zero. Reference to the related plots in Fig. 14-5 shows that the dispersion of the points about a diagonal axis has increased until, in set f, the points happen to be symmetrically located about the X- and Y-axes, and any appearance of a diagonal axis has disappeared. Thereafter, further changes in pairing produced negative values of r and finally led to set k for which $r = -1$. In these sets, a diagonal axis with negative slope begins to be sensed, finally becoming clear as the line $Y = 5.5 - 1.5X$, along which set k exactly falls.

Now let us do something which seems quite unconventional. Suppose we treat these data *as though* they were regression data. Since we have not claimed to be able to select and measure either variable without error, we have no basis for selecting one as the independent variable. Let us see what happens if we use first one, then the other. To keep ourselves straight, let us use subscripts, so that when X is treated as the independent variable we shall be seeking the line,

$$Y_L = a_{Y.X} + b_{Y.X}X \tag{14.7.1a}$$

and when Y is considered the independent variable we shall be seeking the line,

$$X_L = a_{X.Y} + b_{X.Y}Y \tag{14.7.1b}$$

Proper application of our regression formulas leads to

$$b_{Y.X} = \frac{\Sigma(X - \overline{X})(Y - \overline{Y})}{\Sigma(X - \overline{X})^2} \tag{14.7.2a}$$

and

$$b_{X.Y} = \frac{\Sigma(X - \overline{X})(Y - \overline{Y})}{\Sigma(Y - \overline{Y})^2} \tag{14.7.2b}$$

Notice some results of this experiment. In the first place,

$$b_{Y.X}b_{X.Y} = \frac{[\Sigma(X - \overline{X})(Y - \overline{Y})]^2}{\Sigma(X - \overline{X})^2\Sigma(Y - \overline{Y})^2} = r^2 \tag{14.7.3}$$

This result may seem, at first, surprising. But notice that, whichever model we assume, certain elements appear in our formulas: $\Sigma(X - \overline{X})(Y - \overline{Y})$, $\Sigma(X - \overline{X})^2$, and $\Sigma(Y - \overline{Y})^2$, so it is really not so surprising that various formulas developed for one of the models should combine to equal formulas or combinations of formulas for the other model.

Let us follow this idea further. Notice that, as we moved from set to set in order of decreasing r's, the values of $b_{Y.X}$ also decreased, becoming zero for set f and finally reaching -1.5 for set k. Reference to the plots in Fig. 14-5 will show that the corresponding lines became more nearly parallel to the X-axis as the numerical value of $b_{Y.X}$ and of r decreased. The values of $b_{X.Y}$ started at $0.\dot{6}$ ($= 1/1.5$) for set a and decreased to 0 for set f, for which $r = 0$, then further decreased to $-0.\dot{6}$ ($= 1/[-1.5]$) for set k, for which $r = -1$. The lines became more nearly parallel to the Y-axis as the numerical value of $b_{X.Y}$ and r decreased.

Another result of some interest is a little more involved to see. Recall that the regression coefficient, $b_{Y.X}$ measures the slope of its line relative to the X-axis, and is, in fact, the ratio of the difference between two Y-values to the difference between the corresponding X-values for points on the line. In a similar way, $b_{X.Y}$ measures the slope of its line, but relative to the Y-axis, as the ratio of X-differences to Y-differences. If we take its reciprocal, $1/b_{Y.X}$, we express the slope with reference to the X-axis, as the ratio of Y-differences to X-differences along the line X_L. Now if we multiply $b_{Y.X}$ by $1/b_{X.Y}$ for any set, we shall have

$$
\begin{aligned}
(b_{Y.X})(1/b_{X.Y}) &= \frac{b_{Y.X}}{b_{X.Y}} \\
&= \left[\frac{\Sigma(X-\overline{X})(Y-\overline{Y})}{\Sigma(X-\overline{X})^2}\right]\left[\frac{\Sigma(Y-\overline{Y})^2}{\Sigma(X-\overline{X})(Y-\overline{Y})}\right] \\
&= \frac{\Sigma(Y-\overline{Y})^2}{\Sigma(X-\overline{X})^2} \qquad (14.7.4)
\end{aligned}
$$

which tells us that the product is not affected by the rearrangement of pairs. But for set a, we already noted that $b_{X.Y} = 1/b_{Y.X}$, so for that set, $b_{Y.X}(1/b_{X.Y}) = b_{Y.X}^2$, which is the square of the slope of the line along which the points of that set fell exactly. The same statement is true for set k. Thus it appears that, for any of these sets, $b_{Y.X}(1/b_{X.Y})$ is the square of the slopes of the two lines which the data, upon suitable rearrangement of pairs, will exactly fall along, one line having the square root of the product as its slope, the other, the negative of that value.

Lest you fear that our results are affected by the high degree of symmetry of the X- and Y-values, consider the sets in Table 14-4 and Fig. 14-6, in which this symmetry has been eliminated. Here we start with points which exactly fall along the line $Y = 10 + 0.5X$, but neither the X-values nor the Y-values are symmetrically distributed about their mean. Yet, in all pairings, $b_{Y.X}(1/b_{X.Y}) = 0.25 = 0.50^2$, the square of the slope of the original line. In this set, of course, no rearrangement yields a perfect fit to a line of negative slope, yet we have a feeling of dispersion of values about a line with slope of -0.50, as the graphs will help you to see.

Table 14-4 Synthetic Data to Illustrate Correlation Problems, with Computations Thereon. Values Not Symmetric About Their Means

Variable	X	Y	Y	Y	Y	Y	Y	Y
Set	*All*	*a*	*b*	*c*	*d*	*e*	*f*	*g*
	2	11	12	14	11	12	21	21
	4	12	11	12	14	21	12	17
	8	14	14	11	21	14	17	14
	14	17	21	21	12	11	11	12
	22	21	17	17	17	17	14	11
ΣX	50		ΣY	75			$\Sigma(X-\overline{X})^2\Sigma(Y-\overline{Y})^2$	17,424
ΣX^2	764		ΣY^2	1191				
$\overline{X}$	10		$\overline{Y}$	15			$\sqrt{\Sigma(X-\overline{X})^2\Sigma(Y-\overline{Y})^2}$	132
$\Sigma(X-\overline{X})^2$	264		$\Sigma(Y-\overline{Y})^2$	66				
ΣXY		882	848	832	788	748	688	632
$\Sigma(X-\overline{X})(Y-\overline{Y})$		132	98	82	38	−2	−62	−118
r		1.00000	0.74242	0.62121	0.28787	−0.01515	−0.46969	−0.89393
$[\Sigma(X-\overline{X})(Y-\overline{Y})]^2$		17424	9605	6724	1444	4	3844	13924
r^2		1.00000	0.55119	0.38590	0.08287	0.00022	0.22061	0.79912
$b_{Y.X}$		0.50000	0.37121	0.31060	0.14393	−0.00757	−0.23484	−0.44696
$a_{Y.X}$		10.0000	11.2879	11.8940	13.5607	15.0757	17.3484	19.4696
$b_{X.Y}$		2.00000	1.48484	1.24242	0.57575	−0.03030	−0.93939	−01.78787
$a_{X.Y}$		−20.0000	−12.2726	−8.6363	+1.36375	10.4545	24.09085	36.81085

Fig. 14-6. Plot of data from Table 14-4, to illustrate meaning of correlation. Note that, due to asymmetry, complete reversal of the order of pairing, which developed set g from set a, cannot produce a linear relationship among the points.

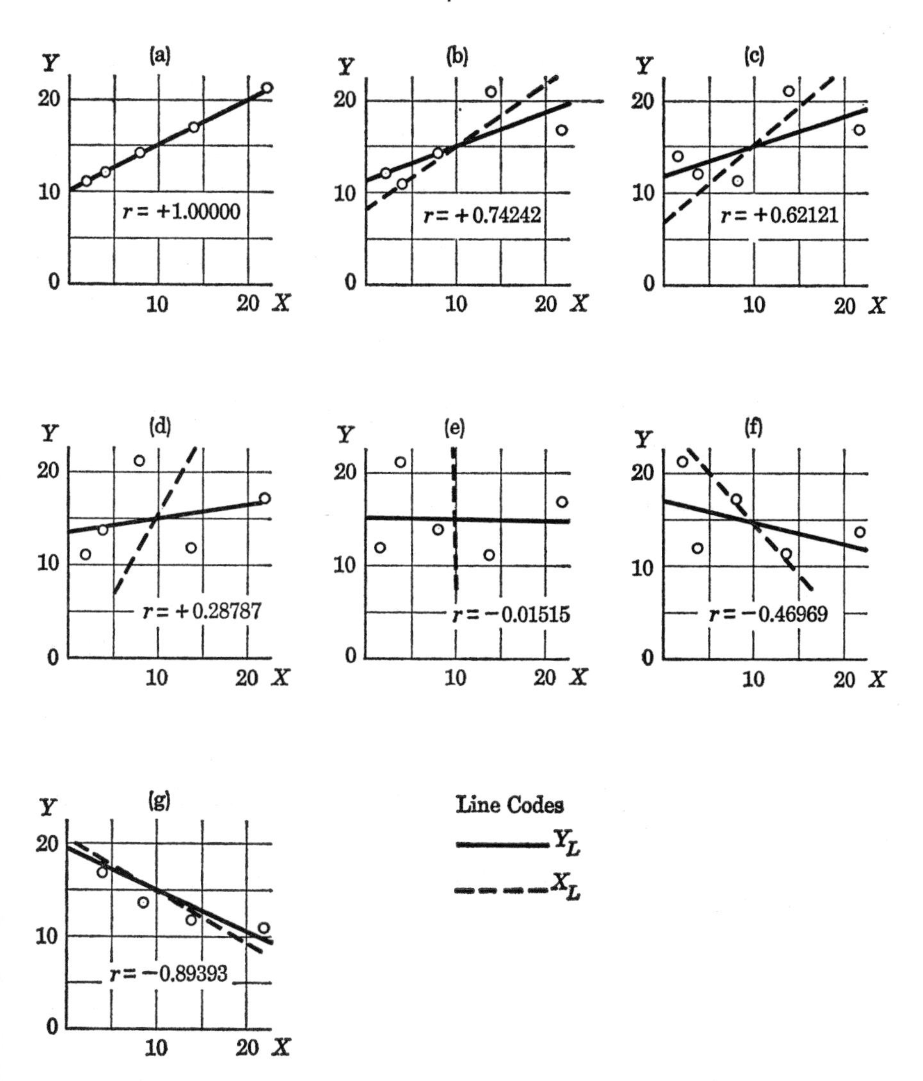

14.8 Correlation and Standardized Variables

In our previous work, we have found it useful to express our values in standard form, that is, as the ratio of their deviation from their mean to their standard deviation. Because, with only sample data at our disposal, we cannot know the population mean and standard deviation, we then consider

$$x' = (X - \overline{X})/s_X \tag{14.8.1a}$$

and

$$y' = (Y - \overline{Y})/s_Y \tag{14.8.1b}$$

as the standardized forms.

If we treat sets of data, such as those of Tables 14-3 and 14-4, by first transforming them to standard form, then making other computations of interest on these standardized values, we find, of course, that $\overline{x'} = \overline{y'} = 0$. In consesequence, when we make regression computations, $a_{y'.x'} = a_{x'y'} = 0$, so that

$$y'_L = b_{y'.x'} \tag{14.8.2a}$$

$$x'_L = b_{x'.y'} \tag{14.8.2b}$$

Now suppose we set up the calculations for $b_{y'.x'}$ but then transform our values back to their original form:

$$b_{y'.x'} = \frac{\Sigma(x' - \overline{x'})(y' - \overline{y'})}{\Sigma(x' - \overline{x'})^2} = \frac{\Sigma x'y'}{\Sigma x'^2}$$

$$= \frac{\sum \left[\frac{X - \overline{X}}{s_X}\right]\left[\frac{Y - \overline{Y}}{s_Y}\right]}{\sum \frac{(X - \overline{X})^2}{s_X^2}} \tag{14.8.3a}$$

But recall that $s_X^2 = \Sigma(X - \overline{X})^2/(N - 1)$, $s_Y^2 = \Sigma(Y - \overline{Y})^2/(N - 1)$ and therefore $s_X s_Y = \sqrt{\Sigma(X - \overline{X})^2 \Sigma(Y - \overline{Y})^2}/(N - 1)$. By making these substitutions in 14.8.3a, we find

$$b_{y'.x'} = \frac{\Sigma(X - \overline{X})(Y - \overline{Y})}{\left[\frac{\sqrt{\Sigma(X - \overline{X})^2 \Sigma(Y - \overline{Y})^2}}{N - 1}\right]} \Bigg/ \frac{\Sigma(X - \overline{X})^2}{\left[\frac{\Sigma(X - \overline{X})^2}{N - 1}\right]}$$

$$= \frac{\Sigma(X - \overline{X})(Y - \overline{Y})}{\sqrt{\Sigma(X - \overline{X})^2 \Sigma(Y - \overline{Y})^2}} = r \tag{14.8.3b}$$

and similar work would show that $b_{x'.y'} = r$ also. Thus, in standardized form, each regression coefficient is simply the correlation coefficient. Thus y'_L and x'_L coincide at an angle of 45° with both axes when $|r| = 1$. The line rises to the right if $r = +1$ and falls if $r = -1$. As $|r|$ decreases the lines move apart, y'_L toward the x'-axis and x'_L toward the y'-axis. The angles between each line and its nearer axis remain equal for the two lines for any set.

14.9 Testing Hypotheses Concerning ρ and ρ^2

We have become so accustomed to the idea that we can test the hypothesis that any parameter we have encountered equals, exceeds, or falls short of any value we may be interested in, that it will come as something of a shock to us to learn that we have exact procedures for testing only the hypothetical value zero when we are concerned with ρ and ρ^2. Only under these conditions is a test statistic truly known. For other hypothetical values, only approximate procedures are available, whose utility we shall subsequently consider. But first, let us consider the case in which we have an exact method.

To illustrate that method, suppose we use the data of Table 14-2e to test $H_0 : \rho = 0$. Our assumption that our data conform to the correlation model can be shown by mathematicians to make our test statistic:

$$t = \frac{r\sqrt{N-2}}{\sqrt{1-r^2}} = \sqrt{\frac{r^2(N-2)}{1-r^2}} \tag{14.9.1}$$

which will have Student's t-distribution with $n = N - 2$ degrees of freedom. Since our data have $N = 12$ pairs of values, if we choose an alpha risk of 0.050, our critical values will be $\pm t_{1/2\alpha,n} = \pm t_{0.025,10} = \pm 2.228$. Our observed value will be

$$t = \sqrt{\frac{0.06925 \times 10}{0.93075}} = 0.862$$

which is not in our critical region, and we would not reject the hypothesis.

As you might expect, we could test the same fact, namely, the absence of an underlying linear relationship, by testing the hypothesis $H_0 : \rho^2 = 0$, which, under the assumption of the correlation model, gives as a test statistic:

$$F = t^2 = \frac{r^2(N-2)}{1-r^2} \tag{14.9.2}$$

which will have the F-distribution with 1 numerator and n denominator degrees of freedom. In our case, at the same alpha risk, our critical value will be $F_{1-\alpha,1/n} = F_{0.950,1/10} = 4.96$ and our observed value will be 0.744, with the result that our null hypothesis is not rejected.

Had we applied the same tests to the data of Table 14-2b, our observed values of t and F would have been 3.447 and 11.88, respectively, and we would have rejected the hypotheses of no correlation.

14.10 Further Relationships Between Correlation and Regression

In our discussion of the meaning of correlation, we have already found that if we had treated the data in a correlation problem as though they were regression data, the product of the two regression coefficients is the coefficient of determination, i.e., $b_{Y.X}b_{X.Y} = r^2$, and that, if the data were first standardized,

$b_{y'.x'} = b_{x'.y'} = r$. These results followed from the fact that, although the correlation and regression models are different, the statistics employed with both models involve the same elements in related combinations. This is really not surprising, for, in either case, we are involved in investigating a possible linear relationship. Let us explore the consequences of this fact somewhat further.

A. *The Coefficient of Alienation and the Residual Variance.* In dealing with our regression problem, we found that, at the time, the easiest formula for $\Sigma(Y - Y_L)^2$, the numerator of $s_{Y.X}^2$, was

$$\Sigma(Y - Y_L)^2 = \Sigma Y^2 - a\Sigma Y - b\Sigma XY$$

But let us replace a by its equivalent, $\bar{Y} - b\bar{X}$, and continue with some algebraic simplifications:

$$\Sigma(Y - Y_L)^2 = \Sigma Y^2 - (\bar{Y} - b\bar{X})\Sigma Y - b\Sigma XY \quad (14.10.1a)$$

$$= \Sigma Y^2 - \bar{Y}\Sigma Y + b\bar{X}\Sigma Y - b\Sigma XY \quad (14.10.1b)$$

$$= \Sigma Y^2 - \bar{Y}\Sigma Y - b(\Sigma XY - \bar{X}\Sigma Y) \quad (14.10.1c)$$

$$= \Sigma(Y - \bar{Y})^2 - b\Sigma(X - \bar{X})(Y - \bar{Y}) \quad (14.10.1d)$$

Now let us replace b by its equivalent,

$$b = \frac{\Sigma(X - \bar{X})(Y - \bar{Y})}{\Sigma(X - \bar{X})^2}$$

to obtain

$$\Sigma(Y - Y_L)^2 = \Sigma(Y - \bar{Y})^2 - \frac{[\Sigma(X - \bar{X})(Y - \bar{Y}]^2}{\Sigma(X - \bar{X})^2} \quad (14.10.1e)$$

Notice that the second term on the right lacks only $\Sigma(Y - \bar{Y})^2$ in the denominator to be exactly the formula for r^2. We can multiply numerator and denominator by this quantity to obtain

$$\Sigma(Y - Y_L)^2 = \Sigma(Y - \bar{Y})^2 - r^2\Sigma(Y - \bar{Y})^2 \quad (14.10.1f)$$

$$= (1 - r^2)\Sigma(Y - \bar{Y})^2 \quad (14.10.1g)$$

Thus it appears that, though we have a regression model, the use of formulas which would have been employed with the correlation model leads to a very expeditious computation of the sum of squared residuals. Of course, it follows immediately that

$$s_{Y.X}^2 = \frac{(1 - r^2)\Sigma(Y - \bar{Y})^2}{(N - 2)} \quad (14.10.2)$$

This result was sufficiently attractive so that it will be worth while to pursue the idea of possible relations between the computing formulas in regression and correlation problems further. Recall equation 14.4.9b for testing hypotheses concerning B, and note that for $H_0 : B = 0$ this becomes

$$F = \frac{b^2\Sigma(X - \overline{X})^2}{s_{Y.X}} \tag{14.10.3a}$$

Let us replace b^2 and $s_{Y.X}^2$ by their equivalents,

$$F = \frac{[\Sigma(X - \overline{X})(Y - \overline{Y})]^2\Sigma(X - \overline{X})^2(N - 2)}{[\Sigma(X - \overline{X})^2]^2(1 - r^2)\Sigma(Y - \overline{Y})^2} \tag{14.10.3b}$$

$$= \frac{[\Sigma(X - \overline{X})(Y - \overline{Y})]^2(N - 2)}{\Sigma(X - \overline{X})^2\Sigma(Y - \overline{Y})^2(1 - r^2)} \tag{14.10.3c}$$

and note that this is simply

$$F = \frac{r^2(N - 2)}{1 - r^2} \tag{14.10.3d}$$

But this is identical in form with 14.9.2, which we used to test the hypothesis $H_0 : \rho^2 = 0$ when our data conformed to a correlation model.

This warrants still further thought. Recall that F, as we originally encountered it as a statistic for testing the equality of two variances, was the ratio of two sample variances. As we later used it in analysis of variance, it was the ratio of two estimates of a common variance. This would suggest that it should be a ratio of variances here. Suppose we multiply the numerator and denominator of 14.10.3d by $\Sigma(Y - \overline{Y})^2$ to obtain

$$F = [r^2\Sigma(Y - \overline{Y})^2]\left[\frac{N - 2}{(1 - r^2)\Sigma(Y - \overline{Y})^2}\right] \tag{14.10.3e}$$

We already recognize the right-hand bracket as the reciprocal of $s_{Y.X}^2$, the residual variance, or measure of the dispersion of the values about the line. The quantity inside the left-hand bracket turns out to be $\Sigma(Y_L - \overline{Y})^2$, as algebra of the type we have been doing will show, and it has associated with it one degree of freedom. It is thus a variance measuring the dispersion of the Y_L-values, or values calculated from the regression equation, about the mean of Y. It can be shown, in fact, that

$$\Sigma(Y - \overline{Y})^2 = \Sigma(Y - Y_L)^2 + \Sigma(Y_L - \overline{Y})^2 \tag{14.10.4a}$$

$$= (1 - r^2)\Sigma(Y - \overline{Y})^2 + r^2\Sigma(Y - \overline{Y})^2 \tag{14.10.4b}$$

and that what we have been doing is performing an analysis of variance on the Y-values. In a very real sense, r^2, our coefficient of determination, is the fraction of the total sum of square which may be inferred from or, more loosely, "accounted for" by our regression line, whereas $1 - r^2$, our coefficient of alienation, is the fraction not inferrable from, or "accounted for," by our line. It is very convenient to set our computations up in an anov table, as we have done in Table 14.3.

This concept of analysis of variance in connection with problems of relationships stimulates still further thinking, but before getting into it, let us see where we now stand. We have seen the following general principles:

1. When we are studying the relationship between two variables, we must distinguish clearly, in our thinking, between the regression and the correlation models.

2. Each model leads formally to its own specific estimates of the population parameters involved, and to its own specific tests of hypotheses concerning their values.

3. In the process of treating such data, whichever model applies, formulas involving the same intermediate computations are employed.

4. In consequence, when we are concerned with a regression model and a test of $H_0 : B = 0$, or its equivalent, $H_0 : B^2 = 0$, we shall be able to effect a saving in time and possible errors in computation if we make the computations that would have been used to test $H_0 : \rho^2 = 0$ with a correlation model.

5. The use of r^2 and $1 - r^2$ for the analysis of $\Sigma(Y - \bar{Y})^2$ into portions inferrable from and not inferrable from the regression line gives them further merit as computing tools in regression problems.

In the following chapter, we shall see how the analysis of variance concept we explored briefly here can be extended to permit us to handle many types of curvilinear relationships quite effectively. In this chapter, we have worked so extensively with our synthetic samples that we believe you will derive more benefit from considering the problems at the end of the chapter than from perusing further examples involving actual data.

General Study

1. At a number of places in this chapter, we stated that certain formulas could be developed by following a plan we had just used for related formulas. Develop these formulas to test your understanding of the principles we have been studying.

2. Consider a number of problems involving relationships that involve fields of particular interest to you. Decide which cases could yield true regression data and which could yield only correlation data. Indicate in each case the reasons why one should be interested in establishing the relationship.

Specific Problems

1–4. Treat each of the following sets of data in two ways. First, assume the regression model and make the analysis using only strict regression procedures. Then assume the correlation model, and analyze again, noting the points of equivalence in the values obtained.

Problem	1		2		3		4	
	X	Y	X	Y	X	Y	X	Y
	4	7	2	−1	3	4	7	2
	5	5	4	2	3	6	7	1
	7	3	5	3	5	8	5	3
	8	2	7	4	5	7	5	4
	9	0	8	4	6	8	3	4
			8	6	6	9	3	6
			9	8	8	9	1	7
					8	10	1	8
							−1	9
							−1	10

5. The following are the heights in inches, H, and the weights in pounds, W, for 40 freshman coeds at a university one fall:

H	W	H	W
66.5	116.	67.5	143.
66.75	121.	65.5	139.
69.	140.	65.	133.5
65.	129.	61.25	104.
65.	128.5	63.	107.25
62.5	100.	64.75	126.
68.	138.	64.5	105.5
66.5	145.	67.	145.
63.5	103.	67.	135.
63.25	131.75	67.	106.
64.	107.	62.5	121.
63.5	118.	66.	110.
63.5	120.	63.	103.
65.	107.	65.	125.
70.	190.	60.	108.5
66.	147.	62.	119.75
64.	129.5	60.5	110.
67.75	116.	65.5	147.
63.75	101.	64.75	117.
65.5	177.5	66.75	192.5

The heights were reported to the nearest quarter inch and the weights to the nearest quarter pound, but the fractions have been converted to decimals for your convenience. The data conform to the correlation model. Explain why. Is there evidence of a linear correlation between height and weight of freshman coeds? State the hypothesis and the alpha risk you used in reaching your conclusion. Determine the two regression lines related to this correlation.

6. In Problem 5, the data strictly conform to a correlation model. However, general knowledge tells us that, generally, the height of an individual varies very slowly with time at the age of these students, while there is appreciable day-to-day and even hour-to-hour variation in weight. Therefore, aside from the fact that the heights were not preselected, the data essentially conform to a regression model with

height as the independent variable. Compute 95% confidence limits for that regression line. How can you reasonably interpret the value of a and the confidence limits you obtained for it?

7. A recent annual report shows the annual expenditures for wages and salaries of E. I. duPont de Nemours & Co. to have been, in millions of dollars,

Year	*Amount*	*Year*	*Amount*
1950	330.1	1955	491.2
1951	382.5	1956	534.8
1952	414.6	1957	575.6
1953	467.6	1958	579.8
1954	458.3	1959	592.9

Extract as much information from these data as you can. Predict the values for subsequent years from your results. Compare these predictions with figures reported in later annual reports. Interpret the differences.

15

Curvilinear Relationships

15.1 The Curvilinear Concept

In considering the regression problem generally in the preceding chapter, we recognized that we would be concerned with a population of values of Y which could be considered as consisting of subpopulations at the various levels of X. These subpopulations were to be normal distributions, all with the same variance, $\sigma_{Y.X}^2$, and with means, $\mu_{Y.X} = f(X)$, which were some function of X, that is, they would fall along some curve in the XY-plane. All this was implied in our model,

$$Y = \mu_{Y.X} + \epsilon(0,\sigma_{Y.X}^2) = f(X) + \epsilon(0,\sigma_{Y.X}^2)$$

During the rest of that chapter, we confined our considerations to linear functions, $f(X) = A + BX$, whose graphs are straight lines.

Now we must face the fact that $f(X)$ may often be a function represented by an equation whose graph is a line with some real curvature. In some cases we may be able to claim that we know the form, or the most involved possible form, of the function, and our problem will be to estimate the parameters involved and test hypotheses concerning them. Under other circumstances, the form of the function may not be known.

When we know the form of the function, and know that it is nonlinear, we are involved in curvilinear regression. When we do not know the form of the function, we are not yet involved in regression analysis, but first have the mathematical problem of developing some hypothesis as to the form. Then we shall be involved in a regression analysis to test the hypothesis that that function is correct. We shall presently gain some insight into the way a mathematician develops ideas concerning possible functions, but first let us consider two kinds of functions which we shall often encounter in practice.

15.2 Polynomial Functions

An equation of the form,

$$\mu_{Y.X} = A + BX + CX^2 + \ldots + NX^n \tag{15.2.1a}$$

is said to be a *polynomial equation*, and the variable $\mu_{Y.X}$ is said to be a *polynomial function* of X. The term involving the highest power of X is known as the *leading term* and its coefficient is known as the *leading coefficient.* The designation stems from the fact that such polynomials are often written in the order of decreasing powers. The *degree* of the equation or function is the index of the highest power of X in it. We shall find it more convenient, for many purposes, to use B's with subscripts indicating the power of X to which they apply as our coefficients instead of using the letters of the alphabet serially. In this form, the equation would be

$$\mu_{Y.X} = B_0 + B_1X + B_2X^2 + \ldots + B_nX^n \tag{15.2.1b}$$

and it may be expressed in very condensed form as

$$\mu_{Y.X} = \sum_{i=0}^{n} B_iX^i \tag{15.2.1c}$$

A. *Curve-fitting Properties.* If we had observations of Y_{ij} at k different levels, X_i, of X, we could make a plot of the k means, $\overline{Y}_{i+}$, against their values of X_i. We would have, as a result, k points $(X_i, \overline{Y}_{i+})$. It can be demonstrated that the following two statements are true:

1. There is one specific polynomial equation of degree $n = k - 1$ which will exactly fit these points, that is, whose graph will contain all of them.
2. This equation will be the polynomial equation of that degree which will represent the least squares fit of such a polynomial to the individual points (X_i, Y_{ij}).

It might appear, then, that because we know that a polynomial equation can always be found which will fit our data, in this sense we would need no other kinds of functions. To see why this is not so, let us examine other characteristics of polynomial functions.

B. *Extreme Values.* Not only is there a correspondence between the forms of equations and the forms of their graphs, so that either implies the other, but, when the variables in the equations express measurements of quantitative aspects of concepts under consideration, there is a similar correspondence between the behavior of these quantities and the form of the equation. The behavior of the quantities requires a specific function for its expression, and the function implies specific behavior.

When the values of a function rise to some specific level, then fall as X increases, we say that the function has a *local maximum*, whereas when the function decreases to a specific value, then increases, we say that it has *a local minimum*. The term *extreme value* designates both maxima and minima. The term *local* merely reminds us that a function may have several extremes, one of which may be "the" maximum or minimum, or the function may ultimately increase or decrease without limit.

For polynomial functions, the abscissas of the extremes may be located by solving an equation of the form,

$$B_1 + 2B_2X + 3B_3X^2 + \ldots + nB_nX^{n-1} = 0 \qquad (15.2.2a)$$

which may be written compactly as

$$\sum_{i=1}^{n} iB_iX^{i-1} = 0 \qquad (15.2.2b)$$

The equation is derived with the aid of calculus, but its form is easy to recall. Starting with B_1, each coefficient is multiplied by its subscript and applied to X to a power one less than the subscript. The sum of the resulting terms is equated to zero. If the degree of the resulting equation is cubic or less, there are well-established and not too difficult methods of solution available. For the fourth degree the problem is more difficult, and for higher degrees approximations generally have to be employed. However, in fact, we rarely need equations of high degree.

Some general statements concerning extremes are useful:

1. Polynomial functions of *even* degree must have one extreme and may have any *odd* number through $n - 1$.

2. Polynomial functions of *odd* degree will have either no extreme or an *even* number of extremes.

3. Maxima and minima alternate as X increases, either type of extreme being free to initiate the succession.

C. *Behavior at Large Values of X.* All polynomial functions, after passing through their extremes, ultimately assume indefinitely large numerical values as X assumes large numerical values. The sign of the function is inferrable from the sign of its leading coefficient and the degree of the function by the following rules:

1. For even functions, the sign of the function ultimately becomes that of the leading coefficient regardless of the sign of X.

2. For odd functions, the sign of the function ultimately becomes that of X if the leading coefficient is positive; otherwise, the opposite.

D. *Inadequacy of Polynomial Functions.* The combination of the extreme value properties and the behavior at large values of X means that all even polynomial functions must have graphs consisting of one or more U's or inverted U's, while all odd functions must consist of one or more somewhat S-shaped portions. But, although a polynomial of finite degree will always fit a finite number of points $(X_i, \overline{Y}_{i+})$, our background information may tell us that the proper function has actually quite different characteristics. It may approach some value asymptotically as X increases or decreases in value, and have neither an extreme value nor an S-shape or it may have other properties which are incompatible with the polynomial form. So, although polynomial functions are quite easy to work with, as we shall see, we shall often be forced to other forms.

15.3 The Exponential or Semilogarithmic Function

One of the very useful functions whose implications often describe situations which are incompatible with polynomial functions is the *exponential function*,

$$\mu_{Y.X} = AB^X \tag{15.3.1}$$

As its name suggests, the X appears as an exponent, and we shall restrict our considerations to cases in which B is positive. If A is also positive, then we can describe the behavior of the function as follows:

1. As a little algebra will show, the ratio of the value of the function at any value of X to its value at $X - 1$ is always B.

2. If $B > 1$, the function will increase indefinitely as X increases and approach zero asymptotically as X decreases. It has no extreme.

3. If $B < 1$, the function approaches zero asymptotically as X increases and increases indefinitely as X decreases. It has no extreme.

4. If $B = 1$, we have the trivial case that Y is constant at A.

If A is negative, the function is always negative, and its behavior is the "mirror image" of that described above.

Unfortunately, this function cannot be fitted by the method of least squares, as polynomials can. However, the use of logarithms permits a simple but effective transformation from which we can obtain a close approximation to a least squares fit. If you are already familiar with the nature and use of logarithms, you will be able to grasp the idea immediately. Otherwise, you should study Appendix XV or a more extensive discussion of these useful mathematical devices.

By taking the logarithms of both sides of 15.3.1 we have

$$\log \mu_{Y.X} = \log A + \log B^X \tag{15.3.2a}$$

$$= \log A + X(\log B)$$

But notice that log A and log B are constants, which we designate as C and D, respectively. Thus our equation can be written in the form,

$$\log \mu_{Y.X} = C + DX \tag{15.3.2b}$$

whence the name *semilogarithmic* (*semilog*, for short) *equation* and *function* came: one variable appears as its logarithm while the other appears as itself. If we make the convenient further substitution $\log \mu_{Y.X} = Z$, the equation takes the final form,

$$Z = C + DX \tag{15.3.2c}$$

and we see that Z is a linear function of X, a fact of which we shall later take advantage.

15.4 Other Functions and Polynomial Approximations

As we have mentioned, there are an unlimited number of functions which could express the relation between $\mu_{Y.X}$ and X. The polynomial and exponential functions will be of tremendous service to us, however, and we shall find them relatively easy to use. The sound use of the other functions would generally require more mathematical background than we assume on the part of our readers or should attempt to develop here. There is, however, one important use of polynomial functions which we should discuss, namely, their use as approximations to other functions.

We defined polynomial functions by means of equation 15.2.1, where we tacitly assumed that the degree of the function, n, was finite. What would happen if n were infinite? Our equation 15.2.1c, expressing the polynomial equation, would not become:

$$\mu_{Y.X} = \sum_{i=0}^{\infty} B_i X^i \tag{15.4.1}$$

and such an expression is said to be an *infinite series*. It requires calculus to prove it, but it is true that many functions can be represented by such infinite series with properly chosen coefficients. Furthermore, while the exact representation requires an infinity of terms, quite finite numbers of terms often approximate the value adequately for our purposes.

Recall the standard form of the normal distribution, which involved the troublesome (for us!) quantity, $\exp(-\frac{1}{2}z^2)$. Suppose we let $w = -\frac{1}{2}z^2$, so that our quantity becomes $\exp(w) = e^w$. It is known that

$$e^w = \sum_{i=0}^{\infty} \frac{w^i}{i!} = 1 + w + \frac{w^2}{2!} + \frac{w^3}{3!} + \cdots \tag{15.4.2}$$

In Table 15-1, we show the computation of the values for $|z| = 0.4$ ($w = -0.8$) and $|z| = 2.0$ ($w = -2.0$). Notice how rapidly the values become stable to

Table 15-1 POLYNOMIAL APPROXIMATIONS TO EXP $(-\frac{1}{2}z^2) = e^w$ USING FINITE NUMBERS OF INITIAL TERMS OF THE SERIES

$$e^w = \sum_{i=0}^{\infty} w^i/i!$$

Part A. $|z| = 0.4$, $z^2 = 0.16$, $w = -0.08$

i	w^i	$i!$	$w^i/i!$	$\Sigma w^i/i!$
0	1.0000000000	1	1.0000000000	1.0000000000
1	−0.0800000000	1	−0.0800000000	0.9200000000
2	+0.0064000000	2	+0.0032000000	0.9232000000
3	−0.0005120000	6	−0.0000853333	0.9231146666
4	+0.0000409600	24	+0.0000017066	0.9231163733
5	−0.0000032768	120	−0.0000000273	0.9231163460
6	+0.0000002621$_{44}$	720	+0.0000000003	0.9231163463
7	−0.0000000209$_{715}$	5040	−0.0000000000	0.9231163463

Part B. $|z| = 2.0$, $z^2 = 4.00$, $w = -2.0$

i	w^i	$i!$	$w^i/i!$	$\Sigma w^i/i!$
0	+1	1	1.0000000000	1.0000000000
1	−2	1	−2.0000000000	−1.0000000000
2	+4	2	+2.0000000000	+1.0000000000
3	−8	6	−1.3333333333	−0.3333333333
4	+16	24	+0.6666666666	+0.3333333333
5	−32	120	−0.2666666666	+0.0666666666
6	+64	720	+0.0888888888	+0.1555555555
7	−128	5040	−0.0253968253	+0.1301587302
8	+256	40320	+0.0063492063	+0.1365079365
9	−512	362880	−0.0014109347	+0.1350970018
10	+1024	3628800	+0.0002821869	0.1353791887
11	−2048	39916800	−0.0000513067	0.1353278820
12	+4096	479001600	+0.0000085511	0.1353364331
13	−8184	6227028984	−0.0000013142	0.1353351189

progressive numbers of decimals. In fact, then, these finite polynomials become approximations to the function that was so unwieldy. In many circumstances we shall find it desirable to use polynomials of relatively low degree as approximations to known functions that are unwieldy. In still other situations we may not know the exact function, and we shall employ a polynomial, or the exponential function, as a reasonable description of the relationship so long as the implications of the function we do employ are not in appreciable conflict with our total knowledge. Sometimes, to a mathematician used to working with series, the relative sizes of the coefficients of a finite polynomial will bear a sufficient resemblance to the first few coefficients of an infinite series equivalent to a known function so that he may suggest this function as the real one we are seeking. So it will be well worth our while to learn how to work with these functions.

15.5 Polynomial Regression and Analysis of Variance

Let us imagine that we have a problem that requires the investigation of a polynomial regression. It may be that our background information has convinced us that the true functional form is a polynomial, or it may be the case that we are using our polynomial as either an approximation to the true function or as a guide toward its recognition. If it is the true form, let us suppose that we are not sure of the degree of the polynomial, but only that it can't be higher than the fourth. If we are using it either as an approximation or a guide, let us suppose that, again, we do not feel interested in a polynomial of higher than the fourth degree.

In either event we shall require data at five levels of the independent variable, X, and, for reasons we shall discuss later, we shall choose equally spaced levels and obtain the same number of observations at each level. Our data will, of course, conform to the regression model. We have provided a synthetic set of such data as Table 15-2. So far as the values of Y are concerned, we may initially think of them as having arisen from a one-way classification with $k = 5$ treatments (the levels of X) and $N_i = 4$ observations at each treatment.

We already know how to make an initial analysis of such data into "among" and "within" components. We shall have $n_a = k - 1 = 4$ and $n_w = N - k = 15$ among and within degrees of freedom, respectively. The results of such an analysis are included in Table 15-2. Our previous experience with analysis of variance will not let us remain content with this gross analysis. We know that the four among degrees of freedom indicate that we can make four sets of orthogonal linear comparisons among the means which should yield us more detailed information. How can we find a set pertinent to regression analysis?

To gain a lead, let us recall our linear regression analysis. There our model took the form, in our present notation,

$$Y = B_0 + B_1X + \epsilon(0,\sigma_{Y.X}^2) \tag{15.5.1}$$

and we were concerned with testing the hypothesis, $H_0 : B_1 = 0$. After we became familiar with the relation between regression and correlation formulas, we found a very convenient test for the purpose using the statistic,

$$F = \frac{r^2(N - 2)}{1 - r^2} \tag{15.5.2}$$

which had the F-distribution with 1 numerator and $(N - 2)$ denominator degrees of freedom. This suggested that the F-value must be a ratio of mean squares, or variance estimates. In section 14.10, we explored this idea further and found that we could multiply numerator and denominator of 15.5.2 by $\Sigma(Y_{ij} - \bar{Y}_{++})^2$ and carry out some algebra. We found that $r^2\Sigma(Y_{ij} - \bar{Y}_{++})^2 = \Sigma(Y_L - \bar{Y}_{++})^2$ was a measure of the deviations of our line values from the

Table 15-2 SYNTHETIC DATA TO ILLUSTRATE POLYNOMIAL REGRESSION ANALYSIS

i	1	2	3	4	5
X_i	1	3	5	7	9
Y_{ij}	7.5	0.0	11.0	4.0	8.5
	9.5	4.0	5.0	2.0	12.5
	3.5	8.0	7.0	8.0	16.5
	5.5	4.0	9.0	10.0	12.5
T_{i+}	26.0	16.0	32.0	24.0	50.0
$\bar{Y}_{i+}$	6.5	4.0	8.0	6.0	12.5

Degree	*Orthogonal Coefficients*				
1	−2	−1	0	+1	+2
2	+2	−1	−2	−1	+2
3	−1	+2	0	−2	+1
4	+1	−4	+6	−4	+1

Degree	$\Sigma l_i T_i$	$(\Sigma l_i T_i)^2$	$N_i \Sigma l_i^2$	$ss = ms$
1	56	3136	40	78.40000
2	48	2304	56	41.14285
3	8	64	40	1.60000
4	108	11664	280	41.65714

N	20	N_i	4	k	5
ΣX	100	$\Sigma Y = T_{++}$	148	T_{++}^2/N	1095.2
ΣX^2	660	ΣY^2	1402	$\Sigma T_{i+}^2/N_i$	1258.0
$\bar{X}$	5.0	$\bar{Y}$	7.4		
$\Sigma(X - \bar{X})^2$	160.0	$\Sigma(Y - \bar{Y})^2$	306.8		

Anov for Y

Source	*ss*	*df*	*ms*	*F*	F_{cr}	*Decision*
Total	306.80000	19	—	—	—	
Among	162.80000	4	40.70000	4.24	3.06	Reject
1°	78.40000	1	78.40000	8.17	4.54	Reject
Bal.	84.40000	3	28.13333	2.93	3.29	Accept
2°	41.14285	1	41.14285	4.29	4.54	Accept
Bal.	43.25715	2	21.62857	2.25	3.68	Accept
3°	1.60000	1	1.60000	0.17	4.54	Accept
Bal.	41.65715	1	41.65715	4.34	4.54	Accept
4°	41.65714	1	45.65714	4.34	4.54	Accept
Within	144.00000	15	9.60000	—		

Linear equation adopted.
$Y_1 = 3.90 + 0.70X$

grand mean and that it had one associated degree of freedom. We recognized that this variance was, in a real sense, a measure of the improvement in our ability to predict Y-values by the use of the regression line. Similarly, $(1 - r^2)\Sigma(Y_{ij} - \overline{Y}_{++})^2 = \Sigma(Y_{ij} - Y_L)^2$ and its associated $(N - 2)$ degrees of freedom measured the uncertainty remaining in our predictions.

It is rather striking that the ratio of these two measures should be so directly related to the hypothesis that $B_1 = 0$. Is there a possibility of extending this idea still further? Suppose we imagine that we first treated our data as though we were going to use a linear equation, then a quadratic, then a cubic, and finally a quartic equation. It is a fact that each progressively higher degree of polynomial will fit our data at least as well as the previous degree, just as a linear equation told us at least as much as the grand mean. This suggests that we should be able to find sums of squares measuring the improvement resulting from each higher degree, and that these sums of squares ought ultimately to lead to test statistics.

Instead of using letter subscripts on Y to indicate the kind of equation employed, we shall now use a numeral indicating the degree of the polynomial, so that our former Y_L now becomes Y_1. In our specific problem we shall need $\Sigma(Y_1 - \overline{Y}_{++})^2$, $\Sigma(Y_2 - Y_1)^2$, $\Sigma(Y_3 - Y_2)^2$, and $\Sigma(Y_4 - Y_3)^2$ to measure our specific stages of improvement. We shall expect, and it is true, that each sum of squares will have one associated degree of freedom, and we hope that they will be related to a set of orthogonal linear comparisons for the further analysis of our among sum of squares. How can we be sure that this is so, and how can we calculate the values?

It has been proved rigorously that, provided our data conform to the regression model and provided we have equal numbers of observations at each level, these sums of squares are related to a set of orthogonal linear comparisons, and that the necessary orthogonal coefficients by which they may be computed are as shown in Appendix VIII. With these coefficients, the computation procedures are exactly those employed for any set of orthogonal linear comparisons. The results, for our data, are shown in Table 15-2.

15.6 Choosing the Proper Degree of Polynomial

Our previous experience with such analyses would lead us to form an F-value as the ratio of each of the mean squares yielded by our analysis to the within mean square and to compare its value with a critical value, $F_{1-\alpha,1/(N-k)}$. If our observed ratio exceeds the critical value, we would reject the related hypothesis. But we haven't stated the hypothesis! As a matter of fact, we have deliberately avoided doing so because this is a situation in which our procedure is relatively simple, but the thinking involved in its application is a little more complex.

Suppose we consider the line in our anov table which we have indicated corresponding to degree 3, where our sum of squares took the form $\Sigma(Y_3 - Y_2)^2$. We have actually measured the improvement in fit of a third degree, or cubic, equation over a second degree, or quadratic equation. Thus we might consider that at this stage we were temporarily considering that our polynomial was at the most of the third degree and were testing the hypothesis that its leading coefficient is zero. The same sort of reasoning applies to each stage of the analysis. For the data of Table 15-2, the only stage of fitting whose related hypothesis was rejected was the first, and perhaps we can conclude that our polynomial is of the first degree only, with the coefficients on all higher terms zero.

Before adopting that position solidly, however, let us notice that after each stage involving the m-th degree we have a sum of squares of the form $\Sigma(\bar{Y}_{i+} - Y_m)^2$ representing the remainder, or balance, of the among sum of squares and that it will have $n_a - m = k - m - 1$ degrees of freedom. It then leads to a mean square and an F-test. What does it mean? Recall that we mentioned that a polynomial of degree $k - 1$ would exactly fit k points $(X_i, \bar{Y}_{i+})$ and that therefore the calculated values from the highest degree polynomial we are considering are identical with the group means. In our specific example $Y_4 = \bar{Y}_{i+}$, so that $\Sigma(\bar{Y}_{i+} - Y_m)^2 = \Sigma(Y_4 - Y_m)^2$ measures the deviations of the group means from the m-th degree polynomial values. Thus the related F-test may be interpreted as a test of the hypothesis that no higher degree of polynomial is required.

It thus appears that we may have two criteria as to the degree of polynomial required by the data under study. We might consider that the highest degree whose individual improvement leads to a rejection of its related hypothesis is the degree to be adopted. Or we might say that we should use that degree which leads to a nonsignificant remainder. No problem would arise if all data behaved like those of Table 15-2 in which both viewpoints led to the same conclusion, that only a linear equation is warranted. Another synthetic set of data is shown in Table 15-3. Actually, they are the same groups of Y-values, but paired with different values of X. Again, both viewpoints lead to the same conclusion — that a fourth degree equation must be employed.

But now let us examine the same data in still another pairing with X-values, as shown in Table 15-4. Here, if we fit to the highest degree whose individual improvement is significant, we shall stop at degree zero, that is, we shall have no polynomial regression. But if we adopt the viewpoint that we must continue through that degree whose balance becomes nonsignificant, we must fit a third degree equation. Real data often lead to similar and, sometimes, even more confusing situations. How can we resolve the difficulty?

First, let us consider why it arises. In presenting our data, we said that they would represent such data as we would obtain either if our background knowledge made us confident that the true relationship was polynomial in form or if we were employing a polynomial as an approximation to or guide toward the true form. In case we thought the true function was a polynomial, we could be mistaken, and a result such as that in Table 15-4 would, if we were prudent,

Table 15-3 SYNTHETIC DATA TO ILLUSTRATE POLYNOMIAL REGRESSION ANALYSIS. Data from Table 15-2 with Different Association of Subsets with X-values

i	1	2	3	4	5
X_i	1	3	5	7	9
Y_{ij}	7.5	0.0	8.5	4.0	11.0
	9.5	4.0	12.5	2.0	5.0
	3.5	8.0	16.5	8.0	7.0
	5.5	4.0	12.5	10.0	9.0
T_{i+}	26.0	16.0	50.0	24.0	32.0
$\overline{Y}_{i+}$	6.5	4.0	12.5	6.0	8.0

Degree	*Orthogonal Coefficients*				
1	−2	−1	0	+1	+2
2	+2	−1	−2	−2	+2
3	−1	+2	0	−2	+1
4	+1	−4	+6	−4	+1

Degree	$\Sigma l_i T_i$	$(\Sigma l_i T_i)^2$	$N_i \Sigma l_i^2$	$ss = ms$
1	20	400	40	10.00000
2	−24	576	56	10.28571
3	−10	100	40	2.50000
4	198	39204	280	140.01428

N	20	N_i	4	k	5
ΣX	100	$\Sigma Y = T_{++}$	148	T_{++}^2/N	1095.2
ΣX^2	660	ΣY^2	1402	$\Sigma T_{i+}^2/N_i$	1258.0
$\overline{X}$	5.0	$\overline{Y}$	7.4		
$\Sigma(X - \overline{X})^2$	160.0	$\Sigma(Y - \overline{Y})^2$	306.8		

Anov for Y

Source	*ss*	*df*	*ms*	*F*	F_{cr}	*Decision*
Total	306.80000	19	—			
Among	162.80000	4	40.70000	4.24	3.06	Reject
1°	10.00000	1	10.00000	1.04	4.54	Accept
Bal.	152.80000	3	50.93333	5.31	3.29	Reject
2°	10.28571	1	10.28571	1.07	4.54	Accept
Bal.	142.51429	2	71.25714	7.42	3.68	Reject
3°	2.50000	1	2.50000	0.26	4.54	Accept
Bal.	140.01429	1	140.01429	14.58	4.54	Reject
Within	144.00000	15	9.60000	—		

Fourth degree equation adopted.
$Y_4 = 33.54 - 41.90X + 17.388X^2 - 2.60445X^3 + 0.12892X^4$

warn us to reappraise our total information. In case we were merely using our polynomial as an approximation, it would seem proper to agree in advance to

Table 15-4 Synthetic Data to Illustrate Polynomial Regression Analysis.

Data from Table 15-1 with Different Association of Subsets with X-Values. See Text for Particular Problem Involved

i	1	2	3	4	5
X_i	1	3	5	7	9
Y_{ij}	7.5	4.0	11.0	0.0	8.5
	9.5	2.0	5.0	4.0	12.5
	3.5	8.0	7.0	8.0	16.5
	5.5	10.0	9.0	4.0	12.5
T_{i+}	26.0	24.0	32.0	16.0	50.0
$\bar{Y}_{i+}$	6.5	6.0	8.0	4.0	12.5

Degree	*Orthogonal Coefficients*				
1	−1	−1	0	+1	+2
2	+2	−1	−2	−1	+2
3	−1	+2	0	−2	+1
4	+1	−4	+6	−4	+1

Degree	$\Sigma l_i T_i$	$(\Sigma l_i T_i)^2$	$N_i \Sigma l_i^2$	$ss = ms$
1	40	1600	40	40.00000
2	48	2304	56	41.14285
3	40	1600	40	40.00000
4	108	11664	280	41.65714

N	20	N_i	4	k	5
ΣX	100	$\Sigma Y = T_{++}$	148	T_{++}^2/N	1095.2
ΣX^2	660	ΣY^2	1402	$\Sigma T_{i+}^2/N_i$	1258.0
$\bar{X}$	5.0	$\bar{Y}$	7.4		
$\Sigma(X - \bar{X})^2$	160.0	$\Sigma(Y - \bar{Y})^2$	306.8		

Anov for Y

Source	*ss*	*df*	*ms*	*F*	F_{cr}	*Decision*
Total	306.80000	19	—			
Among	162.80000	4	40.70000	4.24	3.06	Reject
1°	40.00000	1	40.00000	4.17	4.54	Accept
Bal.	122.80000	3	40.93333	4.26	3.29	Reject
2°	41.14285	1	41.14285	4.29	4.54	Accept
Bal.	81.65715	2	40.82858	4.25	3.68	Reject
3°	40.00000	1	40.00000	4.17	4.54	Accept
Bal.	41.65715	1	41.65715	4.34	4.54	Accept
4°	41.65714	1	41.65714	4.34	4.54	Accept
Within	144.00000	15	9.60000	—		

No degree, individually, is significant; third degree required to make balance non-significant. Third degree equation adopted.

$Y_3 = 2.60 + 4.75X - 1.348X^2 + 0.10418X^3.$

fit to the last degree whose individual improvement was significant or until the balance became nonsignificant, whichever degree was higher. In case we are using polynomials merely to guide us toward a true functional form, we would have to recognize that a polynomial of as low degree as we are investigating will give us very little information in this case.

15.7 Finding the Values of the Coefficients

In our linear regression analysis, we found that the values of our estimates of the coefficients in the regression equation resulted from the solution of the normal equations of the method of least squares. In that particular case the solution was so simple and compact that we were able to reduce it to a formula for each of the coefficients. For higher degree equations this is no longer feasible, and it is desirable to work directly with the normal equations. We shall use the symbol b_i to denote our estimate of the parameter B_i in our regression equations, so that the nth degree estimating equation becomes

$$Y_n = b_0 + b_1X + b_2X^2 + \ldots + bX^n \tag{15.7.1}$$

The normal equations become

$$\begin{cases} b_0N + b_1\Sigma X + b_2\Sigma X^2 + \ldots + b_n\Sigma X^n = \Sigma Y \\ b_0\Sigma X + b_1\Sigma X^2 + b_2\Sigma X^3 + \ldots + b_n\Sigma X^{n+1} = \Sigma XY \\ b_0\Sigma X^2 + b_1\Sigma X^3 + b_2\Sigma X^4 + \ldots + b_n\Sigma X^{n+2} = \Sigma X^2Y \\ \ldots \quad \ldots \quad \ldots \quad \ldots \quad \ldots \quad \ldots \\ b_0\Sigma X^n + b_1\Sigma X^{n+1} + b_2\Sigma X^{n+2} + \ldots + b_n\Sigma X^2 = \Sigma X^nY \end{cases} \tag{15.7.2}$$

The pattern is really simpler than it may at first appear. The left side of the first equation is like the right side of 15.7.1 except that a summation sign precedes each power of X. (Note that $X^0 = 1$ so that $\Sigma X^0 = N$.) The right side is similarly related to the left side of 15.7.1 in that Y_n has been replaced by ΣY. In each subsequent line the power of X in all summations has been increased by one step per line. There are $n + 1$ lines, or equations, which permit the evaluation of the $n + 1$ unknown values, b_0 through b_n.

You may know an efficient method for solving such sets of simultaneous linear equations. If so, you may wish to use it. Possibly, however, if you are using this text in connection with an academic course, your instructor may recommend a method which will make particularly effective use of the computing facilities at your school. Otherwise, we suggest that you become familiar with the method shown in Appendix VIII, which is well adapted to use with good desk calculators. In the appendix, the data of Table 15-3 are used for illustration.

Solution of the equations for the degree polynomial that our analysis indicated was warranted led to the following regression equations for our three sets of data:

For Table 15-2 —

$$Y_1 = 3.90000 + 0.70000X$$

For Table 15-3 —

$$Y_2 = 33.53856 - 41.90077X + 17.33788X^2 - 2.60445X^3 + 0.12892X^4$$

For Table 15-4 —

$$Y_3 = 2.60451 + 4.75385X - 1.34842X^2 + 0.10418X^3 \qquad (15.7.3)$$

Two comments should be made at this point. First, we have given all coefficients to five decimals, although we have not yet determined confidence limits for the line, and therefore we do not know how many places will be needed to avoid serious rounding errors in the use of the equations. This is characteristic of sound statistical practice: we carry more figures during computations than we expect to need finally in order that rounding during computations will not affect our needed results.

Second, although in Table 15-3 our analysis of variance showed only the fourth degree equation producing a statistically significant improvement, notice that our final equation has nonzero values for all coefficients, b_0 through b_4. These findings are not inconsistent but will throw further light on our discussion in section 15.6. There we indicated that our analysis of variance had in mind the fitting of successively increasing degrees of polynomials. As each degree is fitted, we measure its improvement over the preceding degree in fit to the data. We use this improvement to test the idea that the population value of the leading coefficient of an equation of the degree we have just fitted is zero. Unless we permit the coefficients on other terms to vary freely, we shall find that we have put restrictions, which we quite possibly did not intend, on our equation and its curve. For example, if in the quadratic equation $Y = b_0 + b_1X + b_2X^2$, we were to demand that b_0 and b_1 both be zero, we would restrict ourselves to parabolas having their extreme value at (0,0) and their axes vertical. By letting these two coefficients vary, we can have our extreme value at any point whatsoever.

15.8 Further Interpretation of Polynomial Regressions

If you re-examine our analyses of variance, you will find that we reached our conclusion concerning the appropriate degree of equation to use in consequence of several different patterns of values in the anov table. It is always prudent to plot the data and the finally chosen regression lines as we have done for Tables 15-2, 15-3, and 15-4 in Figs. 15-1, 15-2, and 15-3, respectively. The

Fig. 15-1. Plot of data of Table 15-2 with fitted regression line.

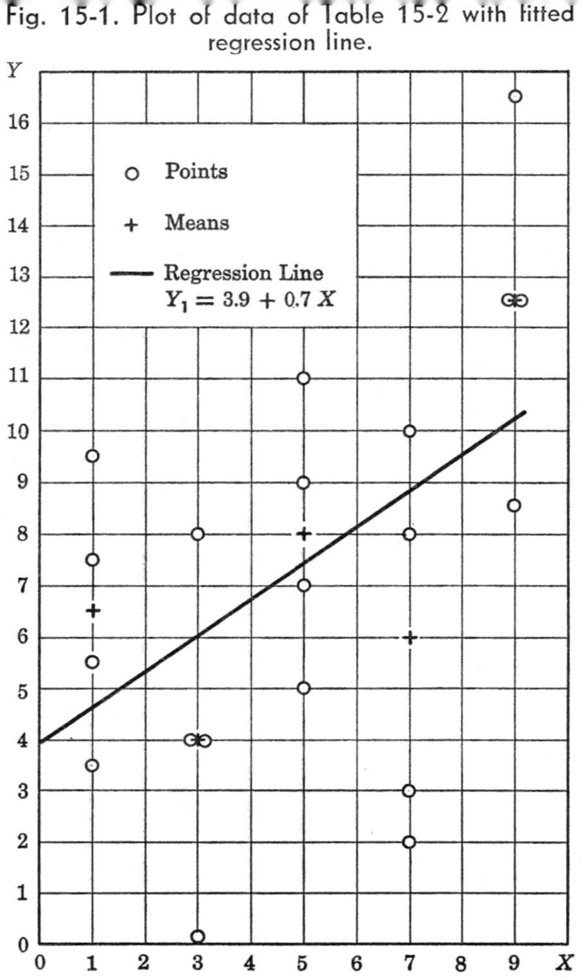

Fig. 15-2. Plot of data of Table 15-3 with fitted regression line.

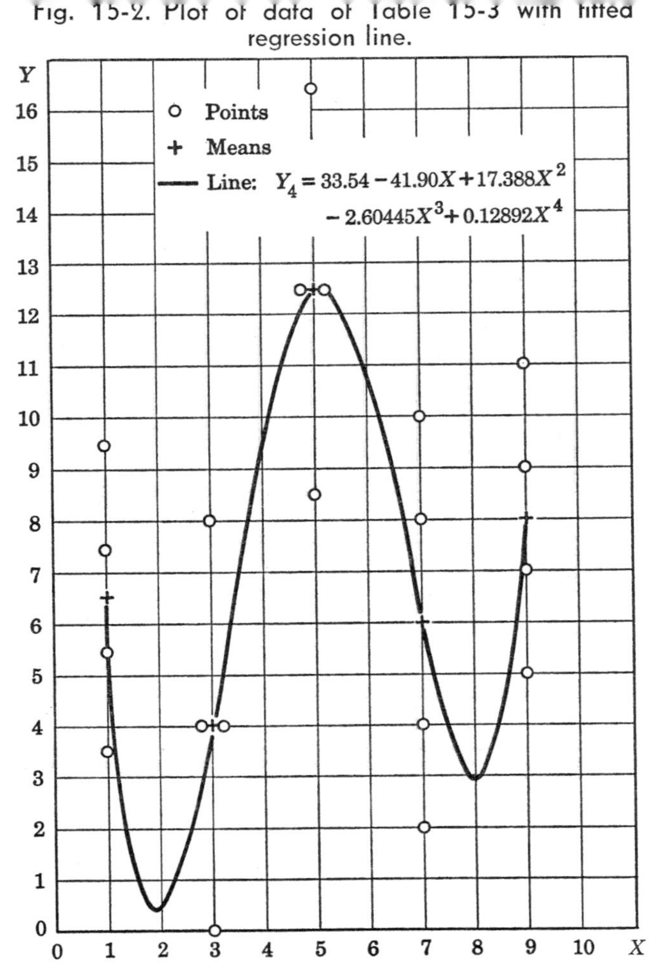

Fig. 15-3. Plot of data of Table 15-4 and fitted regression line.

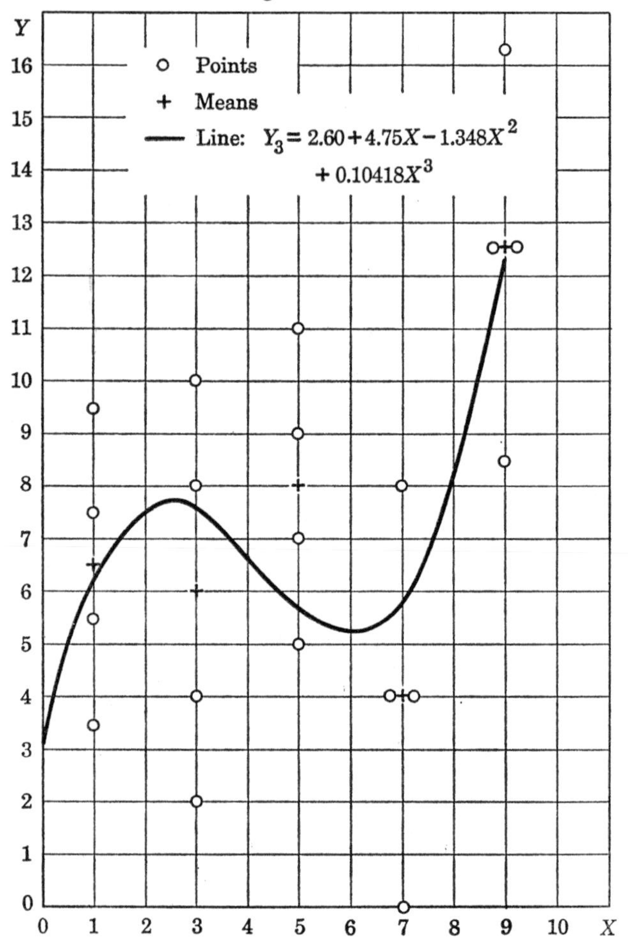

maximum and minimum points shown were located by the algebraic procedure we indicated.

To help us gain a more sound understanding of the meaning of these polynomial equations, we have shown, in Figs. 15-4, 15-5, and 15-6, respectively, the group means and the four possible polynomials, together with the grand mean (which we may, as we have suggested, think of as a zero degree polynomial). Let us consider how the different curves fit the means in each case.

In the first set, Table 15-2 and Fig. 15-4, the grand mean passes through none of the group means and misses some of them by a considerable amount. The linear, or first degree, equation passes quite close to the points, as the anov

Fig. 15-4. Plot of group means from Table 15-2, with the grand mean and first four degrees of polynomial fitted by the method of least squares.

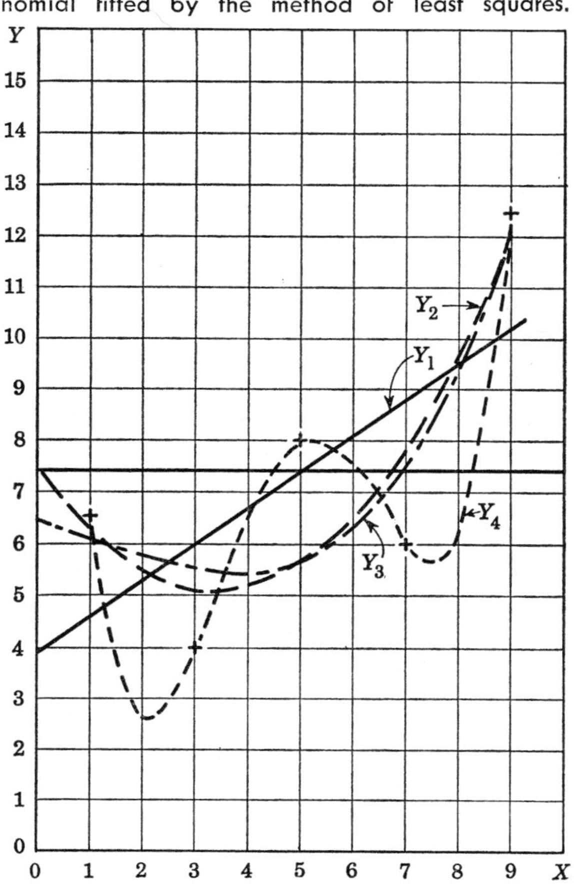

Fig. 15-5. Plot of group means from Table 15-3, with grand mean and first four degrees of polynomial fitted by method of least squares.

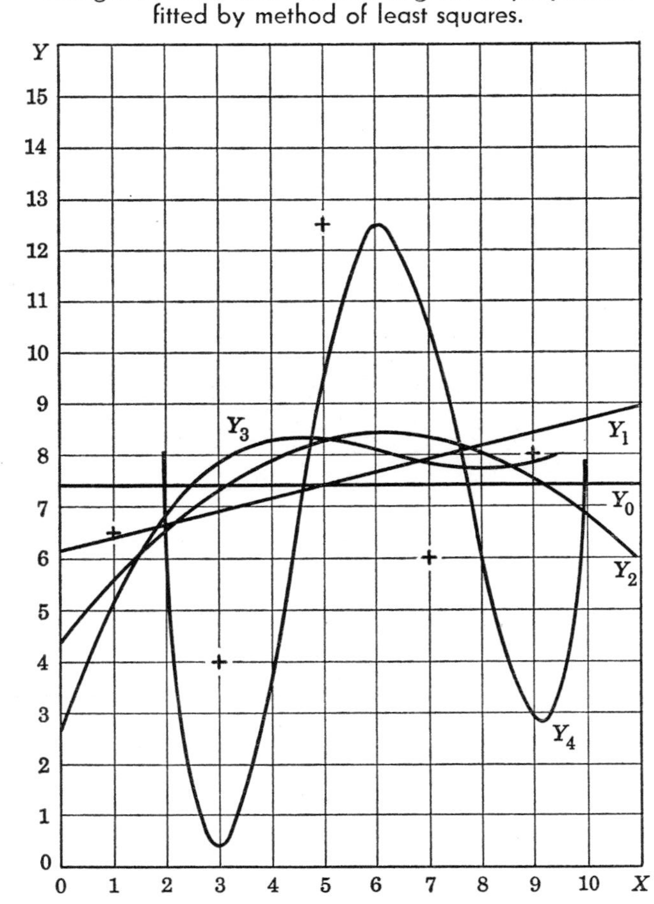

Fig. 15-6. Plot of group means from Table 15-4, with grand mean and first four degrees of polynomial fitted by method of least squares.

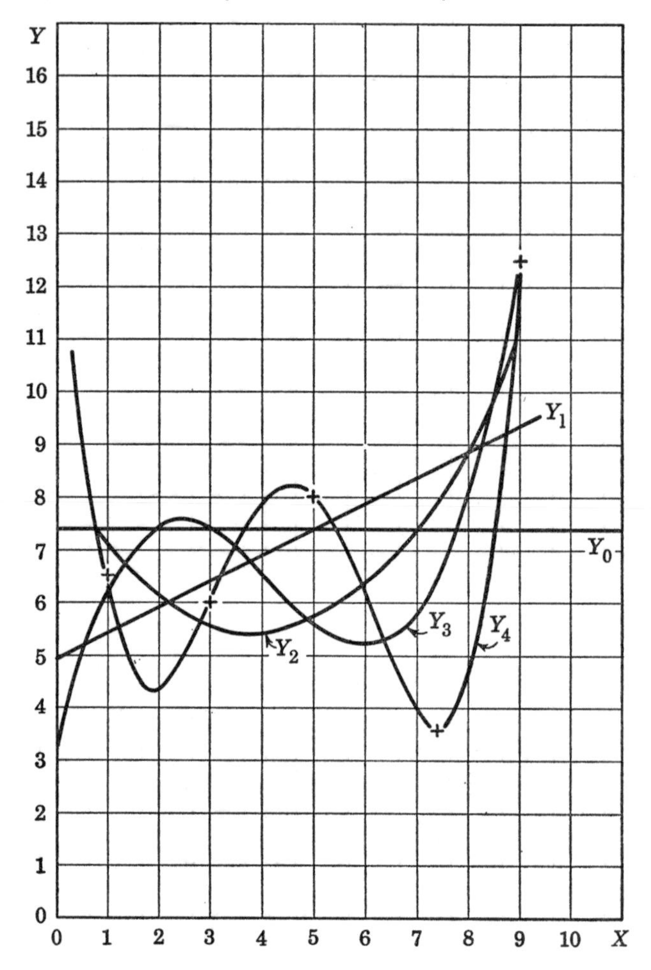

indicates by its quite small remainder. Higher degree equations introduce relatively minor bends into the curves but, in view of the large variations of the individual values about the group means, the improvement in fit is not sufficient to represent any indication that the linear equation inadequately portrays the underlying relationship. Even though the fourth degree equation fits the means perfectly, as it must, its improvement is not sufficient to make us believe the true relationship is of the fourth degree.

In the case of the second set of data, Table 15-3 and Fig. 15-5, no equation makes any real improvement in our fit until the perfectly fitting fourth degree is reached. Its improvement, even over the third degree, is outstanding, and we may use this equation with considerable confidence that it is correct, subject only to the reservation that we were justified in our original idea that a polynomial equation was the proper type and that the degree could not be higher than the fourth.

The third set of data, in Table 15-4 and Fig. 15-6, pose a more serious problem. Here, actually, no single stage of fitting made a significant improvement. In fact, the improvements were about equally divided among the four stages. This fact we somewhat sense by eye in studying the graph and confirm in the analysis of variance. Our adoption of the third degree equation arose, you will recall, from the fact that until we went to the third degree, the remainders were all significant. Had these been real data concerning a serious problem, we should face the following possibilities:

1. If we had considered that the underlying relationship was a polynomial of degree not greater than four, we were probably mistaken, and either the true relationship is not polynomial or its degree is greater than four. After considering all facts known to us, we might expect to reach some new hypothesis concerning the function involved and proceed, with new data, to test it.

2. If we were using the polynomial as an approximation, it is quite evidently an unsatisfactory one, and we should consider some more effective function to approximate the true one.

3. If we had intended to use the polynomial as a guide toward the true function, we must conclude that we are unlikely to gain much information from a polynomial of not greater than the fourth degree in the case of this function.

4. We may happen, as recognized in our alpha risk, to be dealing with an unusual sample from a population which does, in fact, conform to our model and assumptions, a fact which new and possibly more abundant data will help to confirm.

Here you see another example of the principle we have repeatedly attempted to draw to your attention. Our statistical methods can only do as good a job as our skill in selecting and using them permits. If we employ unwarranted assumptions, we may reach false conclusions and surely will reach unwarranted conclusions. We should always scrutinize our final conclusions in the light of our previous knowledge to be sure that the new conclusions "make sense." If they don't, we accept the fact as a warning to scrutinize our analysis, the model on which it is based, and our previous knowledge, together with the procedure by which the data were obtained. By so doing we shall ultimately come a step nearer to truth.

15.9 Confidence Limits

It is unhappily the case that, once we leave the linear equations, the computation of confidence limits for our curves becomes, except at the levels of X at which we actually made observations, a task fraught with arithmetic and algebraic intricacies. It is our feeling that the values at the observed levels convey a sufficient idea of the reliability with which the curves are established to be adequate for most purposes, and we shall therefore discuss only these limits.

With the usual relation we have employed between P and α, $P\%$ confidence limits for the m-th degree polynomial at the i-th level of X are

$$\mu_{Y.X} = Y_{mi} \pm t_{1/2\alpha,n} s_{Y_m.X^2} \sqrt{(1/N) + \Sigma(l_i^2/[N_i \Sigma l_i^2])} \qquad (15.9.1)$$

Even this is a somewhat disturbing formula, we fear! We have used a highly coded notation in writing it because a more detailed notation doesn't seem to make it easier to read. Let us explain the elements in it. Y_{mi} indicates the value of Y calculated from the fitted polynomial of the m-th degree at the i-th level of X. $s_{Y_m.X}^2$ is an estimate of the population variance of Y at X_i, that is, of $\sigma_{Y.X}^2$ of our model. Its numerator, or sum of squares, is the total of the remainder sum of squares after fitting the m-th degree equation plus the within sum of squares, found in our anov table. Its denominator, which we may call n, is the sum of the corresponding degrees of freedom. The value of t needed is found at this number of degrees of freedom.

The summation indicated by the second term under the radical is obtained in the following way. At the i-th level of X, each of the orthogonal coefficients used in our analysis of variance is divided by the value of $N_i \Sigma l_i^2$ for the group of coefficients of which it is a part. These quotients, for degrees through the m-th, are then added. This sum, when added to $1/N$, gives the complete radicand. Table 15-5 shows the computations for our several sets of data.

These computations, like so many we encounter, seem to be much more intricate to describe, and to follow the first time, than they actually are to accomplish. We urge you to follow through the results shown in Table 15-5 and to apply the thinking to analyses of data which are of real concern. We also urge you to treat the data for one of the sets as a problem in linear regression by the methods of the previous chapter. You will find that the regression equation and confidence limits will be exactly those we have obtained by the newer method here.

15.10 Background for Studying Exponential Regressions

In our introductory discussion of the exponential function, $\mu_{Y.X} = AB^X$, in section 15.3, we mentioned that the method of least squares will not work to

Table 15-5 COMPUTATION OF 95% CONFIDENCE LIMITS FOR THE POLYNOMIAL REGRESSION EQUATIONS ADOPTED IN TABLES 15-2, 15-3, AND 15-4

Basic Computations

		l_i				$l_i^2/N_i\Sigma l_i^2$			
i	X_i	1°	2°	3°	4°	1°	2°	3°	4°
1	1	−2	+2	−1	+1	0.10000	0.07142	0.02500	0.00357
2	3	−1	−1	+2	−4	0.02500	0.01785	0.10000	0.05714
3	5	0	−2	0	+6	0.00000	0.07142	0.00000	0.12857
4	7	+1	−1	−2	−4	0.02500	0.01785	0.10000	0.05714
5	9	+2	+2	+1	+1	0.10000	0.07142	0.02500	0.00357

In the balance of the table, $A = 1/N + \Sigma[l_i^2/(N_i\Sigma l_i^2)]$.

For Table 15-2

$$Y_1 = 3.90000 + 0.70000X$$
$$s_{Y.X}^2 = 12.68888,\ s_{Y.X} = 3.56214,\ t_{0.975,18} = 2.101$$
$$K = ts = 7.48406$$

i	A	$\sqrt{A}$	$K\sqrt{A}$	Y_1	Y_U	Y_L
1	0.15000	0.38729	2.89850	4.60000	7.49850	1.70150
2	0.07500	0.27386	2.04958	6.00000	8.04985	3.95015
3	0.05000	0.22360	1.67344	7.40000	9.07344	5.72656
4	0.07500	0.27386	2.04958	8.80000	10.84958	6.75042
5	0.15000	0.38729	2.89850	10.20000	13.09850	7.30150

For Table 15-3

$$Y_4 = 33.53856 - 41.90077 + 17.33788X^2 - 2.60445X^3 + 0.12892X^4$$
$$s_{Y.X}^2 = 9.60000,\ s_{Y.X} = 3.09838,\ t_{0.975,15} = 2.131$$
$$K = ts = 6.60265$$

i	A	$\sqrt{A}$	$K\sqrt{A}$	Y_4	Y_U	Y_L
1	0.25000	0.50000	3.30132	6.50000	9.80132	3.19868
2	0.25000	0.50000	3.30132	4.00000	7.30132	0.69868
3	0.25000	0.50000	3.30132	12.50000	15.80132	9.19868
4	0.25000	0.50000	3.30132	6.00000	9.30132	2.69868
5	0.25000	0.50000	3.30132	8.00000	11.30132	4.69868

For Table 15-4

$$Y_3 = 2.60451 + 4.75385X - 1.34842X^2 + 0.10418X^3$$
$$s_{Y.X}^2 = 11.60357,\ s_{Y.X} = 3.40640,\ t_{0.975,16} = 2.120$$
$$K = ts = 7.22157$$

i	A	$\sqrt{A}$	$K\sqrt{A}$	Y_3	Y_U	Y_L
1	0.24642	0.49640	3.58479	6.11412	9.69891	2.52933
2	0.19285	0.43914	3.17128	7.54314	10.71442	4.37186
3	0.12142	0.34845	2.51636	5.68576	8.20212	3.16940
4	0.19285	0.43914	3.17128	5.54262	8.71390	2.37134
5	0.24642	0.49640	3.58749	12.11436	15.69915	8.52957

give us the needed estimates, a and b, of the parameters, A and B, respectively. This arises from the fact that if we write our estimating equation in the form,

$$Y_e = ab^X \tag{15.10.1}$$

(the subscript refers to the exponential equation), the sum of squares we are to minimize may be written as

$$\Sigma(Y_{ij} - Y_e)^2 = \Sigma(Y_{ij} - ab^X)^2 \tag{15.10.2a}$$

$$= \Sigma(Y_{ij}^2 - 2ab^X Y + a^2 n^{2X}) \tag{15.10.2b}$$

$$= \Sigma Y_{ij}^2 - 2a\Sigma b^X Y + a^2 \Sigma b^{2X} Y \tag{15.10.2c}$$

With the aid of calculus, the normal equations are found to be

$$\begin{cases} a\Sigma b^{2X} = \Sigma b^X Y \\ a\Sigma X b^{2X-1} = \Sigma X b^{X-1} Y \end{cases} \tag{15.10.3}$$

You can see immediately that the unknown value of b is involved in the various sums, which is what renders the method inoperative.

We have at least three alternative ways around this difficulty. First, as we mentioned, the exponential function may be transformed to the semilog form:

$$Z = \log \mu_{Y.X} = C + DX \tag{15.10.4}$$

and we may find the estimates, c and d, of the parameters C and D by the method of least squares. Our estimating equation then becomes

$$Z_{sl} = c + dX \tag{15.10.5}$$

and we can transform values obtained this way back to the forms needed in connection with the exponential form by means of the equations,

$$a = \text{antilog } c \tag{15.10.6}$$

$$b = \text{antilog } d \tag{15.10.7}$$

$$Y_{sl} = \text{antilog } Z_{sl} \tag{15.10.8}$$

Here again we prudently use the subscript $_{sl}$ to remind ourselves that the values originated in the semilog form of the equation. This procedure offers no particular computational difficulties, but, as we shall see when we examine it in detail shortly, it has some surprising faults in principle.

The second alternative is to find the required a and b values for the least squares estimates by successive approximation. While there are a number of mathematical tools that aid this process, it is, at best, tedious and fraught with possibilities of mistakes. We might not let this deter us, but again we shall find some disturbing faults of principle, which we must examine in due course.

A third alternative would be to alter our criterion of the best estimating equation. This would simplify our task of finding values of a and b but would require us to become familiar with test statistics that we have decided to omit from this text.

You may wonder why, if this function poses these difficulties, we discuss it here. The reason is that it is a highly necessary function, as we have said, to describe a number of real relationships we encounter in the "real world," and we must know how to work with it. Furthermore, the methods are so often not understood or are misused that we feel you should, for your own protection, have some understanding of them.

15.11 Using the Semilog Transformation

Suppose that we are about to investigate a regression that we expect to be exponential in form, but we have some concern that the exponential function may not be exactly the correct function to describe the relationship. This would tell us to use more than the two levels of X required to provide estimates of the parameters. We shall imagine that we have actually used five levels, and have made $N_i = 4$ observations of Y at each level. We have synthesized some simple data in Table 15-6 that will make it relatively easy to follow our thinking. We shall assume the regression model.

We shall, however, transform our exponential function to the semilog form. We know that we may make an analysis of variance of the resulting $Z = \log Y$ values, and that we shall have four among degrees of freedom. If we have no better suggestion, we might investigate the possibility that $\mu_{Z.X}$ is a polynomial function of X, of degree as high as four. We know how to make such an analysis, for once we have transformed our Y's to Z's the analysis proceeds as in sections 15.5–15.7. The results are shown in our table and lead to the conclusion that the linear relation is clearly warranted and that no higher degree is justified.

In terms of our present variables, the usual linear regression formulas yield

$$d = \frac{\Sigma XZ - \overline{X}\Sigma Z}{\Sigma X^2 - \overline{X}\Sigma X} = \frac{N\Sigma XZ - \Sigma X \Sigma Z}{N\Sigma X^2 - (\Sigma X)^2} \tag{15.11.1}$$

$$c = \overline{Z} - d\overline{X} \tag{15.11.2}$$

The numerical values are $c = 0.29027$ and $d = 0.17696$, so that our estimating line is $Z_{sl} = 0.29027 + 0.17696X$. A plot of the data and the line is shown in Fig. 15-7. We can go on to compute confidence limits for the line in the usual way. The computations are shown in Table 15-7, and we find gratifyingly narrow limits — too narrow, in fact, to be shown on our graph in the usual way.

We may now transform our coefficients, calculated values, and confidence limits back into terms of Y values by the use of equations 15.10.6–15.10.8, with the results shown in the latter part of Table 15-7 and the graph of Fig. 15-8. In making this back-transformation, we must again remember that we minimized the sum of squared differences between observed and calculated values of Z, not of Y, and we may properly wonder whether this fact makes a difference. We shall see presently.

Table 15-6 SYNTHETIC DATA TO ILLUSTRATE EXPONENTIAL REGRESSION PROBLEM TREATED AFTER TRANSFORMATION TO SEMILOG FORM (NOTE: FOR SIMPLICITY, $X_i = i$)

	$i = 1$		$i = 2$		$i = 3$		$i = 4$		$i = 5$
Y_{1j}	Z_{1j}	Y_{2j}	Z_{2j}	Y_{3j}	Z_{3j}	Y_{4j}	Z_{4j}	Y_{5j}	Z_{5j}
2	0.30103	3	0.47712	8	0.90309	11	1.04139	14	1.14613
3	0.47712	4	0.60206	6	0.77815	10	1.00000	15	1.17609
4	0.60206	6	0.77815	6	0.77815	9	0.90309	16	1.20412
3	0.47712	5	0.69897	8	0.90309	10	1.00000	15	1.17609
T_{i+}	1.85733		2.55630		3.36248		3.94448		4.70243
$\bar{Z}_{i+}$	0.46433		0.63908		0.84062		0.98617		1.17561

Degree	*Orthogonal Coefficients*				
1	−2	−1	0	+1	+2
2	+2	−1	−2	−2	+2
3	−1	+2	0	−2	+1
4	+1	−4	+6	−4	+1

Degree	$\Sigma l_i T_{i+}$	$(\Sigma l_i T_{i+})^2$	$N_i \Sigma l_i^2$	$ss = ms$
1	+7.07838	50.10346	40	1.25258
2	−0.10622	0.01128	56	0.00020
3	+0.06874	0.00473	40	0.00011
4	+0.73152	0.53512	180	0.00191

$N = 20$ $N_i = 4$ $k = 5$

$\Sigma X = 60$ $\Sigma Z = 16.42302$ $T_{++}^2/N = 13.48578^-$

$\Sigma X^2 = 220$ $\Sigma X^2 = 14.86472^-$ $\Sigma T_{i+}^2/N_i = 14.74060^-$

$\bar{X} = 3.0$ $\bar{Z} = 0.8211510$ $\Sigma XZ = 56.34744$

$\Sigma(X - \bar{X})^2 = 40.0$ $\Sigma(Z - \bar{Z})^2 = 1.37894$

Anov for Z (alpha risk: 0.050)

Source	*ss*	*df*	*ms*	*F*	F_{cr}	*Decision*
Total	1.37894	19	—	—		
Among	1.25482	4	0.31371	38.78	3.06	Reject
1°	1.25258	1	1.25258	154.83	4.54	Reject
Rem.	0.00224	3	0.00074	0.09	3.29	Accept
2°	0.00020	1	0.00020	0.02	4.54	Accept
Rem.	0.00204	2	0.00102	0.13	3.68	Accept
3°	0.00011	1	0.00011	0.01	4.54	Accept
Rem.	0.00193	1	0.00193	0.24	4.54	Accept
4°	0.00191	1	0.00191	0.24	4.54	Accept
Within	0.12412	15	0.00809	—		

$$Z_{sl} = 0.29027 + 0.17696X$$

Fig. 15-7. Data of Table 15-6 after logarithmic transformation, and the fitted semilog regression line, $Z_{sl} = 0.29027 + 0.17696X$.

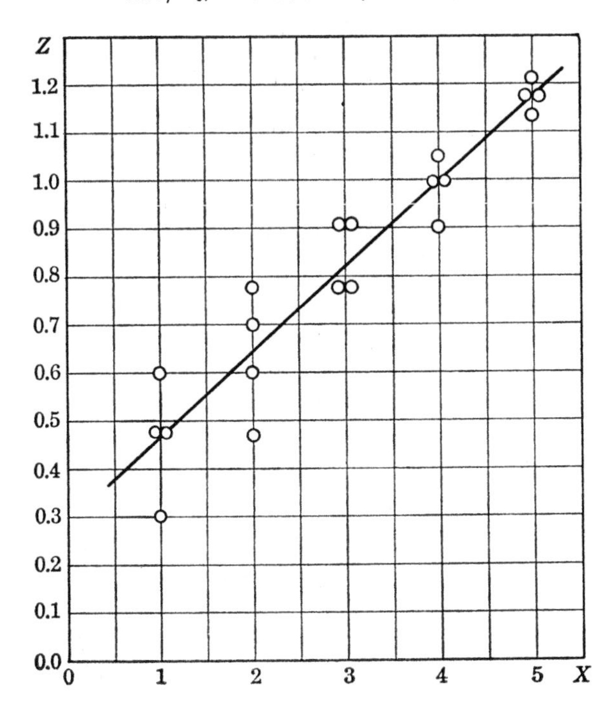

Table 15-7 COMPUTATION OF VALUES AND 95% CONFIDENCE LIMITS FOR THE REGRESSION LINE ADOPTED IN TABLE 15-6, WITH BACK-TRANSFORMATION TO Y-VALUES

$t = t_{0.975,18} = 2.101$; $s_{Y.X}^2 = 0.00702$; $s_{Y.X} = 0.00265$; $K = ts_{Y.X} = 0.00557$.

i	X_i	Δ	Δ^2	$B = \Delta^2/\Sigma\Delta^2$	$A = 1/N + B$	$\sqrt{A}$	$K\sqrt{A}$
1	1	−2	4	0.10000	0.15000	0.38729	0.00216
2	2	−1	1	0.02500	0.07500	0.27386	0.00153
3	3	0	0	0.00000	0.05000	0.22360	0.00125
4	4	+1	1	0.02500	0.07500	0.27386	0.00153
5	5	+2	4	0.10000	0.15000	0.38729	0.00216

i	X_i	Z_{sl}	Z_U	Z_L	Y_{sl}	Y_U	Y_L
1	1	0.46723	0.46939	0.46507	2.9325	2.9471	2.9179
2	2	0.64419	0.64572	0.64266	4.4705	4.4230	4.3920
3	3	0.82115	0.82240	0.81990	6.6244	6.6436	6.6054
4	4	0.99811	0.99964	0.99658	9.9566	9.9918	9.9215
5	5	1.17507	1.17723	1.17291	14.965	15.039	14.891

In the table, $\Delta = X_i - \overline{X}$.

Fig. 15-8. Data of Table 15-6, with line obtained by back-transformation of the semilog regression line to the form, $Y = (1.9510)(1.5030^X)$.

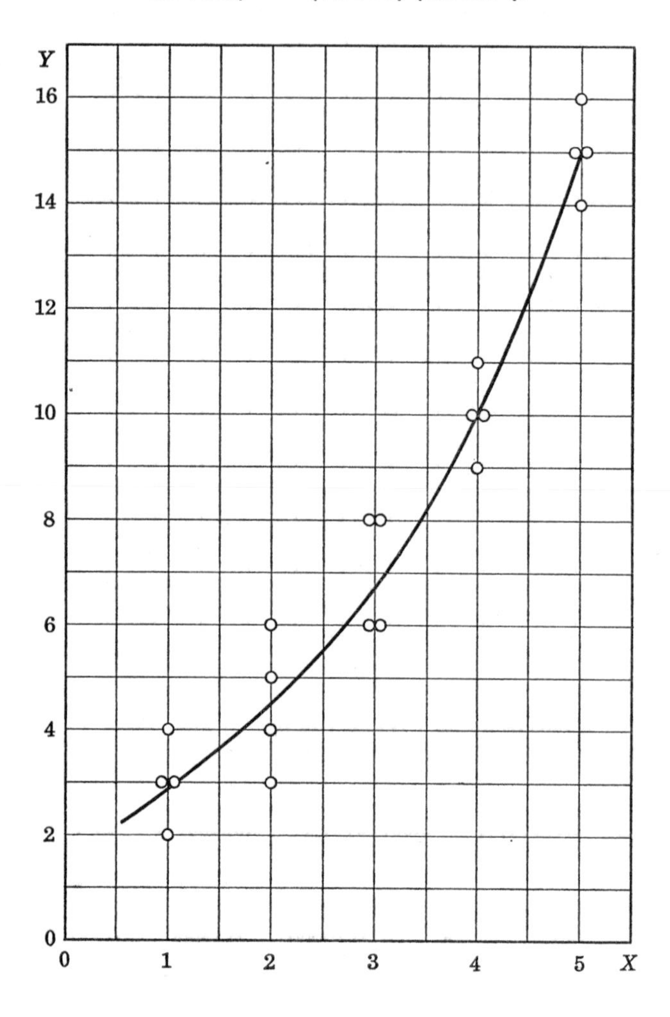

One other fact we should notice. We assumed the regression model for our Y-values. This means that we assumed that $\sigma_{Y.X}{}^2$ was the same at all values of X. If that is true, then the transformation will make the values of $\sigma_{Z.X}{}^2$ different at the different values of X so that, strictly, we have no right to make our regression analysis on the Z's. This is one of those situations we have discussed before in which, if our assumptions are not valid, our results will not be strictly correct, but in which we accept the consequences of small departures from rigor, as discussed earlier.

15.12 Direct Use of the Exponential Function with the Least Squares Approximation

When we transformed our semilog equation back to exponential form, we found $a = 1.9510$ and $b = 1.5030$, so that the transformed estimating equation becomes $Y_{sl} = (1.9510)(1.5030^X)$. Does this represent the least squares regression line in terms of Y's? If we refer to our normal equations, 15.10.3, we find that, although we cannot apply them to find both values, we can solve the first for a in terms of b:

$$a = \Sigma b^X Y / \Sigma b^{2X} \tag{15.12.1}$$

Thus we can assume different values of b, compute the corresponding values of a, and, with the aid of equation 15.10.2c, calculate the sum of squares we are trying to minimize. Proceeding in an orderly manner, we can move toward as close an approximation as we wish to the values giving the minimum sum of squares of differences, $\Sigma(Y_{ij} - Y_e)^2$. For reasons that will presently emerge, we don't want to dwell on this method. Suffice it to say that we found that the required values are approximately $a = 2.06989$ and $b = 1.48595$, so that $Y_e = (2.06989)(1.48959^X)$.

Now let us make an analysis of variance using the values of Y. We have no difficulty in the initial stage involving the analysis of the total into the among and within parts, as shown in Table 15-8. When we come to the further

Table 15-8 Analysis of Variance on the Y-Values from Table 15-6, Initial Phase Only

$i = X_i$	1	2	3	4	5
Y_{ij}	2	3	8	11	14
	3	4	6	10	15
	4	6	6	9	16
	3	5	8	10	15
T_{i+}	12	18	28	40	60

T_{++}	158	T_{++}^2/N	1248.2
ΣY_{ij}^2	1628	$\Sigma T_{i+}^2/N_i$	1613

Anov with $\alpha = 0.050$

Source	*ss*	*df*	*ms*	*F*	F_{cr}
Total	379.8	19	—		
Among	364.8	4	91.2	91.2	3.06
Within	15.0	15	1.0	—	

analysis of the among sum of squares, we note that it depends on the following equivalents:

$$\begin{aligned}\Sigma(\bar{Y}_{i+} - \bar{Y}_{++})^2 &= \Sigma[(\bar{Y}_{i+} - Y_e) + (Y_e - \bar{Y}_{++})]^2 \\ &= \Sigma[(\bar{Y}_{i+} - Y_e)^2 + 2(\bar{Y}_{i+} - Y_e)(Y_e - \bar{Y}_{++}) + (Y_e - \bar{Y}_{++})^2 \\ &= \Sigma(\bar{Y}_{i+} - Y_e)^2 + \Sigma(Y_e - \bar{Y}_{++})^2 \\ &\quad + 2\Sigma(\bar{Y}_{i+} - Y_e)(Y_e - \bar{Y}_{++})\end{aligned} \tag{15.12.2}$$

We have no simple computing equivalents for the final form, and we must make the substitutions indicated and carry out the computations (of course using each mean and computed value once and multiplying the final sums by $N_i = 4$ to save time). Our computations show that $\Sigma(\overline{Y}_{i+} - Y_e)^2 = 0.25053$ and $\Sigma(Y_e - \overline{Y}_{++})^2 = 362.96654$, and that their sum is 363.21707, which lacks 1.58293 of being equal to the among sum of squares. This is disturbing, indeed, but notice that the cross-product term in 15.12.1, namely,

$$2\Sigma(\overline{Y}_{i+} - Y_e)(Y_e - \overline{Y}_{++}) = 1.58293$$

just accounts for this discrepancy. What does this mean?

Unhappily, it means that the least squares fit of our regression equation not only cannot be obtained by direct methods, but that it does not provide an analysis of our among sum of squares into two orthogonal components. If we had studied all our previous analyses of variance, where we did have orthogonal components of the among sum of squares, we would have found that the cross-product sums were each zero. Now we find our approximation to the least squares values leads to nonorthogonality.

Could this be due just to the approximation element? We can, by further trial and error, seek the values of a and b which make the cross-product term zero. These values turn out to be approximately $a = 2.05927$, and $b = 1.48774$, yielding what we may designate as $Y_\epsilon = (2.05927)(1.48774^X)$ as our estimating equation. The sums of squares are $\Sigma(\overline{Y}_{i+} - Y_\epsilon)^2 = 0.25302$ and $\Sigma(Y_\epsilon - \overline{Y}_{++})^2 = 364.54775$, for a total of 364.80077. This is 0.00077 larger than the among sum of squares, and the cross-product term exactly accounts for the discrepancy, which could have been reduced to any required degree by the use of further significant figures.

Now we find ourselves with a least squares fit yielding a nonorthogonal analysis of our among sum of squares, and a fit computed to provide an exact breakdown of the among sum of squares that is not a least squares fit. While we are at it, let us see what would have happened had we made similar computations with Y_{sl}, the back transformation of our least squares semilog equation. Here $\Sigma(\overline{Y}_{i+} - Y_{sl})^2 = 0.62919$, $\Sigma(Y_{sl} - \overline{Y}_{++})^2 = 371.20758$, and $2\Sigma(\overline{Y}_{i+} - Y_{sl})(Y_{sl} - \overline{Y}_{++})^2 = -6.40758$. This attack, then, gives us neither a least squares nor a zero cross-product-sum fit.

We have assembled the pertinent figures for your consideration in Table 15-9 so that you may see the discrepancies among the several computed values as well as the sums of squares we have been discussing. Although it could be argued that the discrepancies in the calculated values over the range of the data are relatively small, it so happens that some of the important uses for this type of equation require extrapolation to higher values of X. At $X = 10$, the three calculated values become

$$Y_e = 108.6$$
$$Y_\epsilon = 109.4$$
$$Y_{sl} = 114.8$$

Whether these discrepancies would be important for our use would depend on the nature of the particular problem of concern to us.

We have discussed the problem of the exponential function more fully, and possibly more honestly, than it is often discussed in texts at this level. Perhaps this discussion has been disturbing to you. Let us see if we can't bring it into focus so that it will finally add to your mental stature.

Table 15-9 Comparison of Calculated Values and Components of the Within Sum of Squares for Regression Lines Fitted by Three Methods to the Data of Table 15-6. Compare Table 15-8

Note: In each case, $\Delta_1 = \bar{Y}_{i+} - Y_c$; $\Delta_2 = Y_c - \bar{Y}_{++}$ and summations are over all values.

Part A. Fitting by Method of Least Squares, to Approximation Discussed in Text

Equation: $Y_c = Y_e = (2.06989)(1.48595^x)$

X_i	$\bar{Y}_{i+-}$	Y_c	Δ_1	Δ_2		
1	3.0	3.07575	−0.07575	−4.82425	$\Sigma\Delta_1^2$	0.25053
2	4.5	4.57042	−0.07042	−3.32958	$\Sigma\Delta_2^2$	362.96654
3	7.0	6.79141	+0.20859	−1.10859		
4	10.5	10.09169	−0.09169	+2.19169	$2\Sigma\Delta_1\Delta_2$	1.58302
5	15.0	14.99575	+0.00425	+7.09575		364.80009

Part B. Fitted to Zero Cross-product Sum, to Approximation Discussed in Text

Equation: $Y_c = Y_\epsilon = (2.05927)(1.48774^X)$

X_i	$\bar{Y}_{i+-}$	Y_c	Δ_1	Δ_2		
1	3.0	3.06366	−0.06366	−4.83534	$\Sigma\Delta_1^2$	0.25302
2	4.5	4.55793	−0.05793	−3.34207	$\Sigma\Delta_2^2$	364.54715
3	7.0	6.78101	+0.21899	−1.11899		
4	10.0	10.08838	−0.08838	+2.18838	$2\Sigma\Delta_1\Delta_2$	−0.00077
5	15.0	15.00888	−0.00888	+7.10888		364.80000

Part C. Fitted by Least Squares to Semilog Transformation

Equation: $Y_c = Y_{sl} = (19510)(1.5030^X)$

X_i	$\bar{Y}_{i+-}$	Y_c	Δ_1	Δ_2		
1	3.0	2.9325	+0.0675	−4.9675	$\Sigma\Delta_1^2$	0.62919
2	4.5	4.4075	+0.0925	−3.4925	$\Sigma\Delta_2^2$	370.57839
3	7.0	6.6244	+0.3756	−1.2756		
4	10.0	9.9566	+0.0434	+2.0566	$2\Sigma\Delta_1\Delta_2$	−6.40757
5	15.0	14.965	+0.035	+7.065		

15.13 Conclusions Concerning Exponential Regressions

First, let us remember that the exponential equation and its semilog transformation, for any fixed pair of coefficients, describes exactly the same relationship. Our problem arises in consequence of estimation difficulties. In the present state of mathematical knowledge, it appears proper to study the regression in terms of the exponential transformation, for in that form established procedures are strictly applicable.

Two comments should be made here. In a number of fields of study, quantities which were found to bear an exponential relationship to an important independent variable are now often replaced by other quantities that are the logarithms of the original quantities. For example, the loudness of sounds is expressed in decibels that are logarithms of the energy involved in their production. It was found that the logarithm was an approximately linear function of the effect on the ear, whereas the energy was an exponential function. The second comment is that, in many cases with real data, the logarithms conform more closely to the regression model requirement of uniform variance at the several levels of X, so that the analysis is more completely justified in this form.

When the Y's rather than their logarithms are clearly more uniform in variance, yet the discrepancy in the analysis of variance arising from the cross-product term is sufficient to be of real concern, it is actually not too difficult to find, particularly with the help of digital computers, the zero cross-product fit. Unfortunately, confidence limit and significance test procedures are not available for this fit. Under such circumstances, it might be wise to enlist the aid of competent assistance to consider the entire question of the proper functional form for your specific data more fully.

15.14 Polynomial Functions as Approximations

We have previously mentioned the utility of polynomial functions as approximations to other types of functions. Let us examine the troublesome data of Table 15-6 in terms of the possibility that Y may be a polynomial function of X. We already know the method from earlier parts of this chapter. The analysis is shown in Table 15-10. You will see that we conclude that a second degree polynomial, having a parabolic graph, fits the data beautifully. Its equation is

$$Y_2 = 2.79997 - 0.26426X + 0.53571X^2$$

and the residual sum of squares, $\Sigma(Y_{ij} - Y_2)^2 = 15.62858$ and has 17 associated degrees of freedom. This yields a residual variance, $s_{Y_2.X}^2 = 0.91933^-$ or a residual standard deviation of $s_{Y_2.X} = 0.959$, which is a little less than $s_{Y.X} = 1.000$. This must be considered an extremely good fit.

Remember, however, that we must examine the implications of the functions we fit. This quadratic function implies a minimum at (0.24664,2.76738) and a value of $Y_2 = 53.7$ at $X = 10$. The exponential functions imply no maximum nor minimum, but indicate that $Y \rightarrow 0$ through positive values as $X \rightarrow -\infty$. The estimates at $X = 10$ were previously listed.

Is there a possibility that the regression is actually polynomial rather than exponential? How could we answer the question? There is, of course, this possibility. The question cannot be answered with the present data, but the

Table 15-10 FITTING A POLYNOMIAL APPROXIMATION TO AN EXPONENTIAL FUNCTION.

(Data from Table 15-6)

X_i	1	2	3	4	5
	2	3	8	11	14
	3	4	6	10	15
	4	6	6	9	16
	3	5	8	10	15
T_{i+}	12	18	28	40	60

Degree	*Orthogonal Coefficients, l_i*				
1	−2	−0	0	+1	+2
2	+2	−1	−2	−1	+2
3	−1	+2	0	−2	+1
4	+1	−4	+6	−4	+1

Degree	$\Sigma l_i T_{i+}$	$(\Sigma l_i T_{i+})^2$	$N_i \Sigma l_i^2$
1	118	13,924	40
2	30	900	56
3	4	16	40
4	8	64	280

Auxiliary Values

$k = 5$	
$N_i = 4$	
$N = 20$	
ΣX	60
ΣX^2	220
$\overline{X}$	3.0
$\Sigma(X - \overline{X})^2$	40
$\Sigma Y = T_{++}$	158
ΣY^2	1,628
$\overline{Y}_{++} = \overline{Y}$	7.90
$\Sigma(Y-\overline{Y})^2$	379.8
T_{++}^2/N	1,248.2
$\Sigma T_{i+}^2/N_i$	1,613.0

Anov table, using $\alpha = 0.050$

Source	*ss*	*df*	*ms*	*F*	F_{cr}	*Decision*
Total	379.80000	19	—	—	—	
Among	364.80000	4	91.20000	91.20	3.06	Reject
1°	348.10000	1	348.10000	348.1	4.54	Reject
Rem.	16.70000	3	5.56666	5.57	3.29	Reject
2°	16.07142	1	16.07142	16.07	4.54	Reject
Rem.	0.62858	2	0.31429	0.31	3.68	Accept
3°	0.40000	1	0.40000	0.40	4.54	Accept
Rem.	0.22858	1	0.22858	0.23	4.54	Accept
4°	0.22857	1	0.22857	0.23	4.54	Accept

clue to obtaining an answer is obtained in the discussion just presented. If we take new data, with an extended range of values of X, preferably including negative as well as larger positive values of X, the data will show good conformity to one of the functions but not the other, thus clarifying the situation, or the data will show good conformity to neither, in which case we must consider other functions.

General Study

1. Explain to your own satisfaction why one may properly use a simple function to interpolate between observed values although it is well known that the function does not represent the true relationship between the values.

2. From your present knowledge or from familiar texts in your major field, prepare a collection of types of equations used to describe relationships between variables. For each equation, make a plot of the curve for typical values of the parameters over the commonly encountered range of the variables.

3. For one or more of the functions such as you found in the preceding problem, study how the form of the equation is considered to be related to the controlling facts in the situation described by the function.

Specific Problems

1. Carry out a complete polynomial regression analysis on the following data:

X	2	4	6	8
Y	1	3	5	7
	3	2	7	6
	2	4	6	8

2. Using the same values of Y as in Problem 1, associate the values of X with them in the following order and perform a new analysis:

4 2 6 8

3–7. Similarly, reanalyze with the following orders of values of X:

4	6	2	8
2	8	4	6
4	8	2	6
8	4	6	2
8	6	4	2

8. Trainees learning radio code were found to be able to receive the following numbers of letters per minute, Y, after the indicated number of weeks of training, X:

X	0	10	20	30	40
Y	10	45	65	92	110
	7	50	64	93	110
	0	47	66	97	115
	5	46	68	95	112
	8	47	65	94	111

Perform an appropriate polynomial regression analysis.

9. For the data of Problem 8, would the equation $Y = A + B \log (X + 1)$ represent the data better than the equation you adopted in Problem 8? Incidentally, why did we use $\log (X + 1)$ instead of $\log X$?

10. Average prices paid for four cereal grains over a period of years at five-year intervals were

Year	1940	1945	1950	1955	1960
Corn	53.2	107.0	115.0	140.0	97.9
Oats	36.3	72.1	70.5	76.8	68.5
Barley	45.9	102.0	110.0	109.0	84.8
Wheat	84.5	146.0	192.0	214.0	178.0

Perform a complete polynomial regression analysis for the relation between price paid for cereal grains and the time. (Note that it would be convenient to let $x = 0$ in 1940, 10 in 1950, etc.)

11. The number of first admissions to public mental institutions, in hundred thousands, for recent years has been:

Year	1952	1953	1954	1955	1956	1957	1958	1959
Admissions	1.18	1.24	1.21	1.22	1.26	1.29	1.37	1.38

What conclusions can you draw from these data?

16

Treating Data Concerning Counts

16.1 The Problem

In our work so far, our data have always consisted of numerical values of some one or more properties of the individuals under study. If we were considering heights of students, for instance, we visualized that each student had a height which was some exact number of inches, and that this height could have any conceivable (positive) value. The fact that our data were reported to the nearest half, quarter, eighth or other fraction, or to some number of decimals we recognized as representing a limitation of our measuring equipment and process, and almost intuitively dealt with it accordingly.

If, however, the matter of concern to us is to which of two or more possible categories the individual should be assigned on the basis of its properties, then our data will consist only of positive integers, the frequency or number of individuals in each category. We may convert these integers to positive fractions, the relative frequencies, by dividing by the total number in our sample or population, but, except in the case of infinite populations, all these proportions will have the total number as their denominator.

We feel at once that this type of number must behave in a somewhat different way from the numbers representing measurements. Yet we also recognize that we are faced with exactly the same problems of inference from samples. We shall need to estimate the population values and test hypotheses concerning these values. Fortunately, our work on probability in Chapter 6 will serve us as a basis here, just as it did in dealing with measurements. It will, in fact, be interesting to you to see that the same pattern will unfold. We shall assume the form of the parent population and make estimates from the sample of the values of the parameters of the population. We shall establish the distribution of these statistics and use this distribution to test hypotheses concerning the parameters or to compute confidence limits for our estimates.

We shall encounter one new difficulty. Even though the distribution we require may be known and the needed values may be capable of computation, we shall find that these computations become exceedingly tedious. Therefore, we shall often make use of approximations to the exact distributions when such approximations will expedite our work without seriously affecting our results. Our encounter with approximations in Chapter 15 should increase our confidence in the wisdom of this procedure.

16.2 A Basic Problem Involving Two Categories

When we discussed the necessity for taking samples, one of the reasons we gave was that the process of obtaining the required information often destroys the individual on which it was obtained. We illustrated this idea in terms of photoflash bulbs. It is desirable that they flash under proper conditions: in order to find out that they will, we flash them and thereby destroy them. Suppose that we need a considerable supply of such bulbs, and we specify that not more than a fraction 0.010 (or 1.0%) shall fail to flash. How can we use information from a sample to determine whether an available brand meets this specification?

Here we recognize that we are clearly involved in the very ideas we discussed in Chapter 6. Every bulb must belong in one or the other of two mutually exclusive categories. The bulb is "good" if it will flash, "bad" if it won't. If the fraction of bulbs in the population in one category is P and in the other category is $Q = 1 - P$, then we know that the number of bulbs, x, in the first category in random samples of n bulbs is described by the binomial distribution. This was originally given as equation 6.12.1, and we restate it here for your convenience, but this time we use $b(x)$ to indicate the frequency:

$$b(x) = \binom{n}{x} P^x Q^{(n-x)} \tag{16.2.1}$$

The use of the $b(x)$ will remind us of the binomial distribution, in distinction to others we shall presently use. In general, we shall associate P with the category constituting the smaller fraction of the parent population.

In effect, our specification for bulbs can quite properly mean that, if P is the population fraction of bad bulbs, we desire to have $P \leq 0.010$. Let us follow our general practice and test the null hypothesis $H_0 : P \geq 0.010$, that is, that the brand is unsatisfactory. If we can reject this hypothesis at an appropriate value of our alpha risk, we may purchase the brand with confidence that it will be satisfactory. Suppose that we use $\alpha = 0.050$ for illustration. Our plan will be to take a sample of n bulbs, test them, and to reject the hypothesis and purchase our needed supply from this brand if and only if the number of bad bulbs, x, is such that it would be in the best 0.050 end of the sample distribution if P were at its borderline value, $P = 0.010$.

We must, therefore, establish two quantities in order to make our plan definite: the number of bulbs to be tested, n, and the number, x, of misfires in our sample which we will allow if we are to reject H_0. It "sounds good" to say that we shall allow no failures in our sample, that is, to require that $x = 0$. This requirement demands that the sample size be such that

$$b(0) = \binom{n}{0} P^0 Q^n = Q^n = \alpha \tag{16.2.2}$$

For our particular case, this means that

$$0.99^n = 0.050$$

The required value of n is readily found after making the logarithmic transformation,

$$n \log Q = \log \alpha \tag{16.2.3a}$$

$$n = (\log \alpha)/(\log Q) \tag{16.2.3b}$$

This, in our case, means that

$$\begin{aligned} n &= (\log 0.050)/(\log 0.99) \\ &= (-1.30103)/(-0.00436) = 298.4 \end{aligned}$$

which, since our sample size must be an integer, we increase to 299. If we substitute this value into 16.2.2, we find

$$b(0) = 0.99^{299} = \alpha$$

Again using logs, we find

$$\begin{aligned} \log \alpha &= 299(\log 0.99) = 299(9.99564 - 10) \\ &= 2988.69636 - 2990 = 8.69636 - 10 \end{aligned}$$

which means that $\alpha = 0.4970$. This represents a slight change from our intended value, 0.050, an unavoidable consequence of the fact that we are dealing with integers as the only possible values for n and x.

The fact that n is so large is of much more concern. Unless we use a very large number of bulbs, the cost of purchasing and testing a sample of 299 bulbs, thereby destroying them, will constitute a disturbing portion of our total cost. Have we been too strict in demanding that there must be no misfires in the sample if we are to use the brand? Let us see what would happen if we agreed to reject H_0 and use the brand if either no misfires or one misfire occurs. This means that we wish

$$b(0) + b(1) = \binom{n}{0} P^0 Q^n + \binom{n}{1} P Q^{n-1} = \alpha \tag{16.2.4}$$

Unfortunately, there is no direct procedure by which we can compute n, and we must resort to approximation, as we did in Table 16-1. After all the

Table 16-1 COMPUTATION DIRECTLY FROM THE BINOMIAL DISTRIBUTION OF THE SAMPLE SIZE REQUIRED FOR THE LAMP BULB TESTING PROBLEM DISCUSSED ON PAGE 309ff.

n	$\log 0.99^n$	$\log 0.01n$	$\log 0.99^{n-1}$	$\log(0.01n)(0.99^{n-1})$	0.99^n	$0.01n\ 0.99^{n-1}$	α
299	8.69638–10	0.47567	8.70072–10	9.17639–10	0.04970	0.15010	0.19980
400	8.25600	0.60206	8.26036	8.86242	0.01803	0.07285	0.09088
500	7.82000	0.69897	7.82436	8.52333	0.00661	0.03337	0.03998
450	8.03800	0.65231	8.04236	8.69557	0.01091	0.04961	0.06052
475	7.92900	0.67669	7.93336	8.61005	0.00849	0.04074	0.04923
470	7.95080	0.67210	7.95516	8.62726	0.00893	0.04239	0.05132
472	7.94208	0.67394	7.94644	8.62038	0.00875	0.04172	0.05047
473	7.93772	0.67486	7.94208	8.61694	0.00866	0.04139	0.05005

Note the tedious computations required for each stage of the approximation.

work shown there, we find that our new plan requires a larger, not a smaller, sample! But the experience will have been valuable if it taught us that the binomial distribution is tedious and awkward to use: perhaps we are now ready to consider approximations seriously.

16.3 Approximations to the Binomial Distribution

In Chapter 6, we mentioned that two other distributions may, under appropriate conditions, be used as adequate and very convenient approximations to the binomial distribution. In section 6.13, we learned that the normal distribution with $\mu = nP$ and $\sigma^2 = nPQ$ approximated the binomial distribution with the approximation improving as $P \rightarrow 0.50$ and as n increased. In section 6.14 we found that the Poisson distribution, with $\mu = nP$, also approximated the binomial distribution. For this approximation to be satisfactory, for the uses which we intend, it is generally agreed that $\mu = nP$ should not exceed 5 and that, as usual, the approximation improves as n increases.

The Poisson distribution, which we originally gave in Chapter 6, we rewrite as

$$p(x) = \frac{\mu^x}{x!}e^{-\mu} \tag{16.3.1}$$

You will find in Appendix IX a useful table of values of $p(x)$ and of $\sum_{x=0}^{x} p(x)$ for a reasonable range of values of μ and x. Its use will be discussed in the following sections.

16.4 Use of the Poisson Distribution to Determine Sample Sizes

Suppose that we consider how we might use the Poisson distribution as an approximation to the binomial distribution to aid us in fixing the sample sizes required for the problem we treated rigorously in section 16.2. We first consider the case in which we required that $x = 0$. We look through Appendix IX on the line $x = 0$ until we come to a value of μ for which $p(0) \doteq 0.050$. We find that at $\mu = 3.0$, $p(0) = 0.0498$, a very close approximation to 0.050. Since $P = 0.010$, our $n = \mu/P = 3.0/0.010 = 300$. This is, indeed, a very close approximation to the value we found, 299, by the more tedious but rigorous use of the binomial distribution. If we take the case in which we allowed either $x = 0$ or $x = 1$, we look in our Appendix in the $x = 1$ line until we come to $\Sigma x \doteq 0.050$. We find that this would occur between $\mu = 4.5$ and $\mu = 5.0$. We may use linear interpolation to find $\mu \doteq 4.77$, from which $n = 4.77/0.010 = 477$. This is again an excellent approximation to our previous value, and was much more readily obtained.

16.5 A Two-Category Problem with Equal Frequencies

In Chapter 6 we recorded a rather extensive experiment in coin tossing, which we used to get some idea of the behavior of an actual coin really tossed in comparison with the behavior of the mathematicians' ideal coin and ideal tossing. Since the ideal situation leads to $P = Q = 0.5$, we shall be concerned with testing $H_0 : P = 0.50$. Here we are dealing with an hypothesis of equality and clearly need a two-tailed test. We must decide upon a value of n and the two values of x, the observed number of heads, which would lead us to reject our hypothesis. Suppose we take our alpha risk, again, as 0.050. We start by trying $n = 10$ which yields the following values for $b(x)$ and $\sum_{x=0}^{x} b(x)$:

x	$b(x)$	$\Sigma b(x)$
0	0.00098	0.00098
1	0.00977	0.01075
2	0.04395	0.05470
3	0.11719	0.17189
4	0.20508	0.37697
5	0.24609	0.62306
6	0.20508	0.82814
7	0.11719	0.94533
8	0.04395	0.98928
9	0.00977	0.99905
10	0.00098	1.00003

Of course, the 3 in the fifth decimal of the final total reflects the accumulated rounding errors. Now we see another example of the difficulties of the binomial distribution. If we agree to reject our hypothesis if we observe 0, 1, 9, or 10 heads our alpha risk becomes $0.01075 + (1 - 0.98928) = 0.01075 + 0.01073$, which, again allowing for rounding error, is $2(0.01075) = 0.02150$. This is far short of the desired 0.050. If we also add 3 or 8 heads we shall have 2(0.05470)

$= 0.10940$, which is more than twice the desired value. We must, then, increase our value of n in order to obtain smaller differences in the values of $b(x)$.

But this is going to involve a great deal of tedious trial computation. Because $P = 0.5$, we should be in ideal circumstances for the use of the normal approximation. The required values of z will be $\pm|z_{1/2\alpha}|$ or, in our case, $\pm|z_{0.025}| = \pm 1.96$. Suppose we think of the lower tail of the distribution, containing small values of x. Since we only observe integral values of x, we consider these values as class marks, and we consider that their frequencies are those given by the normal distribution for values from $x - \frac{1}{2}$ to $x + \frac{1}{2}$. This means that if our critical value at the lower end is to be x_{cr}, we require that

$$z_{1/2\alpha} = \frac{(x_{cr} + 1/2) - \mu}{\sigma} = \frac{(x_{cr} + 1/2) - nP}{\sqrt{nPQ}} \tag{16.5.1}$$

For our particular values,

$$-1.96 = \frac{x_{cr} + 0.5 - n0.5}{\sqrt{n0.5^2}} = \frac{x_{cr} + 0.5 - 0.5n}{0.5\sqrt{n}}$$

Algebraic manipulations yield

$$0.5(-1.96)\sqrt{n} = -0.98\sqrt{n} = (x_{cr} + 0.5) - 0.5n$$
$$0.5n - 0.98\sqrt{n} - (x_{cr} + 0.5) = 0$$

This is easily handled as a quadratic equation in $\sqrt{n}$ which we can solve by the quadratic formula to obtain

$$\sqrt{n} = \frac{0.98 \pm \sqrt{0.98^2 - 4(0.5)[-(x_{cr} + 0.5)]}}{2(0.5)}$$
$$= 0.98 \pm \sqrt{0.9604 + 1.0000 + 2x_{cr}}$$
$$= 0.98 \pm \sqrt{1.9604 + 2x_{cr}}$$

We may now propose various values of x_{cr} and compute the corresponding values of $\sqrt{n}$ and then of n. We shall recognize that the negative sign in the expression leads to values without meaning in our problem, and that, in practice, our normal approximation may not be very good if n turns out to be below 20. Some possible values are shown in Table 16-2. We start with possible values of x_{cr}, compute the required values of n, then take the next integral value as our sample size, and note that we have a critical value for the upper tail which would be $x'_{cr} = n - x_{cr}$. While the required computations are tedious, they are far less tedious than would be the exact computations from the binomial distribution.

Table 16-2 COMPUTATION OF APPROXIMATE SAMPLE SIZE REQUIRED TO TEST H_0: $P = 0.50$ WITH $\alpha = 0.050$, USING THE NORMAL APPROXIMATION TO THE BINOMIAL DISTRIBUTION

x_{cr}	A	$\sqrt{A}$	$\sqrt{n}$	n	n^*	x'_{cr}
0	1.9604	1.40014	2.38014	5.66	6	6
1	3.9604	1.99004	2.97004	8.82	9	8
2	5.9604	2.44139	3.42139	11.71	12	10
3	7.9604	2.82141	3.80146	14.45	15	12
4	9.9604	3.15601	4.13601	17.11	18	14
5	11.9604	3.45838	4.43838	19.70	20	15
10	21.9604	4.68619	5.66619	32.11	33	23
15	31.9604	5.65335	6.63335	44.00	44	29
20	41.9604	6.47768	7.45768	55.62	56	36
25	51.9604	7.20835	8.18835	67.05	68	43
50	101.9604	10.09754	11.07754	122.71	123	73
100	201.9604	14.21127	15.19127	230.77	231	131
500	1001.9604	31.65375	32.63375	1064.96	1065	565
1000	2001.9604	44.74327	45.72327	2090.62	2091	1091

In the table, $A = 1.9604 + 2x_{cr}$ (see text for details) and n^* is the integral value at or above the calculated n.

It would be well to consider another matter at this point. Since, within the limits of approximation, all the possible combinations of sample size and critical values have the same alpha risk, 0.050, does it make any difference which plan we use? It does. The larger the values of n, the more tosses may be required to reach a conclusion. If we were paying for the experiment (as we actually were, though at a token rate in our coin tossing!), this could be serious. But suppose we consider the case in which n turned out to be 56 with critical values of 20 and 36. The value $x = 20$ corresponds to

$$z = \frac{20 + 0.5 - 0.5(56)}{0.5\sqrt{56}} \doteq -2.004$$

for which $p = \frac{1}{2}\alpha = 0.0226$ or $\alpha = 0.0452$. If we had kept n as 56 but increased the critical value to $x = 21$, we would have had, by similar computations, $z = -1.736$, $p = 0.0414$, and $\alpha = 0.0820$ — a considerably different alpha risk. If we had used the plan involving $n = 231$, with critical values of 100 and 131, the actual alpha risk would be 0.0482 while the alpha risk resulting from adding one more value at each end becomes 0.0656. The increased sample size, then, permits us to come closer to our intended alpha risk, and to make the changes resulting from single-step changes in critical values smaller. Whether such a change is desirable will depend, in any specific case, upon economic and technical factors.

Suppose that, for some reason, we had had a value of the sample size, n, more or less determined for us. Perhaps that was as large a sample as was available, or perhaps the cost of obtaining a larger sample would be prohibitive. Under such circumstances, we substitute this value into 16.5.1 and estimate the value of x_{cr} corresponding to the $z_{1/2\alpha}$ resulting from our chosen alpha risk. Of course, the equation is conveniently manipulated to yield

$$x_{cr} = nP + z_{\alpha/2}\sqrt{nPQ} - 0.5$$

which, for our value of P and α, becomes

$$x_{cr} = 0.5n - 1.96(0.5)\sqrt{n} - 0.5$$

$$= 0.5(n - 1 - 1.96\sqrt{n})$$

Just for fun, we calculated the critical values for the values of n in Table 6-6 for which p_H was most remote from 0.5 and for the final value, $n = 1600$. The results are shown in Table 16-3. In no case would we reject the hypothesis that the coin and tossing procedure are normal.

Table 16-3 COMPUTATION OF CRITICAL VALUES FOR THE TEST OF $H_0 : P = 0.50$ WITH $\alpha = 0.050$ FOR THE VALUES OF n IN TABLE 6-6 AT WHICH p WAS MOST REMOTE FROM 0.50, AND FOR THE FINAL VALUE, USING THE NORMAL APPROXIMATION TO THE BINOMIAL DISTRIBUTION

			Exact	*Integral*		
n	$\sqrt{n}$	A	x_{cr}	x_{cr}	x'_{cr}	$x_{obs.}$
50	7.07106	35.14072	17.57	18	32	21
1050	32.40370	985.48875	492.7	493	557	531
1600	40.00000	1520.60000	760.3	761	839	791

Note: $A = n - 1 - 1.96\sqrt{n}$ (see text for details). In no case would we reject H_0.

16.6 Confidence Limits in Two-Category Problems

If we have obtained a sample of n from a population and determined the number of individuals, x, falling into one of the two possible categories involved, we compute $p = x/n$ as an estimate of the value of P, the proportion of individuals in the population falling into the stated category. This is a point estimate, and the question arises as to how we may compute confidence limits. In order to avoid using the same symbol for two purposes we shall, when dealing with these problems, refer to the confidence level by the symbol Π and speak of $\Pi\%$ confidence limits. Of course, the related alpha risk will be $\alpha = (100 - \Pi)/100$.

The rigorous procedure requires that we apply the binomial distribution to find the values, P_U and P_L, such that with our sample size, n, our observed number, x, is just within the $\frac{1}{2}\alpha$ and the $(1 - \frac{1}{2}\alpha)$ tails of the distribution, respectively. As a specific instance, suppose that, in the problem of section 16.2 we adopted the plan calling for $n = 299$ and observed $x = 1$ nonflashing bulbs. We wish 90% confidence limits. Our related $\alpha = 0.100$, $\frac{1}{2}\alpha = 0.050$, and $1 - \frac{1}{2}\alpha = 0.950$. Hence, we require the values of P such that

$$b(0) + b(1) = (1 - P)^{299} + 299P(1 - P)^{298}$$
$$= (1 - P)^{298}(1 + 298P)$$

shall be equal to 0.050 for P_U and 0.950 for P_L. The equation can only be solved by trial, and we show some values we used for the purpose in Table 16-4,

Table 16-4 TRIAL SOLUTIONS, USING LOGARITHMS, OF THE EQUATIONS YIELDING 90% CONFIDENCE LIMITS FOR P FROM THE DATA OF TABLE 6-6

P	$1 - P = A$	$1 + 298P = B$	$\log A$	$\log B$	$\log[b(0) + b(1))$	$b(0) + b(1)$
0.0010	0.9990	1.2980	9.99957–10	0.11327	9.98513–10	0.96634
0.0020	0.9980	1.5960	9.99913–10	0.20303	7.26177–10	0.00182
0.0015	0.9985	1.4470	9.99935–10	0.16047	7.28477–10	0.00193
0.0012	0.9988	1.3576	9.99948–10	0.13277	9.97781–10	0.95018 $\doteq P_U$
0.0100	0.9900	3.9800	9.99654–10	0.59988	9.30000–10	0.19953
0.0200	0.9800	6.9600	9.99123–10	0.84261	8.22915–10	0.01695
0.0150	0.9850	5.4700	9.99344–10	0.73799	8.78311–10	0.06069
0.0160	0.9840	5.7680	9.99300–10	0.76103	8.67503–10	0.04732
0.0157	0.9843	5.6786	9.99313–10	0.75424	8.70698–10	0.05093
0.0158	0.9842	5.7084	9.99308–10	0.75651	8.69435–10	0.04947 $\doteq P_L$

from which we conclude that, correct to four decimals, $P_U = 0.0158$ and $P_L = 0.0012$. Of course, our observed value yields the point estimate, $p = x/n = 1/299 = 0.0033$.

The value of $x = pn = 1$, being considerably less than 5, suggests that we could use the Poisson distribution as an approximation with considerable saving of time and effort. We find the values of μ such that for $x = 1$ the values of $\Sigma p(x)$ are 0.050 and 0.950. By interpolation, we find them to be 4.77 and 0.35, which yield $P_U = 0.016$ and $P_L = 0.0012$, which agree very satisfactorily with the values obtained by the rigorous procedure.

Suppose we consider our coin-tossing data, and wish to establish 90% confidence limits for P after the 50th toss, when x, the number of heads, was 29. Of course, our point estimate is $p = x/n = 29/50 = 0.58$. The rigorous method for establishing the limits would involve tremendous amounts of computation. Here $x = pn = 29$, so that we will legitimately use the normal approximation. Remembering that $\mu = nP$ and $\sigma = \sqrt{nP(1 - P)}$ and remembering our addition and subtraction of $\frac{1}{2}$ unit to x, we require the values of P such that

$$z_{0.050} = -1.645 = \frac{29.5 - 50P}{\sqrt{50P(1 - P)}}$$

and

$$z_{0.950} = +1.645 = \frac{28.5 - 50P}{\sqrt{50P(1 - P)}}$$

Algebraic steps of squaring both sides of the equations, multiplying by the denominator of the right side, and collecting all terms on one side yield the equations,

$$2635.30125P^2 - 3085.30125P + 870.25 = 0$$

and

$$2635.30125P^2 - 2985.30125P + 812.25 = 0$$

The first equation yields the roots $P = 0.69691$ and $P = 0.47384$. Checking by back-substitution shows the second value to be an extraneous root introduced by squaring. Similarly, the second equation yields the roots $P = 0.67864$ and $P = 0.45417$, of which the first is extraneous. Thus we conclude that $P_U = 0.69691$ and $P_L = 0.45417$.

Notice that while these 90% confidence limits do include the expected value, $P = 0.5000$, they are still rather wide. We thought you might be interested in the limits after the 1600 tosses which we recorded, so we calculated them by the same procedure. They were $P_U = 0.51647$ and $P_L = 0.48475$, a narrower set and more symmetrically placed about the expected value, 0.50.

16.7 Problems Involving More Than Two Categories

While there are a great many problems involving counts of individuals in but two categories, there are also numerous problems in which more than two categories are involved. In the academic field we are concerned with the distribution of the several letter grades, or with the number of students remaining in good standing, on academic probation, and dismissed after each semester. More generally, we may be concerned with political or religious preferences, or with which of a group of household appliances families possess, and so on.

If we wish to test an hypothesis about the population distribution on the basis of a distribution in a sample, we must, as always, have some test statistic. Suppose our hypothesis states that the proportion in the i-th category is P_i. In a sample of n individuals taken at random from this population we would have an expected frequency of individuals, which has sometimes been thought of as the "theoretical" frequency, $t_i = P_i n$. Suppose we designate the actual frequencies as a_i. The value of $(a_i - t_i)$ would be a measure of the discrepancy between the actual and theoretical frequency. We are accustomed to the utility of using the squares of such deviations, $(a_i - t_i)^2$, to avoid problems of signs. Now it would seem that a given discrepancy should cause greater concern about the truth of our hypothesis when t_i is small than when it is large, so we might use $(a_i - t_i)^2/t_i$, which we might think of as the relative squared deviation, as our measure of the seriousness of the discrepancy in the i-th category.

It would seem sensible to add these measures for all the categories, obtaining

$$\chi^2 = \Sigma(a_i - t_i)^2/t_i \qquad (16.7.1)$$

and we would expect that the larger this value is the more we should doubt the truth of our hypothesis. All we need to make this quantity into a test statistic is a knowledge of its distribution. It has been shown that, under certain conditions, it has approximately the χ^2-distribution with $k - 1$ degrees of freedom. The conditions are that

1. The number of categories, k, be at least eight and, preferably, at least ten.
2. That the theoretical frequencies, t_i, be at least five in all categories.
3. That, if the theoretical frequencies are rounded to facilitate computations, the rounding error should not exceed 1% of the true t_i value.

The number of degrees of freedom would seem reasonable, from the fact that we must, of course, have the sum of the values of t_i equal the total number of counts.

Now we are in a position to test our hypothesis. We carry out the computations to develop the observed value of χ^2. If, for an alpha risk, α, $\chi^2 \geq \chi^2_{(1-\alpha),(k-1)}$, we must reject our hypothesis. Otherwise, we accept the hypothesis.

Suppose that we first see the application of this idea to a very simple problem. We once purchased some dice to use in making photographs for slides to illustrate some of the probability principles we have discussed. A rather peculiar notice at the counter where we purchased them, together with the results of a close scrutiny of their construction, suggested that they would probably be biased. We decided to use one of them to test this idea, in other words, to test the hypothesis that the probability of the various outcomes was, as predicted by probability theory, $\frac{1}{6}$. We rolled the die 60 times, using no backboard. Each t_i was therefore $(\frac{1}{6})60 = 10$. The actual frequencies, together with the computations needed to test our hypothesis, are shown in Table 16-5. Using an alpha risk, $\alpha = 0.050$, the data from these comparatively few rolls did not lead us to reject the hypothesis.

Table 16-5 TEST OF THE HYPOTHESIS THAT A DIE WAS UNBIASED, I.E., THAT $Pr\{1\} = Pr\{2\} = \ldots = Pr\{6\} = \frac{1}{6}$, WITH A SAMPLE OF $n = 60$ ROLLS WITHOUT A BACKBOARD

x_i = result of roll; a_i = observed frequency; $t_i = (\frac{1}{6})60 = 10$. $\Delta = a_i - t_i$

x_i	a_i	t_i	Δ	Δ^2	Δ^2/t_i
1	7	10	−3	9	0.9
2	6	10	−4	16	1.6
3	10	10	0	0	0.0
4	12	10	+2	4	0.4
5	12	10	+2	4	0.4
6	13	10	+3	9	0.9
Sums	60	60	0	42	$4.2 = \chi^2$

$(\chi^2)_{0.95,5} = 11.07$. Accept H_0.

A rather important use of this procedure is the verification of the validity of the assumption, common to so much of our previous work, that the parent population from which our sample comes is normally distributed. In Chapter 6, where we were considering ways of describing the distributional form, we presented several distributions and fitted normal curves to them. At that time, because we had not introduced methods of inference from samples, we were obliged to consider that we were dealing with complete populations. Now we can be more realistic. Suppose we consider our data concerning freshman indexes, used so often in those early chapters, and, thinking of them as a sample, use them to test the hypothesis that they came from a normal population with mean $\mu = 2.258$ and standard deviation $\sigma = 0.684$. Table 5-6 showed the frequencies required by the normal distribution, f_N, which we would use as t_i in our present symbols, together with the observed frequencies, f_0, which would be our present a_i. We transcribe these data into Table 16-6,

Table 16-6 Comparison of Observed Frequencies and Those of the Fitted Normal Distribution for the Freshman Academic Indexes of Table 5-6

Note that, considering the indexes as a sample from the population of all freshman indexes at the university in question and assuming that the observed mean and variance are those of the population, this is a test of the hypothesis that the population distribution is normal. Class upper boundary = X_u.

X_u	t_i	a_i	Δ	Δ^2/t_i
$+\infty$	11.0	9	−2.0	0.36363
3.605	26.1	34	+7.9	2.39118
3.205	57.4	64	+6.6	0.75888
2.805	90.5	72	−18.5	3.78176
2.405	102.3	101	−1.3	0.01652
2.205	82.9	90	+7.1	0.60808
1.605	48.1	49	+0.9	0.01683
1.205	20.1	25	+4.9	1.19452
0.805	7.5	2	−5.5	4.03333
				$\chi^2 = 13.16474$

$k = 9$, $k - 1 = 8$.
$(\chi^2)_{0.950,8} = 15.51$. Don't reject H_0.

except that we must combine the two highest classes into one class and the three lowest into another in order to meet our requirement of a minimum value of 5 for all t_i. Our computations yield a value of $\chi^2 = 13.16$, whereas the critical value, for $\alpha = 0.050$, is $\chi_{0.950,8}{}^2 = 15.51$. We therefore do not reject our hypothesis, and we do continue to consider the distribution normal.

Let us take a still more realistic look at the problem. Where did our values for μ and σ come from? Actually, they were obtained from the same data. To be strictly correct, we should have used $\overline{X}$ and s, and recognized that they estimate two additional parameters from our data. Then our χ^2 values would have had $k - 3$ associated degrees of freedom. In general, if we are fitting to a distribution whose parameters we have estimated from our data, and there are p parameters, the number of degrees of freedom will be $k - p - 1$.

16.8 Comparing Several Populations

An interesting extension of the thinking of the immediately preceding section permits us to test the hypotheses that several populations have the identical distribution, even though we may know neither the form nor the parameters of the distribution. Suppose that we have, in our populations, k categories, and that we have samples from r such populations. We can denote quantities of interest to us by the following symbols:

a_{ij} = the frequency for the i-th category in the sample for the j-th population,

a_{i+} = the total frequency for the i-th category,

a_{+j} = the total frequency for the j-th sample,

$a_{++} = n$ = the total frequency.

Now we can form an estimate of the needed t_{ij} values by recognizing that we would ideally expect the a_{+j} observations in any sample to be distributed among the k categories in same proportions as in the total of all samples, that is,

$$t_{ij} = (a_{i+}/a_{++})a_{+j} \tag{16.8.1}$$

Another way of thinking of the problem would lead to the idea that the a_{i+} observations in any category would be distributed over the samples in proportion to the total number in the samples, or,

$$t_{ij} = (a_{+j}/a_{++})a_{i+} \tag{16.8.2}$$

Note that the two results are identical, being simply rearrangements of the same algebraic expression. This gives us the needed "theoretical" frequencies, and from then on our computation proceeds as before. Of course, the summation by which χ^2 is ultimately obtained is a double summation over the k categories and r samples:

$$\chi^2 = \frac{\Sigma(a_{ij} - t_{ij})^2}{t_{ij}} \tag{16.8.3a}$$

$$= \sum_{i=1}^{k} \sum_{j=1}^{r} \frac{(a_{ij} - t_{ij})^2}{t_{ij}} \tag{16.8.3b}$$

This statistic will be distributed approximately as χ^2 with $(k - 1)(r - 1) = kr - k - r + 1$ degrees of freedom. We may think of the degrees of freedom as developing as follows. In each sample, except one, we may distribute frequencies "freely," subject to the restriction that we must preserve the sample total. And we may do this in all but one sample: that must be "reserved" to preserve the category totals.

In order for the approximation to the χ^2-distribution to be adequate for our use, either k or r or both should be at least three, and all values of t_{ij} should be at least five. We shall presently discuss modifications to be made when the first condition cannot be met.

A somewhat interesting application of this principle may be made to the data of Table 16-7. The data show the number of fatal accidents classed in various categories in three recent years. Actually, the "observed" frequencies are estimates prepared by the National Safety Council on the basis of a sample of all accident reports, rather than a complete count. It would appear to be impossible to develop a realistic theory to predict the number of accidents in each category for any stated year, so we sensibly use the procedure just outlined to compute our values of t_{ij}. We chose an alpha risk, $\alpha = 0.010$, and the computations and critical value, as shown in our table, lead us to reject the hypothesis that the distribution of fatal accidents remained the same over these three years.

This would be a wise time to consider our conclusion thoughtfully. Basically, we are thinking, under our hypothesis, of our fatal accidents as having a fixed overall distribution of causes, and that those which occur in any one year are a random sample from this population. We conclude that we must reject this hypothesis. This conclusion may have been reached for any of the following causes, and possibly others:

1. The hypothesis is, in fact, false, and there are real variations in the cause of fatalities from year to year.

2. The hypothesis is, in fact, true but the vagaries of random sampling happened to lead to rather extreme variations during these particular three years.

3. The hypothesis is, in fact, true and the years did, in fact, have no striking variation, but the size of the sample and the method of estimating a_{ij} used by the N.S.C. may have been inadequate.

If we were doing serious work with this problem, we should satisfy ourselves concerning possibility No. 3, then study the records in more detail in order to clarify our feelings about the other two.

When both r and k are only two, the approximation of the distribution of the quantities yielded by equation 16.8.3a to the χ^2-distribution is not as good as it should be for our purposes. Under these conditions, it has been found that the quantity

$$\chi^2 = \sum \frac{(|a_{ij} - t_{ij}| - 1/2)^2}{t_{ij}} \tag{16.8.4}$$

Table 16.7 USE OF ESTIMATED FREQUENCIES OF ACCIDENTS IN VARIOUS CATEGORIES IN THE UNITED STATES IN THREE DIFFERENT YEARS TO TEST THE HYPOTHESIS THAT THE RELATIVE FREQUENCIES WERE THE SAME EACH YEAR

Year, j	1956			1957			1958			
Category, i	a_{ij}	t_{ij}	Δ^2/t_{ij}	$-a_{ij}$	t_{ij}	Δ^2/t_{ij}	a_{ij}	t_{ij}	Δ^2/t_{ij}	a_{i+}
Motor Vehicles	39,628	39,231.2	4.01339	38,702	38,807.2	0.28518	37,000	37,291.5	2,27859	115,330
Falls	20,282	20,181.0	0.51547	20,545	19,962.8	16.97942	18,500	19,183.2	24.33182	59,327
Burns	6,405	6,590.4	5.21564	6,269	6,519.1	9.59488	6,700	6,264.5	30.27540	19,374
Drowning	6,263	6,421.0	3.88786	6,613	6,351.6	3.02442	6,400	6,103.5	14.40357	18,876
Railroad	2,696	2,656.7	0.58135	2,614	2,628.0	0.07458	2,500	2,525.3	0.25347	7,810
Firearms	2,202	2,371.3	12.08724	2,369	2,345.7	0.23144	2,400	2,254.0	9.45696	6,971
Poison Gases	1,213	1,226.0	0.15079	1,143	1,213.4	4.10192	1,250	1,166.0	6.05145	3,606
Other Poisons	1,422	1,432.8	0.08140	1,390	1,417.3	0.52585	1,400	1,361.9	1.06587	4,212
a_{+j}	80,111			79,245			76,150			235,506 = a_{++}
Subtotal			26,52314			34.81769			88.11713	

$\alpha = 0.010$. $\chi^2 = 149.45796$. $(\chi^2)_{0.99,14} = 29.14$. Reject H_0.

will have a distribution adequately approximated by the χ^2-distribution with one degree of freedom if the other requirements stated in connection with equation 16.8.3 still apply. By algebraic manipulation, equation 16.8.4 can be converted to

$$\chi^2 = \frac{(|a_{11}a_{22} - a_{12}a_{21}| - n/2)^2 n}{a_{1+}a_{2+}a_{+1}a_{+2}} \tag{16.8.5}$$

It might be interesting to use this idea in connection with the first 50 and second 50 of the first 100 tosses of our half dollar as recorded in Table 6-6 to test the hypothesis that the distribution of heads was the same. The results, using an alpha risk, $\alpha = 0.050$, are shown in Table 16-8, and give us no reason

Table 16-8 USE OF COIN-TOSSING DATA OF TABLE 6-6 TO TEST THE HYPOTHESIS THAT THE PROPORTION OF HEADS IN THE POPULATION SAMPLED BY THE FIRST 50 TOSSES AND BY THE SECOND 50 TOSSES IS THE SAME

	Result, i		
Trial, j	Heads, 1	Tails, 2	a_{+j}
1	29	21	50
2	24	26	50
a_{1+}	53	47	$100 = a_{++}$

$$\chi^2 = \frac{(|29 \times 26 - 24 \times 21| - 50)^2\,100}{53 \times 47 \times 50 \times 50}$$

$$= \frac{(|754 - 504| - 50)^2 100}{6{,}227{,}500}$$

$$= \frac{(250 - 50)^2\,100}{6{,}277{,}500} = \frac{200^2\,100}{6{,}277{,}500}$$

$$= 0.64119$$

$(\chi^2)_{0.950,1} = 3.84$. Accept H_0.

to reject the hypothesis that the coin and tossing procedure are consistent.

16.9 Some Comments on These Methods

In section 16.8 we discussed methods for testing that the distribution of individuals among stated categories in several populations is the same. Suppose that we had a group of individuals with two different characteristics. According to one characteristic they could be placed into one of k categories, and according to the other they could be placed into one of r other categories. If we let the subscript i denote the category of the first characteristic and the subscript j denote the category of the second characteristic, then we shall have actual frequencies, a_{ij}, just as we did in section 16.8. We could develop theoretical frequencies, t_{ij}, in the same way under the hypothesis that the category into which an individual falls with respect to one characteristic is quite independent of its category with respect to the other. Our computation procedures and test statistics would be as described there. Under such conditions the table of frequencies is often known as a *contingency table*, and the test of the hypothesis is known as a test of *independence*.

We would also recognize that, when we were dealing with two samples and two categories, we are, in effect, testing whether $P_1 = P_2$ for two binomial distributions. This would suggest that we might also use the χ^2-distribution idea to test the hypothesis that the value of P for a single population has some stated value, using section 16.7. Suppose we consider the problem of testing the hypothesis that our coin and tossing procedures did conform to the ideal, that is, that $P = 0.50$, and that we wished to test this hypothesis with $\alpha = 0.050$ and $n = 50$ as we did in section 16.5 in the first part of Table 16-3. There we found $x_{cr} = 18$ and 32. Suppose we had observed 18 heads as a_1. Then a_2 would be $50 - 18 = 32$. Our values of t_i would each be 25 and each $(a_i - t_i)^2/t_i$ would be $7^2/25 = 49/25 = 1.96$ and $\chi^2 = 3.92$. But $\chi_{cr}^2 = \chi_{0.95,1}^2 = 3.84$, which agrees within rounding error.

Of course, if P or n or both are small enough so that any of the resulting t_i are below five, then we cannot use our χ^2 procedure. Fortunately, under such circumstances, either our Poisson approximation or direct use of the binomial distribution are usually quite feasible.

16.10 Measurements vs. Counts

Under some circumstances, one may be able to test an hypothesis on the basis either of measurements or of frequency counts. Which method should he prefer? No open-and-shut answer can be given in advance. Generally, for a fixed level of discrimination, the sample size required will be smaller for measured than for counted data. This will be favorable to the use of measurements. But it often happens that the cost per measurement is so much greater than the cost per count that, on an economic basis, counts are preferred. Even here, a reversal of the usual relationship can occur, as in flash bulb testing. Here the cost for counting defective bulbs is high because the accompanying good bulbs are destroyed. A procedure is used in which a voltage below that which will fire the bulbs is applied and their resistance is measured. This does not damage the bulbs, and a high correlation has been established between these resistances and bulb performance. Although the time required per bulb tested is greater, the net economics favors this procedure.

General Study

1. In your areas of particular interest, list those fields in which quantitative studies use measurements, counts of classifications, and both. Are there instances in which the measurements are used chiefly as a basis of classification?

2. In reviewing the foregoing list, does it appear to you that there are cases in which it would be wise to replace the counts by measurements? To replace the measurements by counts? If so, state your proposal, giving reasons, to support it. Can you find out why this has not been done?

3. Examine current news sources for claims that the distribution of counts in some area of public concern has altered. Verify or refute one or more of these claims. Some subjects of possible interest: unemployment, crime, budget analyses, accidents, use of various forms of transportation.

Specific Problems

1–5. In the following problems, test the indicated hypotheses with the stated alpha risks on the basis of the given information. Use at least two procedures wherever possible. Compute $\Pi\%$ confidence limits for P, where $\Pi = 100(1 - \alpha)$.

Problem	H_0	α	x	n	N
1	$P = 0.50$	0.050	40	100	90
2	$P < 0.40$	0.010	30	60	98
3	$P = 0.02$	0.050	1	200	95
4	$P > 0.005$	0.010	0	1000	99
5	$P > 0.05$	0.010	2	50	95

6. General past experience has indicated that about 18% of the students registering for a certain course fail to achieve a passing grade. One semester, 80 students out of 250 registered failed. Test the appropriate hypothesis to determine whether this is a matter for serious concern.

7. In testing a new immunizing procedure, 250 people were given the treatment and 250 were given a placebo (a treatment outwardly resembling the one under study, but with no active ingredients). During the following year, five of the treated and 25 of the untreated people contracted the disease. Would you consider the treatment effective?

8. You wish to guarantee, with 99% certainty of being correct, that a brand of light bulbs will have a fraction not greater than 0.005 failing before 1000 hours. How many bulbs must you test if you allow no failures in your sample? One failure? Suppose you increase your guaranteed fraction to 0.010? Do you know how bulbs are actually tested for this characteristic? If not, find out and explain why the procedure is sound.

PART D

Time Series Analysis: Seasonal and Trend Components

17

The Basic Idea of a Time Series

17.1 A Transition in Thinking

Up to now we have been studying methods which have all followed a common pattern. We have been concerned with populations of varying measurements or counts. We have been able to make certain reasonable assumptions about these populations and the process by which we obtained samples from them. Mathematical developments have then made it possible for us to obtain sound estimates of the parameters of the populations and to test hypotheses concerning the true values. If our assumptions were valid, our procedures were rigorous. In some cases, the rigorous procedure was extremely cumbersome, and mathematicians have sought and found much more convenient adequate approximations.

In the area of time series, which we are about to enter, we are really dealing with an extremely complex regression analysis. The fact is, to be honest, that the model is so extremely complex that, in the case of almost all data, a rigorous analysis would be complicated and costly far beyond its worth. It is also true that data are rarely available to permit such a complete analysis when the series we are dealing with are concerned with business, economic, and sociological matters. Therefore, we must learn to modify our approach to the problem so that we may acquire the information we most urgently require by feasible methods. We shall introduce the ideas by a homely example.

While it is true that the methods have so far been used chiefly in economics and business administration and somewhat in sociology, it is our feeling that the ideas have utility in other areas, and that the way of thinking is well worth study. We hope that it will interest students from other disciplines, and that the study may lead them to constructive thinking in their fields.

17.2 A Familiar Time Series

Any of us who have spent vacations at the shore will recall the predictions of the times of high and low tides published daily in local papers, weekly in souvenir programs, or for the entire season in other forms of advertising. So far as we vacationers were concerned, these predictions were not vitally important, for they merely helped us to plan which hours we would spend at the beach, fishing, or in some other activity, and any errors involved would not have been serious. But these predictions were actually excerpts from much more extensive tables published annually by our government. From these tables we can reliably predict the depth of water at virtually any point along our coast at any instant during the year. If, instead of being idle vacationers, we were pilots of vessels carrying hundreds of passengers and hundreds of thousands of dollars worth of cargo, the reliability of these forecasts would be of very real concern to us. If we could surely predict a very adequate depth of water for our vessel, we could proceed with assurance and dispatch; with but little margin, we would proceed slowly and with great caution; while with inadequate depth, we must wait for the tide or take another route.

How can such predictions be made so that a pilot can thus govern his actions with justified confidence? Essentially, one must first observe the depth of water hour by hour at many locations over long periods of time. Such a series of observations of the changing values of some phenomenon at recorded times constitutes a *time series*. The series itself, however, would give us no help in predicting the future. In order to be able to forecast, we must study these past records and thus discover the underlying pattern of the variations. If such a pattern exists and we discover it, we can extend the pattern into the future as a basis for prediction. The more complete and accurate our recognition of the pattern and the fewer the irregularities of our observations, the more reliable will our predictions be.

In the case of tidal data, we would find that a graph of the depth plotted against time would have a wavelike form from one high tide to a low and back to the next high. But the depth is not the same at each high tide. If we made another plot of the depths of the water at successive high tides, we would find that another wavelike curve resulted, varying from an extreme depth slowly through lesser depths and back to an extreme again. A similar behavior would be shown also by the low-tide depths. If we studied the matter still more thoroughly, we would find that these extreme depths followed still another wavelike pattern, all of which might seem most confusing. But by observation, analysis, and relation to known astronomical data, it turns out that the tidal behavior can be represented, so far, by mathematical statements which are by no means impossible to use.

However, if we compared the depths computed from such formulas with the depths actually observed, we would observe discrepancies, some of them quite serious, and no wieldy formula would avoid this difficulty. But, if we had been wise enough to record other data as well, we might presently notice that, when the wind was from the southwest, the depth was greater than we predicted for a given locality by an amount related to the duration and severity of the blow. Similarly, a northeast wind would lower the depth. Smaller corrections might be made in the light of information related to rainfall in the drainage basins feeding certain rivers, and so on. In the end, we would decide to use the wieldy formula for our published tables, and include notes to guide the pilots in applying corrections based on readily observed local transient conditions.

17.3 Time Series Analysis and Forecasting

Such a study of past data in an effort to discover patterns of behavior is called *time series analysis.* The use of formulas so developed to make future predictions is called *forecasting.* Just as in the case of the Tide Tables, our forecasts, even with adjustments, will not be perfect: our objective will be to make them, like the tidal forecasts, *adequate for their purpose.* That this is true of the Tide Tables is evident from the fact that qualified pilots regularly bring their vessels into port with safety and dispatch, altering their courses and schedules on the basis of the tables.

In this text, we shall not be concerned with tidal data, of course. But many important measures of business behavior follow patterns nearly as discoverable as tidal depths. Some of these patterns are, qualitatively at least, recognizable and understandable with very little effort. Retail store managers, for instance, are well aware of changes in the nature and volume of their business related to the seasons of the year and to our Christmas customs. Bankers are familiar with the noon-hour and end-of-the-day rushes.

We can carry our analogy with tidal data a step further. In the case of the tides, the prudent skipper learns how they behave and how to plan his course accordingly. Having learned what he must do to live with the tides, he may find that in a certain channel the depth is frequently too little for safe navigation. If a sufficient number of his fellow skippers are faced with the same difficulty, they may decide to do something about it. Since they can't alter the level of the top of the water (!) they can only work on the bottom by dredging. Whether this will be expedient will depend on the cost of dredging, affected by the nature of the bottom and the amount of dredging required, compared with the cost of delays, predictable with the aid of Tide Tables. The decision, to be intelligent, must be based on sound knowledge of both costs.

17.4 Using the Results

A. *Retail Food Stores.* Think, for the moment, of the operator of a retail food store. He knows that he will have heavy volumes of sales on Fridays and Saturdays. Fortunately, this rush comes as the result of factors which also make high school students available for part-time help. How many will he need? Here, the *quantitative* aspects of his analysis guide him. But our storekeeper will also find that he requires a minimum staff to operate at all. At the low periods, this staff will not be busy serving customers directly, so he schedules their work to use such periods for inventory taking, reordering and receiving goods, changing displays, and other nonsales activities. Even then, the rush and slack periods are not completely eliminated, so he introduces sales during the slack periods in an effort to attract customers and to modify, partially, their habit of buying at the weekend.

B. *Other Examples.* Similarly, department store managers plan "white sales," fur sales, furniture sales and others in an effort to make their business volume more uniform and thereby to use their sales force more efficiently. Banks found their closing-time rushes were the result, in part, of efforts of their commercial customers to reduce the volume of cash on hand overnight: night depositories are now commonplace. The noontime rush resulted from customers making deposits and withdrawals during their lunch times: deposit-by-mail systems help reduce the rush and save the customer time and trouble as well. A terrific rush in billing departments normally resulted from the custom of mailing statements at the end of each month. What was sacred about that date? Nothing, really, so many business houses stagger such mailing all through the month and so keep a uniform work load. True, some resistance is met, but a suitable adjustment is usually readily made.

17.5 Scope of Our Study

Myriad examples could be offered showing the advantages of a sound knowledge of quantitative aspects of the probable future behavior of any business. Such knowledge comes only from the *analysis* of *appropriate time series* and the formulation of appropriate *forecasts* thereafter. The more complete the information in the series and the more thoughtful and careful the analysis, the more reliable will our forecast be. Our purpose in this course will be to learn how to make the simpler types of analysis, to recognize the extent to which they are complete, and to make and appraise the validity of forecasts based on the series. You will realize that an analysis can become exceedingly complex. We cannot hope, in this brief course, to go far into the complexities but, by understanding the underlying ideas, we can learn to recognize when series with which we may become concerned in our future experience justify such analyses. We can then enlist the services of a specialist in this work, and we shall be much more able to profit by his work because we shall understand the fundamental principles he uses. Our basic techniques will often prove quite adequate, and will point to the need, if one exists, of a more exacting analysis, while giving good temporary guidance pending the completion of the more elaborate study.

17.6 Our Plan of Study

In these notes, we are departing to some extent from the conventional methods of presenting the subject. Time series analysis is, by its very nature, mathematical. Unless one has been exposed to a fairly extensive mathematical training, it is not obvious that a given proposed procedure is necessary or sound in a stated situation, nor even that it really "works." Since most of our readers have not had such prior training, and since we certainly cannot undertake it here, we have adopted the idea of showing how a series would be produced if we knew the laws governing its formation. Then we turn around and show how the procedures work to take the series apart and return the underlying laws to us. Such a process in no sense constitutes a proof of the validity of the methods we are learning, but it will help increase our confidence in the mathematicians who developed the procedures, and it will certainly (past experience has shown) justifiably increase the assurance with which we select and apply appropriate analyses.

The formulas you will use will be quite simple, but the necessary computations, though they are simple, must by the very nature of the subject be extensive if you are to gain any real grasp of the meaning of the subject. The understanding of the meaning of formulas and the facility you should have acquired with computing tools during your study of the previous material will stand you in good stead here. You will find that an orderly plan of your work sheets will be well rewarded in facilitating your work and reducing the chances of mistakes. We hope you will discover, as we did, a certain pleasure in being able to tackle a maze of confusing data and in developing some useful meaning from them.

General Study

1. List some forecasts which have been of interest to you, either in connection with your field of study, matters affecting your school, or public affairs. Indicate which forecasts were probably based on study of a time series. If possible, indicate the series you think was used.

2. List as many instances as you can in which study of past series has led to a modification of the plans of some business or other organization with beneficial results. Consider the cases in enough detail to appreciate the thinking involved.

3. List as many instances as you can in which similar study of past series has led to modification of some community customs with benefit to the community and to the organization involved. What were the benefits? How were the changes effected?

Specific Problems

1. For some subject in which you are personally interested, select a time series whose analysis you would expect to yield valuable information. Transcribe at least quarterly information concerning it over a period of at least 10 years and annual information over at least another 10 years. Be sure to record adequate auxiliary information, including units, source of data, and any notes that may have been included with the source.

2. List the title, call number, and shelf location in your library of time series which may be important in connection with your major field of study.

18

Components of Time Series

18.1 The Basic Statistical Pattern

In our previous study of statistical analysis, we learned that the human mind is unable to cope meaningfully with large masses of figures. One of the important functions of statistical analysis turns out to be the substitution for a maze of data of a few figures which display a recognizable and meaningful portion of the information contained in the data. At the price of a sacrifice of part of the information, we secure a real grasp of the vital parts. Actually, the sacrifice is hardly one of *real* information, because the information lost was not in *usable* form. For instance, suppose we had a complete record of the actual individual expenditures by the students in a specific group, numbering about 2000, during the academic year just passed. We would have all the information concerning the expenditures of these students in that year, but of what use is it in that form? We could answer none but trivial questions concerning student expenditures on the basis of such a hodgepodge.

But suppose we calculate the mean expenditure. Immediately we have a sense of the "target" value. In fact, we know further that the sum of the differences between the mean and all larger individual expenditures is numerically equal to the sum of similar discrepancies in the opposite direction. We could not sense these ideas from the raw data. If we also calculate the variance or standard deviation, we have a grasp of the magnitude of variations from the mean. If we add a statement as to the approximate form of the distribution, we know a great deal about student expenditures, indeed.

If we also had data on the incomes of the families from which the students came, and developed information about the relation between income and expenditures, we could soundly advise the parents of prospective students as to the amounts they should be prepared to make available for their students' expenditures. In accomplishing this result, we have made use of a few statistics and the principles guiding their interpretation. *We have made sense out of figures.*

18.2 Modifications for Time Series

In a similar way, procedures have been developed to aid us in attacking the confusing variations in an extensive time series so that we can see through these variations to the relatively simple rules governing them. We shall find that these rules will often enable us to describe most of the variations observed in the past, leaving only a small part "unexplained." If these rules are consistent with a reasonable explanation of the facts, we can then with confidence extend them into the future, so as to make forecasts in which we can properly place a considerable degree of confidence. If we are not successful in our effort to reduce the unexplained portion of our variation, this fact itself will rightly warn us as to the unreliability of our forecast.

It is convenient to recognize four basic types of rules or laws governing the changing values observed in any time series. These variations have been given the names *secular trend*, *seasonal variation*, *cyclical variation*, and *irregular variation*. The recognition and quantitative estimation of these four types of variation is the problem of time series analysis.

18.3 The Secular Trend

First, consider *secular trend* (or, more simply and commonly, *trend*). It has been observed in most industries which have gone through their complete existence that they show an initial period of slow increase in volume. This is followed by a period of increasingly rapid rise, then by a period of slower rise to a peak or maximum volume. Then follows the decline, slow at first, then more rapid, and finally more slowly again until the industry vanishes from the scene. In the lifetime of our parents, or anyway of our grandparents, the world saw just such a story concerning the electric streetcar. Starting as a new invention, this means of transportation developed slowly at first, then meteorically until its development again slowed as the peak was reached. With the development of the automobile, the expansion of the trolley ceased, then a decline set in until today, when the streetcar exists in but a few cities in this country. A graph of this story is shown in Fig. 18-1. Other industries which have shown a similar history include whale fisheries (although it should be remarked that the use of whale oil in margarine has somewhat revived the industry, see Fig. 18-2), transportation by small inland canals, and the manufacture of gas lighting fixtures.

Other types of industries and many economic variables, as for example the total production of textile fibers, wholesale prices of farm products, or the amount of money in circulation, have a different underlying pattern of behavior, in that the maximum and subsequent decline are not to be expected. But whatever the form of this underlying pattern, it constitutes the secular trend. We shall find that it can be represented by a mathematical equation. In the case of the streetcar industry, the equation is not simple, but fortunately

Fig. 18-1. Total miles of electric railway track operated in the United States. Source: Statistical Abstract of the United States (1947), Tables 583 and 584. It is interesting to notice that recent issues of the abstract no longer tabulate the statistics for the years prior to 1940.

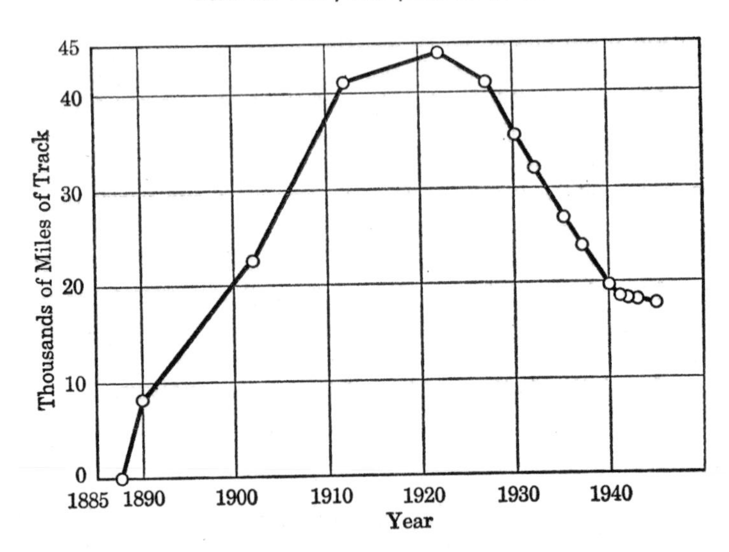

Fig. 18-2. Tonnage of U.S. vessels employed in whale fisheries. Source: Statistical Abstract of the United States (1947), Table 603. Note: 1 gross ton = 100 cubic feet of enclosed space in the hull and superstructure.

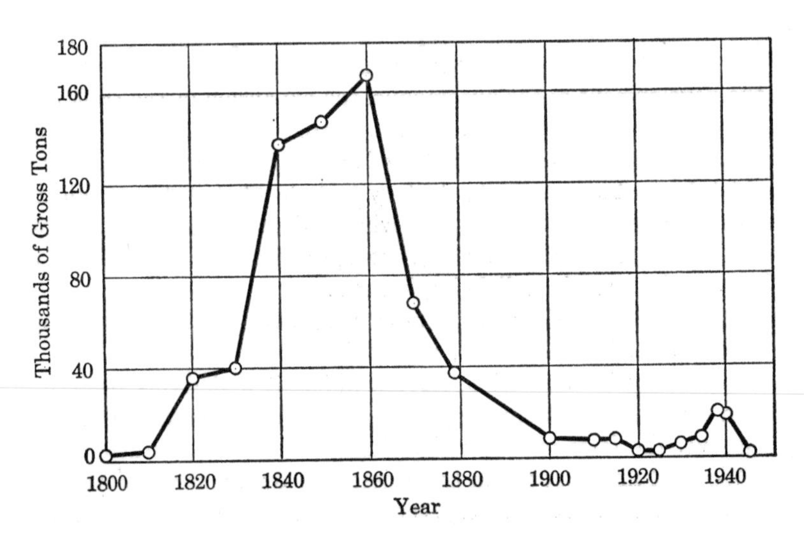

many of our problems deal with industries with such long life that we can treat the period in which we are involved by a much simpler equation that is adequate for our purposes of reasonable prediction. Those industries and economic measures in which a trend peak is not credible turn out often to be representable by equally simple equations. Whatever its form, the trend may be thought of as the core of the behavior of our time series.

18.4 Seasonal Variation

Seasonal variation is the term applied to certain of the up-and-down variations about the smooth core of the trend. Such an oscillatory behavior is describable mathematically in terms of two properties: period and amplitude. The *period* is the *time required to go* from a given value *through a complete set of values* to the original value. The time between two peaks, or two hollows, or two middle values (*provided* the changes are in the same direction) is the period. *Amplitude* is an unfortunately tricky term, for it is one common to many fields. Sometimes it refers to the amount by which the variation, at either extreme, departs from the central value. This is quite convenient in describing simple patterns, like the swing of a pendulum or the changing voltage in the circuit supplying typical power lines. But in other cases it is more convenient to think of it as the *total difference between the maximum and minimum* values in a cycle, and that definition will be more desirable in time series analysis. Oscillatory variations having a period not greater than one year we shall call seasonal variations.

18.5 Measuring Seasonal Variations: Seasonal Indexes

The mathematician can describe seasonal variations in terms of formulas, but these formulas tend to become rather complicated, and we shall find a more convenient way. It has been found that, as a business or economic factor subject to seasonal variation grows, the effect of the variation is a constant proportion of the trend: the greater the level, the greater the variation imposed by seasonal variation. The amount by which the level represented by the trend would need to be multiplied to produce the actual observed value, if only trend and seasonal variation were operating, we call the *seasonal index*. We shall find it most convenient to describe seasonal variation simply by listing the seasonal indices for convenient times during the period. The hour-by-hour variation in the number of customers in a bank is a seasonal variation with a period of one day. The variations in volume of business in a retail food store show a pronounced period of one week, whereas the volume of business in department stores has a clearly defined period of one year. Often a given series will have two or more seasonal variations superimposed. For instance, in addition to the variation with a one-year period, department store sales have another seasonal variation with a period of one week and a third with a period of one month. We shall see presently how to cope with such problems.

18.6 Cyclical Variations

Another type of up-and-down variation about the trend line has been called the *cyclical variation.* Its distinguishing characteristic is that its period is longer than one year. This, in itself, would be a highly arbitrary reason for the distinction, and would hardly justify its being made. There are, however, three reasonable justifications for the distinction. First, the periods are usually by no means uniform from one cycle to another. Second, we rarely have sufficiently extensive data to apply effectively the methods we use for characterizing the seasonal variation. Third, to the extent that they are understood, the causes for cyclical variations are quite different from those for seasonal variation.

It is perhaps fair to state that to a mathematician the two kinds of variation have much in common, and that with more extensive data than are generally available well-understood mathematical methods might develop information not brought out by the procedures we shall study here. It is even possible that the custom of considering cyclical variation as distinguishable from seasonal variation may actually be a barrier to ultimate progress of knowledge. Be that as it may, one who is just learning about time series must become acquainted with the methods now in use.

18.7 Irregular Variations

The fourth type of variation, *irregular*, is really a catch-all for those variations which we cannot (or did not) identify under the other three categories. Actually, these irregular variations can be subdivided into two categories. The first kind manifests itself as a large departure from expected values for reasons which were identifiable after the fact but whose future recurrence is not predictable. Such variations are termed *episodic* and may be caused by fires, floods, explosions, epidemics and other severe but unusual causes. The second kind, the *random* variations, usually relatively small, result from the operation of a host of minor causes that often defy individual identification, and to them we shall apply the methods of elementary statistics.

18.8 Our Time Series Model

Now we can conveniently introduce a few symbols so as to be able to express our ideas more compactly. For any time, t, let

T = the value computed from our trend equation,

S = the factor expressing the effect of seasonal variation,

C = the factor expressing the effect of cyclical variation,

I = the factor expressing the effect of irregular variation, and

Y = the observed level of the quantity of interest to us.

Then, very simply, $Y = TSCI$. If there are several different periodic variations, we write

$$Y = T(S_1S_2S_3\ldots)(C_1C_2C_3\ldots)I$$

The laws of algebra tell us that we may multiply these factors in any order that we wish, and that we may divide Y by any one or more of the factors to produce a new series from which the effect of that factor is removed. We shall use these ideas in our efforts to analyze series.

18.9 Synthesis of Artificial Series

Before we proceed to learn how to analyze a series, however, it will be helpful to see how a series would be built up, or *synthesized*. This will be desirable for two reasons. In the first place, by trying our analyses on a series which we have synthesized, we shall see that our analytic procedures do work quite effectively, but that they have real limitations against which we must protect ourselves. Second, we shall gain an increased understanding of the meaning and consequences of the types of variation we have just defined.

Let us then pretend that we are a sort of superman, and that we have decided to take control of the affairs of the *QRS* Corporation in January 1955, but to conceal our control from the mere mortals who operate the business. We permit the volume to increase at the rate of \$100 per month from the \$5000 per month level at which it was operating when we took over. Thus we establish a trend law which can be expressed by the very simple equation:

$$T = 5000 + 100\,t \tag{18.7.1}$$

where t is the number of months after January 1955. Next we shall decree a seasonal variation with the following indices for the 12 months of its one-year period:

January	1.20	May	1.10	September	1.30
February	0.90	June	1.00	October	1.00
March	0.70	July	0.70	November	1.20
April	0.80	August	1.30	December	1.30

We shall not trouble the firm with any cyclical variation at present, but we shall confuse the picture by decreeing a major equipment breakdown for June and July of 1956, forcing the company to operate at 20% of its proper level, while in March and April of 1958 we introduce another episodic variation in the form of a disaster for another firm which causes it to place orders with QRS leading to overtime work and a sales volume 150% of normal. During the rest of the time we introduce random variations by factors read from a table of random normal numbers with mean 1.00 and variance 0.05. In Table 18-1 and Fig. 18-3 we show the components of this series month by month and how these components build the actual volume which our mortals would observe.

Table 18-1 SYNTHESIS OF A TIME SERIES. TREND EQUATION: $T = 5{,}000 + 100\,t$. OTHER INDICES AS SHOWN. ALL VALUES IN DOLLARS.

Year	*Mo.*	*t*	*T*	*S*	*TS*	*I*	*TSI = Y*
1955	J	0	5,000	1.2	6,000	1.04	6.240
	F	1	5,100	0.9	4,590	1.00	4,590
	M	2	5,200	0.7	3,640	1.14	4,150
	A	3	5,300	0.8	4,240	1.09	4,622
	M	4	5,400	1.1	5,940	1.13	6,712
	J	5	5,500	1.0	5,500	1.08	5,940
	J	6	5,600	0.8	4,480	1.11	5,372
	A	7	5,700	0.7	3,990	0.84	3,352
	S	8	5,800	1.3	7,540	0.92	6,937
	O	9	5,900	1.0	5,900	1.13	6,667
	N	10	6,000	1.2	7,200	0.89	6,408
	D	11	6,100	1.3	7,930	0.80	6,344
1956	J	12	6,200	1.2	7,440	0.99	7,366
	F	13	6,300	0.9	5,670	1.13	6,407
	M	14	6,400	0.7	4,480	0.81	3,629
	A	15	6,500	0.8	5,200	0.98	5,096
	M	16	6,600	1.1	7,260	0.86	6,244
	J	17	6,700	1.0	6,700	0.20	1,340
	J	18	6,800	0.8	5,440	0.20	1,088
	A	19	6,900	0.7	4,830	1.09	5,265
	S	20	7,000	1.3	9,100	1.02	9,282
	O	21	7,100	1.0	7,100	0.81	5,751
	N	22	7,200	1.2	8,640	0.87	7,517
	D	23	7,300	1.3	9,490	1.06	10,059
1957	J	24	7,400	1.2	8,880	0.95	8,436
	F	25	7,500	0.9	6,750	0.85	5,738
	M	26	7,600	0.7	5,320	1.01	5,373
	A	27	7,700	0.8	6,160	1.05	6,468
	M	28	7,800	1.1	8,580	1.22	10,468
	J	29	7,900	1.0	7,900	0.99	7,821
	J	30	8,000	0.8	6,400	0.88	5,632
	A	31	8,100	0.7	5,670	1.17	6,633
	S	32	8,200	1.3	10,660	1.03	10,980
	O	33	8,300	1.0	8,300	0.94	7,802
	N	34	8,400	1.2	10,080	1.02	10,282
	D	35	8,500	1.3	11,050	1.09	12,045

Table 18-1 (*Continued*)

Year	*Mo.*	*t*	*T*	*S*	*TS*	*I*	*TSI* = *Y*
1958	J	36	8,600	1.2	10,320	0.86	8,875
	F	37	8,700	0.9	7,830	0.96	7,517
	M	38	8,800	0.7	6,160	1.50	9,240
	A	39	8,900	0.8	7,120	1.50	10,680
	M	40	9,000	1.1	9,900	1.01	9,999
	J	41	9,100	1.0	9,100	0.86	7,826
	J	42	9,200	0.8	7,360	1.05	7,728
	A	43	9,300	0.7	6,510	1.03	6,705
	S	44	9,400	1.3	12,200	0.85	10,387
	O	45	9,500	1.0	9,500	0.97	9,215
	N	46	9,600	1.2	11,520	0.96	11,059
	D	47	9,700	1.3	12,610	1.03	12,988
1959	J	48	9,800	1.2	11,760	1.05	12,348
	F	49	9,900	0.9	8,910	1.08	9,623
	M	50	10,000	0.7	7,000	1.01	7,070
	A	51	10,100	0.8	8,080	0.90	7,272
	M	52	10,200	1.1	11,220	1.00	11,220
	J	53	10,300	1.0	10,300	0.74	7,622
	J	54	10,400	0.8	8,320	0.95	7,904
	A	55	10,500	0.7	7,350	0.93	6,836
	S	56	10,600	1.3	13,780	0.94	12,953
	O	57	10,700	1.0	10,700	0.88	9,416
	N	58	10,800	1.2	12,960	0.94	12,182
	D	59	10,900	1.3	14,170	1.07	15,162
1960	J	60	11,000	1.2	13,200	1.01	13,332
	F	61	11,100	0.9	9,990	1.16	11,588
	M	62	11,200	0.7	7,840	0.98	7,683
	A	63	11,300	0.8	9,040	1.05	9,492
	M	64	11,400	1.1	12,540	0.90	11,286
	J	65	11,500	1.0	11,500	0.87	10,005
	J	66	11,600	0.8	9,280	0.96	8,909
	A	67	11,700	0.7	8,190	0.95	7,780
	S	68	11,800	1.3	15,340	1.17	17,948
	O	69	11,900	1.0	11,900	1.04	12,376
	N	70	12,000	1.2	14,400	0.78	11,232
	D	71	12,100	1.3	15,730	0.79	12,427
1961	J	72	12,200	1.2	14,640	1.11	16,250
	F	73	12,300	0.9	11,070	0.88	9,742
	M	74	12,400	0.7	8,680	1.03	8,940
	A	75	12,500	0.8	10,000	0.97	9,700
	M	76	12,600	1.1	13,860	1.01	13,999
	J	77	12,700	1.0	12,700	1.05	13,335

Table 18-1 (*Continued*)

Year	*Mo.*	*t*	*T*	*S*	*TS*	*I*	*TSI* = *Y*
1961	J	78	12,800	0.8	10,240	0.96	9,830
(*Cont.*)	A	79	12,900	0.7	9,030	0.78	7,043
	S	80	13,000	1.3	16,900	1.00	16,900
	O	81	13,100	1.0	13,100	0.82	10,742
	N	82	13,200	1.2	15,840	0.96	15,206
	D	83	13,300	1.3	17,290	0.94	16,253
1962	J	84	13,400	1.2	16,080	1.29	20,743
	F	85	13,500	0.9	12,150	1.12	13,680
	M	86	13,600	0.7	9,520	0.98	9,330
	A	87	13,700	0.8	10,960	0.90	9,864
	M	88	13,800	1.1	15,180	1.01	15,332
	J	89	13,900	1.0	13,900	0.97	13,483
	J	90	14,000	0.8	11,200	0.94	10,528
	A	91	14,100	0.7	9,870	0.80	7,896
	S	92	14,200	1.3	18,460	1.04	19,198
	O	93	14,300	1.0	14,300	0.97	13,871
	N	94	14,400	1.2	17,280	1.04	17,971
	D	95	14,500	1.3	18,850	0.95	17,908

Fig. 18-3a. Plot of the trend, *T*, vs. time, *t*, for the data of Table 18-1. Insert shows plot of the seasonal index, *S*, for the months of one year.

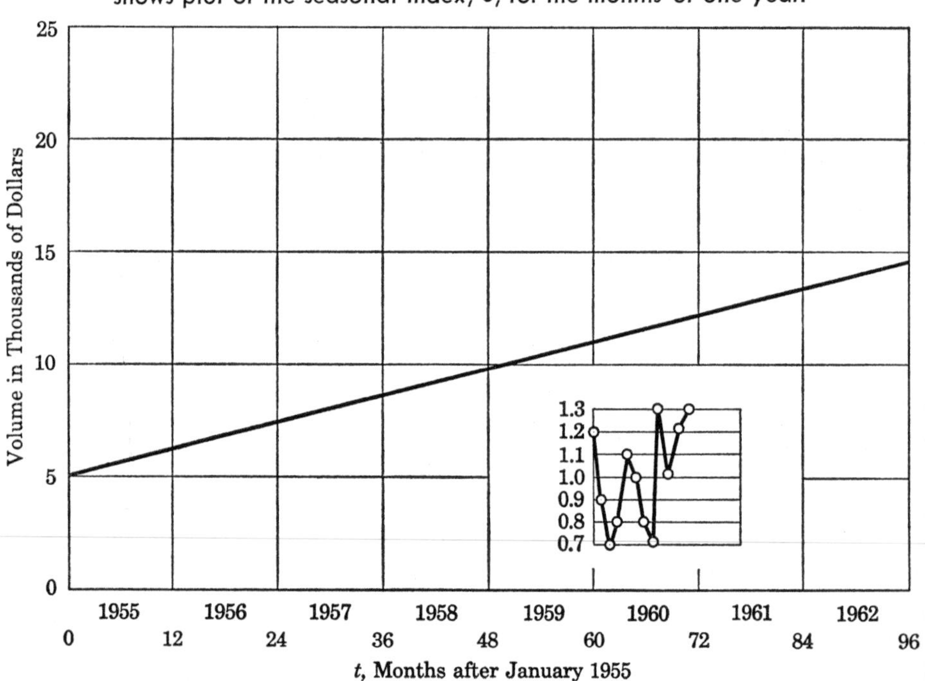

Fig. 18-3b. Plot of TS vs. t for the data of Table 18-1.

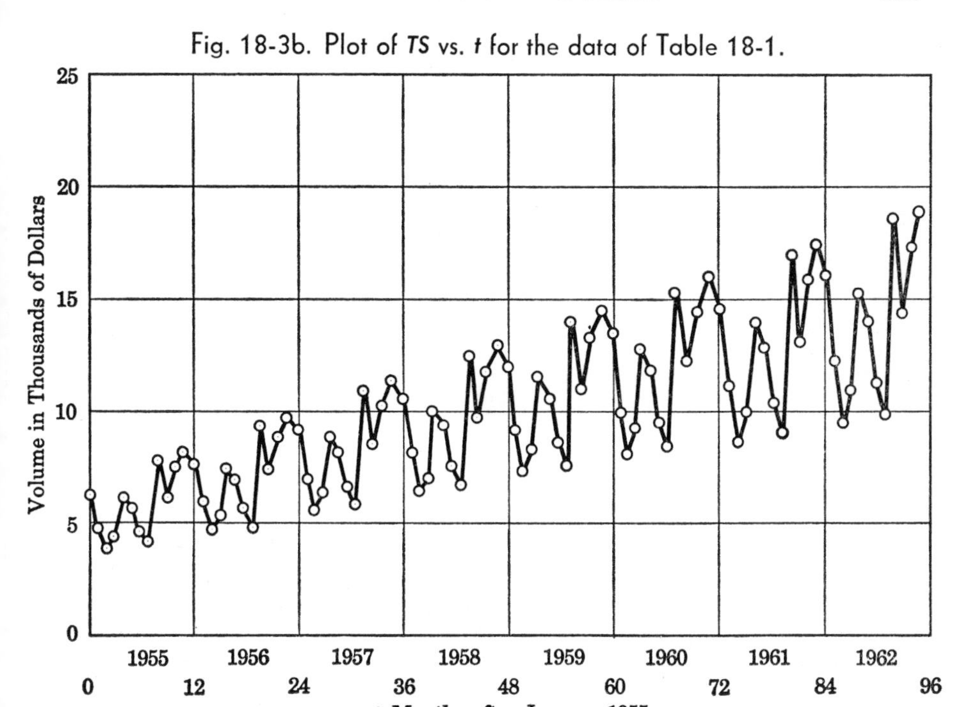

Fig. 18-3c. Plot of final series, $Y = TSI$, vs. t for data from Table 18-1.

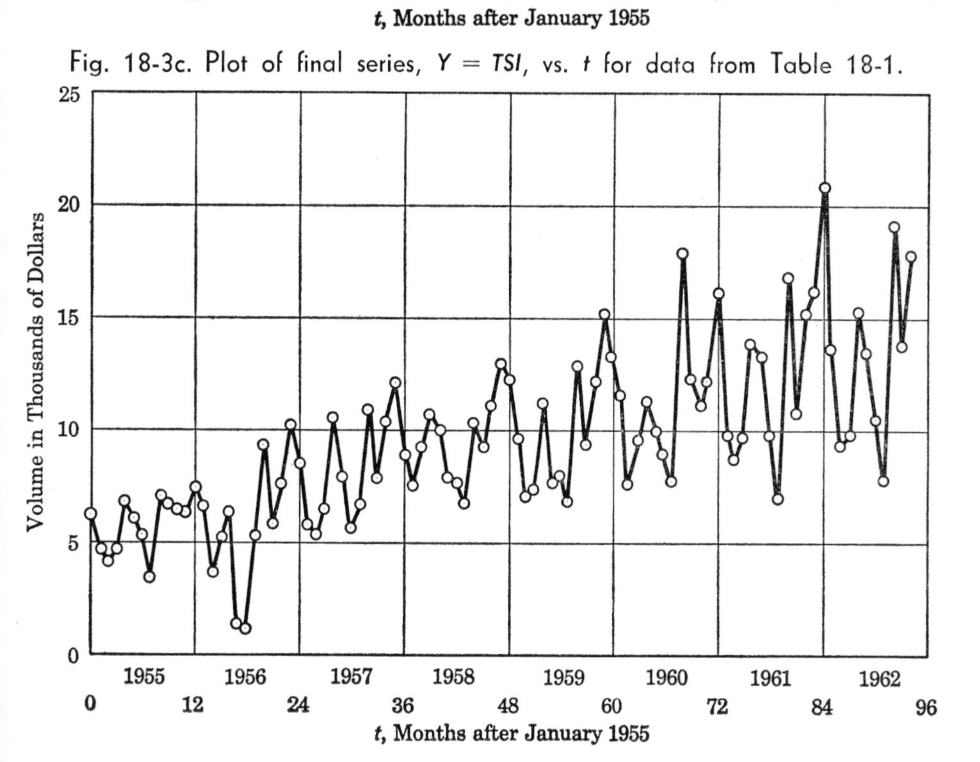

Of course, you must realize that, as mortals, all we ever observe in real series is the equivalent of the dates and the values in the last column of such a table. When we analyze such a series, we seek to infer what the other columns were. To the extent that our inferences are true, and that we understand the causes of the components we have recognized, we are in an effective position to use the information gained to our advantage.

General Study

1. A linear trend has the form $T = A + Bt$. Using values of the parameters of your own choice, compute the monthly values for such a trend for each month of five years. Choose seasonal indexes to produce a seasonal component with a period of one year, and apply them to the trend values. Then choose another set of seasonal indexes with a period of three months and apply them to the previous TS values. Plot the three resulting series on one graph, using suitable line or color codes.

2. A quadratic trend has the equation $T = A + Bt + Ct^2$. Treat such a trend as the linear trend was treated in Problem 1.

3. An exponential trend has the equation $T = AR^t$ where R is positive. Treat such a trend as the linear trend was treated in Problem 1.

19

Analysis of Seasonal Variation

19.1 Our New Approach

We are about to experience a rude shock!

That sentence deserves a paragraph all to itself because, in this chapter, many of us are about to find that we cannot do all the things with numbers that we might like to. If we compromise by arranging to do the most important things, we shall find that our methods will unavoidably lead us to make inferences which are not strictly true! Certainly this will shake our faith in the solidity of mathematics, but that shaking is a necessary accompaniment to a growth in maturity of understanding which we shall be making, and we shall come out both wiser and more competent. Let's see what this is all about.

Recall that, in the last chapter, we pointed out that the values in a time series were the result of the operation of four types of components of variation and that, if one of each type was operating, the values would be given by the formula $Y = TSCI$. We mentioned briefly that if we knew the values of S we could divide the observed values, Y, by the appropriate values of S and form a new series, say $Y' = TCI$, having no seasonal variation. Such a series is said to be derived from the observed series by *deseasonalizing* it. Now go back and notice that we chose our values of S for the series we synthesized so that, over a complete period, they had a mean value exactly unity (1.000). We always require that seasonal indices have this property. Why? Suppose that the only variation operating on some series was seasonal. Then the trend would be represented by a fixed value, say A, and C and I would be 1.00. Now unless the values of S did, indeed, average unity, the deseasonalized values would not average A, as they should. This is certainly reasonable and sensible. But presently we shall see that it does get us into some trouble.

Now let us think about analyzing a series such as the one we synthesized in the last chapter. We ought to be able to undertake to determine any one of the components first, remove its effect, then determine any second component, and so on. However, if a series is known or suspected to have one or more seasonal components, it will prove to be wise to determine them first. Obviously, if we could divide our Y's by the product TCI, we should have our required S's, but since we don't know T, C, and I, that is no help. In this dilemma, we have two ways out.

19.2 Moving Averages

The first of these methods allows us to make a useful approximation to the product of TCI (without knowing any of the individual factors) by what is known as the method of *moving averages*. What we shall do is to average the successive Y values over a time equal to the period of the seasonal variation. We shall place this value at the middle of the range of time covered. Then we shall form a new average by starting and ending one Y-value later and enter its result at the middle of its time range, which will be one unit beyond the previous average, and thus we continue, *moving* along the series with averages each based on one complete cycle.

Before we tackle a series such as the one we synthesized in the preceding chapter, let's see how the idea would work on some simpler series. For the purpose, let's make a series in which only seasonal variation operates, producing fluctuations about a value 2.00 as a result of successive index values 1.00, 1.20, 1.00, 0.90 and 0.90 for a cycle with a period of five time units. The first three columns of Table 19-1 show the construction of this series. Now let's apply our idea and start to analyze this series as though column 2 were not known to us.

Simple inspection of the figures in column 3 shows that they repeat in sets of five, which makes it clear that the period is five time units. So we take the average of the Y-values for times 0, 1, 2, 3, and 4, namely, 2.00, and write it beside the middle time, $t = 2$. Then we take the average for times 1, 2, 3, 4, and 5 and write it opposite $t = 3$, and so on. Notice several things about this procedure. First, we have no moving average to place beside the first two and last two times. This is unavoidable by the very nature of the averaging process, but it does hamper us in using the method on relatively short series. Second, in this case, our moving average was exactly the constant value to which our seasonal indices were applied when we synthesized the series. In other words, we have, in fact, "averaged out" the effects of seasonal variation. If we divide each Y by its related moving average, we shall exactly recover the values of S from column 2.

19.3 Establishing the Period of Seasonal Variations

Suppose that the variation had not been so clearly defined and we had failed to recognize the true period. What would have happened? For con-

Table 19-1 SYNTHESIS AND ANALYSIS OF A TIME SERIES CONTAINING ONLY A SEASONAL VARIATION: $Y = 2.00S$, WHERE S TAKES THE SUCCESSIVE VALUES 1.00, 1.20, 1.00, 0.90, AND 0.90

(1) t	(2) S	(3) Y	(4) $\bar{Y}_5$	(5) $\bar{Y}_3$	(6) $\bar{Y}_7$
0	1.00	2.00	—	—	—
1	1.20	2.40	—	2.13	—
2	1.00	2.00	2.00	2.07	—
3	0.90	1.80	2.00	1.87	2.06
4	0.90	1.80	2.00	1.87	2.06
5	1.00	2.00	2.00	2.07	1.97
6	1.20	2.40	2.00	2.13	1.94
7	1.00	2.00	2.00	2.07	1.97
8	0.90	1.80	2.00	1.87	2.06
9	0.90	1.80	2.00	1.87	2.06
10	1.00	2.00	2.00	2.07	1.97
11	1.20	2.40	2.00	2.13	1.94
12	1.00	2.00	2.00	2.07	1.97
13	0.90	1.80	2.00	1.87	2.06
14	0.90	1.80	2.00	1.87	2.06
15	1.00	2.00	2.00	2.07	—
16	1.20	2.40	—	2.13	—
17	1.00	2.00	—	—	—

Fig. 19-1. Plot of data from Table 19-1.

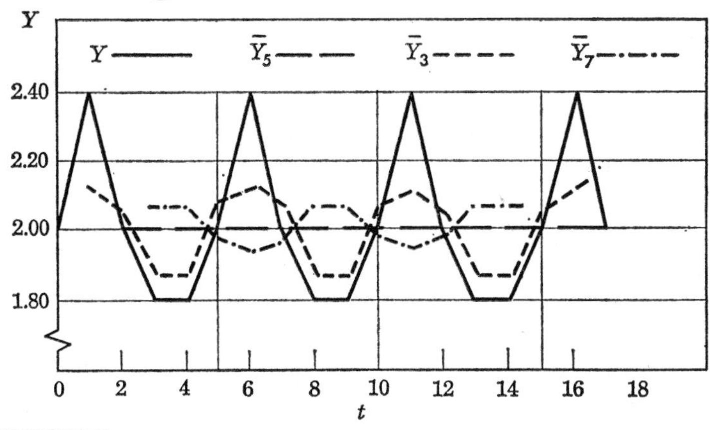

venience, suppose we place a subscript on $\bar{Y}$ to indicate the period covered. The averages we have just considered we shall denote as $\bar{Y}_5$. The remaining columns of our table show the values of $\bar{Y}_3$ and of $\bar{Y}_7$. In Fig. 19-1 the data and the three moving averages are plotted on the same chart. Notice that the average covering the correct period neatly obliterates all effects of seasonal variation. Those with incorrect periods reduce, but do not completely remove, the effects of this variation. Furthermore, the averages with too *short* a period have their peaks and hollows on the *same* side of the central line as the data; those with too *long* a period have them *reversed.* This is fundamental, and the fact can be used to help uncover the true period length when we are uncertain.

19.4 An Imperfection in the Method

So far, the moving average idea looks good, but suppose we push it a bit farther and see how it holds up. In Table 19-2 we have constructed a series with a trend represented by the formula $T = 2.00 + 0.1t$ and with the same seasonal indices we used in Table 19-1. The synthesis is shown in the first four columns and the moving average in column 5. The original Y's, the trend line, and the moving averages are plotted in Fig. 19-2. The results are distressing, are they not? Our moving average is 0.01 unit above the trend line at $t = 5$ and every five units thereafter. Similarly, it is 0.01 unit above at $t = 4$ and every five units later. It is 0.02 unit below the trend at $t = 2$ and at $t = 3$ and every five units after each of those values, and is correct only at $t = 6$ and subsequent five-unit intervals. This raises two rather vital questions: why did it happen and what can we do about it?

To see why it happened, examine the seasonal indices from which the series was constructed. Notice that two values were 1.00, the average value. One was 1.20, or 0.20 unit above the average, and it was balanced by two values of 0.90, each 0.10 unit below the average. In other words, our indices are not symmetrically placed about their mean. If you examine carefully how the $\overline{Y}_5$ values are obtained, you will see just how the observed discrepancies developed and you will realize that the difficulty is unavoidable.

19.5 Coping with the Flaw

Since we can't prevent it, can we offset its effects? Notice that in column 6 we have shown the ratio of $Y/\overline{Y}_5$ that we wish was S but, because we know it isn't, we have designated it S', to indicate that it is our first approximation to S. In Table 19-2B, we have retabulated these S' values, placing in one column values for the same part, or phase, of the cycle on the successive cycles. It is convenient to designate the different cycles by successive values of n. Thus the values for $t = 0$, 5, 10, etc. can be described by saying that $t = 0 + 5n$, while $t = 6$, 11, etc., are simply described as $t = 1 + 5n$, and so on.

In any given column, notice that our values are approaching closer and closer to what we know are the true values. If you are somewhat acquainted with mathematical ideas, you might very properly suggest that we could plot these values and find whether they are approaching the true value as a limit. Then with real data having unknown true values, we could just find the limit and consider it the true value. Your thinking would be sound as far as it goes, but the task of establishing the limit, particularly when we have real data with other components of variation, is a long one and, in some cases, most unsatisfactory. Fortunately, there is another device we can use.

Return again to the consideration of any one column. The items constitute a set of scattering values attempting to portray the true value of S. Suppose we think about elementary statistics and find a central value. Actually, we have our choice of two sensible ones, the median and the mean. Since we have only a few values here, it would be quite proper to use the median, which we have shown for each column. If we take the mean of these five medians, we shall find that it is not 1.00 exactly in this case, so we multiply each median by 1 divided by the actual mean, i.e., by 1.00000/1.00009, obtaining values which we designate as S'', our second and final approximation to the true values for the several S's. Comparison shows that we have closely recovered our original indices, with discrepancies beginning at the third decimal place. In view of the irregularities present in most real series, we shall find this is quite adequate.

Suppose we had had more periods in our data, so that the median would have been more difficult to locate in addition to the fact that it would then be a quite inefficient statistic. In that case we would use the mean instead of the median for each column and carry out our adjustment to obtain S'' just as we did here. These computations are also shown in Table 19-2, Part C, and you will see that the discrepancies between the two sets of values are slight indeed. It might be taken as a rule of thumb to use the mean whenever data include 10 or more cycles of variation, but to use the median when fewer cycles are available, although different firms establish their own rules.

19.6 The Method in More Complicated Series

Perhaps now we don't feel quite so badly treated by mathematics, but our troubles are not yet over. Let's complicate things by putting in a trend line which curves. Such a line would be given, for example, by the equation $T = 2.00 + 0.10t^2$. We use this trend and the same set of seasonal indices as before to form the series in Table 19-3 and proceed to analyze it by the method we have just applied. We might not notice it unless we were close observers, but if we look at Fig. 19-3, we shall find that 16 of the moving averages lie above the trend values, while only five lie below it. We certainly have a bias in our results! To show you what is going on, in Table 19-4 we treat a series with no components except the trend curve we have just employed. Notice here that *every* moving average lies above the trend line. But again, if we continue with our analysis as we planned, we find in both cases that the final result is comfortably close to the truth. What we are doing is making a sensible compromise between complete accuracy and the

Table 19-2 SYNTHESIS AND ANALYSIS FOR SEASONAL VARIATION OF A TIME SERIES $Y = TS$, WHERE $T = 2.00 + 0.10t$ AND S TAKES THE SUCCESSIVE VALUES 1.00, 1.20, 100, 0.90, AND 0.90

Part A. Synthesis and First Phase of Analysis

(1) t	(2) T	(3) S	(4) Y	(5) $\bar{Y}_5$	(6) S'
0	2.00	1.00	2.00	—	—
1	2.10	1.20	2.52	—	—
2	2.20	1.00	2.20	2.19	1.00456
3	2.30	0.90	2.07	2.29	0.90393
4	2.40	0.90	2.16	2.41	0.89626
5	2.50	1.00	2.50	2.51	0.99601
6	2.60	1.20	3.12	2.60	1.20000
7	2.70	1.00	2.70	2.69	1.00371
8	2.80	0.90	2.52	2.79	0.90322
9	2.90	0.90	2.61	2.91	0.89690
10	3.00	1.00	3.00	3.01	0.99667
11	3.10	1.20	3.72	3.10	1.20000
12	3.20	1.00	3.20	3.19	1.00313
13	3.30	0.90	2.97	3.29	0.90273
14	3.40	0.90	3.06	3.41	0.89736
15	3.50	1.00	3.50	3.51	0.99715
16	3.60	1.20	4.32	3.60	1.20000
17	3.70	1.00	3.70	3.69	1.00271
18	3.80	0.90	3.42	3.79	0.90237
19	3.90	0.90	3.51	3.91	0.89769
20	4.00	1.00	4.00	4.01	0.99750
21	4.10	1.20	4.92	4.10	1.20000
22	4.20	1.00	4.20	4.19	1.00238
23	4.30	0.90	3.87	4.29	0.90209
24	4.40	0.90	3.86	—	—
25	4.50	1.00	4.50	—	—

Part B. Retabulation of S' and Computation of S'' Using Median as Central Value

t / n	$0 + 5n$	$1 + 5n$	$2 + 5n$	$3 + 5n$	$4 + 5n$
0	—	—	1.00456	0.90393	0.89626
1	0.99601	1.20000	1.00371	0.90322	0.89690
2	0.99667	1.20000	1.03313	0.90273	0.89736
3	0.99715	1.20000	1.00271	0.90237	0.89769
4	0.99750	1.20000	—	—	—
Median S'	0.99691	1.20000	1.00342	0.90298	0.89713
		Mean of Medians: 1.00009			
S''	0.99682	1.19989	1.00333	0.90290	0.89705

Table 19-2 (*Continued*)

Part C. Retabulation Used for Computation of S'' Using Mean as Central Value

t	$0 + 5n$	$1 + 5n$	$2 + 5n$	$3 + 5n$	$4 + 5n$
Mean S′	0.99683	1.20000	1.00353	0.90306	0.89705
		Mean of Means: 1.00009			
S''	0.99674	1.19989	1.00343	0.90207	0.89696

Fig. 19-2. Plot of data of Table 19-2.

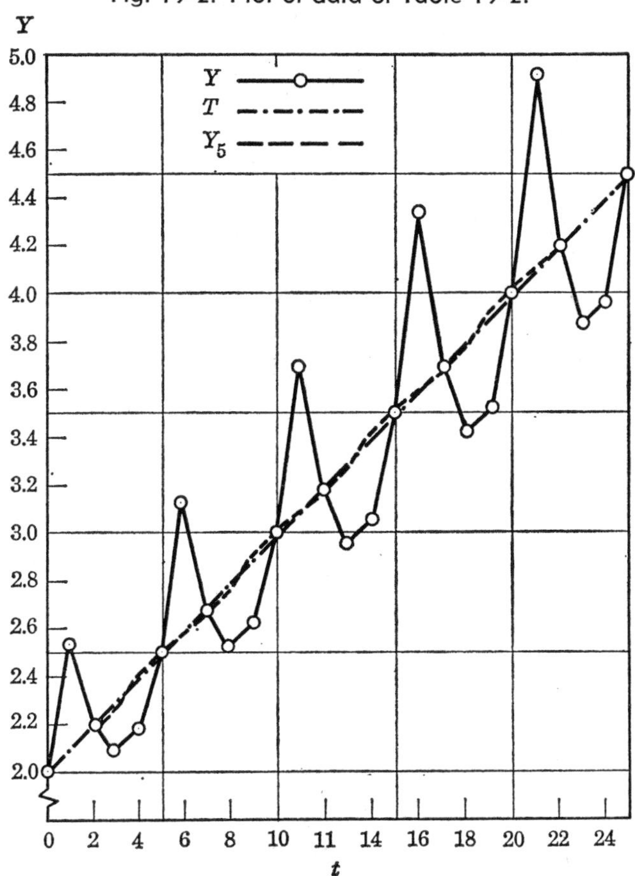

overwhelming cost of securing it. After all, we have done that before: what is the ratio of the circumference of a circle to its diameter? The Bible (II Chronicles 4:2) clearly indicates a value of three! For many purposes, 22/7 is quite adequate, though many of us recall the approximation 3.1416, and modern digital computers are often set to computing the value of π to prodigious numbers of decimals just as a sort of "warm-up." Since we almost

Table 19-3 SYNTHESIS AND ANALYSIS FOR SEASONAL VARIATION OF A TIME SERIES $Y = TS$, WHERE $T = 2.00 + 0.10t^2$ AND S TAKES THE SUCCESSIVE VALUES 1.00, 1.20, 1.00, 0.90, AND 0.90

Part A. Synthesis and First Phase of Analysis

(1) t	(2) t^2	(3) T	(4) S	(5) Y	(6) $\overline{Y}_5$	(7) S'
0	0	2.00	1.00	2.00	—	—
1	1	2.10	1.20	2.52	—	—
2	4	2.40	1.00	2.40	2.554	0.93970
3	9	2.90	0.90	2.61	3.054	0.85789
4	16	3.60	0.90	3.24	3.894	0.83204
5	25	4.50	1.00	4.50	4.794	0.93867
6	36	5.60	1.20	6.72	5.784	1.16182
7	49	6.90	1.00	6.90	6.954	0.99223
8	64	8.40	0.90	7.56	8.454	0.89425
9	81	10.10	0.90	9.90	10.494	0.86620
10	100	12.00	1.00	12.00	12.394	0.96821
11	121	14.10	1.20	16.92	14.284	1.18454
12	144	16.40	1.00	16.40	16.354	1.00281
13	169	18.90	0.90	17.01	18.854	0.90219
14	196	21.60	0.90	19.44	22.094	0.87987
15	225	24.50	1.00	24.50	24.994	0.98024
16	256	27.60	1.20	33.12	27.784	1.19205
17	289	30.90	1.00	30.90	30.754	1.00474
18	324	34.40	0.90	30.96	34.254	0.90384
19	361	38.10	0.90	34.29	38.694	0.88618
20	400	42.00	1.00	42.00	42.594	0.98605
21	441	46.10	1.20	55.32	46.284	1.19522
22	484	50.40	1.00	50.40	—	—
23	529	54.90	.90	49.11	—	—

Part B. Retabulation of S' and Computation of S'' Using Median as Central Value

t / n	$0 + 5n$	$1 + 5n$	$2 + 5n$	$3 + 5n$	$4 + 5n$
0	—	—	0.93970	0.85789	0.83204
1	0.93867	1.16182	0.99223	0.89425	0.86620
2	0.96821	1.18454	1.00281	0.90219	0.87987
3	0.98024	1.19205	1.00474	0.90384	0.88618
4	0.98605	1.19522	—	—	—
Median	0.97422	1.18830	0.99752	0.89822	0.87304
		Mean of Medians: 0.98626			
S''	0.98779	1.20485	1.01142	0.91073	0.88520

Table 19-3 (*Continued*)

Part C. Retabulation Used for Computation of S″ Using Mean as Central Value

	$0 + 5n$	$1 + 5n$	$2 + 5n$	$3 + 5n$	$4 + 5n$
Mean	0.96829	1.18340	0.98487	0.88954	0.86607
		Mean of Means: 0.97843			
S''	0.98693	1.20948	1.00658	0.90915	0.88516

Fig. 19-3. Plot of data from Table 19-3 and, on lower grid, plot of $Y_5 - T$ vs. t for same data.

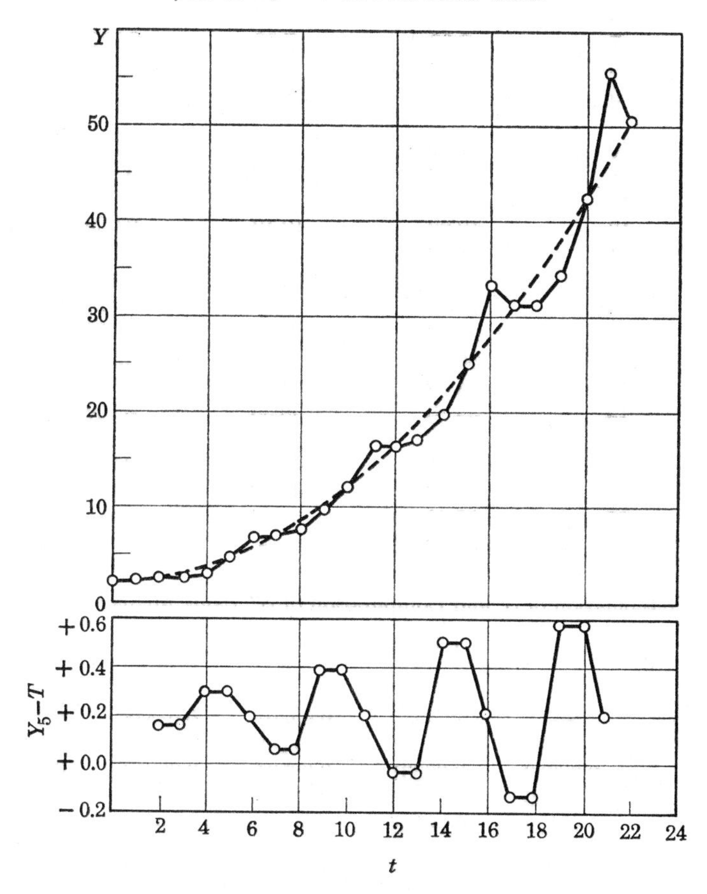

---

unconsciously accept a reasonable approximation to π, should we object to being equally sensible in adopting a course of action which is quite as rational here? Hardly!

Table 19-4 SYNTHESIS AND ANALYSIS FOR SEASONAL VARIATION OF A TIME SERIES CONTAINING ONLY THE CURVILINEAR TREND $T = 2.00 + 0.10t^2$ USED IN TABLE 3-3

Part A. Synthesis and First Phase of Analysis

(1) t	(2) $T = Y$	(3) $\bar{Y}_5$	(4) S'
0	2.00	—	—
1	2.10	—	—
2	2.40	2.60	0.92307
3	2.90	3.10	0.93548
4	3.60	3.80	0.94736
5	4.50	4.70	0.95744
6	5.60	5.80	0.96551
7	6.90	7.10	0.97183
8	8.40	8.60	0.97674
9	10.10	10.30	0.98058
10	12.00	12.20	0.98360
11	14.10	14.30	0.98601
12	16.40	16.60	0.98795
13	18.90	19.10	0.98952
14	21.60	21.80	0.99082
15	24.50	24.70	0.99190
16	27.60	27.80	0.99280
17	30.90	31.10	0.99356
18	34.40	34.60	0.99421
19	38.10	38.30	0.99477
20	42.00	42.20	0.99526
21	46.10	46.30	0.99568
22	50.40	—	—
23	54.90	—	—

Part B. Retabulation of S' and Computation of S'' Using Median as Central Value

t / n	$0 + 5n$	$1 + 5n$	$2 + 5n$	$3 + 5n$	$4 + 5n$
0	—	—	0.02307	0.93548	0.94736
1	0.95744	0.96551	0.97183	0.97674	0.98058
2	0.98360	0.98601	0.98795	0.98952	0.99802
3	0.99190	0.99280	0.99356	0.99421	0.99477
4	0.99526	0.99568	—	—	—
Median	0.98775	0.98940	0.97989	0.98313	0.98570
		Mean of Medians: 0.98517			
S''	1.00262	1.00429	0.99464	0.99793	1.00054

Notice that (1) all $\bar{Y}$'s fall above the T's and inside the curve; (2) therefore all S' values are less than unity; (3) our procedure for computing S'' leads us to indicate that there is a small seasonal variation. However, note that our S'' values differ from unity only in the third decimal place.

19.7 Episodic Variations and Seasonal Analysis

In Table 19-5 we exaggerate another peculiarity by introducing as our sole variation an episodic irregularity with $I = 12$ at $t = 10$. In this case notice that the moving average did not, of course, completely obliterate the effect of this episodic "jump." In fact it "smeared" the effect, at reduced

Table 19-5 SYNTHESIS AND ANALYSIS FOR SEASONAL VARIATION OF A TIME SERIES $Y = 2.00I$ WHERE $I = 12$ WHEN $t = 10$ AND $I = 1.00$ ELSEWHERE

(1) t	(2) I	(3) Y	(4) $\bar{Y}_5$	(5) S'
0	1.00	2.00	—	—
1	1.00	2.00	—	—
2	1.00	2.00	2.00	1.00000
3	1.00	2.00	2.00	1.00000
4	1.00	2.00	2.00	1.00000
5	1.00	2.00	2.00	1.00000
6	1.00	2.00	2.00	1.00000
7	1.00	2.00	2.00	1.00000
8	1.00	2.00	6.40	0.31250
9	1.00	2.00	6.40	0.31250
10	12.00	24.00	6.40	3.75000
11	1.00	2.00	6.40	0.31250
12	1.00	2.00	6.40	0.31250
13	1.00	2.00	2.00	1.00000
and so on.				

Notice that all moving averages, including the value for $t = 10$, are alike and are not at the true core value. Therefore any S' based on them is in error. This example greatly exaggerates the effect of an episodic irregularity. In a real series, such an event would be added to the effects of T, S, and C, and *might* pass unnoticed until the S' values were retabulated.

---

intensity, over five of the averages. Hence, the five values of S' based on these five moving averages are all in error. How can we cope with this sort of thing? Actually, we believe you will find that various organizations that make time series analyses have their own "house rules" for identifying episodic variations and for treating data in which they are reflected. You must become familiar with the rules used by your own future firm. Broadly speaking, all of these rules must provide a basis for identifying the episodic variation, together with means for adjusting the computations. Many of the rules used for identification are somewhat arbitrary, having to do with quasi-statistical procedures for identifying "wild" values of S'. Obviously, if the data are *known* to have been affected during a certain period by an identified extraordinary cause of variation, then these data should certainly be excluded from any computation of S' values, and any moving averages including these figures should not be used. Sometimes it may be quite legitimate to "fair in" by eye a value which Y might be expected to have had if the episodic irregularity had not been present and to use this value in the computation of moving averages. A better plan is to use the method of link-and-chain relatives which will be discussed later in this chapter.

19.8 Centered Moving Averages

Before going on to discuss that method, however, we have one more problem to clear up. Unfortunately, many seasonal variations have a period comprising an even number of time units. Typical is the one-year period, which would be evident in monthly sales volumes of department stores. Suppose we started to analyze such a set of data beginning with the January sales in some stated year. Our first 12 months, from January through December, would be averaged and entered at the middle of the range covered. But the middle of the range is *between* June and July! So we cannot use it as a base in computing either the June or July S' value. This *is* a dilemma, but we overcome it nimbly. We go ahead and place it there and place the next average, from February through the following January, *between* July and August. *Then* we average these two averages and place it between *them*, which lands it right beside our July figure. In that way we end up with a figure for each month from July on until we near the end of our series. This procedure, which we always use with periods comprising even numbers of time units, constitutes what we call the use of a *centered moving average.*

A little more thinking will make the operation more wieldy. Notice that the central value of t for any period is

$$t_c = \frac{t_i + t_f}{2} \tag{19.8.1}$$

where the subscripts c, i, and f denote respectively the central, initial, and final times for the period. As long as the period comprises an odd number of time units, our central value will coincide with one of the times; otherwise, it will fall halfway between two. Thus, in the case of the annual period just considered, the first period would center at

$$t_c = (0 + 11)/2 = 5\tfrac{1}{2} \tag{19.8.2}$$

Our *centered* moving average is placed one-half time unit later. Now let's see if we can't simplify the computation of that average. The average for the first 12 months consisted of

$$\frac{Y_0 + Y_1 + Y_2 + \ldots + Y_{10} + Y_{11}}{12} \tag{19.8.3}$$

Similarly, the next average consisted of

$$\frac{Y_1 + Y_2 + Y_3 + \ldots + Y_{11} + Y_{12}}{12} \tag{19.8.4}$$

When we centered this resulting pair of averages, we added them and divided the sum by two, which means that actually we had

$$\frac{Y_0 + 2Y_1 + 2Y_2 + \ldots + 2Y_{10} + 2Y_{11} + Y_{12}}{24} \tag{19.8.5}$$

In words, we used the first value in the initial period once, all others in that period twice, and the last value in the *next* period once, then divided the sum by twice the period length and placed the value opposite:

$$t_{\text{cm}} = \frac{t_{\text{i}} + t_{\text{f}} + 1}{2} \tag{19.8.6}$$

With the aid of an adding machine and its tape, we can do this job quite handily. We enter the first value once, the next 11 twice, and the 13th once and obtain a subtotal. This is divided by 24 on a calculator in a separate operation. Then we subtract the first and second values once each, add the 13th once and the 14th and obtain a second subtotal, and so on. *It is advisable* once a year to make a direct computation of the appropriate total for comparison to insure that no errors have been made in the continuing set of subtotals, as experience will surely teach you.

19.9 Link and Chain Relatives

Now let's consider a totally different method of finding seasonal indexes. We shall find the ratio of each value of Y to the one before it in the series. This ratio is called, traditionally, a *link relative.* We tabulate each link relative against the time associated with its numerator. Then, as in the case of the S' values from our moving averages, we retabulate these link relatives in columns for corresponding phases of the cycle. The computations are shown for the data we have previously considered in tables of the previous numbers followed by an R (i.e., Tables 19-1R through 19-4R). We eliminate from each column those values known to have been affected by an episodic variation or required by whatever rejection rule our firm uses. Notice that an episodic variation affecting a single month only disturbs two link relatives: that in which that month's value was the numerator, and the following one, in which it was the denominator. Contrast this with the effect of a similar variation on the moving average.

Table 19-1R ANALYSIS OF THE DATA OF TABLE 19-1 FOR SEASONAL VARIATION BY THE METHOD OF LINK AND CHAIN RELATIVES

(1) t	(2) Y	(3) R_L
0	2.00	—
1	2.40	1.20000
2	2.00	0.83333
3	1.80	0.90000
4	1.80	1.00000
5	2.00	1.11111
6	2.40	1.20000
7	2.00	0.83333
8	1.80	0.90000
9	1.80	1.00000

Link relative $= R_L = Y_n/Y_{(n-1)}$

Since this is an ideal series, all values in the future would repeat those shown for two cycles as above. When the values were retabulated, all values in the same column would be alike.

Chain Relative Computation

t	$0 + 5n$	$1 + 5n$	$2 + 5n$	$3 + 5n$	$4 + 5n$
Median	1.11111	1.20000	0.83333	0.90000	1.00000
R_C	1.00000[a]	1.20000	1.00000	0.90000	0.90000
	1.00000[b]				

Mean $R_C = 1.00000$, and so $R_c = S''$

[a]This value is arbitrarily adopted to start the computation of chain relatives.

[b]This value is the result of multiplying 0.90000, the chain relative for $t = 4 + 5n$, by 1.11111, the link relative for $t = 0 + 5n$. Since the value agrees with the starting value, no adjustment is required.

Table 19-2R ANALYSIS OF THE DATA OF TABLE 19-2 FOR SEASONAL VARIATION BY THE METHOD OF LINK-AND-CHAIN RELATIVES

(1) t	(2) Y	(3) $R_L = Y_n/Y_{n-1}$
0	2.00	—
1	2.52	1.26000
2	2.20	0.87301
3	2.07	0.94090
4	2.16	1.04347
5	2.50	1.15740
6	3.12	1.24800
7	2.70	0.86538
8	2.52	0.93333
9	2.61	1.03571

Table 19-2R (*Continued*)

(1) t	(2) Y	(3) $R_L = Y_n/Y_{n-1}$
10	3.00	1.14942
11	3.72	1.24000
12	3.20	0.86201
13	2.97	0.92812
14	3.06	1.03030
15	3.50	1.14379
16	4.32	1.23428
17	3.70	0.85648
18	3.42	0.92432
19	3.51	1.02531
20	4.00	1.13960
21	4.92	1.23000
22	4.20	0.85365
23	3.87	0.92142
24	3.96	1.02325
25	4.50	1.13636

Retabulation and Determination of Seasonal Indices

t / n	$0 + 5n$	$1 + 5n$	$2 + 5n$	$3 + 5n$	$4 + 5n$
0	—	1.26000	0.87301	0.94090	1.04347
1	1.15740	1.24800	0.86538	0.93333	1.03571
2	1.14942	1.24000	0.86021	0.92812	1.03030
3	1.14379	1.23428	0.85648	0.92432	1.02631
4	1.13960	1.23000	0.85365	0.92142	1.02325
5	1.13636	—			
Using Median Values					
Median R_L	1.14379	1.24000	0.86021	0.92812	1.03030
R_C	1.00000[a]	1.24000	1.06666	0.98999	1.01999
	1.16665[b]	Discrepancy: 0.16665			
		Correction Factor: 0.03333			
S'	1.00000	1.20667	1.00000	0.89000	0.88667
		Mean S': 0.99667			
S''	1.00334	1.21070	1.00334	0.89297	0.88963
Using Mean Values					
Mean R_L	1.14531	1.24246	0.86175	0.92962	1.03181
R_C	1.00000[a]	1.24246	1.07069	0.99533	1.02699
	1.17622[b]	Discrepancy: 0.17622			
		Correction Factor: 0.03524			
S'	1.00000	1.21102	1.00021	0.88961	0.88603
		Mean S': 0.99737			
S''	1.00264	1.21421	1.00284	0.89196	0.88837

[a]Assumed.
[b]Computed. See text for details of method.

Table 19-3R ANALYSIS OF THE DATA OF TABLE 19-3 FOR SEASONAL VARIATION BY THE METHOD OF LINK AND CHAIN RELATIVES

(1) t	(2) Y	(3) $L_R = Y_n/Y_{n-1}$
0	2.00	—
1	2.52	1.26000
2	2.40	0.95238
3	2.61	1.08750
4	3.24	1.24137
5	4.50	1.38889
6	6.72	1.49333
7	6.90	1.02678
8	7.56	1.09565
9	9.90	1.30952
10	12.00	1.21212
11	16.92	1.24507
12	16.40	0.96926
13	17.01	1.03719
14	19.44	1.14285
15	24.50	1.26028
16	33.12	1.35183
17	30.90	0.93297
18	30.96	1.00194
19	34.29	1.10755
20	42.00	1.22484
21	55.32	1.31714
22	50.50	0.91106
23	49.11	0.97440

Retabulation and Determination of Seasonal Indices

t / n	$0 + 5n$	$1 + 5n$	$2 + 5n$	$3 + 5n$	$4 + 5n$
0	—	1.26000	0.95238	1.08750	1.24137
1	1.38889	1.49333	1.02678	1.09565	1.30952
2	1.21212	1.41000	0.96926	1.03719	1.14285
3	1.26028	1.35183	0.93297	1.00194	1.10755
4	1.22484	(Remaining values not tabulated to avoid bias in final results.)			
Median R_L	1.24256	1.38092	0.96082	1.06235	1.19211
R_C	1.00000[a]	1.38092	1.32682	1.40955	1.68034
	2.08792[b]	Discrepancy: 1.08792			
		Correction Factor: 0.21758			
S'	1.00000	1.16334	0.89166	0.75681	0.81002
		Mean S': 0.92437			
S''	1.08181	1.25852	0.96461	0.81873	0.87629

[a]Assumed.

[b]Computed. Computation using means as central values may be done by the reader as a check on his understanding.

Table 19-4R Analysis of the Data of Table 19-4 for Seasonal Variation by the Method of Link and Chain Relatives

(1) t	(2) Y	(3) $R_L = Y_n/Y_{n-1}$
0	2.00	—
1	2.10	1.05000
2	2.40	1.14285
3	2.90	1.20833
4	3.60	1.24137
5	4.50	1.25000
6	5.60	1.24444
7	6.90	1.23214
8	8.40	1.21739
9	10.10	1.20238
10	12.00	1.18811
11	14.10	1.17500
12	16.40	1.16312
13	18.90	1.15243
14	21.60	1.14285
15	24.50	1.13425
16	27.60	1.12653
17	30.90	1.11956
18	34.40	1.11326
19	38.10	1.10755
20	42.00	1.10236
21	46.10	1.09761
22	50.40	1.09327
23	54.90	1.08928

Retabulation and Computation of Seasonal Indices

t / n	$0 + 5n$	$1 + 5n$	$2 + 5n$	$3 + 5n$	$4 + 5n$
0	—	1.05000	1.14285	1.20833	1.24137
1	1.25000	1.24444	1.23214	1.21739	1.20238
2	1.18811	1.17500	1.16312	1.15243	1.14285
3	1.13425	1.12653	1.11956	1.11326	1.10755
4	1.10236	Omitted to avoid bias.			
Median R_L	1.16118	1.15076	1.15298	1.18038	1.17262
R_C	1.00000[a]	1.15076	1.32680	1.56613	1.83648
	2.13248[b]	Discrepancy: 1.13248			
		Correction Factor: 0.22650			
S'	1.00000	0.92426	0.87380	0.88663	0.93098
		Mean S': 0.92303			
S''	1.08339	1.00133	0.94666	0.96056	1.00807

[a]Assumed.
[b]Computed.

From this table, we determine a central value for each phase, using the median or mean, depending, as in the moving average method, on the number of periods covered. From these values, we compute the chain relative by the following procedure. We arbitrarily take a value 1.000 (to as many decimals as we need) for the first phase. This we multiply by the link relative for the second phase to obtain the chain relative for the second phase. This we multiply in turn by the link relative for the third phase to obtain the chain relative for that phase. Finally, we multiply the chain relative for the last phase by the link relative for the first phase to obtain a *calculated* value for that phase. Generally the calculated value will not agree with the value of unity we started with, so we divide the discrepancy by the number of time units in one period to obtain the correction per unit time, or correction factor. We apply this correction once to the first chain relative after our assumed value of 1.00000, twice to the second value, and so on. Thus we obtain a set of values which do close the circuit, returning to the starting value, 1.00000. We consider these values analogous to the S' values obtained in the moving average method. Generally they will not average exactly 1.00000, as we demand that our seasonal indexes must, so we multiply each value by the reciprocal of the mean of all of them, that is, by $1.00000/\overline{S'}$, to obtain the S'' values which we use as our estimates of the true S values. Notice that, in both the moving average and relative methods, we used the same number of values in each column of our retabulation. This avoids a bias that might be present if we had more values for one part of the cycle than for another.

19.10 Comparison of Methods

Comparison of the two methods will bring out the following differences:

1. The moving average method requires more computation.

2. The moving average itself is a good estimate of the core of the series, while no estimate of this core is obtainable from the relative method until the deseasonalized values have been computed.

3. For the straight line trend and the slight curvature of the series used for illustration here, the moving average method came closer to recovering the original values. Had a more sharply curving trend, the equation for which we shall discuss later, been present, the relative method would have been superior in this respect.

Thus, you will find that, in real life, you must make a choice between the methods, taking cognizance of these competing features. As you work with series, you will develop your own experience and judgment.

General Study

1. As you use the methods of seasonal analysis, try to develop your own appraisal of their merits. Can you find ways to handle the analysis which either expedites it or reduces the likelihood of errors?

2. After making an analysis of a series important to it, a firm conceives of a plan for altering the seasonal pattern. How can it determine whether it has been successful in so doing?

Specific Problems

1. Make seasonal analyses of the series you synthesized in connection with Chapter 18, using both the moving average and the link and chain relative method. Record the time required and the number of errors made. Make an appropriate table comparing the true values with the results obtained by the two methods.

2. Make a seasonal analysis of the data obtained in Problem 1 of Chapter 17, using the method that you prefer. Tabulate the estimated seasonal indexes and the deseasonalized values. Are the indexes reasonable? Can you suggest causes for the indicated seasonal variation? What use could be made of the information you have gained?

20

The Secular Trend

20.1 Secular Trend and Regression Analysis

In our opening discussion of the components of time series, we stated that the secular trend is the core of the series. (Incidentally, the term secular has no religious connotation: it is the formal way of saying long-time!) Our problem of trend analysis, then, will involve the recognition of the appropriate form of trend equation and the formation of appropriate estimates of its parameters. In our discussion of regression analysis we paid considerable attention to three forms of equation for the dual reason that these three forms are of great general utility and that they are particularly important to time series analysis.

These forms, in terms of our present symbols, are as follows:

The Linear Trend

$$T = A + Bt \tag{20.1.1}$$

The Quadratic or Parabolic Trend

$$T = A + Bt + Ct^2 \tag{20.1.2}$$

The Exponential, Semilog, or Ratio Trend

$$T = AR^t \tag{20.1.3a}$$

$$\text{or } \log T = \log A + (\log R)t$$

$$= C + Dt \tag{20.1.3b}$$

Actually, if we wished to represent the entire trend of a series whose history is virtually complete, like our whale fishery or streetcar series, a much more complicated equation would be required. But we should be well used to the idea of accepting practical approximations, and it is found by experience that most series which we must investigate in practical problems are well represented by one of these three trends over long periods of time.

20.2 Recognizing Forms of Graphs

Your previous experience with regression analysis will have taught you that the graph of a linear equation is always a straight line. The quadratic equation is always represented by a graph in the form of a smooth arch, with one extreme value, so that it is always concave up or concave down throughout. In fact, the extreme is a maximum if C is negative and a minimum if C is positive, and it occurs when $t = -B/2C$. However, this value may not be within the range of our observations. The exponential equation also is represented by a graph in the form of a single smooth arch for the case in which R is positive (the only case of interest to us), but this curve has no extreme value. It approaches the t-axis as an asymptote as t moves in one direction and increases indefinitely as t moves in the other. If R is greater than one, the curve rises with t; if t is less than one, it falls. But in either case the curve is always concave upward.

These facts give us the basis of graphic procedures by which we can often establish the form of the trend when it is clearly defined. If the time span represented by each value of Y is less than a year, we should first deseasonalize the data and work with the resulting Y'' values. When the points each cover one or more whole years, they have no seasonal component and may be plotted directly. The values of Y or Y'' are plotted on ordinary, or arithmetic, graph paper (The word, arithmetic, is an adjective, and the accent is on the *met*. It denotes that the scales in both directions are uniform.) and the general shape of the trend is appraised by eye. The following conclusions may be reached:

1. If the points are fairly randomly scattered about a straight line, we may presume a linear trend.
2. If the points are randomly scattered about a curve with downward concavity, we may assume a quadratic trend, because the only other curve we consider, the exponential, must be concave upward.
3. If the points are randomly scattered about a curve with an upward concavity and a clearly established minimum, we may presume a quadratic trend.
4. Under all other circumstances, further study is required.

20.3 Semilog Graph Paper

To distinguish between quadratic and exponential trends, we recall that the semilog form of the exponential equation is linear in the independent variable. We could plot $\log Y$ or $\log Y''$ vs. t on arithmetic paper and, if the resulting points appeared to be randomly scattered about a straight line, consider the trend to be exponential. Otherwise, we would consider it to be quadratic. But taking the logarithms, then plotting them, is tedious, so we make use of a very convenient paper known as semilog paper. In principle, we may think of it as having been made by taking arithmetic paper and marking a 2 beside its logarithm, 0.30103, on the vertical scale, then a 3 beside 0.47712, and so on. That is, we mark each number beside the level of its logarithm. Then we draw in new horizontal lines at these levels and remove the original horizontal lines. In practice, of course, far more practical methods are used, but we are going to use the paper, not manufacture it! The resulting paper will have uniformly spaced vertical lines but nonuniformly spaced horizontal lines, which become closer together as we rise.

Further thought shows that $\log 1 = 0.00000$ and $\log 10 = 1.00000$, and that we pass through the complete set of mantissas in the interval. We again pass through this set of mantissas for values of our numbers between 10 and 100, whose logarithm is 2, and again between 100 and 1000, whose logarithm is 3, and so on. Thus as we pass through values between two consecutive powers of 10, we pass through a *cycle* of values of mantissas, and we occupy the same vertical extent on our graph. To meet our needs, we can purchase paper with one, two, three, or more cycles. We show blank paper with different cycles as Fig. 20-1. Notice the characteristic spacing of the lines.

With the aid of this semilog paper, we are spared the tedium of looking up logs. We plot the values of Y or Y'' against t on semilog paper. If the values now appear to be scattered about a straight line, we consider that we have an exponential trend; otherwise it is quadratic.

20.4 Some Simple Examples

These ideas will become clear by some specific examples, using exact equations. We shall use first the equations:

$$\text{Linear} \qquad T = 2 + 3t \qquad (20.4.1)$$

$$\text{Quadratic or Parabolic} \qquad T = 2 + 0.16t^2 \qquad (20.4.2)$$

$$\text{Semilog or Ratio} \qquad T = 2(1.195)^t$$

$$\log T = \log 2 + (\log 1.195)t$$

$$= 0.30103 + 0.07737t \qquad (20.4.3)$$

The computed values of T are shown in Table 20-1 and the graphs on arithmetic paper are shown in Fig. 20-2a. Notice that the linear equation plots as a straight line, while both of the other equations plot as curved lines. Now examine Fig. 20-2b, where the equations are replotted on semilog paper. Notice that, on this paper, the ratio or semilog trend plots as a straight line, while the other two are curved.

Fig. 20-1. A typical sheet of two-cycle semilog graph paper.

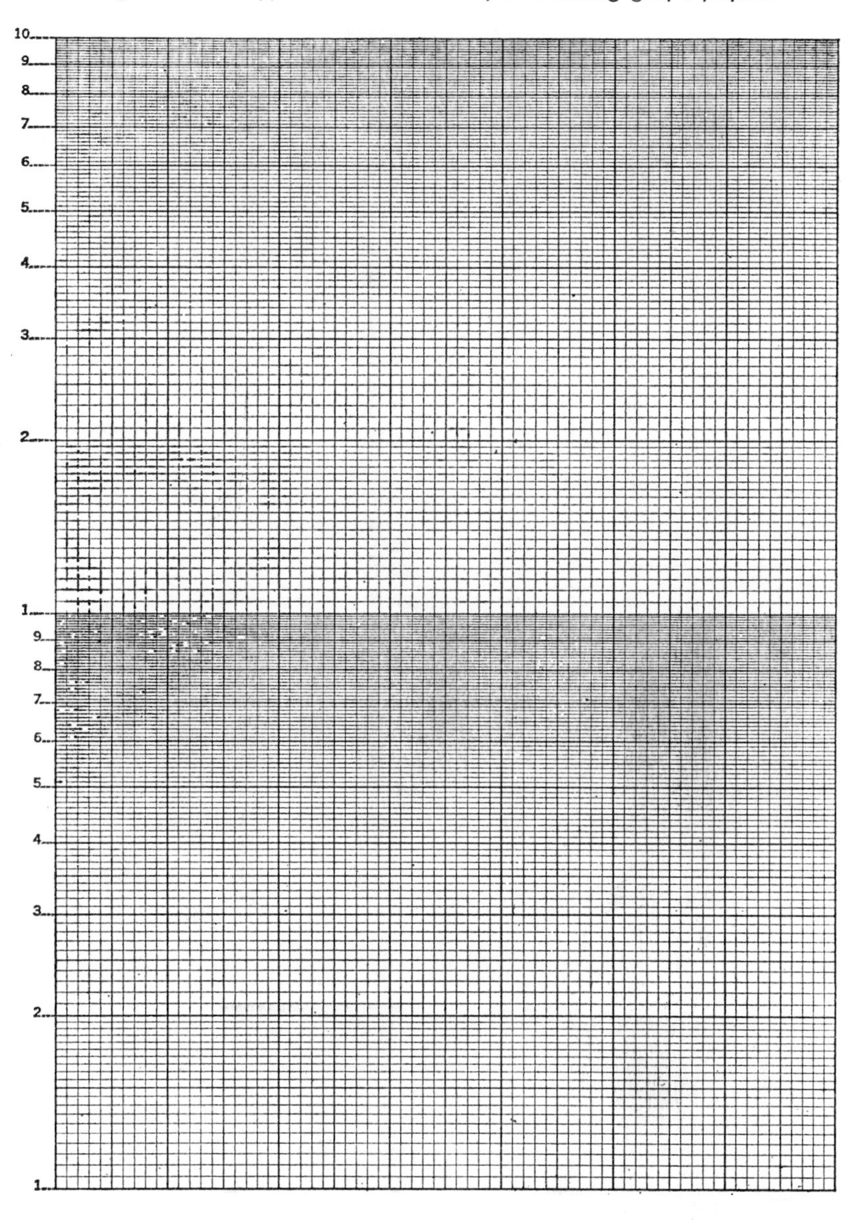

Table 20-1 COMPUTED VALUES OF TREND EQUATIONS, ALL HAVING RISING VALUES

$$\text{Linear, } T_1 = 2 + 3t$$
$$\text{Quadratic } T_2 = 2 + 0.16t^2$$
$$\text{Semilog } T_3 = 2(1.195)^t$$

t	T_1	T_2	T_3
0	2	2.00	2.00
1	5	2.16	2.39
2	8	2.64	2.85
3	11	3.44	3.41
4	14	4.56	4.07
5	17	6.00	4.86
6	20	7.76	5.80
7	23	9.84	6.92
8	26	12.24	8.27
9	29	14.96	9.88
10	32	18.00	11.80
11	35	21.36	14.09
12	38	25.04	16.82
13	41	29.04	20.09
14	44	33.36	23.99
15	47	38.00	28.64
16	50	42.96	34.21
17	53	48.24	40.85
18	56	53.84	56.93
19	59	59.76	56.93

Let us examine three more equations:

$$\text{Linear} \qquad T = 60 - 3t \tag{20.4.4}$$

$$\text{Quadratic} \qquad T = 60 - 0.16t^2 \tag{20.4.5}$$

$$\text{Semilog} \qquad T = 60(0.837)^t$$

$$\log T = \log 60 + (\log 0.837)t$$

$$= 1.77815 + (9.92273 - 10)t$$

$$= 1.77815 - 0.07727t \tag{20.4.6}$$

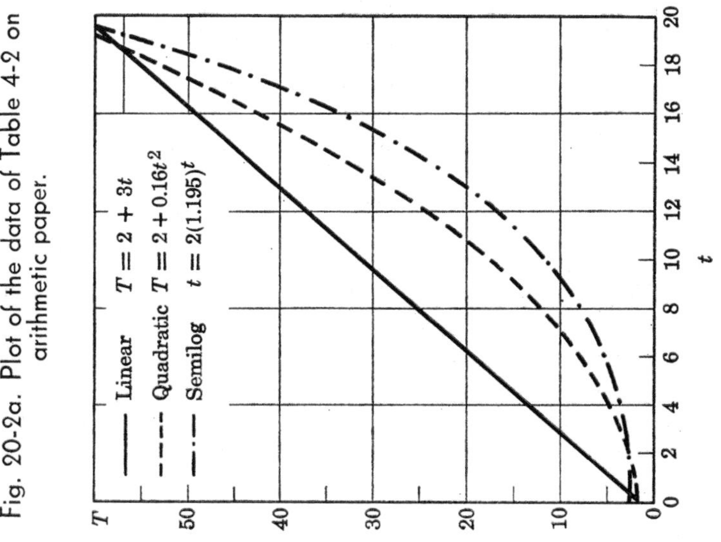

Fig. 20-2a. Plot of the data of Table 4-2 on arithmetic paper.

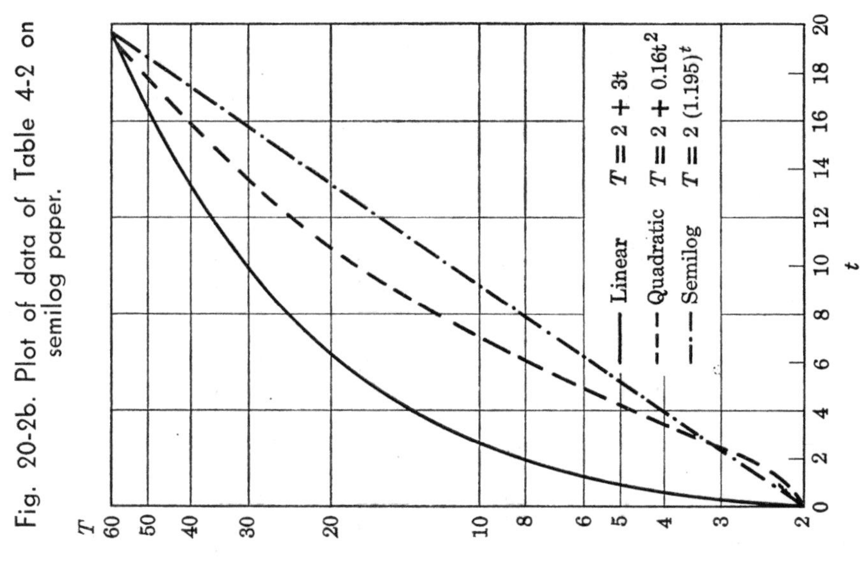

Fig. 20-2b. Plot of data of Table 4-2 on semilog paper.

The necessary values are shown in Table 20-2 and the related plots in Figs. 20-3a and 20-3b. As before, the linear trend is straight on arithmetic

Table 20-2 COMPUTED VALUES OF TREND EQUATIONS, ALL HAVING FALLING VALUES

$$\text{Linear } T_4 = 60 - 3t$$
$$\text{Quadratic } T_5 = 60 - 0.16t^2$$
$$\text{Semilog } T_6 = 60(0.837)^t$$

t	T_4	T_5	T_6
0	60	60.00	60.00
1	57	59.84	50.22
2	54	59.36	42.04
3	51	58.56	35.18
4	48	57.44	29.45
5	45	56.00	24.65
6	42	54.24	20.63
7	39	52.16	17.27
8	36	49.76	14.45
9	33	47.04	12.10
10	30	44.00	10.13
11	27	40.64	8.48
12	24	36.96	7.16
13	21	32.96	6.94
14	18	28.64	4.97
15	15	24.00	4.16
16	12	19.04	3.48
17	9	13.76	2.91
18	6	8.16	2.44
19	3	2.24	2.04

paper and curved on semilog paper, while the reverse is true of the semilog trend. This will always be true. Notice also that, in both cases, the linear equation gave a plot which was *concave downward* on semilog paper. Notice further that the quadratic equation, which was *concave upward* on arithmetic paper, became *concave downward* on semilog paper for the first set of data, while for the second set, the *downward concavity* of the quadratic curve became *more pronounced* on semilog paper.

This behavior is, of course, not peculiar to these specific equations but is a fundamental characteristic of the classes to which they belong. Thus we may summarize our graphical procedure for attempting to recognize the form of trend as follows:

Fig. 20-3. Plots of Data of Table 20-2 on Two Kinds of Paper.

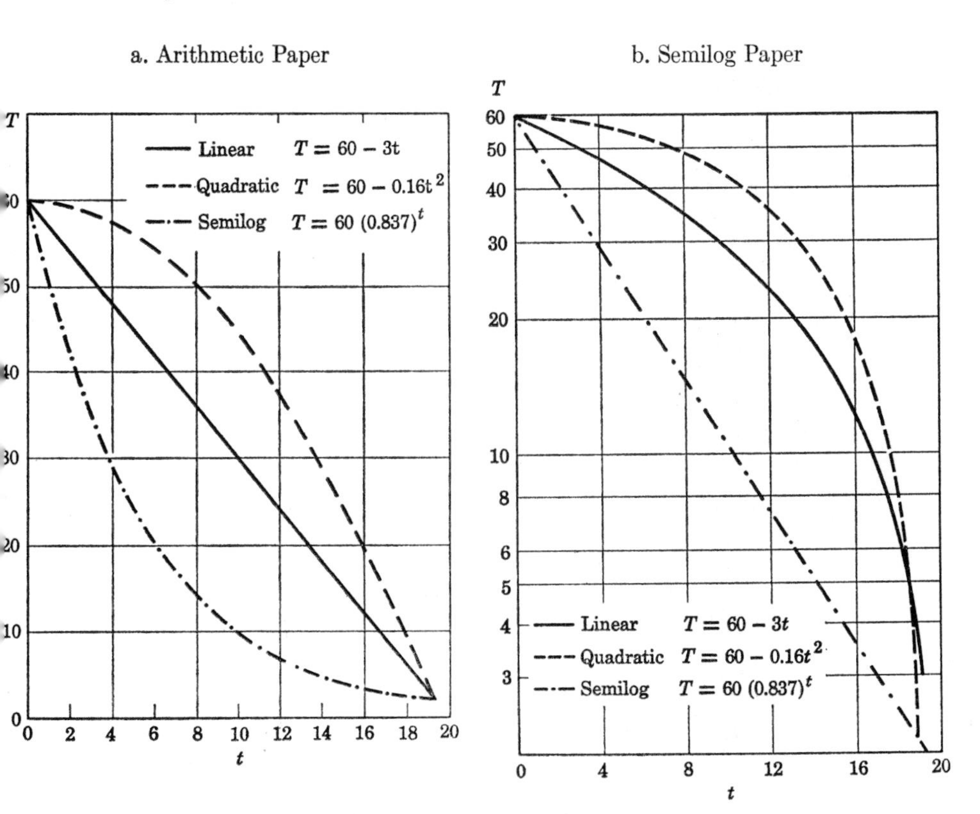

1. Plot the series on arithmetic paper. If the core of the series appears clearly linear, assume a linear trend.

2. If the core appears curvilinear with downward concavity, assume a quadratic trend.

3. If the core is curvilinear, but with upward concavity, replot on semilog paper (or, if it is not available, plot the logarithms of the series on arithmetic paper). If the resulting plot has a linear core, assume the exponential trend. Otherwise, assume the quadratic trend.

20.5 Borderline Decisions

Remember that we are restricting ourselves to but three forms of trend equation to be used, and recall our discussion of approximations when we were considering curvilinear regression problems. You will then easily recognize that we shall often encounter series in which the quadratic and exponential forms are so similar that we shall be unable to choose between them from their graphs. Or the curvature may be so small that we may not be sure the trend is not linear.

Under these circumstances, we may recall our analysis of variance ideas in connection with curvilinear regression analysis. After fitting each equation, we have a variance of estimate, a measure of the discrepancy between the observations and the fitted curve. In our present symbols and for the curves in question, these are

For the Linear Trend

$$s_{Y_1 \cdot t}^2 = (\Sigma Y^2 - a\Sigma Y - b\Sigma Yt)/(N-2) \tag{20.5.1}$$

For the Quadratic Trend

$$s_{Y_2 \cdot t}^2 = (\Sigma Y^2 - a\Sigma Y - b\Sigma Yt - c\Sigma Yt^2)/(N-3) \tag{20.5.2}$$

For the Exponential or Semilog Trend

$$s_{Y_{sl} \cdot t}^2 = \Sigma(Y_{sl} - \bar{Y})^2/(N-2) \tag{20.5.3}$$

In those formulas it is understood that Y should be replaced by Y'' if deseasonalized values were used in estimating the trend equation.

Now we could probably justify the use of the analysis of variance in connection with our decisions concerning the linear and quadratic trend equations, but as soon as we bring in the possibility of the exponential trend, our previous study shows that the analysis of variance is inapplicable. It would generally be considered sound practice to employ the trend equation whose residual variance is lowest provided that

1. The implications of this form of equation are not inconsistent with our total knowledge about the facts of which our series is a part.

2. The reduction in variance over that of any simpler equation also consistent with the facts is sufficient to warrant the complication.

It may seem to you strange that after we have taught you so many fine statistical methods we should advise you to use a procedure rather lacking in refinement here. But this is, in fact, a sound and mature recommendation. You see, we must admit that the actual facts with which we are dealing are extremely complex in most real series, and that we are using available tools as our slaves to aid us: we do not let them become our masters. It is a fact that in much serious and important work with time series, sound analysts often use the simple linear trend because of its great convenience and because of a recognition that changing factors not obvious in the data to the present will be on the point of making important changes in the data ahead.

20.6 Another Precaution

There is another problem that is often present to torment us in time series analysis. You noticed that we warned you to deseasonalize the data before investigating the trend. Suppose you had failed to do so. We show in Table 20-3 the results of estimating the coefficients of the linear trend equation

Table 20-3 ESTIMATES OF PARAMETERS OF TREND EQUATION FROM THE VALUES IN TABLE 19-2

Times Included			
First	*Last*	b	a
0	20	0.09231	2.06737
0	21	0.10314	1.99521
0	22	0.10245	2.00000
0	23	0.09758	2.03754
0	24	0.09373	2.06524
0	25	0.09541	2.05900
1	21	0.10322	1.99410
2	22	0.10841	1.90680
3	23	0.10257	1.95263
4	24	0.09387	2.06486
5	25	0.09101	2.12532

from the data of Table 19-2. These were synthetic values using the trend $T = 2.0 + 0.10t$ and the successive seasonal indexes, 1.00, 1.20, 1.00, 0.90, and 0.90. We first began with $t = 0$ but finished with values from $t = 20$ through $t = 25$. Then we started at $t = 1, 2, 3, 4$, and 5 and ended with the corresponding value in the last cycle.

The following rather striking results appear. First, in no case did we recover our value of $B = 0.10$ exactly. Second, in only one case did we recover our value of $A = 2.00$ exactly, namely, when we began at $t = 0$ and ended at $t = 22$. This is a situation almost certain to develop whenever we fail to deseasonalize before we study our trends on data having seasonal variation. But it is also true that most data with which we deal have cyclical variation, and it operates to disturb our estimates of the trend parameters in a similar way.

If we compute our estimates of the trend parameters from the deseasonalized values, as we did for the same initial and final values of t in Table 20-4, we

Table 20-4 ESTIMATES OF PARAMETERS OF TREND EQUATION FROM THE DESEASONALIZED VALUES OF TABLE 19-2

Times Included			
First	*Last*	b	a
0	20	0.10013	1.99927
0	21	0.10012	1.99933
0	22	0.09994	2.00061
0	23	0.09981	2.00156
0	24	0.09997	2.00032
0	25	0.10009	1.99884
1	21	0.10021	1.99802
2	22	0.10002	1.99954
3	23	0.09975	2.00258
4	24	0.09985	2.00243
5	25	0.10041	1.99380

find that all our values are close to the true value. This is in spite of the fact that our seasonal indexes, S'', were not exactly the true values. So we do work with deseasonalized values when we are studying trends. Should we not, you may well ask, adjust our values for cyclical variation also? That would be desirable, but, you see, we are rapidly approaching the state of suggesting that we perform all other phases of the analysis before we perform any one of them: hardly feasible! You will later learn that cyclical variation poses some very real problems, and we therefore generally do the best we can to analyze for trend before we study the cyclical variations. However, we should work with data over as long a time as is feasible, and should try to avoid starting and ending at markedly different phases of possible cycles.

20.7 Performing the Computations

While it is possible to write out the formulas for the estimates of the several parameters which you will need, it has been our experience that the substitution of the values into these formulas and the ultimate computation of the values required is so fraught with possibilities of mistakes that we prefer to use the Crout procedure discussed in Appendix XV for finding their values. The same figures and procedures are required, but they are carried out and the intermediate steps are tabulated in such a way that intermediate checks are available and the possibility of undetected errors is reduced. We therefore recommend the use of this procedure or a procedure making similar use of any computing facilities at your service.

20.8 Two Synthetic Series

In order to give meaning to some of the ideas we have been considering, let us synthesize two series. The first will have the quadratic trend, $T = 1{,}000 + 35t + t^2$ and successive seasonal indexes, 1.0, 1.2, 0.9, and 0.9. The second will have the exponential trend, $Y = 1{,}000 \times 1.04^t$, with the same seasonal indexes. We might think of the series as representing the quarterly sales of a firm in a rather seasonal business, the values being in thousands of dollars.

We first construct the series as shown in Tables 20-5 and 20-6. Then we make the seasonal analysis, using link-and-chain relatives, and deseasonalize the data. Plots on arithmetic data show concavity upward, and we replot as shown in Figs. 20-4, 20-5, 20-6, and 20-7. The plots are not decisive, so we fit the several equations and compute the residual variances, as shown in the tables containing the data.

Our results will surprise us, perhaps, for we find the exponential trend fits both sets of data better, in spite of the fact that we know that one of the original series was computed with a quadratic trend! How can this be? Very simply! We deliberately selected the two trend equations so that, over the range of the data, they were closely similar in form and values, but so that they had a very real curvature. Then we applied fairly large and unsymmetrical seasonal variations. Finally, we covered a span of only 20 values. These facts, together with the fact that our procedure for estimating seasonal indexes is only an approximation and the difficulties in connection with the exponential equation that we discussed at length in Chapter 15 all conspire to lead to the erroneous conclusion in the case of one of the sets.

We feel that this has been a salutary experience, for it reminds us that our procedures are not rigorous, and that we must be on our guard not to press them "to the last decimal." Actually, the differences between the residual variances after fitting a quadratic trend and after fitting an exponential trend with the aid of the logarithmic transformation are not very great, and the computed values over the range of our observations will not differ greatly. It is only when we attempt a long extrapolation that we develop discrepancies of serious magnitude. But, after all, one should not depend solely on the information in four years of data such as these to make any appreciable extrapolation.

Table 20-5 SYNTHESIS AND ANALYSIS OF A TIME SERIES FROM THE CURVILINEAR TREND, $T = 1000 + 35t + t^2$, AND THE SUCCESSIVE SEASONAL INDEXES, 1.0, 1.2, 0.2, AND 0.2

t	t^2	T	S	Y	R_L	S''	Y'	Z'
0	0	1000	1.0	1000.0	—	1.00510	994.9	2.99778
1	1	1036	1.2	1243.2	1.24320	1.21138	1026.3	3.01128
2	4	1074	0.9	966.6	0.77775	0.89357	1081.7	3.03411
3	9	1114	0.9	1002.6	1.03724	0.88993	1126.6	3.05177
4	16	1156	1.0	1156.0	1.15300	1.00510	1145.6	3.05903
5	25	1200	1.2	1440.0	1.24567	1.21138	1188.7	3.06507
6	36	1246	0.9	1121.4	0.77875	0.89357	1255.0	3.09864
7	49	1294	0.9	1164.6	1.03852	0.88993	1308.6	3.11681
8	64	1344	1.0	1344.0	1.15404	1.00510	1337.2	3.12620
9	81	1396	1.2	1675.2	1.24642	1.21138	1382.9	3.14079
10	100	1450	0.9	1305.0	0.77901	0.89357	1460.4	3.16447
11	121	1506	0.9	1355.4	1.03682	0.88993	1523.0	3.18270
12	144	1564	1.0	1564.0	1.15390	1.00510	1556.1	3.19204
13	169	1624	1.2	1948.8	1.24603	1.21138	1608.7	3.20648
14	196	1686	0.9	1517.4	0.77863	0.89357	1698.1	3.22996
15	225	1750	0.9	1575.0	1.03795	0.88993	1769.8	3.24792
16	256	1816	1.0	1816.0	1.15301	1.00510	1806.8	3.25691
17	289	1884	1.2	2260.8	1.24493	1.21138	1866.3	3.27098
18	324	1954	0.9	1758.6	0.77786	0.89357	1968.1	3.29405
19	361	2026	0.9	1823.4	1.03684	0.88993	2048.9	3.31152

Computation of S''

n t	$0 + 4n$	$1 + 4n$	$2 + 4n$	$3 + 4n$
0	—	1.24320	0.77775	1.30724
1	1.15300	1.24567	0.77875	1.03852
2	1.15404	1.24642	0.77901	1.03862
3	1.15390	1.24603	0.77863	1.03795
4	1.15301	1.24493	0.77786	1.03684
Median R_L	1.15397	1.24567	0.77863	1.03795
R_C	1.00000	1.24567	0.96992	1.00673
	1.16174	Discrepancy: 16174		
		Correction Factor: 0.04044		
S'	1.00000	1.20523	0.88904	0.88541
		Mean S': = 0.99492		
S''	1.00510	1.21138	0.89357	0.88993

Regression Equations and Residual Variances

Linear: $Y'_1 = 940.20432 + 54.47165t$

$\Sigma(Y' - Y'_1)^2 = 22135.84675$

$s_{Y'.t}{}^2 = 1229.76916$

Quadratic: $Y'_2 = 999.79840 + 34.60696t + 1.04551t^2$

$\Sigma(Y' - Y'_2)^2 = 3077.47617$

$s_{Y'.t}{}^2 = 181.20801$

Table 20-5 (*Continued*)

Exponential (in Semilog Form):

$$Z'_{sl} = \log Y'_{sl} = 2.99675 + 0.01644t$$
$$\Sigma(Y' - Y'_{sl}) = 3097.48$$
$$s_{Y'.t}{}^2 = 172.08222$$

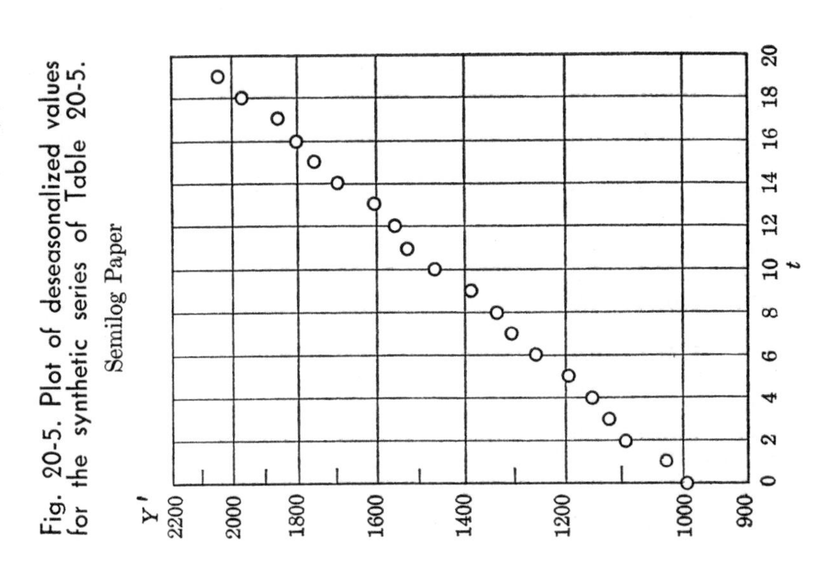

Fig. 20-5. Plot of deseasonalized values for the synthetic series of Table 20-5.

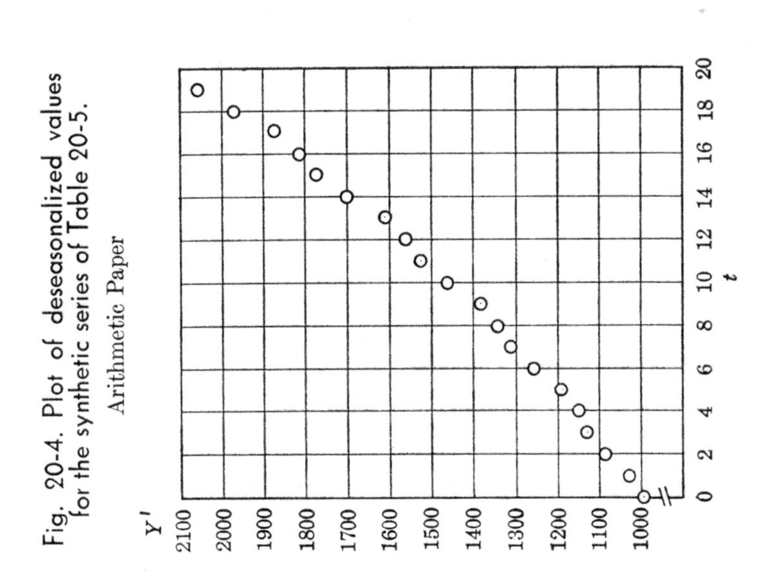

Fig. 20-4. Plot of deseasonalized values for the synthetic series of Table 20-5.

Table 20-6 SYNTHESIS AND ANALYSIS OF A TIME SERIES FROM THE CURVILINEAR TREND, $T = 1000 \cdot 1.04^t$, AND THE SUCCESSIVE SEASONAL INDEXES, 1.0, 1.2, 0.9, AND 0.9

t	t^2	T	S	Y	R_L	S''	Y'	Z'
0	0	1000.0	1.0	1000.0	—	1.00529	994.7	2.99769
1	1	1040.0	1.2	1248.0	1.24800	1.21191	1029.8	3.01276
2	4	1081.6	0.9	973.4	0.77996	0.89317	1089.8	3.03735
3	9	1124.9	0.9	1012.4	1.04006	0.88961	1138.0	3.05614
4	16	1169.9	1.0	1169.9	1.15557	1.00529	1163.7	3.06584
5	25	1216.7	1.2	1460.0	1.24696	1.21191	1204.7	3.08088
6	36	1265.3	0.9	1138.8	0.78000	0.89317	1275.0	3.10551
7	49	1315.9	0.9	1184.3	1.03995	0.88961	1331.2	3.12424
8	64	1368.6	1.0	1368.6	1.15561	1.00529	1361.4	3.13399
9	81	1423.3	1.2	1708.0	1.24799	1.21191	1409.3	3.14900
10	100	1480.2	0.9	1332.2	0.77997	0.89317	1491.5	3.17362
11	121	1539.5	0.9	1385.6	1.04008	0.88961	1557.5	3.19243
12	144	1601.0	1.0	1601.0	1.15545	1.00529	1592.6	3.20211
13	169	1665.1	1.2	1998.1	1.24803	1.21191	1648.7	3.21714
14	196	1731.7	0.9	1558.5	0.77999	0.89317	1744.9	3.24177
15	225	1800.9	0.9	1620.8	1.03997	0.88961	1821.9	3.26053
16	256	1873.0	1.0	1873.0	1.15560	1.00529	1863.1	3.27023
17	289	1947.9	1.2	2337.5	1.24799	1.21191	1928.8	3.28529
18	324	2025.8	0.9	1823.2	0.77997	0.89317	2041.3	3.30991
19	361	2106.8	0.9	1896.1	1.03998	0.88961	2131.4	3.32866

Computation of S''

n	t $0+4n$	$1+4n$	$2+4n$	$3+4n$
0	—	1.24800	0.77996	1.04006
1	1.15557	1.24796	0.78000	1.03995
2	1.15561	1.24799	0.77997	1.04008
3	1.15545	1.24803	0.77999	1.03997
4	1.15561	1.24799	0.77997	1.03998
Median R_L	1.15559	1.24799	0.77997	1.30998
R_C	1.00000	1.24799	0.97339	1.01231
	1.16982	(Discrepancy: 0.16982)		
		(Correction Factor: 0.04246)		
S'	1.00000	1.20553	0.88847	0.88493
		(Mean S': = 0.99473)		
S''	1.00529	1.21191	0.89317	0.88961

Regression Equations and Residual Variances

Linear: $Y'_1 = 937.39715 + 58.27030t$

$\Sigma(Y' - Y'_1)^2 = 28019.92808$

$s_{Y'.t}^2 = 1557.21822$

Quadratic: $Y'_2 = 1004.56139 + 35.88222t + 1.17832t^2$

$\Sigma(Y' - Y'_2)^2 = 3822.40416$

$s_{Y'.t}^2 = 224.84730$

Table 20-6 (*Continued*)

Exponential (in Semilog Form)

$$Z'_{sl} = \text{Log } Y'_{sl} = 2.99942 + 0.01714t$$
$$\Sigma(Y' - Y'_{sl})^2 = 3585.51$$
$$s_{Y'.t}^2 = 199.19500$$

Note: T values were originally computed by multiplication and rounded at the first decimal place.

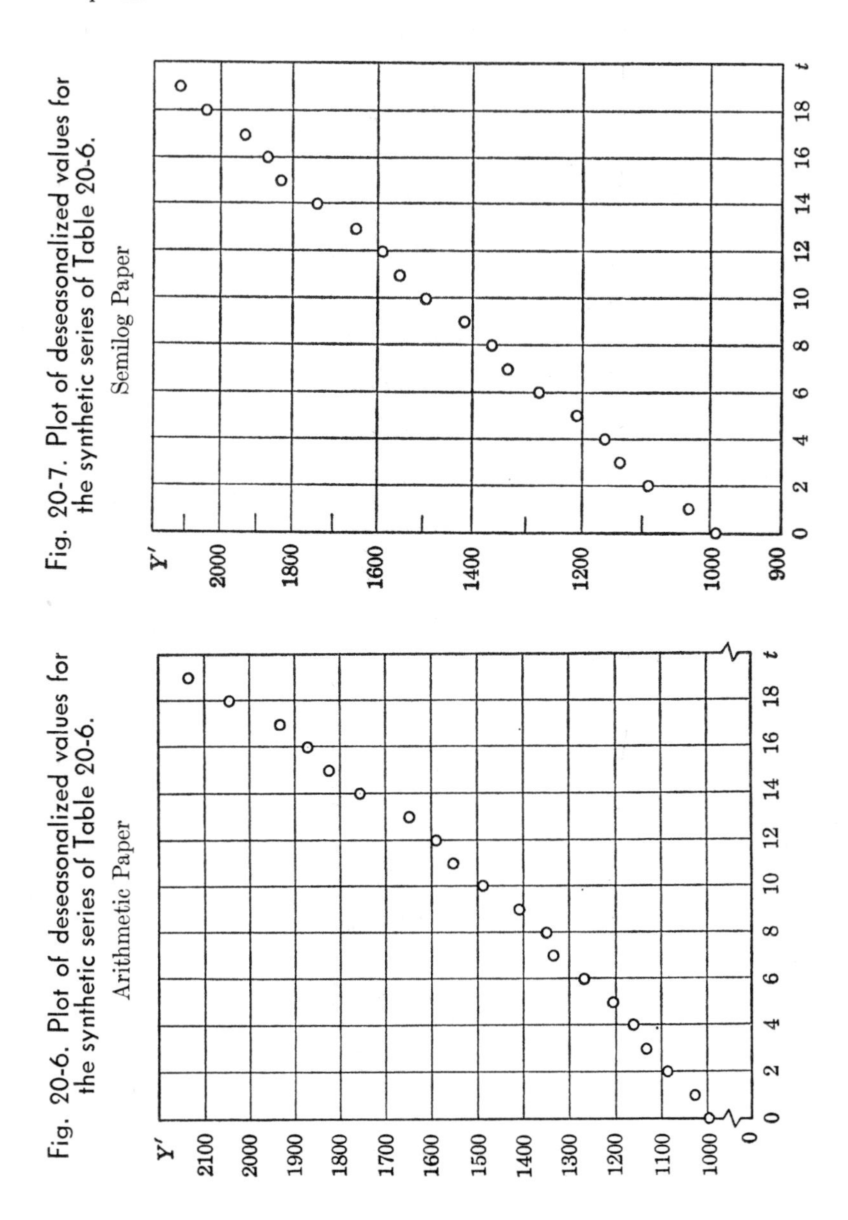

Fig. 20-7. Plot of deseasonalized values for the synthetic series of Table 20-6.

Fig. 20-6. Plot of deseasonalized values for the synthetic series of Table 20-6.

20.9 Treating Real Data

The principle and computational details have been illustrated on synthetic data. Because the computations required for the effective analysis of real data are extensive, and because the proper interpretation of the results requires background knowledge of the field involved, we believe that it is wiser for the reader to select series of real interest to himself, or under study at his school, and make his own analyses, following the plan we have shown. In this way, the real problems and power of the methods will become much more evident, and the effort will be far more rewarding than the boring perusal of pages of printed computations. We urge you to make such analyses.

General Study

1. Consider carefully the consequences of the necessity for using approximate methods which we have discussed in this chapter. For the field in which you are interested, how might your results be affected? How can you protect yourself from reaching misleading conclusions?

2. Under what conditions, in your field, would you have good reasons to expect time series which you encounter to follow each of the types of trends we have discussed? Why would these forms be expected?

Specific Problems

1. Perform seasonal and trend analyses upon the series you have previously synthesized and those you have been following in publications.

21

Some Problems with the Calendar

21.1 The Unequal Months

The universe of which we humans are such a minute part seems to run along pretty smoothly, but we certainly have troubles adjusting ourselves to it! That is particularly apparent when we try to cope with time and form a calendar. It all started with the fact that a year is not a whole number of days long, but is 365 days, 5 hours, 48 minutes and 45.51 seconds long on the kind of clocks we use. That is roughly $365\frac{1}{4}$ days, so we have a calendar that makes three years out of every four 365 days long but adds an extra day every fourth year. But since the 5 hours, 48 minutes and 45.51 seconds isn't quite one quarter of a day (6 hours) we have another adjustment. We add the extra day in any year whose number is divisible by 4 *unless* it is divisible by 100, in which case the number must also be divisible by 400. So 1900 was not a leap year but 2000 will be. Even that isn't perfect, but you and I aren't likely to be concerned with the next adjustment.

Now let's consider the number 365. Unfortunately, it is divisible only by 1, 5, 73, and 365. But somewhere back in ancient times man got his thinking geared to a seven day week. Furthermore, the four more or less obvious seasons (in the Temperate Zones) seem to suggest further subdivisions, and the behavior of the moon seemed to go along with that idea, so we have ended up with our present 12 months of unequal lengths. We all learned the rhyme about "Thirty days hath September," etc., and we keep out of difficulties in most of our affairs.

21.2 Scheduling Customs

But suppose we have figures on the production of viscose rayon in the United States month by month over a period of years and are interested in seasonal variation. Aside from the trouble with February, we shall probably find that the seasonal indexes pretty closely parallel the number of days in the month except in December. Why? The very nature of the process by which viscose rayon is made requires that it operate continuously around the clock and around the week, and that is just what happens. But there are certain maintenance jobs which require the complete shutdown of an entire area periodically, and therefore it is (or, at least, was when the author was in the industry) customary to plan a progressive shutdown once a year. In at least one firm, this was traditionally planned so that as many operators as possible could be at home on Christmas day. Hence the December low.

21.3 Holidays

Now suppose you consider the total monthly transactions of a bank in New Orleans and one in Boston. The seasonal indexes here will be less uniform from year to year because of the number of week ends that creep into the different months. January can have either four or five. Furthermore, legal holidays are established by each state, and Louisiana has a considerable number that Massachusetts does not observe. To make it even more confusing, the Boston area locally observes some holidays that are not Massachusetts legal holidays. Furthermore, Easter wanders back and forth through March and April.

To see how this can really be troublesome, suppose that you have total production figures month by month for plants in an industry which does not have to run continuously and which observes local holidays. Your seasonal indexes will reflect the calendar peculiarities and the holiday customs. If you then use your time series analysis to forecast the time at which a stated amount of material will be produced you can see that the results must be used with great caution.

21.4 Time Rates

Another difficulty arises when we are dealing with reports of production (or sales) per day: per what kind of day? Working? Calendar? Eight-hour or with customary overtime at certain periods? In other words, you must scrutinize the data with which you are working closely to be sure how you should analyze and use them. It must be evident that the possible variations are so numerous that an attempt to compile a comprehensive listing of them would be ludicrous. But sound knowledge of one's general field and of the specific objective of a given study will avoid these pitfalls.

21.5 Changing Time Scales in Trend Equations

A. *Changing Time Scales When the Observations Are Not Rates.* A problem that we must often deal with involves changing the units of time in trend equations. This may be necessary simply for convenience when a trend has been computed with time in years, but we wish to follow the quantities month by month. Or we may need to bring two trend equations, one with time in months and the other with time in years, into a form in which they may better be compared. We first consider how this may be done when the quantities involved are not inherently rates. Suppose we have followed the number of employees on the company payroll at the year end for a number of years and have fitted the trend equation,

$$T = a + bt = 240 + 36t \qquad (21.5.1)$$

where t is in years and is zero in 1940.

Now suppose that we want the time in months. We shall use a subscript, $_m$, when our quantities involve months, so that we are seeking an equation involving t_m. We know that there are 12 months in a year, so we can state that

$$t_m = 12t \qquad (21.5.2a)$$

or

$$t = t_m/12 \qquad (21.5.2b)$$

and we may substitute the latter form into 21.5.1 to obtain

$$T = a + b\,(t_m/12) = a + (b/12)t_m \qquad (21.5.3a)$$

$$= 240 + (36/12)t_m \qquad (21.5.3b)$$

$$= 240 + 3t_m \qquad (21.5.3c)$$

This has converted our time scale to months, but notice that t_m and t are zero at the same time, namely, at the end of the year 1940. We are such creatures of habit that we may well want our zero to be at the end of January, rather than at the end of the year. This is easy: recall that there are 11 months between the end of January and the end of the same year. Using $t_m{}^*$ to denote times with the desired zero, we have

$$t_m{}^* = t_m + 11 \qquad (21.5.4a)$$

or

$$t_m = t_m{}^* - 11 \qquad (21.5.4b)$$

We make the latter substitution into 21.5.3a to obtain

$$T = a + (b/12)\,(t_m{}^* - 11) \qquad (21.5.5a)$$

$$= a - 11b/12 + (b/12)t_m{}^* \qquad (21.5.5b)$$

and into 21.5.3c to obtain, for our specific example,

$$T = 240 + 3(t_m^* - 11) \tag{21.5.5c}$$

$$= 240 - 33 + 3t_m^* \tag{21.5.5d}$$

$$= 207 + 3t_m^* \tag{21.5.5e}$$

It is wise to check your substitutions. At the end of December 1940, $t = 0$ and $t_m^* = 11$, while a year later $t = 1$ and $t_m^* = 23$. Substituting these values in the corresponding equations, we get the same values from either equation: $T = 240$ at the end of 1940 and $T = 276$ at the end of 1941.

The same sort of substitution, with somewhat more algebra involved in simplification, is applicable in the case of the curvilinear trends. Of course, the substitutions can be made in reverse order to convert a monthly trend equation to an annual trend equation. We should also state explicitly that the shifts in zero will not always involve a January-December difference. We may be involved with two fiscal years, one ending December 31 and the other June 30, or we may have two crop years with some other months as the crop-year ends. Careful attention should make it possible to keep the proper substitution straight.

B. *Changing Time Scales When the Observations Are Inherently Rates.* When the quantities we are studying are explicitly or implicitly rates, another element enters into our consideration. To give a specific illustration, suppose that we have studied our annual production in millions of units and have fitted the trend equation,

$$T = a + bt \tag{21.6.1a}$$

$$= 10.8 + 0.18t \tag{21.6.1b}$$

where again t is in years and is zero in 1940. There is no problem in changing to time in months by the substitution represented by equation 21.5.2b, which yields

$$T = a + (b/12)t_m \tag{21.6.2a}$$

$$= 10.8 + (0.18/12)t_m \tag{21.6.2b}$$

$$= 10.8 + 0.015t_m \tag{21.6.2c}$$

Now let us think about the zero on this scale. Here we must recognize that, because our production for the year is interpretable as a rate of production averaged over the entire year, we ought to associate the value with the middle of the year, that is, the midnight between June 30 and July 1 (there are six calendar months either side of that moment), and we might logically associate our time in months with the middle of the month. If we want our monthly scale to have its zero in mid-January, we note that this is $5\frac{1}{2}$ months before the middle of the year, so that we have

$$t_m^* = t_m + 5.5 \tag{21.6.3a}$$

or

$$t_m = t_m^* - 5.5 \tag{21.6.3b}$$

Making the latter substitution in our equations above yields

$$T = a + (b/12)\,(t_m^* - 5.5) \tag{21.6.4a}$$

$$= a - (5.5b/12) + (b/12)t_m^* \tag{21.6.4b}$$

and for our specific case,

$$T = 10.8 + 0.015(t_m^* - 5.5) \tag{21.6.4c}$$

$$= 10.8 - 0.0825 + 0.015t_m^* \tag{21.6.4d}$$

$$= 10.7175 + 0.015t_m^* \tag{21.6.4e}$$

Here we again have an equation expressing annual rates with times in months. Probably we would like to have monthly rates. If the production were at a steady level, the monthly rate would be one-twelfth the annual rate:

$$T_m = T/12 \tag{21.6.5}$$

This suggests that we could divide our last equations by 12 to obtain the desired equations:

$$T_m = T/12 = (a/12) + (b/12^2)\,(t_m^* - 5.5) \tag{21.6.6a}$$

$$= (a/12) + (b/144)\,(t_m^* - 5.5) \tag{21.6.6b}$$

$$= [(a/12) - (5.5b/144)] + (b/144)t_m^* \tag{21.6.6c}$$

or, for our particular case,

$$T_m = (10.7175/12) + (0.015/12)t_m^* \tag{21.6.6d}$$

$$= 0.893125 + 0.00125t_m^* \tag{21.6.6e}$$

It will be instructive to compute the monthly rates for the first two years from equation 21.6.6e and compare their sum with the values of the annual rate for the same years computed from the original equation, 21.6.1b. We show the results in Table 21-1, and they confirm that the two methods

Table 21-1 COMPUTATION OF RATES FROM THE RELATED TREND EQUATIONS: $T_m = 0.893125 + 0.00125t_m^*$ AND $T = 10.8 + 0.18t$

Year	*Month*	t_m^*	T_m	t	T
1940	Jan.	0	0.893125		
	Feb.	1	0.894375		
	Mar.	2	0.895625		
	Apr.	3	0.896875		
	May	4	0.898125		
	June	5	0.899375	0	10.800000
	July	6	0.900625		
	Aug.	7	0.901875		
	Sept.	8	0.903125		
	Oct.	9	0.904375		
	Nov.	10	0.905625		
	Dec.	11	0.906875		
	Total		10.800000		
1941	Jan.	12	0.908125		
	Feb.	13	0.909375		
	Mar.	14	0.910625		
	Apr.	15	0.911875		
	May	16	0.913125		
	June	17	0.914375	1	10.980000
	July	18	0.915625		
	Aug.	19	0.916875		
	Sept.	20	0.918125		
	Oct.	21	0.919375		
	Nov.	22	0.920625		
	Dec.	23	0.921875		
	Total		10.980000		

develop the same value for the sum of the monthly values as for the annual value, as we expect.

Would this result be sound if our trend was curvilinear, that is, quadratic or exponential? Regrettably, the final step of dividing the annual rate equation by 12 to obtain the monthly rate equation is *not* valid. Recall the behavior of our moving averages in seasonal analysis and you will see the sort of thing that will happen. The sum of the 12 monthly productions will be above the annual production if the trend curve is concave upward and below if the curve is concave downward. The algebraic complications necessary to convert annual rates into monthly rates under these conditions are too complex to be practical. Fortunately, many time series in which we are interested have linear trends, and many others have curvatures so slight that the error in conversion is not serious enough to concern us, but it is unavoidably present, and we should be very careful to check the discrepancies in use.

General Study

1. Consider some time series of interest in your field of special study. In each case, list any of the problems discussed in this chapter which would be encountered in using them.

2. As an example of the differences in periods covered by one year, determine when the following years begin:
(a) The fiscal year of any large corporations of interest to you.
(b) The fiscal year of your local government, your state, and the federal government.
(c) The crop year for 1) wheat, 2) corn, 3) cotton, 4) tobacco, and 5) rice.

Specific Problems

1. Determine the legal holidays observed by some producing organization in your region, together with any other scheduling factors, and determine how these would affect seasonal indexes for monthly production totals.

2. The population in a county has followed the trend equation $T = 156{,}000 + 1{,}440t$, where t is in years with $1930 = 0$. What would be the population trend value for each month of 1961?

3. A gas station has shown annual sales in millions of gallons represented by the trend equation $T = 7.2 + 0.288t$ where t is in years with $1956 = 0$. Calculate the monthly sales for 1961.

4. Suppose that the trend in Problem 3 had been of the form $T = 7.2 + 0.288t + 0.035t^2$. Use the (improper) conversion to monthly trend values and find the discrepancy between the sum of these values and the annual value for 1956, 1958, and 1960.

PART E

Index Numbers

22

Index Numbers for Prices

22.1 Orientation

It may seem strange that after we have said that the components of a time series are the trend, seasonal variations, cyclical variation, and irregular variation, we interrupt our discussion after considering only the first two and start to discuss index numbers. Quite possibly it is strange: perhaps we should have discussed index numbers before we considered time series at all. However, we thought that the notion of a time series was something just a little new and different for many of us, and that it might be interesting to open up that idea a bit. But we cannot do much with cyclical and irregular variations without some understanding of index numbers. On the other hand, index numbers have their greatest use in the form of time series. So we have almost the old chicken-and-egg problem. We decided to start on time series, then consider index numbers. Ultimately we shall return to time series and forecasting.

All of us are bound to have an interest in prices. Most of us live on an income which has, from our standpoint, an all too slow upward trend. If the cost of the goods and services we desire rises more rapidly than our income over a period of time, and we are just able to purchase what we want at the beginning of the period, we shall be unable to purchase all that we want at the end. Similarly, if our income drops, but prices drop faster, we shall actually be a little better off! It is, then, important to us to know what is happening to prices.

22.2 The Basic Problem

But just what do we mean by "prices"? Recall all the items that you have, yourself, purchased during the last week, then during the last month, and the last year. Add to your list the items purchased by other members of your family. Then try to recall present prices for these items and prices one year, two years, and five years ago. Next, go on to compare the prices you paid with those paid by similar families living in other parts of the country. Add to the problem that of families with different wants and with habits of purchasing different grades of the same items, and you will begin to see the complexity of making a meaningful statement about what has happened to "prices."

22.3 A Specific Example, with Three Possible Indexes

To make the problem more specific, suppose we consider the cost of the ingredients of a breakfast: orange juice, bacon, eggs, toast, butter, jam, and coffee with cream and sugar. Listed in Table 22-1 are the principal ingredients, their standard commercial units, and possible prices at two times, $t = 0$ and $t = 1$. We also make some computations, showing the percentage ratio, $100P_1/P_0$ for each item, the sum of all the prices, and the percentage ratio, or relative, of these sums, $100\,\Sigma P_1/\Sigma P_0$.

Table 22-1 PRICES OF BREAKFAST INGREDIENTS AT TWO TIMES, WITH COMPARISON OF POSSIBLE PRICE INDEX NUMBERS

Item	Unit	P_0	P_1	$100P_1/P_0$
Oranges	Dozen	\$0.55	\$0.60	109.1
Bacon	Pound	0.45	0.45	100.0
Eggs	Dozen	0.65	0.60	92.3
Bread	Loaf	0.15	0.15	100.0
Butter	Pound	0.75	0.77	102.7
Jam	Jar	0.55	0.52	94.5
Coffee	Pound	1.07	0.90	84.1
Cream	½ Pint	0.29	0.30	103.4
Sugar	Pound	0.12	0.12	100.0
	Sums	\$4.58	\$4.41	886.1

$$100\Sigma P_1/\Sigma P_0 = 96.3$$
$$(\Sigma 100P_1/P_0)/N = 98.5$$

At this point we could compare prices for the two periods by saying that the average of the price relatives was 98.5. (We shall hereafter use the term *price relative* to denote a price ratio expressed as a percentage, and will generally omit the necessary factor of 100 in writing out the formulas involved.) However, the relative of total prices was 96.3. Thus it appears that two ways of considering our information lead to rather different results.

But suppose we look a bit further and ask whether the use of the commercial unit of sale is reasonable. Normally, the individual breakfast involves the following actual amounts, shown as Q in the Table 22-2. Suppose, then, that

Table 22-2 COMPUTATION OF ANOTHER POSSIBLE INDEX FOR THE PRICES FIRST TREATED IN TABLE 22-1

Item	Quantity, Q	P_0	P_0Q	P_1	P_1Q
Oranges	1/8 dozen	$0.55	0.06875	$0.60	0.07500
Bacon	1/16 pound	0.45	0.02812	0.45	0.02812
Eggs	1/6 dozen	0.65	0.10833	0.60	0.10000
Bread	1/16 loaf	0.15	0.00938	0.15	0.00938
Butter	1/48 pound	0.75	0.01562	0.77	0.01604
Jam	1/50 jar	0.55	0.01100	0.52	0.01040
Coffee	1/24 pound	1.07	0.04458	0.90	0.03750
Cream	1/8 of ½ pint	0.29	0.03625	0.30	0.03750
Sugar	1/32 pound	0.12	0.00375	0.12	0.00375
		Sums	0.32578		0.31769

$$\Sigma P_1Q/\Sigma P_0Q = 97.5$$

we calculate next the value (or cost) of the amounts of each food in the breakfasts on the two times in question. Such a value is, of course, the product of the price (dollars per unit) times the quantity (number of units used) or, in symbols, $V = PQ$. The results are shown in Table 22-2.

22.4 Analyzing the Discrepancies

Here we have a quandary: it seems that our attempts to do a little quantitative thinking always produce such quandaries! Why are the three plausible figures we have so far produced so different? Which figure is right? If we re-examine the original data, we see that three of our items (oranges, butter, and cream) rose in price, while three (eggs, jam, and coffee) dropped, and the remaining three (bread, bacon, and sugar) did not change. The average change, expressed as a relative, was 98.5. But notice that the biggest drop was associated with the highest priced item (coffee), while the other drops and all rises were associated with middle-priced items, and two of the three items which did not change were low-priced. Therefore, if we use the relative of the total value of one commercial unit of each item at the two times (which is equivalent to using the relative of the average prices) the large drop in the high-priced item carries more effect, and we have the lower value, 96.3. If we consider our final figure, which reflects the amounts actually used in making a breakfast, it turns out that the eggs are the most important item, oranges next, and so on, and that, so far as the result of all these factors is concerned, ingredients of the actual breakfast dropped very little in price over the period in question. Which index is best? As you have found in connection with other statistical treatments of data, the answer must be, "It depends on what facts you are trying to infer."

22.5 Choosing an Appropriate Index Number

In the present instance, if we are trying to infer the effect of changing prices on our breakfast budget, the last index we computed is clearly the best, for it reflects our actual outgo for breakfasts. If, however, we are considering these prices as representative of many prices and have an idea of the effect of some other economic condition on prices, it may be that the average of price relatives will be more sensibly related to what we want to know. There may be situations in which the relative of the total price is soundly useful, but your author much doubts that. However, the three numbers we have so far considered can all be used as price indexes.

22.6 Summary of Formulas

The first index considered, the average of price relatives, may be called a *simple index*, S.I., and, for N items is computed by the formula,

$$\text{S.I.} = \frac{\Sigma(P_i/P_0)}{N} \tag{22.6.1}$$

where the subscript $_i$ denotes the time of interest and the subscript $_0$ denotes a reference, or *base*, time.

The second index we considered, the ratio of the total value of one commercial unit of each item at the two times, might be thought of as the ratio of values of an aggregate of items, and is sometimes given the name *aggregative price index*. It could be represented by the simple formula,

$$\text{A.I.} = \frac{\Sigma P_i}{\Sigma P_0} \tag{26.6.2}$$

Our final index, in which we found the ratio of the values of the aggregates actually purchased at the two times, is formally called a *weighted aggregative price index*, or simply a weighted index. This name stems from the fact that the quantities used are applied to the individual prices as factors so that they will influence the index more realistically. In statistical parlance, such factors are called weights or weighting factors. This index could be represented by the formula,

$$\text{W.I.} = \frac{\Sigma(P_iQ)}{\Sigma(P_0Q)} \tag{26.6.3}$$

For reasons which will appear presently, we did not place subscripts on the Q's, but we are to understand that the same Q's are to be used in the numerator and in the denominator. That is, the same weights apply to both sets of prices. Notice further that the aggregative index is actually a weighted index where all weights are taken as unity (one).

22.7 Another Example, with More Complications

In the example just given, all indexes agreed that prices had dropped. Will they always? Let's look at some data which are quite typical of the kind of thing that can happen to raw materials for an industry. Suppose that our firm purchases three different raw materials, A, B, and C in the quantities indicated in Table 22-3, and that the prices on two different

Table 22-3 A SECOND SET OF PRICES WITH THREE INDEXES COMPUTED FROM THEM

Item	Q	P_0	P_0Q	P_1	P_1Q	P_1/P_0
A	1	$1.00	1.00	$1.50	1.50	150
B	100	0.50	50.00	0.45	45.00	90
C	1000	0.10	100.00	0.09	90.00	90
	Sums	$1.60	151.00	$2.04	136.50	330

S.I. = 330/3 = 110.0
A.I. = 2.04/1.60 = 127.5
W.I. = 136.5/151.0 = 90.4

occasions were as shown. We compute the three indexes, with the results shown in the table.

Here we have quite a spectacle: three price indexes not only differ in magnitude but tell different stories as to the direction of change. The S.I. says that the prices increased 10%; the A.I. says that they increased by 27.5%; but the W.I. quite as firmly declares that they *decreased* 10%. Surely they can't all be right—or can they? Yes, they can, if we understand and use them correctly. The W.I. tells the story that would be reflected in the company's ledger: expenditures for raw materials did indeed decrease by just 10%. If, somehow, we found a supplier who would ship us the composite set of raw materials in the proportion in which we used them, presumably his price would have dropped 10%. This figure seems quite clear.

Are the A.I. and S.I. equally clear and useful? Generally, we doubt it. For any aggregate in which approximately equal numbers of commercial units are in use for all items, then all three indexes will be about equal, and simplicity of computation will favor the first two. But this is rarely the case, and we believe the W.I. is, in most situations, distinctly to be preferred. Hence, we shall confine our attention largely to it.

Let us clearly understand that although the W.I. is a ratio of *values* it does reflect the price changes, because it is the ratio of values of the same aggregate (perhaps the commonly used term, "market basketful," will sound less frightening?) of goods under two different sets of prices. So only changes in prices alter the index. Is that all there is to price indexes? Not quite: our habits change!

22.8 Choosing Proper Weights

Suppose that the quantities purchased in our company were as shown in Table 22-4. They differ in magnitude from year to year as the result of

Table 22-4 COMPUTATION OF WEIGHTED AGGREGATIVE PRICE INDEXES WHEN BOTH PRICES AND QUANTITIES CHANGE. BOTH INDEXES HAVE 1950 = 100. NO. 1 IS WEIGHTED FOR BASE YEAR QUANTITIES. NO. 2 IS WEIGHTED FOR CURRENT YEAR QUANTITIES

Year	t	Data	Commodity				
			A	B	C	D	Sums
1950	0	P_0	0.50	1.50	5.00	20.00	
		Q_0	1000	500	200	10	
		P_0Q_0	500	750	1000	200	2450
		P_0Q_1	600	780	1100	220	2700
		P_0Q_2	750	900	1100	220	2970
		P_0Q_3	1000	1200	1250	180	3630
		P_0Q_4	1250	1500	1300	100	4150
1951	1	P_1	0.60	1.70	5.20	21.00	
		Q_1	1200	520	220	11	
		P_1Q_0	600	850	1040	210	2700
		P_1Q_1	720	884	1144	231	2979
1952	2	P_2	0.65	1.70	4.90	19.00	
		Q_2	1500	600	220	11	
		P_2Q_0	650	850	980	190	2670
		P_2Q_2	976	1020	1078	209	3282
1953	3	P_3	0.70	1.75	4.80	18.00	
		Q_3	2000	800	250	9	
		P_3Q_0	700	875	960	180	2715
		P_3Q_3	1400	1400	1200	162	4162
1954	4	P_4	0.70	2.00	4.75	15.00	
		Q_4	2500	1000	260	5	
		P_4Q_0	700	1000	950	150	2800
		P_4Q_4	1750	2000	1235	75	5060

Resultant Indexes

Year	*Index No. 1* W.I. = $\Sigma P_iQ_0/\Sigma P_0Q_0$	*Index No. 2* W.I. = $\Sigma P_iQ_i/\Sigma P_0Q_i$
1950	100.0	100.0
1951	110.2	110.3
1952	109.0	110.5
1953	110.8	114.7
1954	114.3	121.9

changes in our total business, of changes in the distribution of products, and in our ways of making them. When we consider constructing weighted indexes, we may use *base year* quantities as weights, or we may use *current year* quantities. (Notice, parenthetically, that we have dropped into the habit of designating times as "years." Actually, the times in question may cover any period whatever. So many indexes have as their base some year that it will avoid tedious circumlocution to use the word, year, in a sort of catchall sense here.) In fact, circumstances will arise in which we may consider the quantities purchased in some designated year other than the base year, or some set of quantities never actually purchased as more representative, and we shall refer to such quantities as *special quantities.* Thus, we have three weighted indexes available for a set of prices over a period of years.

These indexes are constructed with the respective weights shown in the following formulas:

Base Year Weights

$$\text{W.I.}_{\cdot 0} = \frac{\Sigma(P_i Q_0)}{\Sigma(P_0 Q_0)} \tag{22.8.1}$$

Current Year Weights

$$\text{W.I.}_{\cdot i} = \frac{\Sigma(P_i Q_i)}{\Sigma(P_0 Q_i)} \tag{22.8.2}$$

Specified Year Weights

$$\text{W.I.}_{\cdot t} = \frac{\Sigma(P_i Q_t)}{\Sigma(P_0 Q_t)} \tag{22.8.3}$$

Notice that the same weight is used in the numerator as in the denominator for each index. Notice also that the first and third index use one set of weights and one denominator throughout, whereas the second uses a new set of weights and therefore a new denominator each time.

What are the advantages and disadvantages of each modification of the index? Clearly, the use of either base-year or specified-year weights makes the computations much easier. If the aggregate purchased has not changed greatly in the ratios of its components, either index is reasonable. Why, then, use one base year for prices and another for quantities (as in the specified-time index)? To the extent that there has been some change in relative composition of the aggregate, it may be considered that the specified time is more typical, but it may be desirable to relate prices for this aggregate to some other base year to bring the series of indexes into relation with other reference series. In the case of some kinds of prices, technological and sociological changes may affect the composition of the aggregate so rapidly that the current-time weights *may* convey a more realistic picture.

Notice that we say *may!* While we do not wish to frighten you, it is only fair to warn you that the use of indexes is one of the schemes cited in "How to Lie with Statistics" by Darrell Huff (W. W. Norton Inc., New York). *Unless you know how an index was put together, you can be grossly misled by it,* and that fact has, unfortunately, been deliberately used by unscrupulous individuals and groups since the first index number was concocted.

22.9 Base Shifting

Even now, we haven't covered all the possibilities of trouble! Suppose that we are constructing W.I.'s with base year weights and that our base year was 1935. Further suppose that by 1954 our index had reached 250 and for 1955 it was 275. Our immediate reaction is to say (and it is often said) that prices were up 25% in 1955 over 1954. Indeed they were — but 25% of what? Their 1954 level? Not at all! They were up 25% of their 1935 level. They only increased 100(275 − 250)/250 or 10% of their 1954 level or 100(275 − 250)/275 or 9.1% of their 1955 level! Percentages are very handy things to have around, but a wonderful tool of the person who "deals casually with truth." The conscientious user of percentages always makes it perfectly clear what his base is.

In order to reduce the severity of this distortion of facts, it is common practice to change the base of an index after it has moved sufficiently far from 100 in present values. Yet it may still be desirable to use old weighting factors. Suppose that by 1950 our indexes in the series we were just discussing had risen to 200. We might decide that a change of base was needed, so we would refer all values to 1950 as a base. The base, by the way, is often indicated by saying such a thing as "1935 = 100." Here we want to change from 1935 = 100 to 1950 = 100. If we divide all our indexes as originally calculated by 200, the 1950 value, we shall make our 1950 index 100 (as usual we assume the necessary factor to keep our values as percentages) and all other values will work out as percentages of the 1950 value. Thus our 1954 index becomes 125.0 and our 1955 index becomes 137.5, and so the difference between the two values, 12.5, is more nearly but still *not exactly* the percentage of the 1954 prices at which 1955 prices were found. Notice that we continue to use 1935 weights, although we shift the base year to 1950. This is an indication of the kind of thing you must keep constantly in mind in studying and making inferences from published index figures.

22.10 A New Problem with a Long Time Span

Are our troubles over now? Not quite! Suppose you wanted to construct an index of college men's wardrobe prices over the years. The author needed such a wardrobe during the allegedly "roaring" twenties. Standard classroom attire in New England consisted of "plus fours" of quite expensive woolen material, golf stockings which cost several dollars a pair, cotton shirts, necktie, a fancy pullover sweater for spring and fall to which a suit or sport coat was added in winter in the north. If we didn't want to be quite so informal, we either replaced the plus fours with "Oxford bags" or more normal flannel trousers, or wore a suit. For tea dances incident to big week ends in the spring, white flannels with a blue worsted coat were *de rigueur*, while "black tie" demanded a waistcoat, pleated shirt, stand-up collar, and mother-of-pearl studs and links, and special shoes. Now suppose we started out with a typical wardrobe of such items as our "market basketful," and tried to carry on to the present. Several items could be priced only in costume stores in the theatrical district, and many of them are by no means representative of collegiate attire. Actually, the styles changed by several more or less well-defined stages.

And this sort of thing is by no means peculiar to clothing. Think of the bill of goods required per car by automobile manufacturers down the years: alloys are used in large quantities today that were unknown 35 years ago; the finishes and upholstery have totally changed; hydraulic brakes have become universal, and so on. Yet it is important to know how prices have changed. What can be done?

22.11 Splicing Methods

The method used is called "splicing," a quite reasonable term. One constructs an index with one set of weights until it becomes evident that one or more items is being replaced by a different item. Then, for the time period in which that has become apparent, he calculates a value on the old basis and also starts a new index with new quantity weights, involving the new, but not the old, materials. To continue the new figures back to the old base all new index values are then multiplied by the value of the old index for the changeover time.

In a strict sense, it could be argued that the index is not the same and one has no right to continue in such a way, but this is not a very sound argument. Suppose we refer again to the idea of the college man's wardrobe. Certainly college men wear clothes now, and they did in the twenties. Certainly it is of some interest to economists to know how the prices of such wardrobes have changed. By the splicing technic, we have a much more real picture of wardrobe cost changes than we would have had by insisting on trying to price our old costumes in today's market: our prices would be more unrealistic by far than any honest and intelligent effort to keep our quantities representative of what was actually being worn. Similarly, if we were interested in automobile raw material costs, it would be far more sound to consider the changing materials actually being used than to try to carry the old material list forward in a market no longer under the influences prevailing when those materials were in heavy demand for cars.

The important thing, then, is to have a clear idea of what prices you are trying to study and in what kind of a market. If you are reading someone else's index, you *must* know how he answered these questions and how he constructed his index, otherwise you will mislead yourself or fall victim to his calculated effort to mislead you. Perhaps this sounds gloomy, but it is not far from the truth to say that indexes are a most useful tool in the hands of an intelligent and thoughtful user. In the hands of the unscrupulous they can misrepresent facts in a most convincing way.

22.12 Use of Price Relatives in Index Construction

One last bit of mechanics will sometimes save you trouble. Suppose that you have available a set of price relatives, that is, price ratios expressed as percentages, for the commodities in which you are interested over the necessary time period, and that you know the quantities for the required time to use as weights in constructing the W.I. you want. Can you construct the W.I. directly from the relatives without converting them back to actual prices? Yes, you can. All you need is the base year actual prices. Each price relative is simply a ratio, P_i/P_0, so we take advantage of a little simple algebra to write

$$\text{W.I.} = \frac{\Sigma(P_i/P_0)(P_0Q_x)}{\Sigma P_0Q_x} \tag{22.12.1}$$

where the Q_x values of the formula may be the base year, current year, or any arbitrarily specified year quantities. This formula would look even more compact if we let

$$R_P = P_i/P_0 = \text{the price relative and}$$

$$V_t = P_0Q_x = \text{the value of the specified quantity of the commodity at base year prices}$$

Then we see that

$$\text{W.I.} = \Sigma R_P V_t / \Sigma V_t$$

which brings out the fact that we are using *values* as *weights* on *price relatives* to produce our price index.

Appended to this chapter are Tables 22-5 and 22-6 and Fig. 22-1, illustrating briefly a number of the problems and computational methods we have discussed. We urge you to be sure that you grasp the principles involved. In a subsequent chapter we shall discuss some of the better known indexes, published regularly and vital to basic thinking about a variety of business and economic problems. We suspect that you will recognize a number of them by name, and believe that your present study will endow them with a much fuller meaning.

Table 22-5 SPLICING OF A WEIGHTED AGGREGATIVE PRICE INDEX

In 1947, Item $B2$ is used partially in place of Item $B1$ and thereafter replaces it entirely. In 1948, $C2$ similarly partially replaces $C1$ and thereafter replaces it entirely. In 1950, Item D is added to the list of materials purchased. The problem: to construct a meaningful aggregative price index with 1945 = 100

Item	Year													
	1945 = 0		1946 = 1		1947 = 2		1948 = 3		1949 = 4		1950 = 5		1951 = 6	
	P_0	Q_0	P_1	Q_1	P_2	Q_2	P_3	Q_3	P_4	Q_4	P_5	Q_5	P_6	Q_6
A	1.20	1000	1.25	1200	1.20	1500	1.30	1600	1.35	1800	1.40	2000	1.50	2500
$B1$	1.50	1500	1.75	1400	2.00	1000	—	—	—	—	—	—	—	—
$B2$	—	—	—	—	1.40	500	1.35	1700	1.35	1900	1.35	2100	1.40	2300
$C1$	2.20	700	2.20	750	2.35	800	2.40	900	—	—	—	—	—	—
$C2$	—	—	—	—	—	—	2.00	100	1.90	1000	1.85	1200	1.90	1500
D	—	—	—	—	—	—	—	—	—	—	0.75	200	0.70	500
ΣP_iQ_0 [a]	4990		5415		5845									
ΣP_iQ_2 [b]					4380		4545							
ΣP_iQ_3 [c]							4575		4645		4720			
ΣP_iQ_5 [d]											8005		8360	
I_1	100.0		108.5		117.1									
I_2					100.0		103.8							
I_3							100.0		101.5		103.2			
I_4											100.0		104.0	
I_S	100.0		108.5		117.1		121.5		123.3		125.4		130.4	

[a] Sum includes Items A, $B1$, and $C1$. $I_1 = \Sigma P_iQ_0/\Sigma P_0Q_0$ and is a weighted index, 1945 = 100, with 1945 (base year) weights.
[b] Sum includes Items A, $B2$, and $C1$. $I_2 = \Sigma P_iQ_2/\Sigma P_2Q_2$ and is a weighted index, 1947 = 100, with 1947 (*new* base year) weights.
[c] Sum includes Items A, $B2$, and $C2$. $I_3 = \Sigma P_iQ_3/\Sigma P_3Q_3$ and is a weighted index, 1948 = 100, with 1948 (*new* base year) weights.
[d] Sum includes Items A, $B2$, $C2$ and D. $I_4 = \Sigma P_iQ_5/\Sigma P_5Q_5$ and is a weighted index 1950 = 100, with 1950 (*new* base year) weights.
I_S is the spliced index. For 1945–1947 it is simply I_1. For 1947–1948 it is I_2 multiplied by the 1947 value of I_S (= I_1). For 1948–1950, it is I_3 multiplied by the 1948 value of I_S. After 1950, it is I_4 multiplied by the 1950 value of I_S.

Questions for Study

1. Is it proper to think of the resulting spliced index as reflecting prices with 1945 as a base? Clearly justify your conclusions.
2. Is it proper to think of the index as weighted for 1945 quantities? Again, justify your conclusions.
3. How could you explain just how this index reflects prices usefully?

Table 22-6 CHANGE OF BASE OF AN INDEX NUMBER. THE BLS CONSUMERS' PRICE INDEX ON THREE DIFFERENT BASES

Year	1947–49 = 100	1935–39 = 100	1925 = 100
1925	75.0	125.4	100.0
1926	75.6	126.4	100.8
1927	74.2	124.0	98.9
1928	73.3	122.6	97.8
1929	73.3	122.5	97.7
1930	71.4	119.4	95.2
1931	65.0	108.7	86.7
1932	58.4	97.6	77.8
1933	55.3	92.4	73.7
1934	57.2	95.7	76.3
1935	58.7	98.1	78.2
1936	59.3	99.1	79.0
1937	61.4	102.7	81.9
1938	60.3	100.8	80.4
1939	59.4	99.4	79.3
1940	59.9	100.2	79.9
1941	62.9	105.2	83.9
1942	69.7	116.6	93.0
1943	74.0	123.7	98.6
1944	75.2	125.7	100.2
1945	76.9	128.6	102.6
1946	83.4	139.5	111.2
1947	95.5	159.6	127.3
1948	102.8	171.9	137.1
1949	101.8	170.2	135.7
1950	102.8	171.9	137.1
1951	111.0	185.6	148.0
1952	113.5	189.8	151.4
1953	114.4	191.3	152.6
1954	114.8	191.9	153.0
1955	114.5	191.4	152.6
1956	116.2	194.2	154.9
1957	120.2	200.9	160.2
1958	123.5	206.4	164.6
1959	124.6	208.3	166.1
1960	126.5	211.5	168.6

See text for details of procedures used in changing base. Note that two of these series use averages over a period of years instead of a single year as base.

Fig. 22-1. BLS Consumers' Price Index Plotted on Three Different Bases.

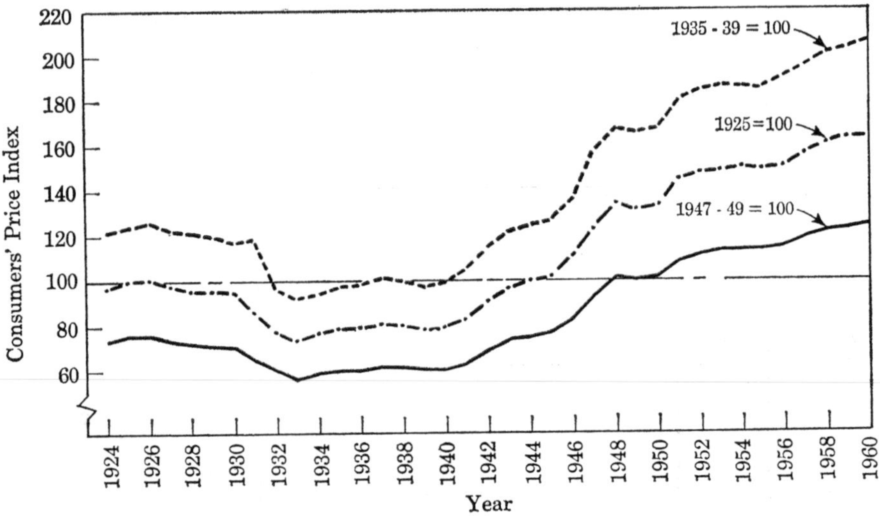

General Study

1. We did not include in our discussion a specific procedure for splicing when a drastic emergency, such as a war, removed one or more items from the market and required a substitution without realistic changeover periods. Use your knowledge acquired to date to develop an appropriate procedure.

2. Use formulas to compare base-shifted values for a simple index and aggregative index, a base-year weighted index, and a current-year-weighted index with indexes computed with the new base. Does the result add any merit to any of the indexes?

3. A number of price indexes of general public interest are available for the years 1789 to date. Consider the question whether they have any real meaning, and suggest arguments on both sides. You can find some of these indexes in *Historical Statistics of the United States, Colonial Times to 1957,* U.S. Department of Commerce, Bureau of the Census, Washington, D.C., 1960, if you wish to examine them. Can you reach any general conclusion concerning their value?

Specific Problems

1. Secure prices on commodities of particular importance to the region in which you live at appropriate intervals over the past several years and construct the several types of indexes. Note their differences and consider their merits for the purposes for which such an index would be useful.

23

Index Numbers for Volume

23.1 Relation to Price Indexes

In the preceding chapter, we confined our discussion of index numbers to indexes of prices. Suppose we now consider the problem of measuring the changes in the quantity (or volume) of materials bought and sold. At first it may seem that this is hardly a matter to involve us in index numbers, for it would appear that all we would need to do would be to count up the total number of units involved at two times of interest to us and express their ratio as a percentage. In other words, we should simply calculate the relative of total volumes. A simple example, admittedly exaggerated, will show the weaknesses of such an index. Imagine a firm selling typewriters at $200 each, paper at $5 per box, and ribbons at $1 each. Suppose that in the base year they sold 10 typewriters, 1000 boxes of paper, and 25 ribbons. Then suppose that in a given year they sold 5 typewriters, 980 boxes of paper, and 50 ribbons. They sold exactly the same total number of items each year and, on our proposed basis, the quantity index would be 100! But is that realistic? Hardly, for the sale of one typewriter ribbon certainly does not carry the same dollar profit as the sale of one typewriter.

23.2 Basic Formulas

We might attempt to compute the relative sales volume for each item, then average the relatives. This would be reminiscent of our simple index for prices, and we would reasonably call the result a *simple index:*

$$\text{S.I.} = \frac{\Sigma(Q_i/Q_0)}{N} \tag{23.2.1}$$

For our case, where the relatives for typewriters, papers, and ribbons are, respectively, 50%, 98%, and 200%, we have

$$\text{S.I.} = \frac{50 + 98 + 200}{3} = \frac{348}{3} = 116 \tag{23.2.2}$$

This index tells us that our quantities have increased.

In our opening paragraph, we actually constructed an index which is somewhat reminiscent of the aggregative price index. It was simply the relative of total quantities, and may reasonably be called the *aggregative* index:

$$\text{A.I.} = \frac{\Sigma Q_i}{\Sigma Q_0} \tag{23.2.3}$$

For our particular data, its value was

$$\text{A.I.} = \frac{10 + 1000 + 25}{5 + 980 + 50} = \frac{1035}{1035} = 1.00 \tag{23.2.4}$$

This index implies that the sales volume remained unchanged.

The thing that we would often be unhappy about in each of these indexes is the very significant fact that they pay no attention to the other component of value, namely, price. In working out a price index, we found that it was desirable to weigh the price changes in terms of the quantities involved. Here, we shall perform a simliar operation and weigh the quantities in terms of fixed prices. The price may be the base year price, the current year price, or some specified year price for each item. The resultant formulas would become

Base Year Weights

$$\text{W.I.}_{\cdot 0} = \frac{P_0 Q_i}{P_0 Q_0} \tag{23.2.5}$$

Current Year Weights

$$\text{W.I.}_{\cdot i} = \frac{P_i Q_i}{P_i Q_0} \tag{23.2.6}$$

Specified Year Weights

$$\text{W.I.}_{\cdot t} = \frac{P_t Q_i}{P_t Q_0} \tag{23.2.7}$$

Assuming that the prices quoted in the above discussion of our small business are base-year quantities, our weighted index with base-year weights would be

$$\text{W.I.}_{\cdot 0} = \frac{(200 \times 5) + (5 \times 980) + (1 \times 50)}{(200 \times 10) + (5 \times 1000) + (1 \times 25)} = \frac{5950}{7025} = 84.7$$

23.3 Comparison of Indexes and Weights

Again we have a problem similar to that involved in our price indexes: here are three indexes with different values. The simple index tells us our sales volume increased 16%; the aggregative index, that it didn't change; and the weighted index, that it decreased 15.3%. It would appear that index numbers lied again! In fact, they didn't, but merely measured different things, and *we* did the lying by failing to recognize that fact in interpreting them. Our simple index showed us what the average "department" in our store would have experienced as a change in volume. The great increase in the relative of ribbon sales offset the small decrease in paper sales and the decrease in typewriter sales. Here no attention is paid to either the value of the items or their physical size. In the aggregative index without weights, we have, as we said, simply the relative counts of actual items: a typewriter and a ribbon for it count equally. Is this realistic? If we are interested simply in the number of transactions that have to be recorded by our accountants, perhaps it is, but as a general measure of our business it seems dubious. The weighted index seems to present a far more realistic picture of the effect of the volume changes on the economics of our little business. We believe you will generally find that an appropriately weighted aggregative index of quantities will be likely to contain the real information needed for guiding business decisions.

Notice that, in the case of the price indexes, the weighted index reflected price changes by obtaining the relative value of the same bill of goods at two different price schedules. Now, in the quantity index, the weighted index reflects quantity changes by determining the relative value of two different bills of goods purchased at the same price schedule.

23.4 Specific Example

It will be instructive to construct quantity indexes, weighted for given year and base year prices, for the data in Table 22-4 of the preceding chapter. All basic computations were already made in that table, and only the final relatives need be computed. The results are summarized in Table 23-1. Notice again that the weights used affect the index appreciably.

Table 23-1 WEIGHTED AGGREGATIVE QUANTITY INDEXES COMPUTED FOR DATA OF TABLE 22-4

Year	*Base Year Weights* $W.I._0 = \frac{P_0Q_i}{P_0Q_0}$	*Current Year Weights* $W.I._i = \frac{P_iQ_i}{P_iQ_0}$
1950	100.0	100.0
1951	110.2	110.3
1952	121.2	122.9
1953	148.2	153.3
1954	169.4	180.7

23.5 Shifting and Splicing

It will be apparent that all the matters of changing base and splicing which we considered in connection with price indexes will concern us with quantity indexes, and that the solution of the problems will follow the principles there established. No detailed explanation seems necessary in this text.

General Study and Specific Problems

Follow the suggestions at the end of the previous chapter in terms of quantities, rather than prices.

24

Some Important Index Numbers and Their Uses

24.1 Introduction

In our discussion of the methods by which index numbers are constructed, we have indicated the importance of being thoroughly familiar with the sampling methods and construction procedures behind any index numbers of which we make serious use. It would require a book larger than this simply to present a summary of this information for our most used indexes. Obviously we cannot do that here. Our serious reader will find *Measuring Business Changes*, by Richard M. Snyder (Wiley, New York, 1955), an excellent source of information of this subject. In general, it gives the source, place and frequency of publication, price, basic sampling information, and construction formulas for all indexes in common use. It also refers to sources of more exhaustive information about those indexes where this information is too voluminous for inclusion in the book. It is a most valuable handbook for the conscientious user of index numbers.

We cannot include this information, of course, but we shall discuss one index in broad terms, show some of its uses and misuses, and mention some other indexes that are useful. We hope our readers who are students of economics and its related fields will be stimulated to make a more complete study of this important area.

24.2 The Consumers' Price Index

One of the most important index numbers today, in the sense that it affects a very large number of people, is that commonly known as the *Consumers' Price Index*, which is constructed and published by the United States Bureau of Labor Statistics. Unfortunately, the short title by which it is commonly known fails to emphasize the fact, contained in its full title, that the index reflects the prices of goods and services purchased by moderate income families in urban communities. The index was originally based on a survey of the "market basketful" of such goods and services actually purchased by some 15,000 families of clerical workers and workers in the skilled trades in a number of our larger cities.

From time to time, revisions have been made on the basis of more recent surveys in an effort to keep it in line with current living conditions. In effect, then, it is a base-year-weighted aggregative price index, which has been subject to splicing and to base shifting. It has been the subject of close scrutiny and sharp criticism by competent students and others, and it is probably as sound a figure as can be obtained for its purpose. An elaborate system of sampling across the country makes it possible to produce separate indexes for different cities and different groups of items, or to combine them into the overall index.

24.3 Escalator Clauses

One important use of the *Consumers' Price Index* has been in connection with the so-called escalator clauses in union contracts, which guarantee specified changes in wages when the *CPI* changes by agreed amounts. Related to these changes are the changes commonly made in salaries of nonunion employees when the *CPI* has changed appreciably.

Unfortunately, it is often misused in that way, because the prices of the goods and services purchased by higher income families, or families in any income bracket in small cities or rural regions, do not necessarily change in the same way as those reflected in the index.

24.4 Other Useful Indexes

The government also makes available the indexes of prices paid by farmers and of prices received by them for farm products. Both indexes are published by the Department of Agriculture. The Bureau of Labor Statistics also publishes an Index of Wholesale Prices, also available by commodity groups as well as in composite form.

24.5 Deflation

One important use of price indexes is to permit the operation known as deflation. Suppose that you consider a worker in a large city who received an income of $3,300 in 1931 and an income of $9,600 in 1950. It sounds as though his income relative was (9,600/3,300)100 = 290.9, doesn't it? But suppose we refer to Table 22-6, which shows the Consumers' Price Index, and use the column with 1935–1939 = 100. The index for 1931 was 108.7. We might say, then, that the basketful which, in the base period, would have cost \$1.00 would cost \$1.087 in 1931. Therefore, our \$3,300 salary would buy 3,300/1.087 or 3035.8 basketsful. In 1950, the index rose to 171.9, or the cost of our basket was now \$1.719, so that our \$9,600 would buy only 9,600/1.719 or 5584.6 basketsful. So that, in terms of the number of standard basketsful we could buy, our income relative would be only 100(5584.6/3035.8) = 184.0, quite different from the 290.9 figure above. If, then, we divide an income or value figure by an appropriate price index (and multiply by 100) we have, in fact, converted our dollar figure into a figure of quantities of goods which the dollars we have would purchase at the current prices. We say that we have *deflated* the dollars *to dollars of fixed value* (or purchasing power), specifically their purchasing power in the base year of the index used.

24.6 Caution: Use an Appropriate Index

A word of caution should be interjected at this point. Suppose we wish to compare the "prosperity" of urban employees and farmers. We may have data on the average wages of the employees, which we deflate by means of the *Consumers' Price Index.* Then we may have information on the income received by farmers in the group with which we are concerned, which we deflate by means of the index of prices of goods bought by farmers. Our first possibility is that we may fail to base both price indexes in the same year. After correcting this error, we may then compute, each year, the ratio of the "real" incomes of the farmers and urban workers. But have we insured that the actual incomes and expenses cover comparable elements? For example, the urban incomes presumably are gross incomes. How has the farmer's livelihood secured directly from his farm (his own vegetables, fruits, dairy products, and meat) been accounted for? Has it been added to his cash income? Or left out of both income and expenses? Where has the cost of his home appeared? And so on. If we use income relatives instead of actual incomes, we tend to be even less critical of the composition of the figures and may mislead ourselves (or others) seriously.

Another aspect of indexes is somewhat related to this one. Separate Consumers' Price Indexes, for instance, are published for different cities. One might note that the price index most recently available for City A was considerably above the index for City B and erroneously infer from that fact that it costs more to live in City A than in City B. A little thought will make it clear that the indexes tell nothing about the relative costs in the two cities but only how they have changed from the costs in each at the base year. To know which city costs more today we must either know directly the value of the "basketful" in each today, or their values in some other year and apply our indexes to compute their values now, and then make our direct comparison of costs.

24.7 The Value of the Dollar

An interesting use of a price index arises by simply using it to deflate $1.00, which simply means taking the reciprocal of the index, with due allowance for the factor of 100 associated with percentages, as usual. As the index rises, values less than 1.00 will be obtained, while, as the index falls below 100.0, values greater than 1.00 will be obtained. The figures reflect the value of the dollar at the stated time compared to its value in the base year of the index, in purchasing the items reflected in the index. It must be borne in mind that (a) the value applies only to these items and (b) it is in reference to an arbitrary base time.

24.8 A Rewarning

It seems to us not amiss to repeat, in somewhat different words after this discussion, the warning we gave you before. Reference to your texts in economics will show you a number of other indexes of various sorts which are useful in various aspects of economic theory and its applications. We hope that what we have said here has persuaded you that index numbers, properly constructed and used, are a most valuable tool, for they can be a very enlightening measure of "typical" changes in a complex situation. The thoughtful user of any index, however, owes it to himself to determine the following facts about any index he uses:

1. Basically, what type of index is it?
2. How many items are included and how are they selected?
3. How is the information concerning the values to be used in its computation secured?
4. When and how have splices and changes of base entered the published figures?

With this information at hand, the index may be soundly used.

We should also mention that there are many highly specialized figures which are indexes of a sort, and that similar questions concerning them will elucidate their meaning and use. We urge you again: be careful to know what you are using.

General Study

1. This chapter deals clearly with applications of index numbers to various aspects of the economy. Therefore, we should consider the ideas in relation to the uses we encounter in course dealing with these subjects, where an understanding of index numbers is generally assumed. We should also become increasingly aware of the appearance of index numbers in news publications and should consider the appropriateness of the uses made of them and the conclusions drawn.

Specific Problems

1. Again, specific problems are most valuable when they apply to items of current and local or general interest, to which background information can apply. If this is being used as a class test, we suggest that the development of index numbers of some concern to the class, school, or community be undertaken, and that these indexes be put to appropriate uses.

PART F

Time Series Analysis, Continued: Cyclical and Irregular Components and Forecasting

25

Cyclical Variation

25.1 Return to Time Series

Now that we have some knowledge of what index numbers mean, it is time to return to our problem of analyzing time series. We have already learned how to analyze for and eliminate trend and seasonal variation, so as to produce a series, $Y/TS = CI$, which contains only cyclical and irregular components. We know that the cyclical variations are, by definition, up-and-down variations having a period greater than one year and that, in fact, their apparent periods are very irregular in length.

25.2 An Initial Attack on Cyclical Variation

A first attack on the problem of analyzing cyclical variation consists of plotting the values of Y/TS vs. t on graph paper and then, by eye, drawing a smooth curve through the somewhat irregular waves we will usually see and reading from the curves the values of C. If the irregular variations are not too large relative to the cyclical variations, this procedure may give us all the information that we require. Or we may go on to tabulate the dates and magnitudes of successive peaks and hollows, the time intervals between them, and other information suggested by the economics involved in our particular series.

25.3 Some Further Considerations

However, and particularly when we are interested in forecasting, we may be somewhat unhappy about leaving so much to the dubious judgment of our eyes. Here is where indexes come in to help us. Suppose we have a series for the volume of sales of our particular product. It presumably will be subject to many of the factors which influence sales generally, but it certainly is subject to its own individual factors, both cyclical and irregular. If we have plots of our series and also of some index of sales based on a large number of products and stores, it is quite possible that we may recognize some gross similarities in the more conspicuous peaks and hollows of the two series. However, we are almost certain to notice three important differences between the two series, namely,

1. The index series is quite likely to have less irregular variation because it is, in fact, an average. This means that the wave form of the cyclical variation will be clearer.
2. The two series may have different amplitudes. This will make it deceptive to our eyes to compare the series.
3. Their evidently comparable features may occur regularly some time after, in one series, the time at which they occurred in the other. In this case, the earlier series is said to *lead* the other, or the later series to *lag* the first by the stated amount.

25.4 Facilitating Comparisons

Our problem, then, is to bring the two series into a more useful relation so that we can use the smoothness of the index series, with its more evident cyclical indexes, as a basis for formulating cyclical indexes for our particular series. This becomes especially useful when our series lags the index series. Our first step is to develop from each series its related "standardized" series. For this purpose we compute for each series the mean and standard deviation of the observed *CI* (which we might call Y'') values, then express each value as $z = (Y'' - \overline{Y''})/s_{Y''}$. This will tend to make the amplitude of both series about the same.

Our next step is to plot the two series on separate pieces of graph paper to the same scale, with at least one on tracing paper. Then we superpose the two graphs and slide one of them relative to the other until we have found, by eye, approximately the correct lead or lag. Then we determine the correlation coefficient between the two z-series at this and nearby leads or lags and consider as our true lead or lag the value which produces the highest correlation coefficient.

25.5 The Relating Equation

Finally, using this lead or lag, we compute the linear regression equation for the two series. Of course this will only be useful for forecasting if the standard series *leads* ours by an amount sufficiently great to permit us to take constructive action. For clarity, suppose that we designate the value of our own series at a given time as Y''_t and the value of L time units earlier from the reference series as X''_{t-L}. We simply compute the a and b for the equation,

$$Y''_{t_c} = a + bX''_{t-L} \tag{25.4.1}$$

from the formulas

$$b = \frac{\Sigma Y''_t X''_{t-L} - \overline{X''}_{t-L}\Sigma Y''_t}{\Sigma(X''_{t-L})^2 - \overline{X''}_{t-L}\Sigma X''_{t-L}} \tag{25.4.2}$$

$$a = \overline{Y''}_t - b\overline{X''}_{t-L} \tag{25.4.3}$$

which you recognize as the familiar regression formulas with the customary Y and X replaced by Y''_t and X''_{t-L}, respectively. The symbol Y''_{t_c} denotes the value calculated from the equation, to distinguish it from Y''_t, which denotes the observed values.

In the event that our reference series is a smoothed estimate of cyclical values, then we can use our calculated values as the best estimate of C and divide our $Y'' = CI$ values by them to estimate I, the irregular variation, that is, $I = CI/C = Y''_t/Y''_{t_c}$.

25.6 Comments on Methods

Thus we have two ways of forming an estimate of C. We can smooth in a curve by eye through our own data, or we can relate our series to a "standard" series which is either smoother by its nature or has been smoothed. It will come as a disappointment to some of us that there are no more exact methods available for common use. It is quite true that there are excellent methods available (not for too common use) to mathematicians for unscrambling complicated and irregular-looking cyclical variations, but it is unfortunately the case that, except for some standard series, few data appear to have sufficient reliability and comparability over a long enough period of time to justify the expense of the analysis.

25.7 Expressing Irregular Variation

What do we do about irregular variations? In our introduction to the ideas of time series, we suggested that irregular variations might be subclassified into episodic and random variations. The episodic variations are those which are large and reasonably associated with causes recognized (after the fact, to be sure) not likely to recur frequently. After identifying these variations, we express the remaining irregularities as their standard deviation. If our seasonal and cyclical variations have been computed as indexes in ratio form (that is, varying about 1.000), our irregular indexes will also vary about

1.000 and, in fact, their mean should be so close to unity that we may consider it to be unity and compute the standard deviation simply as

$$s = \sqrt{\frac{\Sigma I^2 - N}{N - 1}}$$

What will this mean, in effect? We assume that irregular variations will be normally distributed about their mean, 1.000, with the estimated standard deviation, so that we can use the standard z distribution to estimate the probability of experiencing various values of I at future times. We cannot, of course, predict, except in this sense, the value we shall actually experience at any stated time.

Problems

It would be desirable to carry out the cyclical analysis of one or more of the series you have been studying in connection with seasonal and trend analysis.

26

Hindsight and Foresight, or the Gentle Art of Forecasting the Future

26.1 Introduction

Our title for this chapter sounds a bit frivolous, but it could hardly be more frivolous than some forecasts which are taken very seriously. Actually, it is intended to remind us that the only guide we have to the future is the past and a more or less tacit faith that something can be learned of the future from a study of the past. As we have implied, our real purpose in learning something about the analysis of time series is to permit us to make more valid predictions about the future and to take some action to modify the future for our benefit.

26.2 A Survey of Our Accomplishments

What have we learned? We have learned to classify the variations we see in the past into trends, seasonal variations, cyclical variations, and irregular variations. And we have learned how to take series apart and make more or less good estimates of these components. So far as seasonal and trend components were concerned, our methods worked quite well in recovering the facts on known, synthesized series. Cyclical behavior posed more of a problem, and our measure of irregular variation really reflected both actual irregularities and our errors in estimating the other factors. Now suppose we want to predict the future. How do we go about it?

26.3 The Tacit Assumptions in Simple Forecasting

First of all, we think of the trend as the core of our series. The *computation* of future values from our trend equation is no problem. But do they mean anything? In having the temerity to propose these values as the future core, we are tacitly assuming that the factors that have operated on our series in the past will continue. But how sure can we be that a new technical development will not wipe out our business? Who makes wooden automobile body frames today? How many gaslight mantles are produced annually in this country now? How many horsecars operate? Yet these were all important items not so long ago as to have been forgotten. We bring these ideas to your attention not to persuade you that forecasting is futile, but to warn you that the forecast will be correct only if certain assumptions remain true. The extension of your trend line is certainly the only sensible thing to do if you have no knowledge which suggests you do otherwise. But if you are engaged in a certain business and an intelligent reading of technical and financial journals makes it increasingly evident that technical developments which would seriously affect your business are about to "break," you would be something less than wise to follow the old trend line blindly.

Seasonal patterns are likewise subject to change as a result of many causes: changing social customs, deliberate campaigns to modify them, and technological changes, to mention but a few. Constant alertness to these conditions is a "must" for a good forecaster.

Cyclical variation presents the most severe problem. For short term forecasts, the use of a leading series is naturally very desirable, but we doubt that you will often find a series with more than a six month lead. Much sound study is being made of business cycles, and reasonable theories are being developed which are of some help in predicting future cyclical behavior in the light of the past. This is a subject in itself and is beyond the scope of this book. As you become familiar with a specific field of business, you will develop information which will help you make useful choices among the various ideas developed for cyclical forecasting.

26.4 Some Common Sense

All this comes down to the fact that you can, with some justification, extend your trend into the future and multiply the trend values by the recent estimates of seasonal variation to obtain TS values. If you have a good method for forecasting cycles, you can multiply by these indexes to obtain TSC predictions.

Some indication of the effect of irregular variations may be obtained by using $1.000 \pm z_P s$ as an upper and lower value of I, multiplying the TSC values by these two I's, and thinking of the resulting values as reasonable limits for the predicted $Y = TSCI$ values. Our z_P is the absolute value of the standard normal distribution variable, z, such that the range $-z_P \leq z \leq z_P$ includes $P\%$ of the distribution. We must immediately caution you that these limits are not to be thought of as confidence limits in any statistical sense nor as tolerance limits. In fact, the problem of determining what are proper limits is unresolved, for the matter is only in part a statistical problem.

26.5 Some Sound Precautions

We have already indicated some of the factors that operate to make the future less than perfectly predictable from the past. Many more can be suggested. More penetrating analysis of the data than we have been able to discuss here can sometimes throw additional light on relationships within and between series which often aids our understanding of factors operating. But the future is still far from certain.

One of the best ways we can suggest for gaining an understanding of the nature and importance of these problems is to take known series and make appropriate analyses on the data up to various times in the past, use these analyses to prepare forecasts as though we had been living at the past time, then compare our forecasts with the actual subsequent values. The series for Portland cement production, crude oil production, consumption of various textile fibers, anthracite coal production, and oleomargarine consumption, among others, are illuminating in this way. Not only is this idea useful for gaining understanding of the problem, but it is necessary in serious forecasting: as time moves on, yesterday's future is today's present and tomorrow's past. We must constantly check yesterday's predictions against today's experience to secure a better guide to tomorrow.

If you try the experiments we just suggested with known series, you will presently come face to face with the fact that you may have no very good long-range prediction of cyclical behavior. What can you do? A procedure not without merit is to treat all the *CI* variations in the past as though they were irregular. Generally, this will have the effect of considerably increasing your standard deviation of "irregular" variations, and will therefore widen the spread of the two lines you place about the *TS* line. But isn't this realistic? After all, it implies that you expect continuing cyclical variations, but have no exact knowledge of when their peaks and troughs will occur. And it puts you on notice not to be too sure of your predictions.

What we have been saying may have given you the impression that time series analysis is folly. That is not our intention. Time series analysis does indeed permit us to clarify much of the information that the past offers. Often trend and seasonal variation are the principal components of a series of interest to us. Often long-range forecasts, which are our poorest forecasts, are not important to us. If we can learn what the past *does* teach and what it *does not* teach, and use this information wisely, we shall surely be better off than running blindly. We can only be seriously in error when we foolishly think that a little information is all of wisdom.

Appendix 1 Explanation

This particular form of presentation was developed to make it possible to have in compact form both an adequate table of ordinates of the standard normal curve and a good, reasonably large-scale graph of its curve.

With the page in its usual reading position, the first column of the table shows values of z by increments of 0.2 units, and the second column shows the height of the corresponding ordinate, y.

If the page is turned so that the bound edge is up, the z values become the abscissas of the curve, while the y values could be (roughly) read from the scale on the left.

Of course, the vertical scale has been much enlarged, as usual. The ratio of enlargement will make the curve *appear* more or less peaked, just as scales other than those having equal units make the equations of circles *appear* to plot as ellipses. See Chapter 5.

Appendix I Normal Ordinates

Plot and Ordinates of the Standard Normal Distribution Curve

$$y = (1/\sqrt{2\pi})e^{-(1/2)z^2}$$

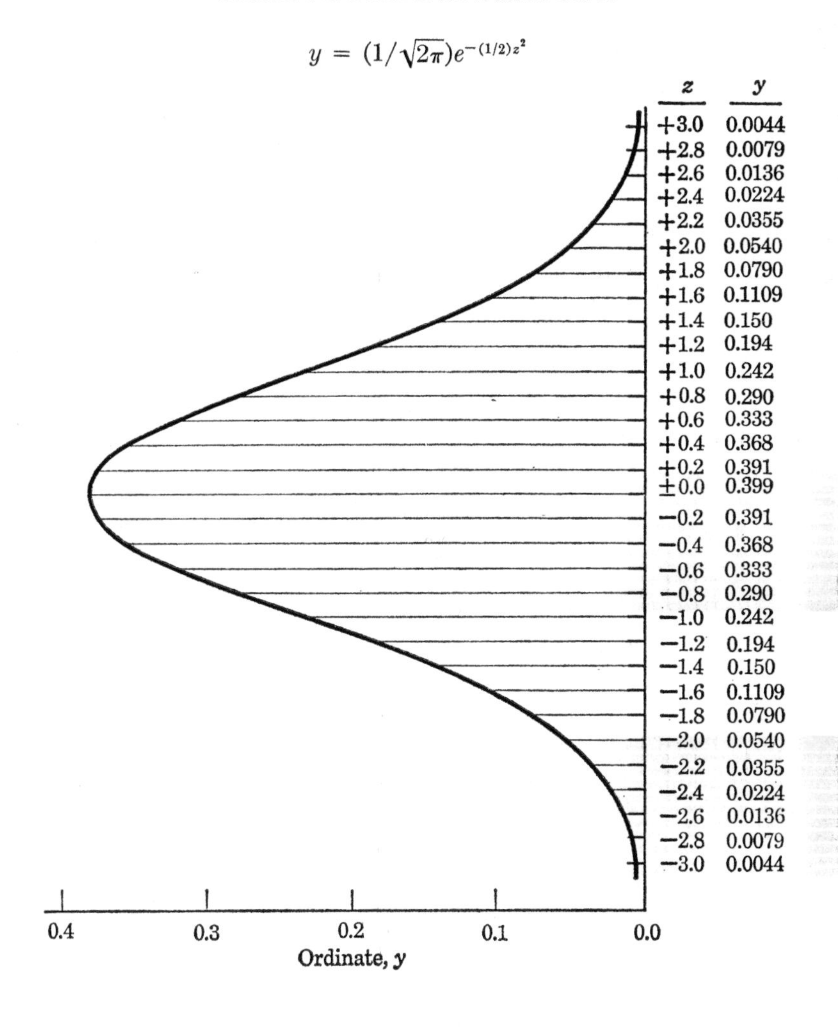

z	y
+3.0	0.0044
+2.8	0.0079
+2.6	0.0136
+2.4	0.0224
+2.2	0.0355
+2.0	0.0540
+1.8	0.0790
+1.6	0.1109
+1.4	0.150
+1.2	0.194
+1.0	0.242
+0.8	0.290
+0.6	0.333
+0.4	0.368
+0.2	0.391
±0.0	0.399
−0.2	0.391
−0.4	0.368
−0.6	0.333
−0.8	0.290
−1.0	0.242
−1.2	0.194
−1.4	0.150
−1.6	0.1109
−1.8	0.0790
−2.0	0.0540
−2.2	0.0355
−2.4	0.0224
−2.6	0.0136
−2.8	0.0079
−3.0	0.0044

Appendix II Explanation of Table and Chart

The particular form of presentation in this table and chart was developed to make the meaning of the values appearing in the usual tables more vivid to beginning students.

With the page in the normal reading position, the first column gives the values of z; the second gives p, the proportion of the area under the standard normal distribution curve to the left of an ordinate at the stated values of z. In this pair of columns, the values of z are in increments of 0.1. Linear interpolation may be used to secure values to 0.01 unit of z adequately for most practical purposes.

The last two columns give similar pairs of values for those values of p most often needed in testing hypotheses and computing confidence limits.

By turning the page so that the bound edge is up, the first column of z values becomes the abscissa of the ogive of p vs z. The vertical scale is double, with values of p on the left and of $1 - p$, the area above the ordinate, on the right. The values of p correspond to areas such as the shaded portion of the sketch below illustrates; those of $1 - p$ correspond to the unshaded portion.

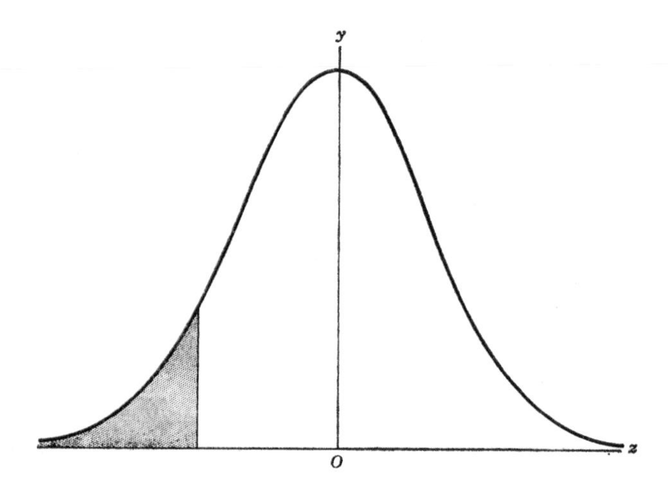

Appendix II Normal Areas

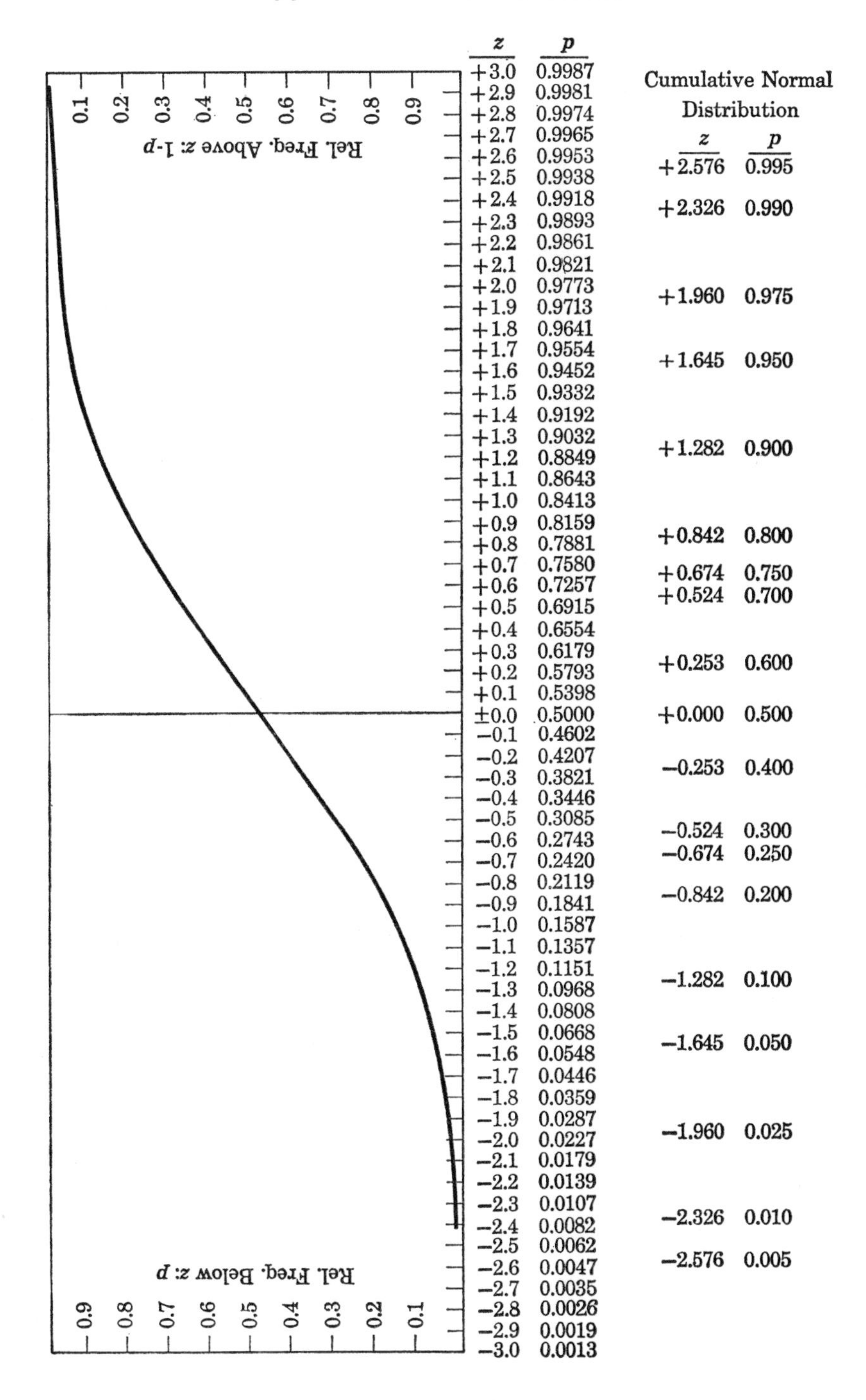

z	p
+3.0	0.9987
+2.9	0.9981
+2.8	0.9974
+2.7	0.9965
+2.6	0.9953
+2.5	0.9938
+2.4	0.9918
+2.3	0.9893
+2.2	0.9861
+2.1	0.9821
+2.0	0.9773
+1.9	0.9713
+1.8	0.9641
+1.7	0.9554
+1.6	0.9452
+1.5	0.9332
+1.4	0.9192
+1.3	0.9032
+1.2	0.8849
+1.1	0.8643
+1.0	0.8413
+0.9	0.8159
+0.8	0.7881
+0.7	0.7580
+0.6	0.7257
+0.5	0.6915
+0.4	0.6554
+0.3	0.6179
+0.2	0.5793
+0.1	0.5398
±0.0	0.5000
−0.1	0.4602
−0.2	0.4207
−0.3	0.3821
−0.4	0.3446
−0.5	0.3085
−0.6	0.2743
−0.7	0.2420
−0.8	0.2119
−0.9	0.1841
−1.0	0.1587
−1.1	0.1357
−1.2	0.1151
−1.3	0.0968
−1.4	0.0808
−1.5	0.0668
−1.6	0.0548
−1.7	0.0446
−1.8	0.0359
−1.9	0.0287
−2.0	0.0227
−2.1	0.0179
−2.2	0.0139
−2.3	0.0107
−2.4	0.0082
−2.5	0.0062
−2.6	0.0047
−2.7	0.0035
−2.8	0.0026
−2.9	0.0019
−3.0	0.0013

Cumulative Normal Distribution

z	p
+2.576	0.995
+2.326	0.990
+1.960	0.975
+1.645	0.950
+1.282	0.900
+0.842	0.800
+0.674	0.750
+0.524	0.700
+0.253	0.600
+0.000	0.500
−0.253	0.400
−0.524	0.300
−0.674	0.250
−0.842	0.200
−1.282	0.100
−1.645	0.050
−1.960	0.025
−2.326	0.010
−2.576	0.005

Appendix III Factorials and Their Logarithms

N	$N!$	Log ($N!$)
1	1	0.000000
2	2	0.301030
3	6	0.778151
4	24	1.380211
5	120	2.079181
6	720	2.857332
7	5,040	3.702431
8	40,320	4.605521
9	362,880	5.559763
10	3,628,800	6.559763
11	39,916,800	7.601156
12	479,001,600	8.680354
13	6,227,020,800	9.794280
14	87,178,291,200	10.940408
15	1,307,674,368,000	12.116500

Appendix IV Random Sampling Numbers

23 15	75 48	59 01	83 72	59 93	76 24	97 08	86 95	23 03	67 44
05 54	55 50	43 10	53 74	35 08	90 61	18 37	44 10	96 22	13 43
14 87	16 03	50 32	40 43	62 23	50 05	10 03	22 11	54 38	08 34
38 97	67 49	51 94	05 17	58 53	78 80	59 01	94 32	42 87	16 95
97 31	26 17	18 99	75 53	08 70	94 25	12 58	41 54	88 21	05 13
11 74	26 93	81 44	33 93	08 72	32 79	73 31	18 22	64 70	68 50
43 36	12 88	59 11	01 64	56 23	93 00	90 04	99 43	64 07	40 36
93 80	62 04	78 38	26 80	44 91	55 75	11 89	32 58	47 55	25 71
49 54	01 31	81 08	42 98	41 87	69 53	82 96	61 77	73 80	95 27
36 76	87 26	33 37	94 82	15 69	41 95	96 86	70 45	27 48	38 80
07 09	25 23	92 24	62 71	26 07	06 55	84 53	44 67	33 84	53 20
43 31	00 10	81 44	86 38	03 07	52 55	51 61	48 89	74 29	46 47
61 57	00 63	60 06	17 36	37 75	63 14	89 51	23 35	01 74	69 93
31 35	28 37	99 10	77 91	89 41	31 57	97 64	48 62	58 48	69 19
57 04	88 65	26 27	79 59	36 82	90 52	95 65	46 35	06 53	22 54
09 24	34 42	00 68	72 10	71 37	30 72	97 57	56 09	29 82	76 50
97 95	53 50	18 40	89 48	83 29	52 23	08 25	21 22	53 26	15 87
93 73	25 95	70 43	78 19	88 85	56 67	16 68	26 95	99 64	45 69
72 62	11 12	25 00	92 26	82 64	35 66	65 94	34 71	68 75	18 67
61 02	07 44	18 45	37 12	07 94	95 91	73 78	66 99	53 61	93 78
97 83	98 54	74 33	05 59	17 18	45 47	35 41	44 22	03 42	30 00
89 16	09 71	92 22	23 29	06 37	35 05	54 54	89 88	43 81	63 61
25 96	68 82	20 62	87 17	92 65	02 82	35 28	62 84	91 95	48 83
81 44	33 17	19 05	04 95	48 06	74 69	00 75	67 65	01 71	65 45
11 32	25 49	31 42	36 23	43 86	08 62	49 76	67 42	24 52	32 45

64 75	58 38	85 84	12 22	59 20	17 69	61 56	55 95	04 59	59 47
10 30	25 22	89 77	43 63	44 30	38 11	24 90	67 07	34 82	33 28
71 01	79 84	95 51	30 85	03 74	66 59	10 28	87 53	76 56	91 49
60 01	25 56	05 88	41 03	48 79	79 65	59 01	69 78	80 00	36 66
37 33	09 46	56 49	16 14	28 02	48 27	45 47	55 44	55 36	50 90
47 86	98 70	01 31	59 11	22 73	60 62	61 28	22 34	69 16	12 12
38 04	04 27	37 64	16 78	95 78	39 32	34 93	24 88	43 43	87 06
73 50	83 09	08 83	05 48	00 78	36 66	93 02	95 56	46 04	53 36
32 62	34 64	74 84	06 10	43 24	20 62	83 73	19 32	35 64	39 69
97 59	19 95	49 36	63 03	51 06	62 06	99 29	75 95	32 05	77 34
74 01	23 19	55 59	79 09	69 82	66 22	42 40	15 96	74 90	75 89
56 75	42 64	57 13	35 10	50 14	90 96	63 36	74 69	09 63	34 88
49 80	04 99	08 54	83 12	19 98	08 52	82 63	72 92	92 36	50 26
43 58	48 96	47 24	87 85	66 70	00 22	15 01	93 99	59 16	23 77
16 65	37 96	64 60	32 57	13 01	35 74	28 36	36 73	05 88	72 29
48 50	26 90	55 65	32 25	87 48	31 44	68 02	37 31	25 29	63 67
96 76	55 46	92 36	31 68	62 30	48 29	63 83	52 23	81 66	40 94
38 92	36 15	50 80	35 78	17 84	23 44	41 24	63 33	99 22	81 28
77 95	88 16	94 25	22 50	55 87	51 07	30 10	70 60	21 86	19 61
17 92	82 80	65 25	58 60	87 71	02 64	18 50	64 65	79 64	81 70
94 03	68 59	78 02	31 80	44 99	41 05	41 05	31 87	43 12	15 96
47 46	06 04	79 56	23 04	84 17	14 37	28 51	67 27	55 80	03 68
47 85	65 60	88 51	99 28	24 39	40 64	41 71	70 13	46 31	82 88
57 61	63 46	53 92	29 86	20 18	10 37	57 65	15 62	98 69	07 56
08 30	09 27	04 66	75 26	66 10	57 18	87 91	07 54	22 22	20 13

*Reproduced with the permission of Professor E. S. Pearson from M. G. Kendall and B. Babington Smith, *Tables of Random Sampling Numbers* (Tracts for Computers, No. 24), Cambridge Univ. Press.

89 22	10 23	62 65	78 77	47 33	51 27	23 02	13 92	44 13	96 51
04 00	59 98	18 63	91 82	90 32	94 01	24 23	63 01	26 11	06 50
98 54	63 80	66 50	85 67	50 45	40 64	52 28	41 53	25 44	41 25
41 71	98 44	01 59	22 60	13 14	54 58	14 03	98 49	98 86	55 79
28 73	37 24	89 00	78 52	58 43	24 61	34 97	97 85	56 78	44 71
65 21	38 39	27 77	76 20	30 86	80 74	22 43	95 68	47 68	37 92
65 55	31 26	78 90	90 69	04 66	43 67	02 62	17 69	90 03	12 05
05 66	86 90	80 73	02 98	57 46	58 33	27 82	31 45	98 69	29 98
39 30	29 97	18 49	75 77	95 19	27 38	77 63	73 47	26 29	16 12
64 59	23 22	54 45	87 92	94 31	38 32	00 59	81 18	06 78	71 37
07 51	34 87	92 47	31 48	36 60	68 90	70 53	36 82	57 99	15 82
86 59	36 85	01 56	63 89	98 00	82 83	93 51	48 56	54 10	72 32
83 73	52 25	99 97	97 78	12 48	36 83	89 95	60 32	41 06	76 14
08 59	52 18	26 54	65 50	82 04	87 99	01 70	33 56	25 80	53 84
41 27	32 71	49 44	29 36	94 58	16 82	86 39	62 15	86 43	54 31
00 47	37 59	08 56	23 81	22 42	72 63	17 63	14 47	25 20	63 47
86 13	15 37	89 81	38 30	78 68	89 13	29 61	82 07	00 98	64 32
33 84	97 83	59 04	40 20	35 86	03 17	68 86	63 08	01 82	25 46
61 87	04 16	57 07	46 80	86 12	98 08	39 73	49 20	77 54	50 91
43 89	86 59	23 25	07 88	61 29	78 49	19 76	53 91	50 08	07 86
29 93	93 91	23 04	54 84	59 85	60 95	20 66	41 28	72 64	64 73
38 50	58 55	55 14	38 85	50 77	18 65	79 48	87 67	83 17	08 19
31 82	43 84	31 67	12 52	55 11	72 04	41 15	62 53	27 98	22 68
91 43	00 37	67 13	56 11	55 97	06 75	09 25	52 02	39 13	87 53
38 63	56 89	76 25	49 89	75 26	96 45	80 38	05 04	11 66	35 14

02 49	05 41	22 27	94 43	93 64	04 23	07 20	74 11	67 95	40 82
11 96	73 64	69 60	62 78	37 01	09 25	33 02	08 01	38 53	74 82
48 25	68 34	65 49	69 92	40 79	05 40	33 51	54 39	61 30	31 36
27 24	67 30	80 21	48 12	35 36	04 88	18 99	77 49	48 49	30 71
32 53	27 72	65 72	43 07	07 22	86 52	91 84	57 92	65 71	00 11
66 75	79 89	55 92	37 59	34 31	43 20	45 58	25 45	44 36	92 65
11 26	63 45	45 76	50 59	77 46	34 66	82 69	99 26	74 29	75 16
17 87	23 91	42 45	56 18	01 46	93 13	74 89	24 64	25 75	92 84
62 56	13 03	65 03	40 81	47 54	51 79	80 81	33 61	01 09	77 30
62 79	63 07	79 35	49 77	05 01	30 10	50 81	33 00	99 79	19 70
75 51	02 17	71 04	33 93	36 60	42 75	76 22	23 87	56 54	84 68
87 43	90 16	91 63	51 72	65 90	44 43	70 72	17 98	70 63	90 32
97 74	20 26	21 10	74 87	88 03	38 33	76 52	26 92	14 95	90 51
98 81	10 60	01 21	57 10	28 75	21 82	88 39	12 85	18 86	16 24
51 26	40 18	52 64	60 79	25 53	29 00	42 66	95 78	58 36	29 98
40 23	99 33	76 10	41 96	86 10	49 12	00 29	41 80	03 59	93 17
26 93	65 91	86 51	66 72	76 45	46 32	94 46	81 94	19 06	66 47
88 50	21 17	16 98	29 94	09 74	42 39	46 22	00 69	09 48	16 46
63 49	93 80	93 25	59 36	19 95	79 86	78 05	69 01	02 33	83 74
36 37	98 12	06 03	31 77	87 10	73 82	83 10	83 60	50 94	40 91
93 80	12 23	22 47	47 95	70 17	59 33	43 06	47 43	06 12	66 60
29 85	68 71	20 56	31 15	00 53	25 36	58 12	65 22	41 40	24 31
97 72	08 79	31 88	26 51	30 50	71 01	71 51	77 06	95 79	29 19
85 23	70 91	05 74	60 14	63 77	59 93	81 56	47 34	17 79	27 53
75 74	67 52	68 31	72 79	57 73	72 36	48 73	24 36	87 90	68 02

29 93	50 69	71 63	17 55	25 79	10 47	88 93	79 61	42 82	13 63
15 11	40 71	26 51	89 07	77 87	75 51	01 31	03 42	94 24	81 11
03 87	04 32	25 10	58 98	76 29	22 03	99 41	24 38	12 76	50 22
79 39	03 91	88 40	75 64	52 69	65 95	92 06	40 14	28 42	29 60
30 03	50 69	15 79	19 65	44 28	64 81	95 23	14 48	72 18	15 94
29 03	99 98	61 28	75 97	98 02	68 53	13 91	98 38	13 72	43 73
78 19	60 81	08 24	10 74	97 77	09 59	94 35	69 84	82 09	49 56
15 84	78 54	93 91	44 29	13 51	80 13	07 37	52 21	53 91	09 86
36 61	46 22	48 49	19 49	72 09	92 58	79 20	53 41	02 18	00 64
40 54	95 48	84 91	46 54	38 62	35 54	14 44	66 88	89 47	41 80
40 87	80 89	97 14	28 60	99 82	90 30	87 80	07 51	58 71	66 58
10 22	94 92	82 41	17 33	14 68	59 45	51 87	56 08	90 80	66 60
15 91	87 67	87 30	62 42	59 28	44 12	42 50	88 31	13 77	16 14
13 40	31 87	96 49	90 99	44 04	64 97	94 14	62 18	15 59	83 35
66 52	39 45	96 74	90 89	02 71	10 00	99 86	48 17	64 06	89 09
91 66	53 64	69 68	34 31	78 70	25 97	50 46	62 21	27 25	06 20
67 41	58 75	15 08	20 77	37 29	73 20	15 75	93 96	91 76	96 99
76 52	79 69	96 23	72 43	34 48	63 39	23 23	94 60	88 79	06 17
19 81	54 77	89 74	34 81	71 47	10 95	43 43	55 81	19 45	44 07
25 59	25 35	87 76	38 47	25 75	84 34	76 89	18 05	73 95	72 22
55 90	24 55	39 63	64 63	16 09	95 99	98 28	87 40	66 66	66 92
02 47	05 83	76 79	79 42	24 82	42 42	39 61	62 47	49 11	72 64
18 63	05 32	63 13	31 99	76 19	35 85	91 23	50 14	63 28	86 59
89 67	33 82	30 16	06 39	20 07	59 50	33 84	02 76	45 03	33 33
62 98	66 73	64 06	59 51	74 27	84 62	31 45	65 82	86 05	73 00

27 50	13 05	46 34	63 85	87 60	35 55	05 67	88 15	47 00	50 92
02 31	57 57	62 98	41 09	66 01	69 88	92 83	35 70	76 59	02 58
37 43	12 83	66 39	77 33	63 26	53 99	48 65	23 06	94 29	53 04
83 56	65 54	19 33	35 42	92 12	37 14	70 75	18 58	98 57	12 52
06 81	56 27	49 32	12 42	92 42	05 96	82 94	70 25	45 49	18 16
39 15	03 60	15 56	73 16	48 74	50 27	43 42	58 36	73 16	39 90
84 45	71 93	10 27	15 83	84 20	57 42	41 28	42 06	15 90	70 47
82 47	05 77	06 89	47 13	92 85	60 12	32 89	25 22	42 38	87 37
98 04	06 70	24 21	69 02	65 42	55 33	11 95	72 35	73 23	57 26
18 33	49 04	14 33	48 50	15 64	58 26	14 91	46 02	72 13	48 62
33 92	19 93	38 27	43 40	27 72	79 74	86 57	41 83	58 71	56 99
48 66	74 30	44 81	06 80	29 09	50 31	69 61	24 64	28 89	97 79
85 85	07 54	21 50	31 80	10 19	56 65	82 52	26 58	55 12	26 34
08 27	08 08	35 87	96 57	33 12	01 77	52 76	09 89	71 12	17 69
59 61	22 14	26 09	96 75	17 94	51 08	41 91	45 94	80 48	59 92
17 45	77 79	31 66	36 54	92 85	65 60	53 98	63 50	11 20	96 63
11 26	37 08	07 71	95 95	39 75	92 48	99 78	23 33	19 56	06 67
48 08	13 98	16 52	41 15	73 96	32 55	03 12	38 30	88 77	17 03
76 27	72 22	99 61	72 15	00 25	21 54	47 79	18 41	58 50	57 66
98 89	22 25	72 92	53 55	07 98	66 71	53 29	61 71	56 96	41 78
88 69	61 63	01 67	61 88	58 79	35 65	08 45	63 38	69 86	79 47
12 58	13 75	80 98	01 35	91 16	18 36	90 54	99 17	68 36	85 06
08 86	96 36	14 09	43 85	51 20	65 18	06 40	52 17	48 10	68 97
33 81	05 51	32 48	60 12	32 44	08 12	89 00	98 82	79 17	97 22
05 15	99 28	87 15	07 08	66 92	53 81	69 42	02 27	65 33	57 69

80 30	23 64	67 96	21 33	36 90	03 91	69 33	90 13	34 48	02 19
61 29	89 61	32 08	12 62	26 08	42 00	31 73	31 30	30 61	34 11
23 33	61 01	02 21	11 81	51 32	36 10	23 74	50 31	90 11	73 52
94 21	32 92	93 50	72 67	23 20	74 59	30 30	48 66	75 32	27 97
87 61	92 69	01 60	28 79	74 76	86 06	39 29	73 85	03 27	50 57
37 56	19 18	03 42	86 03	85 74	44 81	86 45	71 16	13 52	35 56
64 86	66 31	55 04	88 40	10 30	84 38	06 13	58 83	62 04	63 52
22 69	58 45	49 23	09 81	98 84	05 04	75 99	27 70	72 79	32 19
23 22	14 22	64 90	10 26	74 23	53 91	27 73	78 19	92 43	68 10
42 38	59 64	72 96	46 57	89 67	22 81	94 56	69 84	18 31	06 39
17 18	01 34	10 98	37 48	93 86	88 59	69 53	78 86	37 26	85 48
39 45	69 53	94 89	58 97	29 33	29 19	50 94	80 57	31 99	38 91
43 18	11 42	56 19	48 44	45 02	84 29	01 78	65 77	76 84	88 85
59 44	06 45	68 55	16 65	66 13	38 00	95 76	50 67	67 65	18 83
01 50	34 32	38 00	37 57	47 82	66 59	19 50	87 14	35 59	79 47
79 14	60 35	47 95	90 71	31 03	85 37	38 70	34 16	64 55	66 49
01 56	63 68	80 26	14 97	23 88	59 22	82 39	70 83	48 34	46 48
25 76	18 71	29 25	15 51	92 96	01 01	28 18	03 35	11 10	27 84
23 52	10 83	45 06	49 85	35 45	84 08	81 13	52 57	21 23	67 02
91 64	08 64	25 74	16 10	97 31	10 27	24 48	89 06	42 81	29 10
80 86	07 27	26 70	08 65	85 20	31 23	28 99	39 63	32 03	71 91
31 71	37 60	95 60	94 95	54 45	27 97	03 67	30 54	86 04	12 41
05 83	50 36	09 04	39 15	66 55	80 36	39 71	24 10	62 22	21 53
98 70	02 90	30 63	62 59	26 04	97 20	00 91	28 80	40 23	09 91
82 79	35 45	64 53	93 24	86 55	48 72	18 57	05 79	20 09	31 46

37 52	49 55	40 65	27 61	08 59	91 23	26 18	95 04	98 20	99 52
48 16	69 65	69 02	08 83	08 83	68 37	00 96	13 59	12 16	17 93
50 43	06 59	56 53	30 61	40 21	29 06	49 60	90 38	21 43	19 25
89 31	62 79	45 73	71 72	77 11	28 80	72 35	75 77	24 72	98 43
63 29	90 61	86 39	07 38	38 85	77 06	10 23	30 84	07 95	30 76
71 68	93 94	08 72	36 27	85 89	40 59	83 37	93 85	73 97	84 05
05 06	96 63	58 24	05 95	56 64	77 53	85 64	15 95	93 91	59 03
03 35	58 95	46 44	25 70	31 66	01 05	44 44	62 91	36 31	45 04
13 04	57 67	74 77	53 35	93 51	82 83	27 38	63 16	04 48	75 23
49 96	43 94	56 04	02 79	55 78	01 44	75 26	85 54	01 81	32 82
24 36	24 08	44 77	57 07	54 41	04 56	09 44	30 58	25 45	37 56
55 19	97 20	01 11	47 45	79 79	06 72	12 81	86 97	54 09	06 53
02 28	54 60	28 35	32 94	36 74	51 63	96 90	04 13	30 43	10 14
90 50	13 78	22 20	37 56	97 95	49 95	91 15	52 73	12 93	78 94
33 71	32 43	29 58	47 38	39 96	67 51	64 47	49 91	64 58	93 07
70 58	28 49	54 32	97 70	27 81	64 69	71 52	02 56	61 37	04 58
09 68	96 10	57 78	85 00	89 81	98 30	19 40	76 28	62 99	99 83
19 36	60 85	35 04	12 87	83 88	66 54	32 00	30 20	05 30	42 63
04 75	44 49	64 26	51 46	80 50	53 91	00 55	67 36	68 66	08 29
79 83	32 39	46 77	56 83	42 21	60 03	14 47	07 01	66 85	49 22
80 99	42 43	08 58	54 41	98 05	54 39	34 42	97 47	38 35	59 40
48 83	64 99	86 94	48 78	79 20	62 23	56 45	92 65	56 36	83 02
28 45	35 85	22 20	13 01	73 96	70 05	84 50	68 59	96 58	16 63
52 07	63 15	82 30	66 23	14 26	66 61	17 80	41 97	40 27	24 80
39 14	52 18	35 87	48 55	48 81	03 11	26 99	03 80	08 86	50 42

Appendix V Chi-square and Chi-square-over-*n*

Values of χ^2 (Upper Row) and χ^2/n (Lower Row) Below Which the Fraction, p, of the Respective Distributions Falls.

n \ p	0.005	0.010	0.025	0.050	0.950	0.975	0.990	0.995
1	0.000039	0.00016	0.00098	0.0039	3.84	5.02	6.63	7.88
	0.000039	0.00016	0.00098	0.0039	3.84	5.02	6.63	7.88
2	0.0100	0.0201	0.0506	0.1026	5.99	7.38	9.21	10.60
	0.00501	0.0100	0.0253	0.0513	3.00	3.69	4.61	5.30
3	0.0717	0.115	0.216	0.362	7.81	9.35	11.34	12.84
	0.0239	0.0383	0.0719	0.117	2.60	3.12	3.78	4.28
4	0.207	0.297	0.484	0.711	9.49	11.14	13.28	14.86
	0.0517	0.0743	0.121	0.178	2.37	2.79	3.32	33.72
5	0.412	0.554	0.831	1.15	11.07	12.83	15.09	16.75
	0.0823	0.111	0.166	0.229	2.21	2.57	3.02	3.35
6	0.676	0.872	1.24	1.64	12.59	14.45	16.81	18.55
	0.113	0.145	0.206	0.273	2.10	2.41	2.80	3.09
7	0.989	1.24	1.69	2.17	14.07	16.01	18.48	20.28
	0.141	0.177	0.241	0.310	2.01	2.29	2.64	2.90
8	1.34	1.65	2.18	2.73	15.51	17.53	20.09	21.96
	0.168	0.206	0.272	0.342	1.94	2.19	2.51	2.74
9	1.73	2.09	2.70	3.33	16.92	19.02	21.67	23.59
	0.193	0.232	0.300	0.369	1.88	2.11	2.41	2.62
10	2.16	2.56	3.25	3.94	18.31	20.48	23.21	25.19
	0.216	0.256	0.325	0.394	1.83	2.05	2.32	2.52
11	2.60	3.05	3.82	4.57	19.68	21.92	24.73	26.76
	0.237	0.278	0.347	0.416	1.79	1.99	2.25	2.43
12	3.07	3.57	4.40	5.23	21.03	23.34	26.22	28.30
	0.256	0.298	0.367	0.435	1.75	1.94	2.18	2.36
13	3.57	4.11	5.01	5.89	22.36	24.74	27.69	29.82
	0.274	0.316	0.385	0.453	1.72	1.90	2.13	2.29
14	4.07	4.66	5.63	6.57	23.68	26.12	29.14	31.32
	0.291	0.333	0.402	0.469	1.69	1.87	2.08	2.24
15	4.60	5.23	6.26	7.26	25.00	27.49	30.58	32.80
	0.307	0.349	0.417	0.484	1.67	1.83	2.04	2.19
16	5.14	5.81	6.91	7.96	26.30	28.85	32.00	34.27
	0.321	0.363	0.432	0.498	1.64	1.80	2.00	2.14
17	5.70	6.41	7.56	8.67	27.52	30.19	33.41	35.72
	0.335	0.377	0.445	0.510	1.62	1.77	1.96	2.10
18	6.26	7.01	8.23	9.39	28.87	31.53	34.81	37.16
	0.348	0.390	0.457	0.522	1.60	1.75	1.93	2.06
19	6.84	7.63	8.91	10.12	30.14	32.85	36.19	38.58
	0.360	0,402	0.469	0.532	1.59	1.75	1.90	2.03
20	7.43	8.26	9.59	10.85	31.41	34.17	37.57	40.00
	0.372	0.413	0.480	0.543	1.57	1.71	1.88	2.00

n	p	0.005	0.010	0.025	0.050	0.950	0.975	0.990	0.995
25		10.52	11.52	13.12	14.61	37.65	40.65	44.31	46.93
		0.421	0.461	0.525	0.584	1.51	1.63	1.77	1.88
30		13.79	14.95	16.79	28.49	43.77	46.98	50.89	53.67
		0.460	0.498	0.560	0.616	1.46	1.57	1.70	1.79
40		20.71	22.16	24.43	26.51	55.76	59.34	63.69	66.77
		0.518	0.554	0.611	0.663	1.39	1.48	1.59	1.67
50		27.99	29.71	32.36	34.76	67.50	71.42	76.15	79.49
		0.560	0.594	0.647	0.695	1.35	1.43	1.52	1.59
100		67.33	70.06	74.22	77.93	124.34	129.56	135.81	140.17
		0.673	0.701	0.742	0.779	1.24	1.29	1.35	1.40

Appendix VI Student's *t*-Distribution

Part A. *The Cumulative Student t-Distribution,* Shown for 1, 10, and ∞ degrees of Freedom. p = fraction below t; n = degrees of freedom.

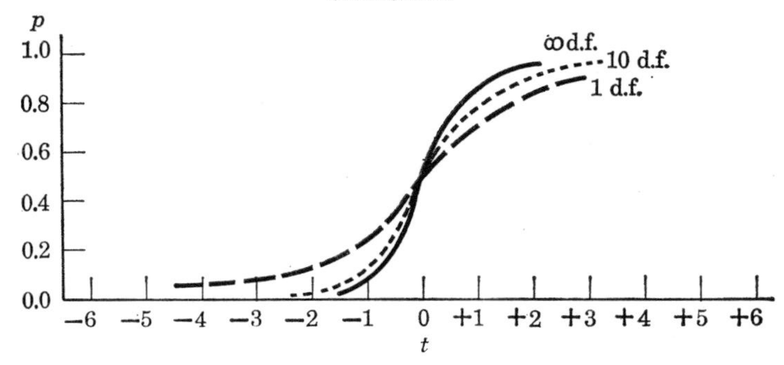

Part B. Table of Absolute Values of t Beyond Which Commonly Needed Fractions of *Student's t-Distribution Fall.*

n \ p	0.005	0.010	0.025	0.050	0.100
1	63.657	31.821	12.706	6.314	3.078
2	9.925	6.965	4.303	2.920	1.886
3	5.841	4.541	3.182	2.353	1.638
4	4.604	3.747	2.776	2.132	1.533
5	4.032	3.365	2.571	2.015	1.476
6	3.707	3.143	2.447	1.943	1.440
7	3.499	2.998	2.365	1.895	1.415
8	3.355	2.896	2.306	1.860	1.397
9	3.250	2.821	2.262	1.833	1.383
10	3.169	2.764	2.228	1.812	1.372
14	2.977	2.624	2.145	1.761	1.345
15	2.947	2.602	2.131	1.753	1.341
19	2.861	2.539	2.093	1.729	1.328
20	2.845	2.528	2.086	1.725	1.325
24	2.797	2.492	2.064	1.711	1.318
25	2.787	2.485	2.060	1.708	1.316
30	2.750	2.457	2.042	1.697	1.310
60	2.660	2.392	2.000	1.671	1.296
∞	2.576	2.326	1.960	1.645	1.282

Interpolation between given degrees of freedom should be done by using reciprocals of degrees of freedom.

Appendix VII Cumulative F-Distribution

n_A/n_B	$F_{0.950}$	$F_{0.975}$	$F_{0.990}$	$F_{0.995}$
1/1	161	648	4,052	16,211
1/2	18.5	38.5	98.5	198
1/3	10.1	17.4	34.1	55.6
1/4	7.71	12.2	21.2	31.3
1/5	6.61	10.0	16.3	22.8
1/6	5.99	8.81	13.7	18.6
1/7	5.59	8.07	12.2	16.2
1/8	5.32	7.57	11.3	14.7
1/9	5.12	7.21	10.6	13.6
1/10	4.96	6.94	10.0	12.8
1/11	4.84	6.72	9.65	12.2
1/12	4.75	6.55	9.33	11.8
1/13	4.67	6.41	9.07	11.4
1/14	4.60	6.30	8.86	11.1
1/15	4.54	6.20	8.68	10.8
1/20	4.35	5.87	8.10	9.94
1/25	4.24	5.69	7.77	9.48
1/30	4.17	5.57	7.56	9.18
1/40	4.08	5.42	7.31	8.83
1/60	4.00	5.29	7.08	8.49
1/120	3.92	5.15	6.85	8.18
1/∞	3.84	5.02	6.63	7.88
2/1	200	800	5,000	20,000
2/2	19.0	39.0	99.0	199
2/3	9.55	16.0	30.8	49.8
2/4	6.94	10.6	18.0	26.3
2/5	5.79	8.43	13.3	18.3
2/6	5.14	7.26	10.9	14.5
2/7	4.74	6.54	9.55	12.4
2/8	4.46	6.06	8.65	11.0
2/9	4.26	5.71	8.02	10.1
2/10	4.10	5.46	7.56	9.43
2/11	3.98	5.26	7.21	8.91
2/12	3.89	5.10	6.93	8.51
2/13	3.81	4.97	6.70	8.19
2/14	3.74	4.86	6.51	7.92
2/15	3.68	4.77	6.36	7.70
2/20	3.49	4.46	5.85	6.99
2/25	3.39	4.29	5.57	6.60
2/30	3.32	4.18	5.39	6.35
2/40	3.23	4.05	5.18	6.07
2/60	3.15	3.93	4.98	5.80
2/120	3.07	3.80	4.79	5.54
2/∞	3.00	3.69	4.61	5.30

n_A/n_B	$F_{0.950}$	$F_{0.975}$	$F_{0.990}$	$F_{0.995}$
3/1	216	864	5,403	21,615
3/2	19.2	39.2	99.2	199
3/3	9.28	15.4	29.5	47.5
3/4	6.59	9.98	16.7	24.3
3/5	5.41	7.76	12.1	16.5
3/6	4.76	6.60	9.78	12.9
3/7	4.35	5.89	8.45	10.9
3/8	4.07	5.42	7.59	9.60
3/9	3.86	5.08	6.99	9.60
3/10	3.71	4.83	6.55	8.08
3/11	3.59	4.63	6.22	7.60
3/12	3.49	4.47	5.95	7.23
3/13	3.41	4.35	5.74	6.93
3/14	3.34	4.24	5.56	6.68
3/15	3.29	4.15	5.42	6.48
3/20	3.10	3.86	4.94	5.82
3/25	2.99	3.69	4.68	5.46
3/30	2.92	3.59	4.51	5.24
3/40	2.84	3.46	4.31	4.98
3/60	2.76	3.34	4.13	4.73
3/120	2.68	3.23	3.95	4.50
3/∞	2.60	3.12	3.78	4.28
4/1	225	900	5,625	22,500
4/2	19.2	39.2	99.2	199
4/3	9.12	15.1	28.7	46.2
4/4	6.39	9.60	16.0	23.2
4/5	5.19	7.39	11.4	15.6
4/6	4.53	6.23	9.15	12.0
4/7	4.12	5.52	7.85	10.1
4/8	3.84	5.05	7.01	8.81
4/9	3.63	4.72	6.42	7.96
4/10	3.48	4.47	5.99	7.34
4/11	3.36	4.28	5.67	6.88
4/12	3.26	4.12	5.41	6.52
4/13	3.18	4.00	5.21	6.23
4/14	3.11	3.89	5.04	6.00
4/15	3.06	3.80	4.89	5.80
4/20	2.87	3.51	4.43	5.17
4/25	2.76	3.35	4.18	4.84
4/30	2.69	3.25	4.02	4.62
4/40	2.61	3.13	3.83	4.37
4/60	2.53	3.01	3.65	4.14
4/120	2.45	2.89	3.48	3.92
4/∞	2.37	2.79	3.32	3.72

n_A/n_B	$F_{0.950}$	$F_{0.975}$	$F_{0.990}$	$F_{0.995}$
5/1	230	922	5,764	23,056
5/2	19.3	39.3	99.3	199
5/3	9.01	14.9	28.2	45.4
5/4	6.26	9.36	15.5	22.5
5/5	5.05	7.15	11.0	14.9
5/6	4.39	5.99	8.75	11.5
5/7	3.97	5.29	7.46	9.52
5/8	3.69	4.82	6.63	8.30
5/9	3.48	4.48	6.06	7.47
5/10	3.33	4.24	5.64	6.87
5/11	3.20	4.04	5.32	6.42
5/12	3.11	3.89	5.06	6.07
5/13	3.03	3.77	4.86	5.79
5/14	2.96	3.66	4.70	5.56
5/15	2.90	3.58	4.56	5.37
5/20	2.71	3.29	4.10	4.76
5/25	2.60	3.13	3.86	4.43
5/30	2.53	3.03	3.70	4.23
5/40	2.45	2.90	3.51	3.99
5/60	2.37	2.79	3.34	3.76
5/120	2.29	2.67	3.17	3.55
5/∞	2.21	2.57	3.02	3.35
6/1	234	937	5,859	23,437
6/2	19.3	39.3	99.3	199
6/3	8.94	14.7	27.9	44.8
6/4	6.16	9.20	15.2	22.0
6/5	4.95	6.98	10.7	14.5
6/6	4.28	5.82	8.47	11.1
6/7	3.87	5.12	7.19	9.16
6/8	3.58	4.65	6.37	7.95
6/9	3.37	4.32	5.80	7.13
6/10	3.22	4.07	5.39	6.54
6/11	3.09	3.88	5.07	6.10
6/12	3.00	3.73	4.82	5.76
6/13	2.92	3.60	4.62	5.48
6/14	2.85	3.50	4.46	5.26
6/15	2.79	3.41	4.32	5.07
6/20	2.60	3.13	3.87	4.47
6/25	2.49	2.97	3.63	4.15
6/30	2.42	2.87	3.47	3.95
6/40	2.34	2.74	3.29	3.71
6/60	2.25	2.63	3.12	3.49
6/120	2.18	2.52	2.96	3.28
6/∞	2.10	2.41	2.80	3.09

n_A/n_B	$F_{0.950}$	$F_{0.975}$	$F_{0.990}$	$F_{0.995}$
7/1	237	948	5,928	23,715
7/2	19.4	39.4	99.4	199
7/3	8.89	14.6	27.7	44.4
7/4	6.09	9.07	15.0	21.6
7/5	4.88	6.85	10.5	14.2
7/6	4.21	5.70	8.26	10.8
7/7	3.79	4.99	6.99	8.89
7/8	3.50	4.53	6.18	7.69
7/9	3.29	4.20	5.61	6.88
7/10	3.14	3.95	5.20	6.30
7/11	3.01	3.76	4.89	5.86
7/12	2.91	3.61	4.64	5.52
7/13	2.83	3.48	4.44	5.25
7/14	2.76	3.38	4.28	5.03
7/15	2.71	3.29	4.14	4.85
7/20	2.51	3.01	3.70	4.26
7/25	2.40	2.85	3.46	3.94
7/30	2.33	2.75	3.30	3.74
7/40	2.25	2.62	3.12	3.51
7/60	2.17	2.51	2.95	3.29
7/120	2.09	2.39	2.79	3.09
7/∞	2.01	2.29	2.64	2.90
8/1	239	957	5,982	23,925
8/2	19.4	39.4	99.4	199
8/3	8.85	14.5	27.5	44.1
8/4	6.04	8.98	14.8	21.4
8/5	4.82	6.76	10.3	14.0
8/6	4.15	5.60	8.10	10.6
8/7	3.73	4.90	6.84	8.68
8/8	3.44	4.43	6.03	7.50
8/9	3.23	4.10	5.47	6.69
8/10	3.07	3.85	5.06	6.12
8/11	2.95	3.66	4.74	5.68
8/12	2.85	3.51	4.50	5.35
8/13	2.77	3.39	4.30	5.08
8/14	2.70	3.28	4.14	4.86
8/15	2.64	3.20	4.00	4.67
8/20	2.45	2.91	3.56	4.09
8/25	2.34	2.75	3.32	3.78
8/30	2.27	2.65	3.17	3.58
8/40	2.18	2.53	2.99	3.35
8/60	2.10	2.41	2.82	3.13
8/120	2.02	2.30	2.66	2.93
8/∞	1.94	2.19	2.51	2.74

n_A/n_B	$F_{0.950}$	$F_{0.975}$	$F_{0.990}$	$F_{0.995}$
9/1	241	963	6,023	24,091
9/2	19.4	39.4	99.4	199
9/3	8.81	14.5	27.3	43.9
9/4	6.00	8.90	14.7	21.1
9/5	4.77	6.68	10.2	13.8
9/6	4.10	5.52	7.98	10.4
9/7	3.68	4.82	6.72	8.51
9/8	3.39	4.36	5.91	7.34
9/9	3.18	4.03	5.35	6.54
9/10	3.02	3.78	4.94	5.97
9/11	2.90	3.59	4.63	5.54
9/12	2.80	3.44	4.39	5.20
9/13	2.71	3.31	4.19	4.94
9/14	2.65	3.21	4.03	4.72
9/15	2.59	3.12	3.89	4.54
9/20	2.39	2.84	3.46	3.96
9/25	2.28	2.68	3.22	3.64
9/30	2.21	2.57	3.07	3.45
9/40	2.12	2.45	2.89	3.22
9/60	2.04	2.33	2.72	3.01
9/120	1.96	2.22	2.56	2.81
9/∞	1.88	2.11	2.41	2.62
10/1	242	969	6,056	24,224
10/2	19.4	39.4	99.4	199
10/3	8.79	14.4	27.2	43.7
10/4	5.96	8.84	14.5	21.0
10/5	4.74	6.62	10.1	13.6
10/6	4.06	5.46	7.87	10.3
10/7	3.64	4.76	6.62	8.38
10/8	3.35	4.30	5.81	7.21
10/9	3.14	3.96	5.26	6.42
10/10	2.98	3.72	4.85	5.85
10/11	2.85	3.53	4.54	5.42
10/12	2.75	3.37	4.30	5.09
10/13	2.67	3.25	4.10	4.82
10/14	2.60	3.15	3.94	4.60
10/15	2.54	3.06	3.80	4.42
10/20	2.35	2.77	3.37	3.85
10/25	2.24	2.61	3.13	3.54
10/30	2.16	2.51	3.13	3.34
10/40	2.08	2.39	2.80	3.12
10/60	1.99	2.27	2.63	2.90
10/120	1.91	2.16	2.47	2.71
10/∞	1.83	2.05	2.32	2.52

n_A/n_B	$F_{0.950}$	$F_{0.975}$	$F_{0.990}$	$F_{0.995}$
15/1	246	985	6,157	24,630
15/2	19.4	39.4	99.4	199
15/3	8.70	14.3	26.9	43.1
15/4	5.86	8.66	14.2	20.4
15/5	4.62	6.43	9.72	13.1
15/6	3.94	5.27	7.56	9.81
15/7	3.51	4.57	6.31	7.97
15/8	3.22	4.10	5.52	6.81
15/9	3.01	3.77	4.96	6.03
15/10	2.85	3.52	4.56	5.47
15/11	2.72	3.33	4.25	5.05
15/12	2.62	3.18	4.01	4.72
15/13	2.53	3.05	3.82	4.46
15/14	2.46	2.95	3.66	4.25
15/15	2.40	2.86	3.52	4.07
15/20	2.20	2.57	3.09	3.50
15/25	2.09	2.41	2.85	3.20
15/30	2.01	2.31	2.70	3.01
15/40	1.92	2.18	2.52	2.78
15/60	1.84	2.06	2.35	2.57
15/120	1.75	1.95	2.19	2.37
15/∞	1.67	1.83	2.04	2.19
20/1	248	993	6,209	24,836
20/2	19.4	39.4	99.4	199
20/3	8.66	14.2	26.7	42.8
20/4	5.80	8.56	14.0	20.2
20/5	4.56	6.33	9.55	12.9
20/6	3.87	5.17	7.40	9.59
20/7	3.44	4.47	6.16	7.75
20/8	3.15	4.00	5.36	6.61
20/9	2.94	3.67	4.81	5.83
20/10	2.77	3.42	4.41	5.27
20/11	2.65	3.23	4.10	4.86
20/12	2.54	3.07	3.86	4.53
20/13	2.46	2.95	3.66	4.27
20/14	2.39	2.84	3.51	4.06
20/15	2.33	2.76	3.37	3.88
20/20	2.12	2.46	2.94	3.32
20/25	2.01	2.30	2.55	3.01
20/30	1.93	2.20	2.55	2.82
20/40	1.84	2.07	2.37	2.60
20/60	1.75	1.94	2.20	2.39
20/120	1.66	1.82	2.03	2.19
20/∞	1.57	1.71	1.88	2.00

n_A/n_B	$F_{0.950}$	$F_{0.975}$	$F_{0.990}$	$F_{0.995}$
40/1	251	1,006	6,287	25,148
40/2	19.5	39.5	99.5	199
40/3	8.59	14.0	26.4	42.3
40/4	5.72	8.41	13.7	19.8
40/5	4.46	6.18	9.29	12.5
40/6	3.77	5.01	7.14	9.24
40/7	3.34	4.31	5.91	7.42
40/8	3.04	3.84	5.12	6.29
40/9	2.83	3.51	4.57	5.52
40/10	2.66	3.26	4.17	4.97
40/11	2.53	3.06	3.86	4.55
40/12	2.43	2.91	3.62	4.23
40/13	2.34	2.78	3.43	3.97
40/14	2.27	2.67	3.27	3.76
40/15	2.20	2.59	3.13	3.58
40/20	1.99	2.29	2.69	3.02
40/25	1.87	2.12	2.45	2.72
40/30	1.79	2.01	2.30	2.52
40/40	1.69	1.88	2.11	2.30
40/60	1.59	1.74	1.94	2.08
40/120	1.50	1.61	1.76	1.87
40/∞	1.39	1.48	1.59	1.67
60/1	252	1,010	6,313	25,253
60/2	19.5	39.5	99.5	199
60/3	8.57	14.0	26.3	42.1
60/4	5.69	8.36	13.7	19.6
60/5	4.43	6.12	9.20	12.4
60/6	3.74	4.96	7.06	9.12
60/7	3.30	4.25	5.82	7.31
60/8	3.01	3.78	5.03	6.18
60/9	2.79	3.45	4.48	5.41
60/10	2.62	3.20	4.08	4.86
60/11	2.49	3.00	3.78	4.45
60/12	2.38	2.85	3.54	4.12
50/13	2.30	2.72	3.34	3.87
60/14	2.22	2.61	3.18	3.66
60/15	2.16	2.52	3.05	3.48
60/20	1.95	2.22	2.61	2.92
60/25	1.82	2.05	2.36	2.61
60/30	1.74	1.94	2.21	2.42
60/40	1.64	1.80	2.02	2.18
60/60	1.53	1.67	1.84	2.08
60/120	1.43	1.53	1.66	1.87
60/∞	1.32	1.39	1.47	1.67

n_A/n_B	$F_{0.950}$	$F_{0.975}$	$F_{0.990}$	$F_{0.995}$
120/1	253	1,014	6,339	25,253
120/2	19.5	39.5	99.5	199
120/3	8.55	13.9	26.2	42.1
120/4	5.66	8.31	13.6	19.6
120/5	4.40	6.07	9.11	12.4
120/6	3.70	4.90	6.97	9.12
120/7	3.27	4.20	5.74	7.31
120/8	2.97	3.73	4.95	6.18
120/9	2.75	3.39	4.40	5.41
120/10	2.58	3.14	4.00	4.86
120/11	2.45	2.94	3.69	4.45
120/12	2.34	2.79	3.45	4.12
120/13	2.25	2.66	3.25	3.87
120/14	2.18	2.55	3.09	3.66
120/15	2.11	2.46	2.96	3.48
120/20	1.90	2.16	2.52	2.92
120/25	1.77	1.98	2.27	2.61
120/30	1.68	1.87	2.11	2.42
120/40	1.58	1.72	1.92	2.18
120/60	1.47	1.58	1.73	1.96
120/120	1.35	1.43	1.53	1.75
120/∞	1.22	1.27	1.32	1.53
∞/1	254	1,018	6,366	25,465
∞/2	19.5	39.5	99.5	200
∞/3	8.53	13.9	26.1	41.8
∞/4	5.63	8.26	13.5	19.3
∞/5	4.37	6.02	9.02	12.1
∞/6	3.67	4.85	6.88	8.88
∞/7	3.23	4.14	5.65	7.08
∞/8	2.93	3.67	3.17	5.95
∞/9	2.71	3.33	4.31	5.19
∞/10	2.54	3.08	3.91	4.64
∞/11	2.40	2.88	3.60	4.23
∞/12	2.30	2.72	3.36	3.90
∞/13	2.21	2.60	3.17	3.65
∞/14	2.13	2.49	3.00	3.44
∞/15	2.07	2.40	2.87	3.26
∞/20	1.84	2.09	2.42	2.69
∞/25	1.71	1.91	2.17	2.38
∞/30	1.62	1.79	2.01	2.18
∞/40	1.51	1.64	1.80	1.93
∞/60	1.39	1.48	1.60	1.69
∞/120	1.25	1.31	1.38	1.43
∞/∞	1.00	1.00	1.00	1.00

Appendix VIII Orthogonal Coefficients

Orthogonal Coefficients Useful in Polynomial Regression

The body of the table contains the coefficients, l_i, needed in polynomial regression analysis. If a dependent variable, say Y, is assumed to be a polynomial function of an independent variable, X, then the sum of squares which measures the improvement in fit resulting from the use of a polynomial of degree k in place of one of degree $(k - 1)$ is given by

$$\text{SS} = (\Sigma l_i T_i)^2 / N_i \Sigma l_i^2$$

where

T_i = total of Y's at the ith level of X
N_i = number of values of Y at the ith level of X

It is required that the levels of X be equally spaced and that all values of N_i are equal. The values of l_i are given in the body of the table. See Chapter 15 for details.

i / k	1	2	3	4	5	6	Σl_i^2
1	−1	0	+1				2
2	+1	−2	+1				6
1	−3	−1	+1	+3			20
2	+1	−1	−1	+1			4
3	−1	+3	−3	+1			20
1	−2	−1	0	+1	+2		10
2	+2	−1	−2	−1	+2		14
3	−1	+2	0	−2	+1		10
4	+1	−4	+6	−4	+1		70
1	−5	−3	−1	+1	+3	+5	70
2	+5	−1	−4	−4	−1	+5	84
3	−5	+7	+4	−4	−7	+5	180
4	+1	−3	+2	+2	−3	+1	28
5	−1	+5	−10	+10	−5	+1	252

Appendix IX Poisson Distribution

P = the proportion of the population in the designated category
n = the sample size
r = the number of individuals in the stated category in the sample
$P\{r\}$ = the probability that a sample will contain r individuals in the stated category
$\Sigma P\{r\}$ = the probability that a sample will contain r or fewer individuals in the stated category
$\mu = Pn$ = the population mean value of r

μ	0.1		0.2		0.3		0.4	
r	$P\{r\}$	$\Sigma P\{r\}$	$P\{r\}$	$\Sigma P\{r\}$	$P\{r\}$	$\Sigma P\{r\}$	$P\{r\}$	$\Sigma P\{r\}$
0	.9048	.9048	.8187	.8187	.7408	.7408	.6703	.6703
1	.0905	.9953	.1637	.9824	.2222	.9630	.2681	.9384
2	.0045	.9998	.0164	.9988	.0333	.9963	.0536	.9920
3	—	—	.0011	.9999	.0033	.9996	.0072	.9992
4	—	—	—	—	.0003	.9999	.0007	.9999

μ	0.5		0.6		0.8		1.0	
r	$P\{r\}$	$\Sigma P\{r\}$	$P\{r\}$	$\Sigma P\{r\}$	$P\{r\}$	$\Sigma P\{r\}$	$P\{r\}$	$\Sigma P\{r\}$
0	.6065	.6065	.5488	.5488	.4493	.4493	.3679	.3679
1	.3033	.9098	.3293	.8781	.3595	.8088	.3679	.7458
2	.0758	.9856	.0988	.9769	.1438	.9526	.1839	.9197
3	.0126	.9982	.0198	.9967	.0383	.9909	.0613	.9810
4	.0016	.9998	.0030	.9997	.0077	.9986	.0153	.9963
5	—	—	—	—	.0012	.9998	.0031	.9994
6	—	—	—	—	.0002	1.0000	.0005	.9999

μ	1.2		1.4		1.6		2.0	
r	$P\{r\}$	$\Sigma P\{r\}$	$P\{r\}$	$\Sigma P\{r\}$	$P\{r\}$	$\Sigma P\{r\}$	$P\{r\}$	$\Sigma P\{r\}$
0	.3012	.3012	.2466	.2466	.2019	.2019	.1354	.1354
1	.3614	.6626	.3452	.5918	.3230	.5249	.2707	.4061
2	.2169	.8795	.2417	.8335	.2584	.7833	.2707	.6768
3	.0867	.9662	.1128	.9463	.1378	.9211	.1805	.8573
4	.0260	.9924	.0395	.9858	.0551	.9762	.0902	.9475
5	.0062	.9986	.0111	.9967	.0176	.9938	.0361	.9836
6	.0012	.9998	.0026	.9993	.0047	.9985	.0120	.9956
7	—	—	.0005	.9998	.0011	.9996	.0032	.9988
8	—	—	.0001	.9999	.0002	.9998	.0009	.9997
9	—	—	—	—	—	—	.0002	.9999

μ	2.5		3.0		3.5		4.0	
r	$P\{r\}$	$\Sigma P\{r\}$	$P\{r\}$	$\Sigma P\{r\}$	$P\{r\}$	$\Sigma P\{r\}$	$P\{r\}$	$\Sigma P\{r\}$
0	.0821	.0821	.0498	.0498	.0302	.0302	.0183	.0183
1	.2052	.2873	.1494	.1992	.1057	.1359	.0733	.0916
2	.2565	.5438	.2241	.4233	.1850	.3209	.1466	.2832
3	.2138	.7576	.2241	.6474	.2158	.5367	.1954	.4336
4	.1336	.8912	.1680	.8154	.1888	.7255	.1954	.6290
5	.0668	.9580	.1008	.9162	.1322	.8577	.1563	.7853
6	.0278	.9858	.0504	.9666	.0771	.9348	.1042	.8895
7	.0099	.9957	.0216	.9882	.0385	.9733	.0596	.9491
8	.0031	.9988	.0081	.9963	.0169	.9902	.0298	.9789
9	.0009	.9997	.0027	.9990	.0066	.9968	.0132	.9921
10	.0002	.9999	.0008	.9998	.0023	.9991	.0053	.9974
11	—	—	—	—	.0007	.9998	.0019	.9993
12	—	—	—	—	—	—	.0006	.9999

μ	4.5		5.0	
r	$P\{r\}$	$\Sigma P\{r\}$	$P\{r\}$	$\Sigma P\{r\}$
0	.0111	.0111	.0067	.0067
1	.0500	.0611	.0337	.0404
2	.1125	.1736	.0842	.1246
3	.1688	.3424	.1404	.2650
4	.1898	.5322	.1755	.4405
5	.1708	.7030	.1755	.6160
6	.1281	.8311	.1462	.7622
7	.0824	.9135	.1045	.8667
8	.0463	.9598	.0653	.9320
9	.0232	.9830	.0363	.9683
10	.0104	.9934	.0181	.9864
11	.0043	.9977	.0082	.9946
12	.0016	.9993	.0034	.9980
13	.0006	.9999	.0013	.9993
14	—	—	.0005	.9998

Appendix X Four-Place Logarithm Tables

N	0	1	2	3	4	5	6	7	8	9
0	....	0000	3010	4771	6021	6990	7782	8451	9031	9542
1	0000	0414	0792	1139	1461	1761	2041	2304	2553	2788
2	3010	3222	3424	3617	3802	3979	4150	4314	4472	4624
3	4771	4914	5051	5185	5315	5441	5563	5682	5798	5911
4	6021	6128	6232	6335	6435	6532	6628	6721	6812	6902
5	6990	7076	7160	7243	7324	7404	7482	7559	7634	7709
6	7782	7853	7924	7993	8062	8129	8195	8261	8325	8388
7	8451	8513	8573	8633	8692	8751	8808	8865	8921	8976
8	9031	9085	9138	9191	9243	9294	9345	9395	9445	9494
9	9542	9590	9638	9685	9731	9777	9823	9868	9912	9956
10	0000	0043	0086	0128	0170	0212	0253	0294	0334	0374
11	0414	0453	0492	0531	0569	0607	0645	0682	0719	0755
12	0792	0828	0864	0899	0934	0969	1004	1038	1072	1106
13	1139	1173	1206	1239	1271	1303	1335	1367	1399	1430
14	1461	1492	1523	1553	1584	1614	1644	1673	1703	1732
15	1761	1790	1818	1847	1875	1903	1931	1959	1987	2014
16	2041	2068	2095	2122	2148	2175	2201	2227	2253	2279
17	2304	2330	2355	2380	2405	2430	2455	2480	2504	2529
18	2553	2577	2601	2625	2648	2672	2695	2718	2742	2765
19	2788	2810	2833	2856	2878	2900	2923	2945	2967	2989
20	3010	3032	3054	3075	3096	3118	3139	3160	3181	3201
21	3222	3243	3263	3284	3304	3324	3345	3365	3385	3404
22	3424	3444	3464	3483	3502	3522	3541	3560	3579	3598
23	3617	3636	3655	3674	3692	3711	3729	3747	3766	3784
24	3802	3820	3838	3856	3874	3892	3909	3927	3945	3962
25	3979	3997	4014	4031	4048	4065	4082	4099	4116	4133
26	4150	4166	4183	4200	4216	4232	4249	4265	4281	4298
27	4314	4330	4346	4362	4378	4393	4409	4425	4440	4456
28	4472	4487	4502	4518	4533	4548	4564	4579	4594	4609
29	4624	4639	4654	4669	4683	4698	4713	4728	4742	4757
30	4771	4786	4800	4814	4829	4843	4857	4871	4886	4900
31	4914	4928	4942	4955	4969	4983	4997	5011	5024	5038
32	5051	5065	5079	5092	5105	5119	5132	5145	5159	5172
33	5185	5198	5211	5224	5237	5250	5263	5276	5289	5302
34	5315	5328	5340	5353	5366	5378	5391	5403	5416	5428
35	5441	5453	5465	5478	5490	5502	5514	5527	5539	5551
36	5563	5575	5587	5599	5611	5623	5635	5647	5658	5670
37	5682	5694	5705	5717	5729	5740	5752	5763	5775	5786
38	5798	5809	5821	5832	5843	5855	5866	5877	5888	5899
39	5911	5922	5933	5944	5955	5966	5977	5988	5999	6010
40	6021	6031	6042	6053	6064	6075	6085	6096	6107	6117
41	6128	6138	6149	6160	6170	6180	6191	6201	6212	6222
42	6232	6243	6253	6263	6274	6284	6294	6304	6314	6325
43	6335	6345	6355	6365	6375	6385	6395	6405	6415	6425
44	6435	6444	6454	6464	6474	6484	6493	6503	6513	6522
45	6532	6542	6551	6561	6571	6580	6590	6599	6609	6618
46	6628	6637	6646	6656	6665	6675	6684	6693	6702	6712
47	6721	6730	6739	6749	6758	6767	6776	6785	6794	6803
48	6812	6821	6830	6839	6848	6857	6866	6875	6884	6893
49	6902	6911	6920	6928	6937	6946	6955	6964	6972	6981
50	6990	6998	7007	7016	7024	7033	7042	7050	7059	7067
N	0	1	2	3	4	5	6	7	8	9

N	0	1	2	3	4	5	6	7	8	9
50	6990	6998	7007	7016	7024	7033	7042	7050	7059	7067
51	7076	7084	7093	7101	7110	7118	7126	7135	7143	7152
52	7160	7168	7177	7185	7193	7202	7210	7218	7226	7235
53	7243	7251	7259	7267	7275	7284	7292	7300	7308	7316
54	7324	7332	7340	7348	7356	7364	7372	7380	7388	7396
55	7404	7412	7419	7427	7435	7443	7451	7459	7466	7474
56	7482	7490	7497	7505	7513	7520	7528	7536	7543	7551
57	7559	7566	7574	7582	7589	7597	7604	7612	7619	7627
58	7634	7642	7649	7657	7664	7672	7679	7686	7694	7701
59	7709	7716	7723	7731	7738	7745	7752	7760	7767	7774
60	7782	7789	7796	7803	7810	7818	7825	7832	7839	7846
61	7853	7860	7868	7875	7882	7889	7896	7903	7910	7917
62	7924	7931	7938	7945	7952	7959	7966	7973	7980	7987
63	7993	8000	8007	8014	8021	8028	8035	8041	8048	8055
64	8062	8069	8075	8082	8089	8096	8102	8109	8116	8122
65	8129	8136	8142	8149	8156	8162	8169	8176	8182	8189
66	8195	8202	8209	8215	8222	8228	8235	8241	8248	8254
67	8261	8267	8274	8280	8287	8293	8299	8306	8312	8319
68	8325	8331	8338	8344	8351	8357	8363	8370	8376	8382
69	8388	8395	8401	8407	8414	8420	8426	8432	8439	8445
70	8451	8457	8463	8470	8476	8482	8488	8494	8500	8506
71	8513	8519	8525	8531	8537	8543	8549	8555	8561	8567
72	8573	8579	8585	8591	8597	8603	8609	8615	8621	8627
73	8633	8639	8645	8651	8657	8663	8669	8675	8681	8686
74	8692	8698	8704	8710	8716	8722	8727	8733	8739	8745
75	8751	8756	8762	8768	8774	8779	8785	8791	8797	8802
76	8808	8814	8820	8825	8831	8837	8842	8848	8854	8859
77	8865	8871	8876	8882	8887	8893	8899	8904	8910	8915
78	8921	8927	8932	8938	8943	8949	8954	8960	8965	8971
79	8976	8982	8987	8993	8998	9004	9009	9015	9020	9025
80	9031	9036	9042	9047	9053	9058	9063	9069	9074	9079
81	9085	9090	9096	9101	9106	9112	9117	9122	9128	9133
82	9138	9143	9149	9154	9159	9165	9170	9175	9180	9186
83	9191	9196	9201	9206	9212	9217	9222	9227	9232	9238
84	9243	9248	9253	9258	9263	9269	9274	9279	9284	9289
85	9294	9299	9304	9309	9315	9320	9325	9330	9335	9340
86	9345	9350	9355	9360	9365	9370	9375	9380	9385	9390
87	9395	9400	9405	9410	9415	9420	9425	9430	9435	9440
88	9445	9450	9455	9460	9465	9469	9474	9479	9484	9489
89	9494	9499	9504	9509	9513	9518	9523	9528	9533	9538
90	9542	9547	9552	9557	9562	9566	9571	9576	9581	9586
91	9590	9595	9600	9605	9609	9614	9619	9624	9628	9633
92	9638	9643	9647	9652	9657	9661	9666	9671	9675	9680
93	9685	8689	9694	9699	9703	9708	9713	9717	9722	9727
94	9731	9736	9741	9745	9750	9754	9759	9763	9768	9773
95	9777	9782	9786	9791	9795	9800	9805	9809	9814	9818
96	9823	9827	9832	9836	9841	9845	9850	9854	9859	9863
97	9868	9872	9877	9881	9886	9890	9894	9899	9903	9908
98	9912	9917	9921	9926	9930	9934	9939	9943	9948	9952
99	9956	9961	9965	9969	9974	9978	9983	9987	9991	9996
100	0000	0004	0009	0013	0017	0022	0026	0030	0035	0039
N	0	1	2	3	4	5	6	7	8	9

Appendix XI Operation of Calculators

XI.1 *Preliminary Comments*

The following suggestions are not intended to provide complete and detailed instructions for the use of calculators, but are offered in the hope that they will clarify some underlying principles, thus making it easy for the reader to become an effective user of any modern machine. All machines consist of a rather marvelous set of mechanical and electrical interlocks so that, *when power is on the machine and no undue force is applied,* no harm can be done to the machine by accidental misoperation. (This assumes, of course, that the machine has been properly maintained.) The following general principles, then, will guide you in operating the machines:

1. Operate a machine which is unfamiliar to you only after you have received instruction, if such instruction is available, or after careful thought and observation of the machine.
2. Verify that the power is connected and on. This can be done most safely by pressing the "Clear" keys described below.
3. Do not normally use more force than you would use to operate the keys of a nonelectric typewriter.
4. If the machine appears to be jammed or "running away" and does not respond to the use of the "Stop" key or lever described below, disconnect the power at the plug and notify the proper member of your organization to have the machine checked. Place an "Out of Order" tag on the machine and record as much as you can of the operation on which the difficulty developed. This will help the service man locate and correct the cause of the difficulty and will reduce your service charges.

XI.2 *General Principles*

If, instead of thinking of the calculator as a mechanical demon which must be handled according to certain very mystic rules, you will think of it as a mechanized pencil, paper, and eraser which will, at your command, perform the basic operations of addition, subtraction, multiplication, and division, you will find the machine easy to use. In fact, it will become your valued servant rather than your feared master! You "write" the numbers with the aid of (a) the keyboard and (b) the add, subtract, or multiply keys. These elements are therefore like the pencil. The results of the operations are written by the machine in one of the two dials (actually, each "dial" in the machine terminology is really a row of ten or twenty individual but connected dials, in the ordinary terminology) which are located on the carriage. The carriage, then, is like the paper. Various keys and levers tell the machine what to do with the numbers and where to put the results. These are the operating keys. Some of the operating keys tell the machine to remove numbers. These are the "Clear" keys, which are like erasers. The rest of them direct the arithmetic and the placement of the results.

The *keyboard* consists of several columns or *banks* of keys numbered from

1 through 9. Machines are made with either eight or ten banks: the latter are much to be preferred for statistical computations. In what follows, we shall first describe the operations as they are performed on a Marchant "Figure-master," then indicate any modifications which apply to the Monroe "CAA" and Friden machines. Minor variations in other models of the several makes should cause little difficulty.

XI.3 *Addition*

Marchant. Press the three "Clear" keys, either separately or simultaneously. All dials should then show only zeros. Enter the first number by depressing the appropriate keys on the keyboard. Verify that the small lever at the extreme upper right corner of the machine is in its "Up" position (more about this lever presently). Then depress the bar marked "+". The number which was on the keyboard will be transferred to the long dial on the carriage to a position directly above that which it occupied on the keyboard and will disappear from the keyboard. Also, a "1" will appear on the short dial directly below a small orange arrow on the machine frame. Now enter the second number on the keyboard, using the same relative position as to decimals and again depress the "+" key. The new number will add to the first, and a "2" will appear on the short dial. Other numbers can be similarly added, and the total will appear in the long dial, while the number of items will appear in the short dial.

Monroe. To the right of the keyboard banks are two round buttons, one plain and the other marked "R": depress the plain button, which permits the figures to leave the keyboard when they have been added. A small lever below the "+" bar has two positions marked "×" (up) and "÷" (down). This is like the small lever at the corner of the Marchant keyboard and should be at the "×" (up) position. Both knobs at the left of the carriage should be pushed fully in.

Friden. A lever marked "Ctr Con" over the auxiliary keyboard at the left of the main keyboard, which acts like the lever at the corner of the Marchant machine, should be in its up position. A lever at the upper right corner of the keyboard marked "Add", which acts like the two red buttons on the Monroe machine, should be pulled down. Both knobs at the right end of the carriage should be turned so that they are parallel to the carriage.

XI.4 *Subtraction*

Marchant. Enter the first figure (minuend) on the keyboard and transfer it to the long dial by pressing the "+" bar. Then enter the second figure (subtrahend) on the keyboard and press the "−" bar. The long dial will show the difference and the short dial will show the net number of items, or 0. When a series of numbers are to be combined, some added and others subtracted, transfer each item to the long dial by pressing the appropriate bar, "+" or "−". If a count of the actual number of items is desired, move the lever at the top right corner of the keyboard (hereafter called the upper dial, or counter, control lever) to the reverse, or down, position before each subtraction and restore it to forward, or up, before each addition.

Monroe. The upper dial control lever should be moved to its down, or reverse, position, which is marked "÷" before each subtraction if an item count is wanted.

Friden. The "Ctr Con" lever must be moved to its down, or reverse, position before each subtraction if a count of items is desired.

XI.5 *Multiplication*

In pencil-and-paper multiplication, we multiply our numbers, then count the total decimals in the two factors and "point off" that many places in the product. We could operate similarly on the machines, but there is a certain efficiency to be gained by presetting our decimals on the machine, then operating so that all numbers are entered with due regard to their decimal location.

For many purposes, it is convenient to have the decimals located at the center of the machine. We shall find that, in multiplication, one factor appears in the short dial while the other is on the keyboard and the product appears on the long dial. By analogy with our pencil-and-paper principle, we operate with the number of decimals on the keyboard plus that on the short dial equal to the number on the long dial. We might remember this as

$$K + S = L$$

Notice, by the way, that we have used "short" and "long" to designate the carriage dials. The makers' names for the dials and their specific location vary from machine to machine, but all short dials, whatever their name or location, contain item counts, factors, and quotients. All long dials contain sums, differences, products, and dividends.

Marchant. A good "standard" setup uses 5 decimals each on the keyboard and short dial and 10 on the long dial. We might call this the 5-5-10 (K-S-L) setup. Decimals are marked on the carriage by turning over the small plates under and between the dial openings to show the bright circular spot. Notice that the number of each dial position, counting from the right, is shown by the number near it. Keyboard decimals are marked by a brilliant orange pointer at the top of the keyboard. Color changes between groups of banks are convenient when 2, 5, or 8 decimals are used on the keyboard.

One factor is entered on the keyboard with respect to the decimal. The other factor goes through the multiplier mechanism. To enter this factor, first set a sliding element near the top of the keyboard so that its part carrying an arrow pointing left (⟵) is visible. The row of buttons below the keyboard, numbered from 1 through 10, are tabulator control buttons. The position on the short dial into which a count or digit of a multiplier enters is directly below the orange arrow. If tabulator button No. 1 is depressed and held down, the carriage will move to the extreme left so that the arrow points to No. 1 position. If the No. 10 button is held down the carriage will move to the extreme right until the orange arrow points to No. 10 position. If the machine is brought to the No. 1 position, then any other button is pressed, that button will stay down but the machine will not move. Pressing the "tab" bar will make the machine move to that position. Another pressure will make the machine move to the next higher numbered position whose tabulator button is down, or to No. 10 position. To make the machine move the carriage toward the left and stop on a *lower* numbered position, tap (don't hold) the No. 1 button.

Returning to multiplication, then, with one factor in the keyboard, tabulate the carriage to the appropriate position for the left-hand digit in the other factor in the short dial. Press the buttons in the bank at the extreme right of the machine to "enter" the digits of the second factor in the short dial. The product shows in the long dial, properly pointed off as to decimals.

Monroe. Enter one factor in the keyboard and transfer it to the multiplier mechanism by pressing the key marked

□
SET
←——
UP

The factor will appear in an auxiliary dial under the carriage. Enter the second factor in the keyboard and press the button marked

CLEAR
←——
MULT

which will clear both dials of the carriage, then transfer the factor from the multiplier to the short dial and the product to the long dial. If the multiplication is a squaring (multiplication of a number by itself) *hold* the set-up key down until the machine *stops*. This will retain the factor on the keyboard as well as transferring it to the multiplier mechanism. Depression of the multiplier key will then produce the square. If the setup key is not held down long enough, the factor will leave the keyboard and you will multiply the factor by zero, producing, regrettably, merely zero!

Friden. The multiplier is controlled through the small keyboard to the left of the main keyboard. The number of decimals in it must be that shown on the short dial. One factor is entered on the keyboard, the other, by means of the auxiliary keyboard, in the multiplier. Pressing the key marked "MULT" transfers this factor to the short dial and the product to the long dial.

XI.6 *Accumulative Multiplication*

Marchant. On the Marchant, if a second multiplication is performed without clearing the carriage, the sum of the two factors which went through the multiplier appears in the short dial and the sum of the two products appears in the long dial. This can be continued indefinitely, and is used in accumulating simultaneously ΣX and ΣX^2 or ΣXY in statistical work.

Monroe. Use the "ACCUM MULT" instead of the "CLEAR MULT" button. This prevents clearing the carriage dials before multiplication and allows the factors and products to accumulate.

Friden. Use the "ACC MULT" button, which prevents clearing the carriage.

XI.7 *Negative Multiplication*

When it is desired to have a new product subtracted from a figure already in the long dial, the process, in machine language, is called "negative multiplication."

Marchant. Before entering the factors in the multiplier, depress the "NEG ×" key. If the factor contains more than one digit, press the "REP" key as well. The factor will subtract from the short dial and the product from the long dial. The reverse lever can be used to make the factor appear in its actual values in the short dial.

Monroe. Use the "NEG MULT" button. The reverse lever can be used to control the short dial as on the Marchant.

Friden. Use the "NEG MULT" and "CTR CON" levers as on the Monroe.

XI.8 *Multiplication by a Constant*

When it is necessary to multiply a constant factor by a succession of other, different factors, the constant factor is entered on the keyboard and the varying factors are then entered through the multiplier. In order to reduce the possibility of accidentally clearing the factor from the keyboard, the lower portion of the split keyboard clearing key may be held down while this factor is being entered. Subsequent depression of this portion of the key will *not* clear the keyboard: the upper portion of the split key must be used.

Often, as in the computations involved in finding the frequencies under the normal distribution curve for several classes, we need to multiply a fixed factor by one which varies in such a way that a number of its digits remain fixed, but one or more change. For example, in the several values of $(1/\sigma)(x - \mu)$, the value of $1/\sigma$ remains fixed, but the values of $(x - \mu)$ usually differ by some fixed amount, say 0.4, or 2, or 50. It is convenient to place the $(1/\sigma)$ in the keyboard and multiply by the smallest numerical value of $(x - \mu)$. Then, without clearing, simply multiply repeatedly by the fixed difference. The short dial will show the successive values of $(x - \mu)$ and the long dial will show the successive values of the product. If only a single digit is changing, further convenience is obtained by depressing the "non-shift" key after the carriage has been positioned to the dial corresponding to the location of the changing digit. The machine will not shift after the successive multiplications, and the work will proceed rapidly.

Monroe. When both factors have approximately equal numbers of digits, or the changing factor has several digits changing, enter the fixed factor in the multiplier and lower the lever at the right of the carriage to its "C" position. This will cause the factor to return to the multiplier after each multiplication is complete, ready for reuse.

When the varying factor changes only one or two digits from value to value, enter its smallest numerical value in the multiplier. Then enter the constant factor in the keyboard with the small red button marked "R" at the right depressed. After the first product is obtained, the add bar may be used to increase the factor shown on the short dial and the product shown on the long dial by simply holding it down with the machine tabulated to the proper position until the new value appears. If two or more digits are changing in the factor, the tabulator buttons in the positions involved may be depressed, and thus used as an aid in stopping the carriage at the proper places with the carriage shifting keys. If several digits are changing, but by fixed amounts, the first product may be obtained as above, then the amount of the change in the varying factor may be entered as a constant in the multiplier and the actually constant factor may be put in the keyboard. Accumulative multiplication will then cause the new products to show in the long dial, while the varying factors show, for verification, in the short dial.

Friden. The control on the multiplier which causes a factor to return for reuse is the lever marked "REP" above and to the left of the multiplier keyboard. In its down position, it causes the factor to return for repeated use. The control which causes keys to remain in the keyboard for repeated addition, analogous to the "R" button on the Monroe, is the lever marked "ADD" at the top of the keyboard. In its upper position, keys remain depressed during addition and subtraction, and thus these operations will continue as long as the add or subtract bars are depressed. The use of these controls is like that on the Monroe machine.

XI.9 *Division*

On the Marchant machine, the carriage is positioned as for addition, and the dividend added to the long dial. The divisor is then entered in the keyboard. If any digits on the dividend are to the left of the left digit in the divisor, the tabulator button as many places to the left of the button used to get the "units" position on the short dial should be depressed, while holding the "units" position button down. When the key marked "÷" and the small key above it are *both* depressed at once, the following sequence of operations occurs:

1. The short dial is cleared.
2. The machine moves to the position of the second tabulator button depressed, so that the left digits of the dividend and divisor are in line.

3. Division continues until all decimals allowed for in the short dial have been obtained.

What happens thereafter depends on the position of a small lever located beside the add bar. If this is up, the machine will stop, leaving the quotient on the short dial, the remainder on the long dial, and the divisor on the keyboard. If the lever is down, the machine will leave the quotient on the short dial, but will clear the long dial and keyboard and return to the position of the first depressed tabulator button. Normally this will be the "units" button, and the machine will thus be ready for addition or a new division.

If the dividend is already in the long dial as a result of a previous computation, simply enter the divisor and continue from there as directed above.

Monroe. Move the carriage to the extreme left. Depress the tabulator button over the "units" position on the short dial. Enter the dividend on the keyboard and press the "DIV'D TAB" button, over the clear keys. The machine will:

1. Tabulate to the units position.
2. Enter the dividend in the long dial.
3. Remove the "1" which showed temporarily in the short dial.

Now enter the divisor on the keyboard and note if there are any figures in the dividend to the left of its left figure. If so, depress the tabulator button as many places to the left of the "units" button as there are "overhanging" digits, move the carriage to that position, and press the "DIV" button below the keyboard. The machine will develop the quotient on the short dial, leave the remainder in the long dial, and the divisor in the keyboard.

If the dividend has been obtained as a result of other operations and is already in the long dial, leave it there, clear the short dial, enter the divisor on the keyboard, and continue as above.

Friden. Depress the tabulator button above the decimal point on the short dial. Enter the dividend on the keyboard and press the "ENTER DIV" key. The machine will tabulate to the units position, after clearing the carriage, and will transfer the dividend to the long dial, but will leave the short dial empty. Enter the divisor on the keyboard and press *both* keys marked "÷." The quotient, remainder, and divisor will appear on the short dial, long dial, and keyboard areas, respectively. The machine will tabulate itself to the proper place to start division. The two "÷" keys have the following functions:

1. The left key causes the quotient to subtract from any value previously in the short dial.
2. The right key, alone, does nothing. Pressed simultaneously with the left, it reverses the action of the left key and causes the quotient to add to the short dial (which was at zero in normal division).

If the dividend was in the long dial as the result of previous computations, leave it there, clear the short dial, enter the divisor on the keyboard and continue.

XI.10 *Gaining Efficiency and Accuracy*

The foregoing discussion covers, very compactly, all the fundamental operations on the three models of calculators specifically considered. Other models of these three makes differ in minor details, in so far as the operator is concerned. Generally speaking, if you have mastered the *principles* of machine operation, which we have tried to bring out, you will have little difficulty in learning to operate any model, even if its manual has been mislaid. If the manual is available, a few minutes thoughtful study of it, and trial of some examples, should put you in command of the machine.

Efficiency and accuracy come from the following principles consistently applied:

1. Plan your work so that it flows smoothly through the machine, avoiding the necessity for reentering a value onto the long dial whenever possible.
2. Whenever possible, make the machine check you. For example, if you must find

$$\frac{A \times B}{C}$$

   notice that this is the same as $(A/C)B$. Divide A by C. Clear the long dial and keyboard. Set the short dial control in reverse. Put A/C through the multiplier with B on the keyboard, using accumulative multiplication. If A/C was correctly entered, the short dial will show zero: its failure to do so will indicate an error which can then be corrected.
3. Try to use the machine in the way it operates fastest. For example, it can multiply by a short $1/N$ faster than it can divide by N.

XI.11 *Variance Computations*

These principles are well illustrated in the computation of variance. By the use of accumulative multiplication, ΣX and ΣX^2 are developed in the short and long dials, respectively. When $1/N$ is "wieldy," that is, complete in a few significant figures, $1/N$ can be put in the multiplier and ΣX in the keyboard, using a temporary decimal setup so that the figures appear at the extreme right or left of the machine. By using accumulative multiplication, μ and $1/N$ will appear, with the new decimal setup, in the long dial and short dial, respectively. The same product is then negatively multiplied, clearing the values just obtained from the machine. Meanwhile, the original sum and sum of squared values are undisturbed. The sum can now be put through the multiplier with the newly found mean on the keyboard, using negative multiplication. The short dial will go to zero if the sum was properly entered in the multiplier and the long dial will show the "sum of squares" ready for division by N to obtain the variance.

If $1/N$ is unwieldy, after accumulating ΣX and ΣX^2, tabulate the machine to the "units" position. Copy ΣX^2 from the long dial to the keyboard. Then either (a) multiply it by $(N - 1)$ or (b) clear the long dial and multiply by N. Then, on the Marchant machine, clear the keyboard and negatively multiply by $N - 1$ or N, whichever was used above, to restore the short dial to ΣX. Now square ΣX, but using negative multiplication. This will, if correctly done, reduce the short dial to zero, and the long dial is ready to be divided by N to produce the sum of squares or by N^2 to produce the variance. On the Monroe and Marchant machines, the non-enter control may be used to prevent the value of $N - 1$ or N from appearing in the short dial during the first step.

If you will carry out the computation as suggested, you will see that it does incorporate the principles of the preceding section, and provides an effective method for computing variances.

Appendix XII Square Roots

XII.1 *Background*

In the course of using statistical methods, one has such frequent need to obtain square roots, as in calculating standard deviations from variances, that it is desirable to be able to accomplish such tasks with ease and speed. Unfortunately, too little attention is usually paid in most math courses either to the procedure or to the principles on which it rests. Because we find both the procedure and the principles interesting, we are presenting here first a brief discussion of the ideas used, then the details of their application to methods for obtaining roots. The methods are particularly useful when a desk calculator is available.

XII.2 *Behavior of Decimals*

Suppose we consider the squares of the nonzero digits:

N	1	2	3	4	5	5	7	8	9
N^2	1	4	9	16	25	36	49	64	81

We know that we cannot obtain a number as large as 100, no matter what decimals we may add to 9: we must square 10. Thus we know that all numbers with one or two digits to the left of their decimal have square roots with one digit to the left of the decimal.

If we multiply each of the digits above by 10, then square the results, our new numbers will range from 10 to 90 and their squares will range from 100 to 8100, and the addition of units and decimals to 90 cannot produce a number whose square is as large as 10,000. Thus all numbers with three or four digits to the left of the decimal will have roots with two digits to the left.

On the other hand, if we divide our original digits by 10 to obtain 0.1, 0.2, . . . 0.9, the squares of the resulting numbers will be between 0.01 and 0.81, and further decimals in the number will not produce a square as large as 1.00. If the original digits are divided by 100, producing 0.01, 0.02, . . . 0.09, the square will range from 0.0001 to 0.0081, and further decimals will not increase the square to 0.0100.

All of this is a consequence of a general principle which leads to the following:

Rule for Locating Decimals. Start at the decimal in the number and mark off groups of two digits. If there are nonzero digits to the left of the decimal, there will be one digit in the root for each group (the extreme left group may contain only one digit) in the number. If there are only zeros to the left of the decimal in the number, there will be one zero to the right of the decimal in the root before the first nonzero digit for each pair of zeros in the number between the decimal and the first nonzero digit.

XII.3 *Relation Between Squares and Roots*

We can learn some interesting things about squares and roots by writing out in symbols what our convention about the value assigned to the position of the digits in our numbers really means. If we denote the digits standing in the hundreds, tens, units, tenths, and hundredths places by H, T, U, t, and h, respectively, then the number which would be written simply as $HTU.th$ is really:

$$N = 100H + 10T + 1U + 0.1t + 0.01h$$

and its square would be:

$$\begin{aligned} N^2 = {} & 10{,}000H^2 + 1{,}000(2HT) + 100(2HU + T^2) \\ & + 10(2Ht + 2TU) + 1(2Hh + 2Tt + U^2) \\ & + 0.1(2Th + 2Ut) + 0.01(2Uh + t^2) \\ & + 0.001(2ht) + 0.0001h^2 \end{aligned}$$

For example, 372.94 is really

$$372.94 = 100\times3 + 10\times7 + 1\times2 + 0.1\times9 + 0.01\times4$$

If we write out each part of the square according to the formula above, and place the corresponding numerical values in a column to the right, we shall have

$10{,}000H^2$	$10{,}000 \times 3^2$	90,000.0000
$1{,}000(2HT)$	$1{,}000 \times 2 \times 3 \times 7$	42,000.0000
$100(2HU + T^2)$	$100(2 \times 3 \times 2 + 7^2)$	6,100.0000
$10(2Ht + 2TU)$	$10(2 \times 3 \times 9 + 2 \times 7 \times 2)$	820.0000
$1(2Hh + 2Tt + U^2)$	$1(2 \times 3 \times 4 + 2 \times 7 \times 9 + 2^2)$	154.0000
$0.1(2Th + 2Ut)$	$0.1(2 \times 7 \times 4 + 2 \times 2 \times 9)$	9.2000
$0.01(2Uh + t^2)$	$0.01(2 \times 2 \times 4 + 9^2)$	0.9700
$0.001(2th)$	$0.001(2 \times 9 \times 4)$	0.0720
$0.0001h^2$	0.0001×4^2	0.0016
N^2		139,084.2436

Now let us see how we could find the square root of the number we have just produced by using a sort of orderly reversal of the process by which we formed it. First we mark off our groups of two digits according to the principle developed in section XII.2:

$$\overline{13}\,\overline{90}\,\overline{84}.\overline{24}\,\overline{36}$$

From this, we know that our root will have three digits to the left of the decimal. The largest digit whose square does not exceed 13 is 3, whose square is 9. So we know that $H = 3$ and that $10{,}000H^2 = 90{,}000$. We subtract this value from our number and have left:

$$\overline{4}\,\overline{90}\,\overline{84}.\overline{24}\,\overline{36}$$

Now note that, when we were building up the square of N, the biggest element after $10{,}000H^2$ was $1{,}000(2HT)$ which we could think of as $100(2H)10T$. We know that $H = 3$ so that $2H = 6$ and $100(2H) = 600$. We note that another component of our square is $100T^2$, which we might think of as $(10T)^2$. Now the product of $[100(2H) + 10T]$ by $10T$ is $100(2H)10T + (10T)^2 = 1{,}000(2HT) + 100T^2$. We may estimate that T is 8, the first digit of the quotient of our previous remainder divided by $100(2H)$:

$$\frac{49{,}084.2436}{600} = 8 \ldots \ldots$$

However, $[100(2H) + 10T]\ 10T = 680 \times 80 = 54{,}400$, which is larger than 49084.2436, so we try $T = 7$ instead and find $[100(2H) + 10T]\ 10T = 670 \times 70 = 46{,}900$. This, subtracted from our 49084.2436, leaves

$$\overline{21}\,\overline{84}.\overline{24}\,\overline{36}$$

Scrutiny of our squaring record shows that we have now subtracted $10{,}000H^2$, $1{,}000(2HT)$ and $100T^2$ from the square whose root we are seeking. One of the parts of what is left is $100(2HU)$, and we therefore seek the units digit next. Again referring to our squaring plan, we see that items involving digits we have already found and the U we are seeking are

$$\begin{aligned} 100(2HU) &= 100(2H)U \\ 10(2TU) &= 10(2T)U \\ 1U^2 &= (1U)U \end{aligned}$$

Suppose we form the number $100(2H) + 10(2T) = 100 \times 6 + 10 \times 14 = 600 + 140 = 740$. The quotient of our previous remainder by it has 2 as its first digit:

$$\frac{2{,}184.2436}{740} = 2 \ldots .$$

so we estimate that $U = 2$ and add this to $100(2H) + 10(2T)$ to obtain $100(2H) + 10(2T) + U = 600 + 140 + 2 = 742$. The product of this number by U is the quantity whose components were detailed above and is, numerically, $742 \times 2 = 1{,}484$. Subtracting this from our previous remainder leaves

$$\overline{\ \,7}\,\overline{00}.\overline{24}\,\overline{36}$$

We again refer to our squaring plan and note that elements involving the next digit, t, are: $2Ht$, $2Tt$, $2Ut$ and t^2, each multiplied by the appropriate power of 10. So we form the number $100(2H) + 10(2T) + 1(2U) = 744$ and note, following reasoning that we have used before, that $700.2436/744 = 0.9 \ldots .$, so we estimate that $t = 9$. Thus we form the product:

$$\begin{aligned} &[100(2H) + 10(2T) + 1(2U) + 0.1t]\ 0.1t \\ &= 10(2Ht) + 1(2Tt) + 0.1(2Ut) + 0.01t^2 \\ &= 744.9 \times 0.9 = 670.41 \end{aligned}$$

and subtraction of this product from our previous remainder leaves

$$\overline{29}.\overline{83}\,\overline{36}.$$

The only remaining components of our root are $2Hh$, $2Th$, $2Uh$, $2th$ and h^2, multiplied by appropriate powers of 10. We therefore form

$$100(2H) + 10(2T) + 1(2U) + 0.1(2t) = 745.8$$

and estimate h as the first digit of the quotient of our previous remainder by it:

$$\frac{29.8336}{745.8} = 0.04 \ldots .$$

Without detailing the algebra (which you should do for yourself) we add 0.04 to 745.8 and multiply by 0.04:

$$745.84 \times 0.04 = 29.8336$$

which, subtracted from our previous remainder, leaves zero, and we conclude that our root is 372.94. This is, of course, correct.

A pencil-and-paper procedure taking advantage of a convenient layout may be familiar to you:

```
3)        139084.2436  )372.94
           9
67)        490
           469
742)        2184
            1484
7449)        70024
             67041
74584)        298336
              298336
                   0
```

You can recognize the numbers by a careful comparison with our work above, and thus see the convenience of the plan.

XII.4 *A Shortcut*

There is a shortcut which we could recognize from our development of the square and our process of extracting the square root. This shortcut seems to be too little known to most students, but is well worth learning. Suppose we had carried our operation through the point of obtaining more than half the digits we required in our root and were on the point of estimating our next digit. In our case, suppose we were just about to estimate the tenths digit, having obtained three digits in our root and decided that we want only two more.

We shall literally carry out the division we previously used to estimate t to obtain two digits of the quotient:

$$\frac{700.2436}{744} = 0.94^{+}$$

and we have thus found both t and h. Why?

Our remainder was, actually,

$$10(2Ht) + 1(2Hh + 2Tt) + 0.1(2Th + 2Ut) + 0.01(2Uh + t^2) + 0.001(2th) + 0.0001h^2$$

and the quotient of this divided by our divisor, which was, symbolically,

$$100(2H) + 10(2T) + 1(2U)$$

is

$$0.1t + .001h$$

with a remainder of $0.01t^2 + 0.001(2th) + 0.0001h^2$.

This remainder is just the fragment that would have been taken care of if we had literally completed our taking of the root instead of using the shortcut as an approximation, but the two figures we sought will not be affected by more than one unit in the second digit.

XII.5 *Application to the Marchant Calculator*

The method we have just demonstrated is readily applied to the Marchant calculator. Suppose we use the usual setup of decimals (5-5-10) and the number whose square root we are seeking on the long dial. (In this particular case, this is conveniently done by placing 1/10 of it on the keyboard and multiplying by 10.) Clear the short dial and keyboard and set the short dial control lever in reverse.

We note that there are three groups of two digits to the left of the decimal in the long dial occupied, so we know our root will start in the hundreds place. We tabulate to that position, No. 8, and estimate the square root of the left group, 13, as 3. We enter the 3 in column No. 8 on the keyboard, then negatively multiply by 3. The three dials will now read as follows:

```
                      v
S              00300.00000
L     0000049084.0000000000
K         00300.00000
```

Note that the decimal points are aligned above just as they will be on the machine. Now we add 3 onto the 3 already in column No. 8 on the keyboard, making it read 00600.00000, and estimate how much the 6 will go into the digits, 49, above and to the left of it on the long dial. It appears to go 8 times. We place an 8 in column No. 7, making the keyboard read 00680.00000. If we don't happen to notice that 680 × 8 is more than 49000, we could negatively multiply by 8 in position No. 7. The long dial would show a series of 9'3 at the left, indicating that the new product was larger than the amount previously on the long dial. We return to position No. 7, multiply by 8 to restore the previous figures, then reduce the keyboard figure to 7 in column No. 7. Now we negatively multiply by 7 in position No. 7 and our machine now shows the following:

```
                              v
S                    0 0 3 7 0.0 0 0 0 0
L  0 0 0 0 0 0 2 1 8 4.0 0 0 0 0 0 0 0 0 0
K              0 0 6 7 0.0 0 0 0 0
```

Now we add another 7 to column No. 7 on the keyboard, making it read 00740.00000. (We really added 70 to 670, making 740, of course.) We estimate that 74, on the keyboard, goes into the digits above and to the left of it on the long dial, 218, twice but not three times. We place a 2 in column No. 6 on the keyboard and negatively multiply by 2 in position No. 6 with the result that the machine now shows the following:

```
                               v
S                    0 0 3 7 2.0 0 0 0 0
L  0 0 0 0 0 0 0 7 0 0.2 4 3 6 0 0 0 0 0 0
K              0 0 7 4 2.0 0 0 0 0
```

We add another 2 in column No. 6 on the keyboard, making the reading 00744.00000. At this point, we may either continue with our extraction of the root, using the same procedure, or we may decide to use the shortcut, if we want only two more digits.

To put the shortcut into operation we must

1. Return the short dial control to normal.
2. Hold one finger on the "STOP" button.
3. While holding the "STOP" button down, depress the division key.
4. Remove the finger from the "STOP" button first, then the other finger from the division key.

The first step is necessary to make the quotient, not its complement, appear on the short dial. The second step prevents the part of the root we have found from disappearing when we start to divide. The fourth step prevents the premature stopping of the division operation. The machine will, if allowed to run out all five decimals of the quotient, finally show 00372.94118 on the short dial, but only the first two decimals are meaningful. Thus our root is 372.94, which is correct.

XII.6 *Another Old Mathematical Idea*

Before the advent of modern calculators, people were much more eager to find ways of making arithmetic easy than they are now! One of the facts they discovered is that the sum of the successive odd digits is simply the square of the number of digits added, thus:

$$1 = 1 = 1^2$$
$$1 + 3 = 4 = 2^2$$
$$1 + 3 + 5 = 9 = 3^2$$
$$1 + 3 + 5 + 7 = 16 = 4^2$$
$$\cdot \quad \cdot \quad \cdot \quad \cdot \quad \cdot \quad \cdot \quad \cdot \quad \cdot \quad \cdot \quad \cdot \quad \cdot \quad \cdot \quad \cdot \quad \cdot \quad \cdot \quad \cdot \quad \cdot \quad \cdot \quad \cdot$$
$$1 + 3 + 5 + 7 + 9 + 11 + 13 + 15 + 17 = 81 = 9^2$$

We could take advantage of this fact with pencil and paper by counting off groups of 2 as usual, then, considering only the left-hand group, we could start subtracting the successive odd digits, recording the number of subtractions we make:

$$\begin{array}{lr}
 & \overline{13}\,\overline{90}\,\overline{84}.\overline{24}\,\overline{36} \\
1 & \underline{1} \\
 & 12 \\
2 & \underline{3} \\
 & 9 \\
3 & \underline{5} \\
 & 4 \\
\not{4} & \underline{\not{7}}
\end{array}$$

We "tried" to subtract the fourth odd digit, 7, and found it too big, so crossed it out. Actually, we did it to prepare our thinking for an adaptation of the process to machine use. Notice that the 3, the number of digits subtracted, is, in fact, the first digit in our root. Notice further that the remainder is just what we had at the same stage of our previous methods, and finally, the odd digit that was too big to be subtracted, 7, when reduced by one, is just twice the digit we have found in the root.

Now we start subtracting 61, 63, etc., from the remainder, 4 from the first group followed by 90, the two digits of the second group. On pencil and paper application, the results would look thus:

$$\begin{array}{lr}
 & 49084.2436 \\
31 & \underline{61} \\
 & 429 \\
32 & \underline{63} \\
 & 366 \\
33 & \underline{65} \\
 & 301 \\
34 & \underline{67} \\
 & 234 \\
35 & \underline{69} \\
 & 165 \\
36 & \underline{71} \\
 & 94 \\
37 & \underline{73} \\
 & 21 \\
\not{3}\not{8} & \underline{\not{7}\not{5}}
\end{array}$$

Again notice that 37 comprises the first two digits of our root, that the remainder is exactly that given by our other methods, and that the odd number which was too large to be subtracted was, when reduced by one, 74, which is just twice the significant digits already determined in the root.

XII.7 *Adaptation to Monroe and Friden Machines*

Using the same decimal setup as on the Marchant machine, 5-5-10, enter the number whose square root is to be determined in the long dial. Set the short dial control lever in reverse, and set the machine for repeated addition ("R" button down on the Monroe machine, "ADD" lever up on the Friden machine). Note that there are three groups to the left of the decimal in the number, so there will be three digits to the left in the root. Start entering the successive odd digits in bank No. 8 on the keyboard and subtract each once while the machine is tabulated to position No. 8. When the first excessive digit is subtracted, press the add bar once and reduce the keyboard digit by 1. The machine will then show the following values:

```
S               0 0 3 0 0.0 0 0 0 0
L   0 0 0 0 0 4 9 0 8 4.2 4 3 6 0 0 0 0 0 0
K         0 0 6 0 0.0 0 0 0 0
```

Now tabulate to position No. 7. Leave the 6 in bank No. 8 and enter the odd digits in bank No. 7, subtracting each once. When the excessive value is subtracted, immediately add it back and reduce the digit in bank No. 7 by one. This will leave the following on the machine:

```
S               0 0 3 7 0.0 0 0 0 0
L   0 0 0 0 0 0 2 1 8 4.2 4 3 6 0 0 0 0 0 0
K               7 4 0.0 0 0 0 0
```

Continue in the same manner until more than half the wanted digits are obtained, then restore the short dial to its normal position and divide to obtain the remaining digits.

This method can be employed on the Marchant machine by using the nonshift key and successive negative multiplication by 1 to accomplish the subtraction of the odd numbers. However, it does not take advantage of the speed of the unique multiplier on the Marchant, and seems an inefficient way to use the machine.

XII.8 *Other Machine Methods*

There are available special methods for the machines which, with the aid of quite simple factors, read from special tables, will enable the machines to develop roots to many significant figures. Unfortunately, the tables of factors seem to have a way of disappearing when they are most needed. Actually, the methods described above are so rapid and require no tables that it is well worth while to master them. We assure you that, like putting on a coat, they are easier to do than to describe!

Appendix XIII Linear Interpolation

In most types of work involving numerical computations, as in statistics, it is very convenient to have tables of values of one quantity, called a *function*, which depend on the values of another quantity, called the *argument*. In Appendix I, the ordinate of the standard normal curve, y, is the function whose values depend on the values of z, the argument. In Appendix II, the proportion of the distribution below z is the function, p, while z itself is the argument. It is readily apparent that tables containing values of the function for all the values of the argument in which we might conceivably be interested would be prohibitively bulky.

Fortunately, such unwieldy tomes are not necessary. To see why, suppose we see how we could use Appendix II to obtain the proportion of the normal distribution below $z = +1.83$. We could make a large-scale plot of p vs. z for the two sets of tabled values next below and next above $z = +1.83$, as we have done in Fig. XIII-1. Now we connect the successive points by straight line segments. Of course, we know that there is a slight curve in the actual plot of p vs. z for all values, but it is quite obvious that the curve will never be far from these straight lines. So, if we read the value of p corresponding to $z = 1.83$ from our straight line, we would have about the value we need. However, it is costly in time and paper to make such a plot every time we need such a value. Let's use a little algebra and geometry.

Suppose we designate the point corresponding to one of our tabled values as P_1, that corresponding to the value we are seeking as P_2, and the point corresponding to the other tabled value as P_3, understanding that P_1 and P_3 are the closest available points to the one we want. We can use the same subscripts on p and z to denote their values at the corresponding points. We now draw in on our graph a horizontal line from P_1 and vertical lines from P_2 and P_3, and denote their points of intersection as points Q_2 and Q_3. Now we have two right triangles, $P_1Q_2P_2$ and $P_1Q_3P_3$, which have the acute angle P_1 in common. Hence they are similar triangles and their corresponding sides have the same ratio. Thus,

$$\frac{P_2Q_2}{P_3Q_3} = \frac{P_1Q_2}{P_1Q_3}$$

But we can express these lengths in terms of the values of p and z:

$$\frac{p_2 - p_1}{p_3 - p_1} = \frac{z_2 - z_1}{z_3 - z_1} \qquad \text{XIII.1}$$

A few algebraic operations yield

$$p_2 - p_1 = \frac{(p_3 - p_1)(z_2 - z_1)}{z_3 - z_1} \qquad \text{XIII.2}$$

$$p_2 = p_1 + \frac{(p_3 - p_1)(z_2 - z_1)}{(z_3 - z_1)} \qquad \text{XIII.3}$$

Fig. XIII-1. DIAGRAM SHOWING PRINCIPLE OF LINEAR INTERPOLATION. Plotted points are values of p vs z for $z = 1.70, 1.80, 1.90$, and 2.00 from Appendix II.

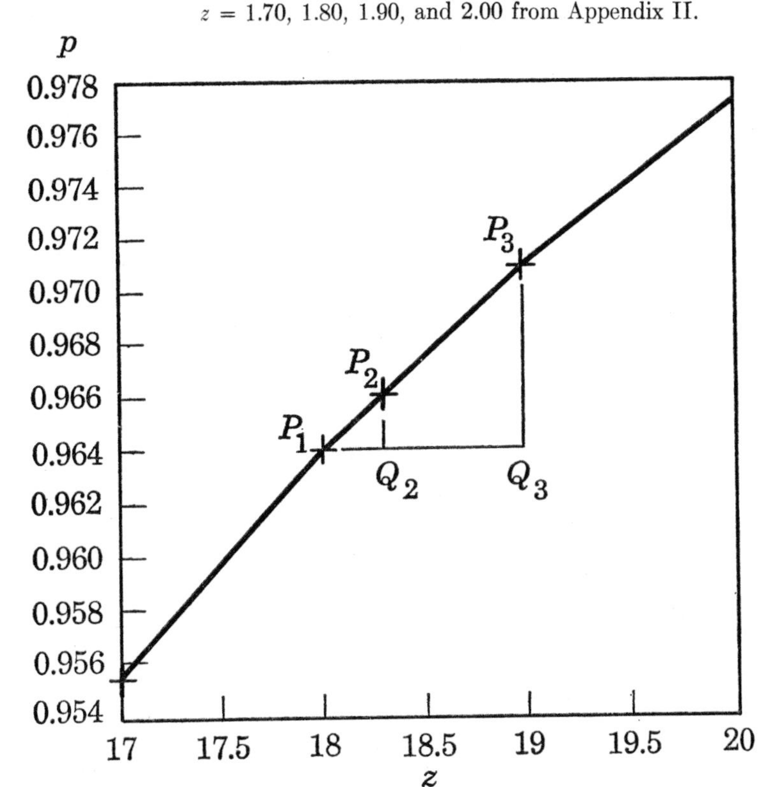

and substitution of numerical values for our particular problem yields

$$p_2 = 0.9641 + \frac{0.0072 \times 0.03}{0.10} \qquad \text{XIII.4}$$

$$= 0.9641 + 0.00216 = 0.96626 \doteq 0.9663. \qquad \text{XIII.5}$$

The value read from a more complete table, which gives values of z out to two decimals, is 0.9664, so we see that our process has given us a good approximation to the required value from a very compact table. The procedure we have used is that generally taught in secondary schools. However, when we have a calculator available, we can make the process even easier for ourselves by doing a little more algebra. Starting with equation XIII.3, we find

$$p_2 = \frac{p_1(z_3 - z_1) + (p_3 - p_1)(z_2 - z_1)}{z_3 - z_1} \qquad \text{XIII.6}$$

$$p_2 = \frac{p_1(z_3 - z_1) + p_3(z_2 - z_1) - p_1(z_2 - z_1)}{z_3 - z_1} \qquad \text{XIII.7}$$

Now we note that $z_3 - z_1 = (z_3 - z_2) + (z_2 - z_1)$. If we make this substitution in the first term of the numerator, we find that $p_1(z_2 - z_1)$ in the result just balances the negative of the same quantity in the last term of the numerator, so we have

$$p_2 = \frac{p_1(z_3 - z_2) + p_3(z_2 - z_1)}{z_3 - z_2} \qquad \text{XIII.8}$$

In our case,

$$p_2 = \frac{0.9641 \times 0.07 - 0.9713 \times 0.03}{0.10} \qquad \text{XIII.9}$$

$$= 0.96626 \doteq 0.9663 \text{ as before.} \qquad \text{XIII.10}$$

This process is easy to keep track of if we think of the arrangement of subscripts, arguments, argument differences, and functions as follows:

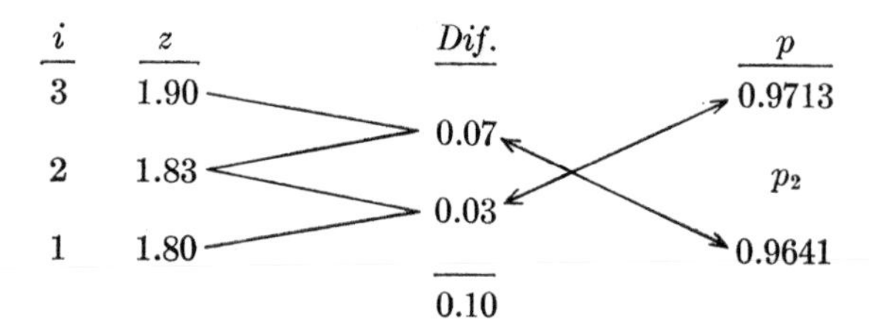

Using accumulative multiplication, simply multiply the upper argument difference by the lower function value, the lower argument difference by the upper function value (the values at the ends of the crossed double arrows) and divide by the total argument difference. Of course, often the total argument differences are such that one can easily divide each difference, mentally, by the total and thus eliminate the final division. That is the case here, where

$$p_2 = 0.9641 \times 0.7 + 0.9713 \times 0.3 = 0.96626$$

If you will use the principle a few times with the aid of a written layout such as we gave above, you will find that before long you can dispense with this aid and will be able to perform extrapolations very rapidly and reliably.

Appendix XIV The Greek Alphabet

It has become customary to use the letters of the Greek alphabet as symbols in much scientific and statistical writing. Because this alphabet is unfamiliar to many of us, it is shown here. The first and second columns show, respectively, the upper and lower case forms, the third column shows the classic name of the letter, and the fourth shows the approximate English transliteration.

Α	α	alpha	a	Ν	ν	nu	n
Β	β	beta	b	Ξ	ξ	xi	x or ks
Γ	γ	gamma	g	Ο	ο	omicron	o
Δ	δ	delta	d	Π	π	pi	p
Ε	ε	epsilon	e	Ρ	ρ	rho	r
Ζ	ζ	zeta	z	Σ	σ	sigma	s
Η	η	eta	ā	Τ	τ	tau	t
Θ	θ	theta	th	Υ	υ	upsilon	ü or o͞o
Ι	ι	iota	ē	Φ	φ	phi	f or ph
Κ	κ	kappa	k	Χ	χ	chi	k or ch
Λ	λ	lambda	l	Ψ	ψ	psi	ps
Μ	μ	mu	m	Ω	ω	omega	ō

Appendix XV The Crout Method

There are a number of problems in statistics which require the solution of sets of simultaneous linear equations. This tedious task is by no means restricted to statistics, and mathematicians, down the centuries, have frequently developed new methods for accomplishing the task, taking advantage of new knowledge and equipment, in an effort to reduce both the effort and the risk of mistakes involved. A method developed by Professor Prescott D. Crout makes very effective use of the capabilities of modern desk calculators and incorporates certain desirable checking features.

The present notes are written in simplified terms to present the particular aspects of the method needed for our specific kinds of problems. The task of finding the coefficients of the fourth-degree equation giving the least squares fit to the data of Table 15-3 is used for illustration. As we explained in the text, this requires the solution of the five normal equations of the type of equation 15.7.2 which have been specifically rewritten as Part A of Table XV-1.

Table XV-1. THE CROUT METHOD

Part A. The Equations to be Solved (From 15.7.2).

$$\begin{aligned}
b_0N + b_1\Sigma X^1 + b_2\Sigma X^2 + b_3\Sigma X^3 + b_4\Sigma X^4 &= \Sigma Y \\
b_0\Sigma X^1 + b_1\Sigma X^2 + b_2\Sigma X^3 + b_3\Sigma X^4 + b_4\Sigma X^5 &= \Sigma XY \\
b_0\Sigma X^2 + b_1\Sigma X^3 + b_2\Sigma X^4 + b_3\Sigma X^5 + b_4\Sigma X^6 &= \Sigma X^2Y \\
b_0\Sigma X^3 + b_1\Sigma X^4 + b_2\Sigma X^5 + b_3\Sigma X^6 + b_4\Sigma X^7 &= \Sigma X^3Y \\
b_0\Sigma X^4 + b_1\Sigma X^5 + b_2\Sigma X^6 + b_3\Sigma X^7 + b_4\Sigma X^8 &= \Sigma X^4Y
\end{aligned}$$

Part B. The Form of the Initial Matrix.

	0	1	2	3	4	5	C
0	$a_{0\,0}$	$a_{0\,1}$	$a_{0\,2}$	$a_{0\,3}$	$a_{0\,4}$	$a_{0\,5}$	$a_{0\,c}$
1	$a_{1\,0}$	$a_{1\,1}$	$a_{1\,2}$	$a_{1\,3}$	$a_{1\,4}$	$a_{1\,5}$	$a_{1\,c}$
2	$a_{2\,0}$	$a_{2\,1}$	$a_{2\,2}$	$a_{2\,3}$	$a_{2\,4}$	$a_{2\,5}$	$a_{2\,c}$
3	$a_{3\,0}$	$a_{3\,1}$	$a_{3\,2}$	$a_{3\,3}$	$a_{3\,4}$	$a_{3\,5}$	$a_{3\,c}$
4	$a_{4\,0}$	$a_{4\,1}$	$a_{4\,2}$	$a_{4\,3}$	$a_{4\,4}$	$a_{4\,5}$	$a_{4\,c}$

Part C. The Form of the Auxiliary Matrix.

	0	1	2	3	4	5	C
0	$x_{0\,0}$	$x_{0\,1}$	$x_{0\,2}$	$x_{0\,3}$	$x_{0\,4}$	$x_{0\,5}$	$x_{0\,c}$
1	$x_{1\,0}$	$x_{1\,1}$	$x_{1\,2}$	$x_{1\,3}$	$x_{1\,4}$	$x_{1\,5}$	$x_{1\,c}$
2	$x_{2\,0}$	$x_{2\,1}$	$x_{2\,2}$	$x_{2\,3}$	$x_{2\,4}$	$x_{2\,5}$	$x_{2\,c}$
3	$x_{3\,0}$	$x_{3\,1}$	$x_{3\,2}$	$x_{3\,3}$	$x_{3\,4}$	$x_{3\,5}$	$x_{3\,c}$
4	$x_{4\,0}$	$x_{4\,1}$	$x_{4\,2}$	$x_{4\,3}$	$x_{4\,4}$	$x_{4\,5}$	$x_{4\,c}$

Part D. The Form of the Final Matrix.

	0	1	2	3	4		
b	b_0	b_1	b_2	b_3	b_4		

Table XV-1 (*Continued*)

Part E. Initial Matrix with Symbols for Values.

	0	1	2	3	4	5	C
0	N	ΣX^1	ΣX^2	ΣX^3	ΣX^4	ΣY	$\Sigma a_{0\ j}$
1	ΣX^1	ΣX^2	ΣX^3	ΣX^4	ΣX^5	ΣXY	$\Sigma a_{1\ j}$
2	ΣX^2	ΣX^3	ΣX^4	ΣX^5	ΣX^6	ΣX^2Y	$\Sigma a_{2\ j}$
3	ΣX^3	ΣX^4	ΣX^5	ΣX^6	ΣX^7	ΣX^3Y	$\Sigma a_{3\ j}$
4	ΣX^4	ΣX^5	ΣX^6	ΣX^7	ΣX^8	ΣX^4Y	$\Sigma a_{4\ j}$

Part F. Initial Matrix with Numerical Values.

	0	1	2	3	4	5	C
0	20	100	660	4,900	38,676	148	44,504
1	100	660	4,900	38,676	316,900	780	362,016
2	660	4,900	38,676	316,900	2,661,780	5,188	3,028,104
3	4,900	38,676	316,900	2,661,780	22,747,300	38,268	25,807,824
4	38,676	316,900	2,661,780	22,747,300	196,834,836	300,148	222,899,640

Part G. Auxiliary Matrix with Numerical Values.

	0	1	2	3	4	5	C
0	20.00000	5.00000	33.00000	245.00000	1,933.80000	7.40000	2,225.20000
1	100.00000	160.00000	10.00000	88.60000	772.00000	0.25000	871.85000
2	60.00000	1,600.00000	896.00000	15.00000	167.71428	−0.10714	183.60714
3	4,900.00000	14,176.00000	13,440.00000	3,686.40000	20.00000	−0.02605	20.97396
4	38,676.00000	123,520.00000	150,272.00000	73,728.00000	8,426.05714	0.12892	1.12894

Part H. Final Matrix with Numerical Values.

	0	1	2	3	4
b	+33.53856	−41.90077	+17.33788	−2.60445	+0.12892

The five unknowns are b_0 through b_4, and we write the equations with the terms involving them in order on the left and the known term on the right.

More exactly, we do not literally write the equations, but enter their elements into a specific array, known as the *initial matrix*. For convenient designation, we number the rows from 0 through 4, following the subscript designation of our unknown b's. We similarly number the first five columns 0 through 4. The remaining columns are numbered 5 and C (standing for "check"), respectively. Thus we can denote any element by a_{ij} where the $_i$ denotes the row and the $_j$ the column in which the element is found. The form of the matrix is shown in Part B, the formulas for the quantities to be substituted are shown in Part E, and the actual values in Part F of Table XV-1. Note that the figure in each row of the check column is simply the sum of the preceding figures in the row. Notice also that, throughout the matrixes, the blocks falling on the diagonal beginning at the upper left corner have been given an extra heavy underlining. These blocks constitute the *principal diagonal* of the matrix and are key positions in the subsequent work.

A second matrix of the same form as the original matrix is then laid out, preferably with the same spacing and directly under the original. It is called the *auxiliary matrix*, and its elements are designated as x_{ij}'s. This matrix is filled by "chevrons," each chevron comprising a principal diagonal and the elements below and to the right of it. In each case, we start with the principal diagonal, then fill the spaces below it and finally those to the right. It is prudent to complete each chevron before starting the next.

In the first chevron, the principal diagonal $x_{00} = a_{00}$. All values in the first column are simply copied from the initial matrix, that is, $x_{i0} = a_{i0}$. In the first row, to the right of the diagonal, all elements are those of the initial matrix divided by the principal diagonal, that is, $x_{0j} = a_{0j}/x_{00}$. To complete the check, add the values in the matrix to the right of the principal diagonal (excluding the check column) and increase the sum by 1: this result should equal the calculated value of x_{0c} with a possible small discrepancy due to rounding.

The principal diagonal of the second chevron is obtained from the formula,

$$x_{11} = a_{11} - x_{10}x_{01}$$

that is, from the value in the corresponding block of the *initial* matrix we subtract the product of the value at the *head* of the *row* by the value at the *head* of the *column* in the auxiliary matrix.

Under the diagonal, a similar pattern continues:

$$x_{21} = a_{21} - x_{20}x_{01}$$

$$x_{31} = a_{31} - x_{30}x_{01}$$

$$x_{41} = a_{41} - x_{40}x_{01}$$

To the right of the principal diagonal the values are

$$x_{12} = \frac{a_{12} - x_{10}x_{02}}{x_{11}}$$

$$x_{13} = \frac{a_{13} - x_{10}x_{03}}{x_{11}}$$

$$x_{14} = \frac{a_{14} - x_{10}x_{04}}{x_{11}}$$

$$x_{15} = \frac{a_{15} - x_{10}x_{05}}{x_{11}}$$

$$x_{1c} = \frac{a_{1c} - x_{10}x_{0c}}{x_{11}}$$

In each case, we again start with the value from the corresponding block of the initial matrix, subtract the product of the values at the heads of the row and column, but we then *divide* the result by the principal diagonal of the auxiliary matrix.

This particular problem, and many like it in statistics, possesses a characteristic which permits us to save considerable work. Note that in the initial matrix the value a given number of spaces to the right of the principal diagonal is identical with the value the same number of spaces below it. Such a matrix is said to be *symmetric* about the principal diagonal. As a result of this symmetry, you will find that the numerators of the x_{ij} values to the right of the principal diagonal (that is, for $j > i$) are identical with the symmetrical values below the diagonal. Therefore, we need only enter the values in the initial matrix on and above the principal diagonal. As we fill the auxiliary matrix, we can enter the numerator of each value to the right of the diagonal in the symmetric position below the diagonal before proceeding with the division by the diagonal.

The third chevron has as its principal diagonal

$$x_{22} = a_{22} - x_{20}x_{02} - x_{21}x_{12}$$

The first element below it is

$$x_{32} = a_{32} - x_{30}x_{02} - x_{31}x_{12}$$

and the element to the right is

$$x_{23} = \frac{a_{23} - x_{20}x_{03} - x_{21}x_{13}}{x_{22}}$$

This pattern continues throughout the chevron, with two products being subtracted from the value taken from the initial matrix. A similar pattern follows for the fourth and fifth chevrons, with three and four products, respectively, being subtracted.

In all chevrons, the check is obtained, as in the first one, by determining that the sum of 1 plus all elements to the right of the principal diagonal except the element in the check column equals the element in the check column, save for minor rounding discrepancies. In all cases, advantage may be taken of symmetry, when it is present, by the procedure discussed in the case of the second chevron.

The final matrix consists of one line and contains the required b values. It is filled starting from the right by the following formulas:

$$b_4 = x_{45}$$

$$b_3 = x_{35} - b_4x_{34}$$

$$b_2 = x_{25} - b_4x_{24} - b_3x_{23}$$

$$b_1 = x_{15} - b_4x_{14} - b_3x_{13} - b_2x_{12}$$

$$b_0 = x_{05} - b_4x_{04} - b_3x_{03} - b_2x_{02} - b_1x_{01}$$

The values may be checked by direct substitution into the original equations. This is readily accomplished by multiplying each b by the value over it on the first line of the initial matrix and letting the sum of the products accumulate: it should equal the value of $a_{0\,5}$, within limits of rounding errors. Similarly, the sum of products of the b's by the values over them in any row of the initial matrix should equal the value for that row in the 5 column.

In first using this method, you will probably find it very confusing to follow the subscripts. If you will watch what they are telling you, you will find that the pattern of operations, thought of in terms of geometric positions, is very simple and easy to recall — it is easier done than described.

Appendix XVI Use of Logarithms

In order to understand logarithms sufficiently to be able to use them effectively, we need reasonable familiarity with the laws of exponents. So we shall review the more fundamental of these laws here, restricting ourselves to the particular conditions of concern for our purpose rather than covering the subject exhaustively. Suppose we have a number, b, the *base*, which, for our purposes, will always be not only positive but greater than unity. Now suppose we have another number, n, the exponent, which we shall at present require be a positive integer. Thus we can define the number, which we write as

$$a = b^n$$

as the product obtained by multiplying together n b's:

$$a = b^n = \overbrace{b \cdot b \cdot b \cdot \cdots \cdot b}^{n \text{ factors}}$$

This, and the laws of multiplication, tell us that if c and d are positive integers,

$$p = b^c b^d = \overbrace{(b \cdot b \cdot \cdots \cdot b)}^{c \text{ factors}} \overbrace{(b \cdot b \cdot \cdots \cdot b)}^{d \text{ factors}}$$

$$= \overbrace{(b \cdot b \cdot \cdots \cdot b)}^{c + d \text{ factors}}$$

$$= b^{c+d}$$

that is, the product of the same base to two powers is the base to the sum of the powers.

A thought on the relationship between multiplication and division would suggest that

$$q = \frac{b^c}{b^d} = b^{c-d}$$

which is true, but in order to validate it we must extend our definitions a little. If, for example, $c = d$ so that $c - d = 0$, we have no meaning for b^0. But if $c = d$, then $b^c = b^d$ and $b^c/b^d = 1$. For this and other reasons, we define $b^0 = 1$. But if $c < d$, then $c - d < 0$, and we have no meaning yet for b^n when n is negative. However, note that

$$q = \frac{b^c}{b^d} = \frac{1}{b^d/b^c} = \frac{1}{b^{d-c}}$$

and $d - c > 0$ so that the last form is defined. Therefore we note that a negative exponent indicates a number which is the reciprocal of that number obtained by raising the base to the absolute value of the exponent.

Suppose we consider the use of another positive integer, m, and consider the idea of the mth power of b^n:

$$P = (b^n)^m = \overbrace{\underbrace{(b \cdot b \cdot \cdots \cdot b)}_{n \text{ factors}} \underbrace{(b \cdot b \cdot \cdots \cdot b)}_{n \text{ factors}} \cdots \underbrace{(b \cdot b \cdot \cdots \cdot b)}_{n \text{ factors}}}^{m \text{ sets}} = b^{mn}$$

The idea of a root, namely, that $R = \sqrt[m]{a}$ means a number such that $R^m = a$, suggests that

$$R = \sqrt[m]{b^n} = b^{n/m}$$

and this now gives meaning to fractional exponents.

We could use, as we said, any base greater than unity for our present purposes, but it is particularly interesting to let the base be ten, that is, to let

Fig. XVI-1 PLOT OF THE EXPONENTIAL CURVE
$Y = 10^N$
(Note the use of unequal units on the two scales.)

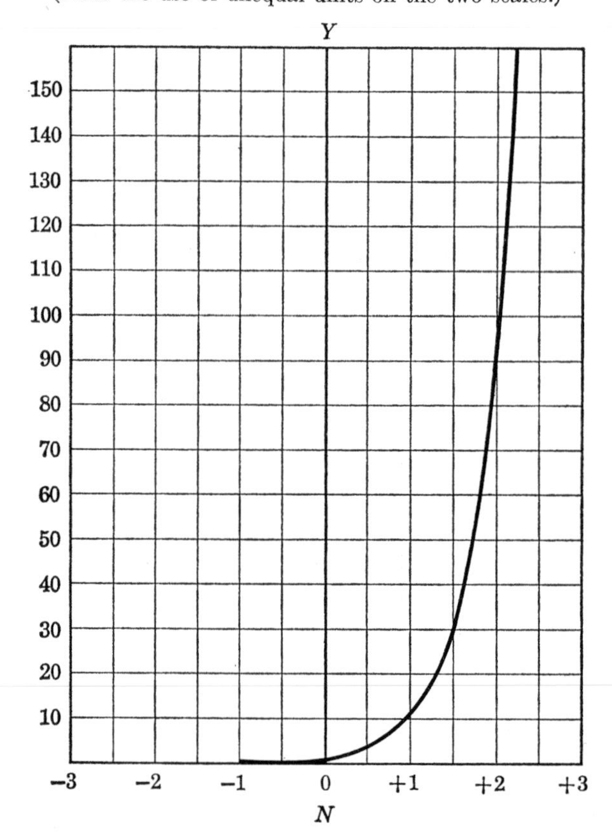

$b = 10$. We could plot a number of values of $y = b^n = 10^n$ and they would soon suggest fairing in the smooth curve as we have done in Fig. XVI-1. There is a little problem we haven't yet taken care of: the n-scale implies that n can have all real values, including irrational numbers, like $\sqrt{2}$ and π, but we have not yet given meaning to $10^{\sqrt{2}}$ and 10^{π}. However, as we have tried to show you before, mathematicians try to "make sense," and their solution to the problem started with the idea of reading the value from the graph, then went on to refine the idea, so that we have sound meaning for 10^n for all real values of n.

Now suppose we use slightly different symbols and consider any number,

$$N = 10^L$$

for which we rightly feel that each L has one and only one N associated with it and, similarly, there is one and only one value of L which will yield a given N. All values of N will, of necessity, be positive. Suppose we now call L the *logarithm* (to the base 10) *of* N and indicate the fact by writing

$$\log N = L$$

from which,

$$N = 10^{\log N}$$

A little careful study of our laws of exponents will show that:

$$\log ab = \log a + \log b \qquad \log a/b = \log a - \log b$$

$$\log a^m = m \log a \qquad \log \sqrt[m]{a} = (1/m) \log a$$

In a sense, this means that the use of logarithms reduces the "complexity" of arithmetic operations by one "step": multiplications and division "reduce" to addition and subtraction; raising to powers and extracting roots, to multiplication and division.

If we draw the graph of $Y = \log N$, as in Fig. XVI-2, and study it carefully, we would presently be reminded that for $1 \leq N < 10$, $0 \leq \log N < 1$, that is, these logs are decimals. For $10 \leq N < 100$, $1 \leq \log N < 2$, that is, these logs are one plus decimals. This pattern continues, and we should presently notice that, for any given sequence of digits in N, the decimal part of the logarithm is the same, and only the part to the left of the decimal changes. This should be so, because any number, N, can be written as the product of a number, S, where $1 \leq S < 10$, multiplied by an integral power of 10:

$$N = 10^c S$$

Thus:

$$34.56 = 10 \cdot 3.456 = 3.456 \times 10^1$$

$$3456 = 10^3\, 3.456 = 3.456 \times 10^3$$

$$0.03456 = 10^{-2}\, 3.456 = 3.456 \times 10^{-2}$$

Fig. XVI-2. Plot of the Logarithmic Function
$Y = \log N$
(Note use of unequal scale divisions.)

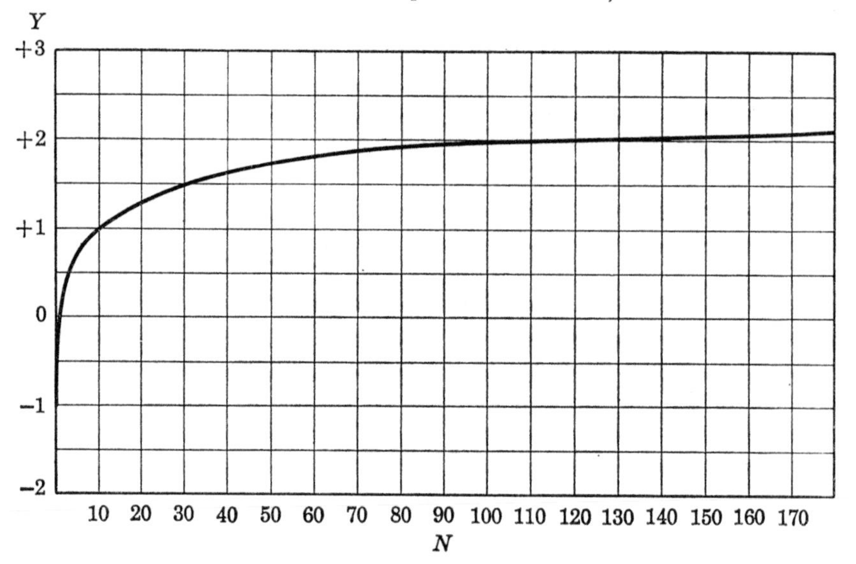

The form of writing given on the right side of these equations is sometimes referred to as the "scientific" notation for the numbers.

From this it would appear that all we need is a table giving $\log n$ for $1 \leq N < 10$, since these same decimals will comprise the decimal part of the logs of all other numbers. These decimals (or decimal parts) are called the *mantissas* of the logarithms. Logarithms to the base ten are formally called *common logarithms*, and what is properly called a table of mantissas of common logarithms is more generally just called a log table. Such a table, with four significant figures in the mantissas, is our Appendix X. Tables with five places are readily available, and tables with six places are reasonably common. More places are available, but are rarely needed, and are bulky and costly. In general, one needs as many places, or more, in his mantissas as he has significant digits in the numbers he is working with.

Log tables are printed with certain conventions and economies. The first two digits in N are given in the column at the left and the third in the row at the top. Thus the log of a number with three digits will be found in the space occurring in the row designated by its first two digits and the column designated by its third. Thus, $\log 3.45 = 0.5378$ and $\log 3.46 = 0.5391$. Notice that no decimals are used in the table, since all mantissas in a four-place table are decimals occupying the first four decimals, and they apply to a stated sequence of digits in N regardless of the location of its decimal.

Now suppose that we want $\log 3.456$. This will require linear interpolation which, if we have a calculator at hand, may readily be done by the method of Appendix XIII. Otherwise, we note that the difference between log 3.46 = 0.5391 and log 3.45 = 0.5378 was 13 in the last two decimal places and that we need to add 6/10 of this amount, or $0.6 \times 13 = 7.1 \doteq 7$ onto log 3.45 to obtain $0.5378 + 0.0007 = 0.5385 = \log 3.456$.

Notice that the logs of integral powers of 10 are, by definition, the indexes of the powers, that is,

$$\log 10^c = c$$

This means that:

$$\log N = \log 10^c s$$

$$= c + \log S$$

This integral value, c, is called the *characteristic* of the logarithm, and serves to identify the decimal location in the original number. For the numbers we considered earlier, we have

$$\log 34.56 = 1 + 0.5385 = 1.5385$$

$$\log 3456 = 3 + 0.5385 = 3.5385$$

$$\log 0.03456 = -2 + 0.5358 = -1.4642$$

This last result seems to contradict our statement about the decimal part of the logarithm being the same for a given sequence of digits regardless of where the decimal is in the sequence. We should have said that the decimal part must always be kept positive. There are several ways of doing this. One would be to write

$$\log 0.03456 \quad \text{as} \quad -2 + 0.5358$$

without combining the negative characteristic and positive mantissa. This is not often done. Another way is to write

$$\log 0.03456 = \bar{2}.5358$$

where the placing of the minus (−) *over* the two indicates that only the 2 is negative. This was more common in the past than it is nowadays. A more common practice is to express a negative characteristic as the difference between a positive number and the negative of an integral multiple of 10, thus:

$$-2 = 8 - 10$$

and combine the positive number with the mantissa:

$$\log 0.03456 = 8.5358 - 10$$

The other use of a log table is to find the number corresponding to a given logarithm. Suppose we have

$$\log N = 6.5432 - 10$$

From the table, we find that 0.5428 is the mantissa of the sequence 349, while 0.5441 is the mantissa of the sequence 350. The difference of the two mantissas is 13, while the difference between our mantissa and the lower one is 4 which, from the table of proportional parts, is closest to 0.3 of 13, so we make the fourth digit in our sequence 3, or the sequence 3493. Our characteristic is $6 - 10 = -4$ and we now know that our number:

$$N = 10^c S = 10^{-4}\,3.493 = 0.0003493$$

Index

Abscissa, 64
Aggregative price index, 394
Alpha risk, 134, 136
  related, 148
"Among" estimate, 217
Amplitude, 337
Analysis, times series, 330
Analysis of variance
  "among" estimate, 218
  basic ideas, 214–216
  factor, 229
    level of, 229
  in polynomial regression analysis, 281–287
  linear comparisons, 227
    development of idea, 223–227
    in two-way classification, 236
    orthogonality, 228
  one-way classification
    first phase, 216–219
  orthogonal sets
    choice of, 229
  table, 220
  "total" estimate, 217
  treatment, 230
  two-way classification, 230-241
    first phase, 232
    interaction, 233
    interpretation, 239
    plan and interpretation, 241
    second phase, 232
    tabulation of data, 230, 231
    third phase, 236
  "within" estimate, 217
Analytic geometery, 61
Anov = analysis of variance (*q.v.*)
Arithmetic mean, 36
Arrangements, number of, 87
Array, 9
Asymptote, 100
Auxiliary hypothesis, 206
Averages, 33
  arithmetic mean, 36
  geometric mean, 42
  harmonic mean, 42
  median, 34
  mid-range, 34
  mode, 35

Beta risk, 134, 137
Binomial distribution
  background of, 104–107
  equation, 107
  for proportions, 116
  normal approximation, 109–118
Bivariate normal distribution
  description of, 247–250
  equation, 247

Cartesian coordinates, 62
Chain relative, 257
Chi-square (χ^2) distribution, 161
Chi-square-over-n (χ^2/n) distribution, 162
Circles, equations of, 67
Class, 11
  open, 19
Class interval, 11
Class mark, 12
Coefficient of correlation, 259
Coefficient of determination, 259
Column heading, 29
Combination, 90
Combinations, number of, 90, 91
Compound event, 93
Confidence limits, 148
  difference of two means
    variances known, 203
    variances unknown but equal, 207
  one mean
    variance known, 146–149
    variance unknown, 183
  one variance, 164

Consistent statistics, 132
Consumers' Price Index, 402
Contingency table, 324
Coordinates
  Cartesian, 62
  rectangular, 62
Correlation analysis
  hypothesis testing, 269
  regression statistics and, 264
  standardized variables in, 267
Correlation coefficient, 259
Correlation problem, 246–251
Counts, 308
  multi-category, 317–320
  two-category
    binomial distribution and, 309
    normal approximation, 313
  Poisson approximation, 311
  vs. measurements, 324
Crossover point, 211
Cumulative frequencies, 22
Curvilinear regression, 275
Cyclical analysis, 415–417
  lag, 416
  lead, 416
  leading series, 416
Cyclical variation, 338

Data, raw, 8
Deduction, 129
Deflation, 409
Degrees of freedom, 160
  (*See* specific statistics)
Deseasonalizing, 345
Determination coefficient, 259
Deviation, standard, 54
  physical meaning, 58
Diagram, step, 23–26
Difference of two means, estimate of
  variances known, 203
  variances unknown but equal, 207
Dispersion, measures of
  comparison of, 56
  mean absolute deviation, 46
  range, 45
  standard deviation, 54
  variance, 47
Distribution, 29
  binomial
    background of, 104–107
    equation of, 107
    for proportions, 116
    normal approximation, 109–118
  bivariate normal
    description, 247–250
    equation, 247
  chi-square (χ^2), 161
  chi-square-over-n (χ^2/n), 162
  F-, 189, 190
  normal
    areas as frequencies, 79–81
    as approximation to binomial, 109–118
    as limit of binomial, 109

Equation
  binomial distribution, 107
  bivariate normal distribution, 247
  chi-square (χ^2) distribution, 161
  explicit form of, 67
  F-distribution, 190
  implicit form of, 66
  linear, 66
  normal distribution, 73, 77
  t-distribution, 181
Equations
  of circles, 67
  of ellipses, 67
  trend
    forms considered, 364
Error, risk of, 5
  alpha, 134, 136
  beta, 134, 137
Escalator clauses
  index numbers and, 409
Estimate
  difference of two means
  variance known, 203
  variances unknown but equal, 207
  interval, 148
  one mean
    variance known, 146–149
    variance unknown, 183
  one variance, 164
  point, 146
  reliability of, 5
Estimation, 146
Event, 93
  compound, 93
  simple, 93
Events
  independent, 93
  successive
    ways of performing, 86
Experiment, sampling
  like "Student's", 172–181

Explicit form, 67
Exponential regression
basic ideas, 294–297
direct least square estimation, 301
orthogonality, 302
summary, 303

Factor (anov), 229
Factorial, 87
Forecasting, 331, 419–421
Freedom, degrees of, 160
(*See* specific statistics)
Frequencies
comparison of distributions, 320
comparison with hypothetical, 317
cumulative, 22
relative, 22
Frequency polygon, 26
Frequency table, 11
Functions of statistics
condensation, 4
hypothesis testing (*q.v.*), 5
planning observations, 5
presentation, 5

Geometric mean, 42

Harmonic mean, 42
Heading, column, 29
Histogram, 14
bar widths, 14
special treatments, 21
Holidays, effect on trend analysis, 382
Hypothesis, 130
null, 137
one-sided, 142
two-sided, 142
Hypothesis testing
basic idea, 130
choice of H_0, 140–144
comments on method, 144–146
correlation, 69
errors, risk of
alpha and beta, 134
errors, types of, I and II, 134
many means (*see* analysis of variance)
one mean, variance known, 135–145
one-tailed, 139–144
two-tailed, 135–138
variance unknown, 182
one variance, 162–164
two means
paired observations, 207
variances known, 202
variances unequal, crossover point, 211
variances unknown, auxiliary H_0, 206
variances unknown but equal, 203
variances unknown and unequal, 212
two variances, 189–194
Implicit form, 66
Independent events, 93
Index, seasonal, 337
Index numbers, price
aggregative, 394
base shifting, 398
basic ideas, 391
choice of type, 394
computing from relatives, 400
Consumers' Price Index
discussion, 408
table and chart, 402
paid by farmers, 409
simple, 394
splicing, 398, 399
types of, 392
use of
deflation, 409
escalator clauses, 409
value of the dollar, 411
weighted, 394
formulas, 397
weights
choice of, 396
Index numbers, selection of appropriate, 410
Index numbers, volume
formulas for, 405
problems with, 406–407
relation to price indexes, 404
Induction, 130
Interaction
in analysis of variance, 233
Intercept, 64
Intermediate table, 9
Interval estimate, 148
Intervals, class, 11
Irregular variation, 338
measuring, 417

Lag, 416
Lead, 416
Leading series, 416
Least squares, in exponential regression, 301

Limits
  asymptote, 100
  mathematical vs. statistical, 99–101
  statistical, 100
Limits, class, 11
Limits, confidence, 148
  difference of two means
    variance known, 203
    variances unknown but equal, 207
  one mean
    variance known, 146–149
    variance unknown, 183
  one variance, 164
Limits, tolerance, 210
Linear comparisons, 227
Linear equation, 66
Linear regression
  confidence limits for line, 256
  estimation in, 256
  hypothesis testing, 254
  statistics, 251
  use of correlation statistics in, 270
Link relative, 357

Mark, class, 12
Mathematical notation, 38
Mathematical probability, 95
Mean, arithmetic
  as balance point, 37
  computation from frequency tables, 40
  estimate of
    variance known, 146–149
    variance unknown, 183
  hypothesis testing
    (*see* hypothesis testing)
    (*see* analysis of variance)
  minimum variance property, 58
Mean absolute deviation, 46
Meaningful, technically, 143
Measurements vs. counts, 324
Measures of central value, 33
  arithmetic mean, 36
  geometric mean, 42
  harmonic mean, 42
  median, 34
  mid-range, 34
  mode, 35
Measures of dispersion
  comparison, 56
  mean absolute deviation, 46
  range, 45
  standard deviation, 54
  variance, 47

Median, 34
Mid-range, 34
Mode, 35
Model
  regression, 245
  time series, 338

Normal distribution
  areas as frequencies, 79–81
  as approximation to binomial, 109–118
  as limit of binomial, 109
  equation, 73
  fitting to histogram, 72–78
  standard form, 77
  use with counts, 313
Notation, mathematical, 38
Null hypothesis, 137
Number
  of combinations, 90, 91
  of permutations, 87
Numbered scale, 62
Numbers, random
tables of, 126, App. IV

Open class, 19
Orders of arrangement, number of, 87
Ordinate
  of normal distribution, Table App. I
  of point, 64
Orthogonality, 228

Parabolas, equations of, 66
Period, 346
Permutations
  definition, 88
  extension of ideas, 88–90
  number of, 88
Plotting, 64
Point estimate, 146
Poisson distribution, 114
  as approximation to binomial, 114
  use with counts, 311
Polygon, frequency, 26
Polynomial regression
  analysis of variance in, 281
  as approximation to exponential, 304
  as approximation to other forms, 279
  basic ideas, 276–278
  choice of degree, 283–287
  confidence limits, 294
  estimation of coefficients, 287,
    App. VIII
  interpretation, 288–293

Pooled sample variance, 194
Population, 5, 32
  two meanings of, 121
Price indexes, 391–401
  (*see also* Index numbers, price)
Price relative, 392
Probability
  basic ideas, 92
  mathematical, 95
  statistical
Proof, 145

Random numbers, 126, Table App. IV
Random sample
  by indirect physical methods, 125
  by physical methods, 124
  by use of tables, 126
  definition, 124
Range, 45
Raw data, 8
Reasoning, deductive, 129
  inductive, 130
Reciprocal, 49
Rectangular coordinates, 62
Regression
  curvilinear, 275
  exponential, 278
    basic ideas, 294–297
    least squares estimates, 301
    orthogonality problem, 302
    semi-log transformation, 297–300
    summary, 303
  linear
    confidence limits for line 256
    estimation, 256
    hypothesis testing, 254
    statistics, 251
    use of correlation statistics, 270
  polynomial
    analysis of variance in, 281
    as approximation to exponential, 304
    as approximation to other forms, 279
    basic ideas, 276–278
    choice of degree, 283–287
    confidence limits, 294
    estimation of coefficients, 287, Table, App. VIII
    interpretation, 288–293
    trend analysis and, 364
Regression model, 245
Regression problem, 244–246
Regression, semi-log, 278
Relative, chain, 357
  link, 357
  price, 392
Relative frequencies, 22
Reliability of estimates, 5
Risk, alpha, 134, 136
  beta, 134, 137
  related alpha, 148
Row stub, 29

Sample, 5
  definition, 122
    of good, 123
  non-random, 124, 127
  random
    by indirect physical methods, 125
    by physical methods, 124
    by use of tables, 126
    definition, 124
  reasons for
    cost of measurement, 122
    destructive measurements, 122
    infinite populations, 123
Sample mean, 131
  distribution of, 132
Sample variance
  basic idea, 154–160
  distribution of, 162
  pooled, 194
Sampling experiment, 172–181
Scale, numbered, 62
Scale units, change in
  effect on histogram, 69
  thermometer illustration, 74–76
  unequal effect of, 68
Scales, changing time
  rates involved, 384
  rates not involved, 382
Scheduling customs, effect on trend analysis, 381
Seasonal analysis
  comparison of methods, 362
  determination of period, 346
  moving averages, 346
    centered, 356
  relatives, link and chain, 357
Seasonal index, 337
Seasonal variation
  amplitude, 337
  period, 346
Secular trend, 335
Semilog paper, use in trend analysis, 365–371
Semilog regression, 278

Semilog transformation, 297–300
Significance, statistical, 143
Simple event, 93
Simple price index, 394
Slope of line, 64
Source of data, 29
Splicing, 399
Standard deviation, 54
  biased estimate, reason for using, 165
  physical meaning, 58
Standard form of normal distribution, 77
Standardized variables in correlation analysis, 267
Statistic, 131
  criteria of, 132
  sample mean, 131
  sample variance, 160
Statistical probability, 95
Statistical proof, 145
Statistically significant, 143
Statistics, 5
  condensation, 4
  hypothesis testing (*q.v.*), 5
  planning observations, 5
  presentation, 5
Step diagram, 23–26
Stub, row, 29
"Student's" t-distribution, 181
  history of, 170–172
Study suggestions, 6
Subtitle, 29
Successive events, 86
Sufficient statistic, 132
Symbols, mathematical
  basic ideas, 38
Synthesis of time series, 339

Technically meaningful, 143
t-distribution
  equation, 181
  history of, 170–172
  use of, 183
Table
  column heading, 29
  row stub, 29
  source, 29
  subtitle, 29
  title, 29
Table, contingency, 324
Table, frequency, 11
Table, intermediate, 9
Tally sheet, 12
Time series
  analysis, 311
    (*See* also separate components)
  definition, 330
  deseasonalizing, 345
  model, 338
  synthesis, 339
Tolerance limits, 210
"Total" estimate, 217
Treatment, 230
Trend analysis and regression anal ysis, 364
  changing time scales
    rates involved, 384
    rates not involved, 382
  effect of holidays, 382
  effect of scheduling customs, 381
  effect of unequal months
  forms considered, 364
  recognizing form, 365
    borderline cases, 372
    use of semilog paper, 365–371
Trend, secular, 335
Trial, 93

Unbiased statistic, 132
Universe, 5, 32

Value, typical, 4
Value of the dollar, 411
Variance, 47
  choice of formulas, 50–54
  computation from frequency table, 56
  estimate of, 164
Variance, analysis of
  (*see* analysis of variance)
Variance, sample
  background, 154–159
  distribution of, 162
  pooled, 194
Variation, 1
  episodic, 338
  irregular, 338
  random, 338
  seasonal
    definition, 337
    period of, 337
  typical, 5
Variations, types of
  errors, 3
  inherent, 4
  mistakes, 3
Volume indexes, 404–407

"Within" estimate, 217

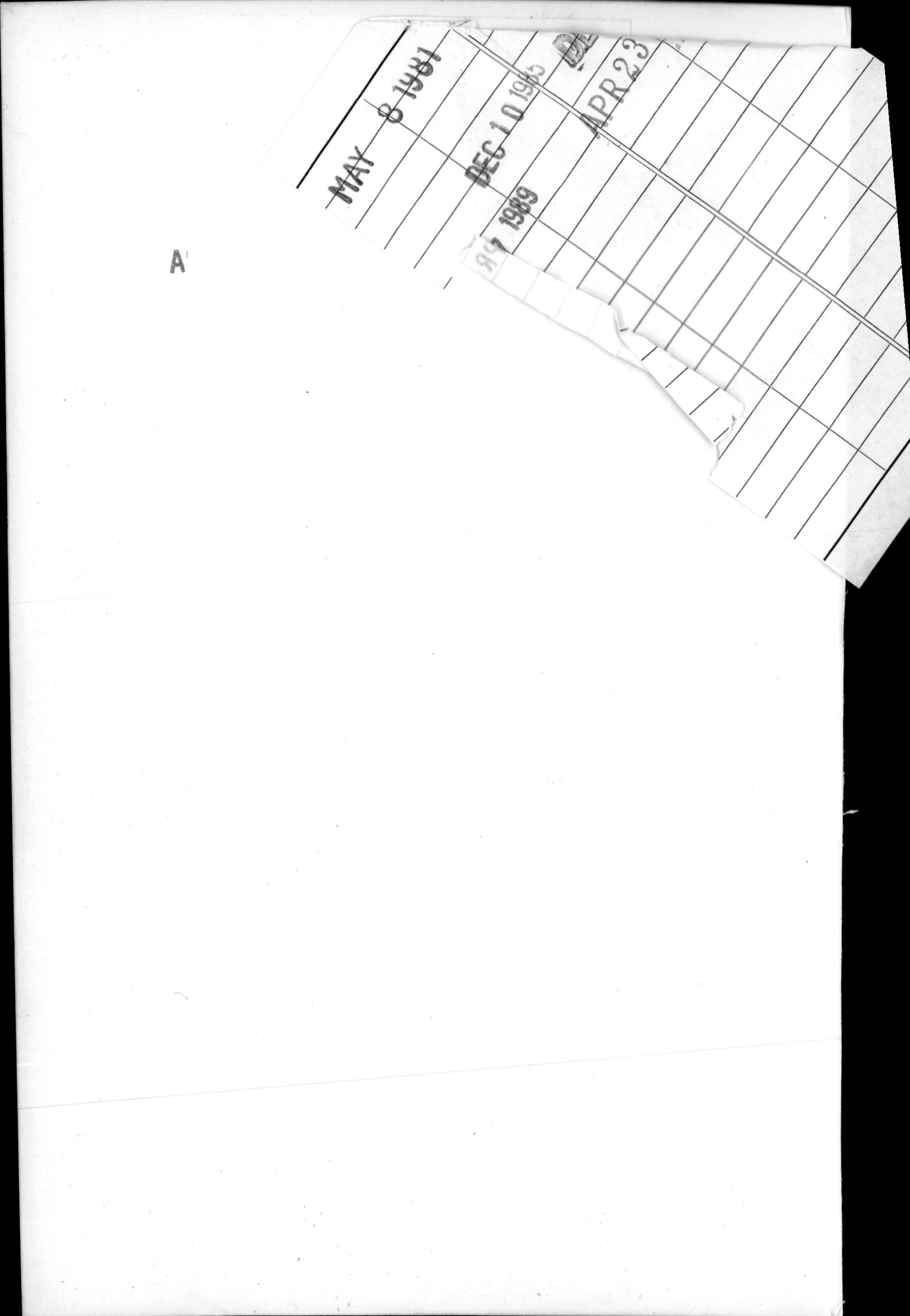
MAY 8 1981
DEC 10 1985
APR 23
1989

A'